EXAMINATION COPY

Published by
M42

SOUTH-WESTERN PUBLISHING CO.
Cincinnati • Chicago • Dallas • New Rochelle, N. Y. • Burlingame, Calif.

Applied

BUSINESS
MATHEMATICS

FOR CONSUMER AND BUSINESS USE

NINTH EDITION

EDWIN B. PIPER

Formerly Supervisor of Business Education
Albany Public Schools, Albany, New York

ROSWELL E. FAIRBANK

Coordinator of Business Education
State University of New York at Albany, Albany, New York

JOSEPH GRUBER

Dean of the School of Continuing Education
Pace College, New York, New York

Library of Congress Catalog Card Number: 71-103642

Printed in the United States of America

1 2 3 4 5 6 7 8 K 6 5 4 3 2 1 0

Preface

This Ninth Edition of APPLIED BUSINESS MATHEMATICS includes many changes and several new features. Throughout the book, the factual data in the topical discussions and problems have been brought up to date. Much of the exercise material has been otherwise revised or rewritten, and many new problems have been supplied in the review assignments and general reviews.

At planned intervals in the exercises and review assignments of the first fifteen sections, there is a brief reminder to the student to make an estimate of each product and quotient, and to check all calculations immediately. These reminders are identified in each instance by a bold-face check mark. It is hoped that these frequent reminders will encourage the student to strive for accuracy in all his computational work.

In most written exercises, which are supplied primarily for classroom practice in gaining initial mastery of new types of problems, the answer is given, in color, for the first problem in each group of similar problems contained within an exercise. The answer is given so that the student may know whether he is solving the problem the right or wrong way and thereby avoid the wrong kind of practice in his work with these problems. The use of this guide answer, or check figure, is explained to the student in Exercise 2 on page 15 of the textbook. An expanded treatment of the use of guide answers is contained in the manual of the Teacher's Edition (pages 8 and 13).

Other new features are the line drawings at numerous points throughout the book for reinforcing some of the ideas developed in the topical discussions, and the divider page, at the beginning of each unit, which portrays pictorially typical points of the unit subject matter.

Although the Ninth Edition contains many changes, the basic organization and development of the subject matter, which contributed to the popularity of the preceding editions, have been retained.

As in the preceding editions, the Ninth Edition contains bonus or optional topics, exercises, and problems. These materials are identified in each instance by an arrow. They may be assigned for the faster or more capable students, or they may be omitted in shorter courses. Such materials provide for individual and class differences. The supplementary problems for each unit can be used for this purpose also.

The book is designed so that the course in business mathematics has value both for consumer use and for business use. The beginning units develop the fundamental principles and operations through a study of problems faced by every individual in his daily life. The problems that illustrate these situations are relatively simple. These units deal with personal money records, banking transactions, buying for personal and household needs, and personal financing.

The principles and processes developed in the beginning units are then applied in subsequent units dealing with savings and investments, home ownership, travel and transportation, taxes, and in units devoted to problems arising in the operation of various types of business enterprise, including problems of the small businessman and the farmer.

In general, each topic is developed by means of a five-step learning pattern that provides:

1) A functional approach that introduces each new principle or process in a meaningful, concrete manner.

2) A simple, concise explanation that furnishes essential background information for an understanding of the new principle or process.

3) An illustrative example with a model solution and a simple and complete explanation of the solution.

4) An exercise for immediate practice consisting of problems similar to the illustrative example.

5) A review of the new type of problem at carefully planned intervals to insure retention of what the student has learned. This spaced review is provided by the review assignments in each section and the general reviews at various points in the text.

The materials are organized into 18 units that include 80 sections. Most sections are divided into two or more parts of convenient length for assignments. New principles and new types of problems are introduced in graded sequence, one at a time. This step-by-step development of subject matter, together with the simple discussions, illustrative examples, and model solutions, enables the student to progress with a minimum of teacher assistance.

We take this opportunity to thank the many teachers who have offered helpful suggestions and the government agencies and businessmen who have supplied factual information and problem materials.

Edwin B. Piper
Roswell E. Fairbank
Joseph Gruber

Table of Contents

UNIT

UNIT

UNIT

UNIT One

Personal Money Records

SECTION 1

Family Cash Records

Many persons and families keep records of cash receipts and cash payments. These records are helpful in planning and in getting the most use from money. Records are also helpful in preparing income tax returns.

PART 1a   Cash Receipts and Cash Payments Records

The personal cash receipts record. The cash receipts record of the Robert Mason family for the week of April 3 is shown below.

DATE		EXPLANATION	AMOUNT	
April	3	Robert; take-home pay Mar. 18-31	200	00
	3	Robert; commission Mar. 18-31	48	75
	4	Federal income tax refund	34	70
	5	Anniversary gift	10	00
	6	Savings bond cashed at maturity	25	00
	7	Refund for return of radio	33	55
	8	Betty; take-home pay Apr. 3-7	20	00
	8	Betty; tips for week	30	50
		Total	402	50

Cash receipts record for the Robert Mason family

Robert Mason is a salesman and earns a regular salary plus a commission on his sales. His wife, Betty, is a part-time waitress who earns a small salary plus tips. All cash received from any source by either Mr. or Mrs. Mason is recorded in their family cash receipts record. The Mason children keep their own cash records.

The Masons total their record each week. As shown above, the total for the week of April 3 is $402.50.

Exercise 1   Written

1. The cash receipts record of the Charles Bellmore family for the week of September 1 is shown below.

Date		Explanation	Amount
19—			
Sept.	*1*	*C. A. Bellmore; take-home salary*	*235 00*
	1	*C. A. Bellmore; bonus*	*40 75*
	3	*Ruth Bellmore; salary*	*62 50*
	4	*Bottle deposit refund*	*1 25*
	5	*Sale of used furniture*	*12 50*
	6	*Dividend on government life insurance*	*20 50*
	6	*Repayment of personal loan*	*20 00*

Find the Bellmores' total cash receipts for the week. To do this, place the edge of a sheet of paper under the last line. Then add the column and write the total on the paper.

2. For the week of June 10, Karl Stanley, an office manager, had the following cash receipts: take-home salary, $248.90; dividend on stock, $35.75; interest on a bond, $71.88; life insurance dividend, $50.27; sale of used lawn mower, $25. What were his total receipts for the week?

3. For October, the Moore family's cash income from work was a take-home salary of $280.24 and commissions of $346.78. They also received $25 as a gift, $80.40 from a savings bond, and $475 from selling their car. What were their total receipts?

4. A high school student received cash during July, as follows: wages for full-time job, $252.80; wages for part-time job, $32.20; tips, $23.45; sale of auto parts, $9.75; bottle refund, $1.28. How much cash did he receive for the month?

WHERE DID OUR MONEY GO ?

WELL, LET'S LOOK AT THE RECORD

The personal cash payments record. Shown below is the cash payments record of the Robert Mason family for the week of April 3.

Cash Payments Record

DATE		EXPLANATION	AMOUNT	
19— April	3	Rent for April	125	00
	3	Electric bill for March	14	68
	3	Fuel bill	21	40
	4	Car payment	78	30
	4	Gas and oil	5	40
	6	Food purchases	43	22
	7	Clothing	28	65
	7	Deposit to savings account	10	00
	8	Weekly allowances — children	4	50
		Total	331	15

Cash payments record for the Robert Mason family

Each payment by Mr. or Mrs. Mason is recorded in the family cash payments record. For the week of April 3 the total, as shown, is $331.15. The Mason children keep records of their own.

Exercise 2   Written

1. The cash payments record of the Charles Bellmore family for the week of September 1 is shown below.

Date		Explanation	Amount	
19— Sept.	1	Mortgage payment on home	90	00
	1	Monthly life insurance premium	22	50
	2	Fuel and electricity	32	45
	3	Food purchases	41	23
	4	Doctor's bill	12	00
	5	Savings bond purchase	18	75
	5	Clothing	28	55
	5	Gas, oil, tune-up	23	25

Find the Bellmores' total cash payments for the week. To do this, place the edge of a sheet of paper under the last line. Then add the column and write the total on the paper.

2. The Santori family uses a cash payments record that has special columns for classifying the payments. The family's payments for one month are shown below.

Pay-ments	Classification of Payments					
	Food	Cloth-ing	Hous-ing	Operat-ing	Develop-ment	Sav-ings
149 90	43 00		60 00	25 40	21 50	
129 10	38 50	4 75		32 10	18 75	35 00
156 30	46 65		60 00	28 75	20 90	
158 85	35 10	30 50		35 25	23 00	35 00
86 10	15 25	35 00		20 60	15 25	

In this form, payments are recorded on one line at the end of each full or partial week within the month. On each line the amounts are entered first in the Classification of Payments columns. Amounts are then added across to find the total for the week, and the sum is entered in the Payments column. Totals for the month are found by adding the columns.

a Place the edge of a sheet of paper under the last line, add the columns, and write the totals on the paper.

b Prove your work by adding across (horizontally) the totals of the six Classification of Payments columns. The sum should equal the total of the Payments column.

3. The Forest family also uses a cash payments record that has special columns but for different types of payments. The payments for one month are shown below.

Pay-ments	Classification of Payments					
	Hous-ing	Food	Cloth-ing	Per-sonal	Trans-portation	Sav-ings
241 50	110 00	30 75		7 00	75 00	18 75
46 05		29 50	9 95	2 50	4 10	
67 25		32 15		12 50	3 85	18 75
113 65		31 20	37 50	39 75	5 20	
37 65		16 80	3 70	14 50	2 65	

Find the column totals and prove your work in the way you did in Problem 2.

Exercise 3   Written

1. Chester Mead's cash receipts record for July is shown below. What was the total of his cash receipts for the month?

Date		Explanation	Amount
July	1	Interest on savings	25 34
	7	Salary	192 70
	7	Commission	175 30
	10	Income tax refund	36 78
	15	Dividends on stock	8 45
	21	Salary	192 70
	21	Commission	196 20

2. Edna Cross, a factory worker, received the following take-home pay for the four weeks of February: $84.80, $87.20, $82.35, and $92.40. During that month she also received $10 from a friend in repayment of a loan, and $25 in cash as an award from her employer for a cost-saving suggestion. Her life insurance policy paid a cash dividend on February 15 of $16.78. What were her total cash receipts for February?

3. The Harris family's payments for the month of January were as follows:

Food	$176.48	Operating Expenses	$143.62
Clothing	94.79	Development	108.25
Housing	145.00	Savings	93.75

What were their total payments for the month?

4. For the first six months of a year, Henry Remick ate in restaurants. His monthly expenditures for food during that time were as follows: $145.25, $157.60, $164.73, $139.10, $153.38, and $147.35. How much did he spend for food?

5. Mr. Luther Anderson, a homeowner, uses fuel oil for heating his house. During the last heating season, from September to June, he bought the following quantities of fuel oil: 215 gal.; 191 gal.; 188 gal.; 212 gal.; 168 gal.; 197 gal.; 184 gal.; 208 gal. How many gallons of fuel oil did he buy?

6. On an automobile trip, Mr. Robb bought gasoline, as follows:

14 gal.........	$5.32	16 gal.........	$6.16
12 gal.........	4.44	10 gal.........	3.90
15 gal.........	5.40	8 gal.........	2.96
11 gal.........	4.07	13 gal.........	4.94

a How many gallons did he buy?

b What was the total cost?

PART 1b Numerals

Meaning of numerals. When you keep a cash record or any record involving numbers, you make certain marks to represent the numbers. These marks are called numerals. Thus, 8, 16, and 136 are numerals.

A *numeral* is a name for a number. Any number may have many different numerals or names representing it. For example, $6 + 2$, $9 - 1$, 2×4, $24 \div 3$, and $\frac{16}{2}$, as well as 8, are all numerals or names for the same number, which is eight. The numeral 8, however, is the most common and simplest numeral or name for the number eight.

THEY ALL NAME THE SAME NUMBER

Number sentences. To show that two numerals are names for the same number, we may write an equal sign ($=$) between them. Thus, we may write $5 + 3 = 4 \times 2$. This statement about $5 + 3$ and 4×2 is called a *number sentence*. It says that the number named by $5 + 3$ is equal to the number named by 4×2.

A number sentence may be either true or false. The sentence $24 \div 3 = 2 + 6$ is true, because $24 \div 3$ and $2 + 6$ are names for the same number. But the sentence $2 \times 4 = 5 + 1$ is false, because 2×4 is the name for 8 whereas $5 + 1$ is the name for 6.

Exercise 4   Oral

For each sentence below, state whether it is true or false.

1. $2+6=6+2$
2. $2\times4=4\times2$
3. $2+4=4\times2$
4. $12-4=4\times2$
5. $4\times3=6\times2$

6. $2\times5=2+5$
7. $9\div1=1\times9$
8. $7+3=8+2$
9. $16\div8=14\div7$
10. $18-12=17-10$

11. $8\div2=8-2$
12. $14+1=5\times3$
13. $2\times3=18\div6$
14. $3+7=5+5$
15. $12\div3=16-12$

Open sentences. A sentence like $6 + 2 = 5 + N$, in which a numeral is missing, is incomplete and is called an *open sentence*. As it stands, it is neither true nor false. We complete it by replacing N with a numeral that makes the sentence true. Obviously, the numeral is 3;

so we may write $6 + 2 = 5 + 3$. The number that makes the sentence true is the value of N. In this case, the value is 3.

Exercise 5   Written

Copy each sentence, replacing the question mark or letter with the numeral that makes the sentence true.

1. $5 + 4 = 4 + ?$
2. $8 + 7 = ? + 8$
3. $N + 6 = 6 + 8$
4. $6 \times 4 = ? \times 6$
5. $8 \times N = 3 \times 8$

6. $N \times 7 = 7 \times 5$
7. $8 + 6 = 10 + N$
8. $12 + ? = 10 + 8$
9. $N + 7 = 5 + 6$
10. $10 + 5 = ? + 3$

11. $12 - 7 = 8 - ?$
12. $3 \times N = 2 \times 6$
13. $N \times 6 = 3 \times 8$
14. $15 + 6 = 7 \times ?$
15. $18 \div 3 = 24 \div ?$

REVIEW ASSIGNMENT   1b

1. Copy each sentence, replacing the question mark or letter with a numeral that makes the sentence true.

a $9 + 4 = ? + 9$
b $5 \times 3 = ? \times 5$
c $5 + 7 = 10 + N$
d $? + 6 = 5 + 5$
e $10 - 7 = 8 - ?$

f $12 - N = 7 - 5$
g $2 \times N = 4 \times 3$
h $12 \times 3 = 4 \times N$
i $18 \div 6 = 21 \div N$
j $14 \div 7 = 8 \div ?$

2. Mr. Field's wages for four weeks in May were $120.65, $118.40, $125.85, and $122.70. Mrs. Field's earnings for the same four weeks were $78.20, $84.60, $80.50, and $85.75. What was the total of their combined earnings for the month?

3. On Monday morning, Roy Snow, a high school sophomore, had $6.17. During the week he received $3.95 for cutting neighbors' lawns and $3.75 for working an afternoon at a gas station.

a What total amount of money did he take in during the week?

b What total amount did he have to spend during the week?

4. On September 1, Donald Gray had 145 gallons of fuel oil on hand. During the heating season he purchased more oil as follows: 195 gal.; 178 gal.; 226 gal.; 242 gal.; 191 gal.; 201 gal.

a How many gallons did he purchase during the season?

b How many did he have available to use during the season?

5. Joe and Alice Miller operate a summer day camp for boys. On July 1 they had 18 pounds of sugar on hand. During July they purchased more sugar as follows: 35 lb., 25 lb., 40 lb., 45 lb. What total quantity did they have available for use during July?

PART 1c Addition

Need for and meaning of addition. Addition is needed in finding the totals of the amount columns of cash receipts and cash payments records. Addition is also required in many other personal and business problems.

Addition is the operation of combining two numbers to give one number. The numbers to be added are called *addends*. The result is called the *sum*.

Principles of addition. There are three general rules or principles that you should keep in mind when doing addition.

1. When you have two numbers to add, the order in which you add them does not affect the sum. Thus, $3 + 4 = 4 + 3$. This is called the *commutative* (kŏ-mū′tȧ-tĭve) *principle of addition*.

   This principle permits us to add numbers either up or down, or to the right or left. We use it when we check addition by adding again in the opposite direction.

2. Addition can be done on only two numbers at a time. When you have three or more numbers to add, the way you group the numbers does not affect the sum. $(3 + 4) + 5 = 3 + (4 + 5)$. This is called the *associative principle of addition*.

   The commutative and associative principles permit us, when adding several numbers, to skip around to find combinations that make 10 or some other number that is easy to add.

3. Adding 0 to a number does not change the number. $5 + 0 = 5$. Therefore, 0 is called the *identity number* for addition.

Exercise 6   Oral

For each sentence below, state what numeral should be substituted for the question mark or letter to make the sentence true.

1. $5+4=?$
2. $8+7=N$
3. $N=9+6$
4. $?=5+8$
5. $74+0=N$
6. $N+0=15$
7. $4+N=9$

8. $?=32+0$
9. $8+4=?+8$
10. $9+N=7+9$
11. $15+N=15$
12. $8=8+?$
13. $0+35=?$
14. $N+2=10$

15. $(7+8)+2=7+(N+2)$
16. $6+(4+9)=(N+4)+9$
17. $8+(N+3)=(8+6)+3$
18. $5+8+4=?$
19. $N=3+8+7+4$
20. $8+4+2+6=N$
21. $N=6+0+8+4$

Exercise 7   Written

Copy each sentence below, replacing the question mark or letter with a numeral that makes the sentence true.

1. $N = 34 + 9$
2. $6 + 78 = ?$
3. $18 + 0 = N$

4. $13 + 9 = N + 13$
5. $? + 42 = 42 + 18$
6. $N + 63 = 63$

7. $(8+9) + 5 = 8 + (? + 5)$
8. $N + (6+7) = (4+6) + 7$
9. $N = 7 + 6 + 4 + 3$

Exercise 8   Written

Show that the following are true. Use the method shown in the example at the right.

1. $(9+6) + 8 = 9 + (6+8)$

2. $(8+9) + 2 = (8+2) + 9$

3. $35 + (15+27) = (35+15) + 27$

4. $(68+75) + 25 = 68 + (75+25)$

Example
$(4 + 5) + 6 = 4 + (5 + 6)$
$9 + 6 = 4 + 11$
$15 = 15$

5. $(18+25) + 12 = (18+12) + 25$

6. $(27+49) + 13 = (27+13) + 49$

Exercise 9   Oral Drill

You can increase your speed in addition by combining two or three numbers mentally, especially those that total 10, and adding them to the others in one amount.

This method is indicated in the first column below. In adding from the bottom up, you would think "10, 24, 34, 44." In checking by adding from the top down, you would think "10, 20, 34, 44."

Add orally, from the bottom up, the columns given below, using groups of two or three numbers wherever possible. Repeat the drill, adding the columns from the top down.

	a	b	c	d	e	f	g	h	i	j
9	5	4	1	5	6	5	4	4	6	9
4	5	6	9	5	4	8	3	8	1	3
1	6	5	9	6	8	4	6	5	8	8
6	4	2	1	2	3	3	2	2	1	4
8	2	1	8	3	7	3	4	5	5	6
6	8	9	1	5	6	0	9	6	3	4
5	4	4	5	2	3	5	1	7	6	5
3	1	6	3	1	2	6	8	3	2	3
2	5	7	2	7	4	4	2	8	7	7

44

Drills for accuracy and speed are provided on pages 515 to 532. One such drill for addition is given on page 515.

Checking addition. The best method of checking a total in addition is by *reverse addition;* that is, by adding a column in the opposite direction from that in which it was added the first time. As this process almost always results in new combinations of numbers, it usually avoids the danger of making the same error twice.

Exercise 10   Written

Copy and add the following problems. Check each result by reverse addition.

1.	2.	3.	4.	5.	6.
$18.79	$ 7.45	$98.45	$55.38	$ 8.32	$16.75
2.11	23.45	10.63	31.02	11.71	90.34
1.92	74.17	2.82	94.46	91.07	1.03
17.28	76.52	30.26	6.74	87.65	82.11
.55	1.48	81.74	10.23	11.32	20.97
21.05	39.40	26.36	84.17	10.13	15.83

Horizontal addition. You saw in the problem at the top of page 5 how horizontal addition is used in a cash payments record. Adding horizontally saves the time and labor that would be required to write the amounts in a column and to add them vertically.

Exercise 11   Written

Copy the following problems and find the missing totals. Get the line totals by horizontal addition and the column totals by vertical addition. Check by adding the column totals horizontally and the line totals vertically. These two totals should be equal.

1. $2 + 5 + 3 =$
   $6 + 3 + 5 =$
   $4 + 9 + 2 =$
   $+ \quad + \quad =$

2. $6 + 8 + 9 =$
   $7 + 2 + 6 =$
   $4 + 7 + 5 =$
   $+ \quad + \quad =$

3. $7 + 1 + 3 + 9 =$
   $5 + 5 + 6 + 8 =$
   $3 + 8 + 2 + 3 =$
   $+ \quad + \quad + \quad =$

4. $31 + 23 =$
   $21 + 19 =$
   $26 + 85 =$
   $33 + 95 =$
   $+ \quad =$

5. $26 + 44 + 37 =$
   $31 + 33 + 56 =$
   $73 + 35 + 56 =$
   $17 + 53 + 37 =$
   $+ \quad + \quad =$

6. $122 + \quad 39 + 221 =$
   $140 + \quad 66 + \quad 84 =$
   $66 + 300 + 219 =$
   $115 + \quad 79 + \quad 6 =$
   $+ \quad + \quad =$

REVIEW ASSIGNMENT 1c

✔ *Check each calculation as soon as you complete it.*

1. Copy each sentence, replacing the question mark or letter with a numeral that makes the sentence true.

   a $N = 0 + 24$ **d** $6 \times N = 3 \times 8$
   b $44 + 8 = N + 44$ **e** $24 \div 8 = 18 \div N$
   c $81 + ? = 81$ **f** $12 - 8 = ? - 20$

2. On September 1, Homer Bell had on hand a quantity of fuel oil that cost him $12.17. During the heating season he purchased additional quantities at the following costs: $34.60; $32.87; $29.46; $41.44; $38.06; $36.27; $39.88. What was the cost of the oil that he had available for use during the season?

3. At the end of the season, Homer Bell (Problem 2) had on hand an unused quantity of oil that cost $22.49. What was the cost of the oil that he used during the season?

4. At the beginning of a heating season, Dexter Jones had on hand a quantity of fuel oil that cost him $16.45. During the season, he purchased additional quantities at a total cost of $301.22. At the end of the season there remained in his fuel tank a quantity of oil that cost $24.95.

   a What was the cost of the oil available during the season?

   b What was the cost of the oil used during the season?

5. On Tuesday morning, Mrs. Blake had $17.36. Before leaving for work, Mr. Blake gave her an additional $35 for shopping purposes. How much money did she have for shopping that day?

6. Mrs. Blake (Problem 5) counted her money Tuesday evening and found that she had $14.78. Assuming that she hadn't lost any of the money, how much did she spend during the day?

7. Friday morning, Ted Grant had $4.13. On the way to school he collected 65 cents from a classmate who owed him that amount. There were no other receipts. How much did he spend if he had $3.42 at the end of the day?

8. Bob Thompson has a Sunday morning paper route. Last Sunday, the papers he sold cost him $25.80 and he received $32.25 for them.

   a How much was his gross profit?

   b How much net profit did he have left after paying his younger brother $1.25 for helping deliver the papers?

   The *gross profit* is the amount remaining after deducting the cost of the papers from the sales. The *net profit* is the amount remaining after deducting the expense ($1.25) from the gross profit. Net profit is often called *net income.*

Personal Checkbook Records

Many persons deposit most of their cash income in a checking account at a bank and make larger payments by check. The checking account is easy to use, and the canceled checks provide a record of payments.

CHECKING ACCOUNTS PROVIDE

SAFETY

CONVENIENCE

RECORD

PART 2a   Records of Deposits and Checks

Using deposit slips. When a person makes a deposit, he records it on a *deposit slip*.

FOR DEPOSIT TO THE ACCOUNT OF		Dollars	Cents
ROBERT MASON	CURRENCY	43	70
	CHECKS *13-1*	*135*	*45*
September 12, 19--	*56-5*	*10*	*50*
FREEDOM NATIONAL BANK			
AKRON, OHIO			
⑆0412⑈0057⑆ 406⑈56500⑈	TOTAL	*189*	*65*

Deposit slip for Robert Mason

The total value of all bills and coins is listed after "Currency." Each check is entered separately and may be identified by its American Bankers Association transit number. This number is the top part of a fraction printed near the upper right corner of the check, as shown on the checks on page 14. All items listed on the deposit slip are added and the total is shown on the last line.

Exercise 1   Written

In each of the following, list in a column the amounts of the total bills, the total coins, and the individual checks. Then find the total deposit.

✓*Check each calculation as soon as you complete it.*

1. Irving Ambler deposited the following items in the First National Bank, Rochester:

> 3 ten-dollar bills and 2 five-dollar bills
> His pay check for $90.86
> A check for $10, which was a gift from his aunt

2. Mary Kilty is treasurer of the Kansas Association of Educational Secretaries. She has the following items for deposit:

> **Bills:**   5 twenties; 4 tens; 8 fives; 15 ones
> **Coin:**   8 halves; 17 quarters; 5 dimes; 17 nickels
> **Checks:** $7.50; $15.00; $22.50; $37.50.

3. Ray Kent, treasurer of the FBLA of the Greenway High School, deposited the following receipts from the sale of boxes of candy:

> **Bills:**   4-10's; 9-5's; 23-1's
> **Coin:**   15 halves; 11 quarters; 7 dimes; 12 nickels
> **Checks:** $1.75; $2.50; $3.25

Using check stubs. A depositor may write orders directing the bank to make payments for him. These orders are known as *checks.*

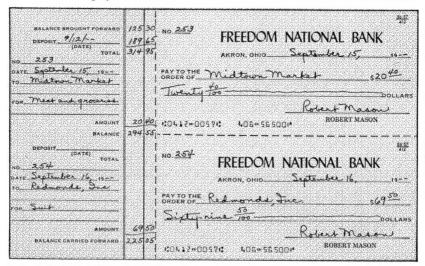

Check stubs and checks for Robert Mason

As shown on the check stubs above, the depositor adds each deposit to, and subtracts each check from, the preceding balance on the stub. In this way he always knows the balance against which checks may be drawn.

Exercise **2**   Written

√*Check each calculation as soon as you complete it.*

1. Karl Jay's check stubs for August show the balance in his account on August 1, his deposits, and the checks which he drew. What is the correct balance after each deposit or check?

Aug.	1 Balance	$231.45		Aug. 15 Check	$18.50
	7 Deposit	28.75		Balance	
	Total			18 Deposit	32.85
	12 Check	37.54		Total	
	Balance			27 Check	21.40
				Balance	

2. Find the new balance in each of the following:

	Previous Balance	Deposits	Checks Issued	New Balance
a	$245.60	$60.00	$7.34; $17.75; $25.56	$254.95*
b	625.25	$92.45; $25.00	$52.45; $13.25; $8.86; $5.25	
c	536.28	$39.41; $62.25	$10.35; $7.44; $45.70	
d	974.53	None	$12.46; $9.56; $21.20; $5.75	
e	521.30	$76.30	$6.85; $25.00; $9.25; $19.50	

3. Gary Cody's checkbook showed a balance of $150.75 on Monday, June 14. Later in the week he deposited $99.80, $21.68, and $18.36. He wrote checks for $28.37, $33.56, $27.43, $3.49, and $78.21. Find his checkbook balance at the end of the week.

REVIEW ASSIGNMENT **2a**

1. Copy each sentence, replacing the question mark or letter with a numeral that makes the sentence true.

a $? = 16 + 0$		**f** $N - 8 = 10$	
b $13 + 14 = N$		**g** $16 - N = 12$	
c $N + 17 = 17$		**h** $3 \times ? = 9 \times 3$	
d $8 + 10 = ? + 8$		**i** $4 \times N = 32$	
e $7 + N = 6 + 4$		**j** $5 = 15 \div N$	

*The answer is supplied for this problem and for others later in the book. If you get the same answer, you are probably solving the problem the right way. If you do not get the same answer, you should check your method of solving the problem and your calculations. Either or both may be incorrect.

✔ *Check each calculation as soon as you complete it.*

2. Lewis Flood's bank balance on September 1 was $782.50. During the month he deposited $94.65 and withdrew $127.70. What was his bank balance at the end of the month?

3. Frank Pierce had a bank balance of $324.36 on the morning of August 15. During the day he made a deposit of $52.38. His bank balance at the end of the day was $282.88. How much did he withdraw from the bank during the day?

4. On September 15, Marvin West, a householder, had on hand a quantity of fuel oil that cost him $18.50. During the heating season he purchased additional oil costing $268.43. At the end of the season there remained in the fuel tank oil that cost $24.15.

a What was the cost of the oil available for use?
b What was the cost of the oil used?

5. Ray Rogers, a college student, operates a roadside stand during the summer months, selling soft drinks, ice cream, fruit, and candy. Last year, his total sales for the month of August were $3,377.14. The goods he sold cost him $2,296.58.

a What was his gross profit for the month?
b His expenses for the month were as follows: rent of stand and equipment, $125; electricity for lights and refrigerator, $22.20; supplies, consisting of paper bags, twine, ice cream cones, and similar items, $45.22; hired help, $192.70. What was the total of his operating expenses?
c What was the amount of his net income (net profit) for the month?

PART 2b   Subtraction

Need for subtraction. You use subtraction when you deduct the amount of each check from your check-stub balance. You will often find subtraction necessary in solving other personal and home problems.

Meaning of subtraction. When you use subtraction, two numbers are given. They are the *minuend* and the *subtrahend*. You subtract the subtrahend from the minuend. The result is called the *difference*.

58 minuend
26 subtrahend

32 difference

(Check: $26 + 32 = 58$)

In the subtraction expression $58 - 26$, 58 represents the sum of two addends. One of them is 26. The other is the number to which 26 was added to give 58. That is, $N + 26 = 58$. To find N, we "undo" the addition by subtracting 26. The difference, 32, is the other addend. Thus, N (the other addend) $= 58 - 26 = 32$.

Hence, when we perform subtraction, we are finding one of the two addends of a given sum where the other addend is known. We find the missing addend by subtracting the known addend from the sum.

Inverse operations of addition and subtraction. If you add 26 to 32 and then subtract 26 from the sum, the result is 32, the number you started with. Subtracting 26 "undoes" what was done by adding 26. Hence, if $N + 26 = 58$, then $58 - 26 = N$, and $N = 32$.

Similarly, if you subtract 26 from 32 and then add 26 to the difference, the result is 32. Adding 26 "undoes" what was done by subtracting 26. Hence, if $N - 26 = 6$, then $6 + 26 = N = 32$.

Operations that "undo" one another are called *inverse operations*. Thus, subtraction is the inverse of addition; and addition is the inverse of subtraction. You use the latter principle when you check subtraction by adding the difference and the subtrahend.

Identity number for subtraction. Subtracting 0 from a number does not change that number. For example, $5 - 0 = 5$. 0 is therefore called the *identity number* for subtraction.

Exercise 3 Oral

State the final result of the operations in each of the following.

1. $7+1-1$ 3. $12-8+8$ 5. $N+6-6$ 7. $60+10-10$
2. $9-5+5$ 4. $25+5-5$ 6. $N-8+8$ 8. $x-4+4$

Exercise 4 Oral

State the value of N in each of the following sentences.

1. $9-8=N$ 6. $8-0=N$ 11. $22=N-6$ 16. $N+0=10$
2. $N=14-8$ 7. $N-8=14$ 12. $17=N-9$ 17. $31=N-0$
3. $N=9+7$ 8. $N-7=13$ 13. $11=N+8$ 18. $15=N+0$
4. $6+9=N$ 9. $N+7=15$ 14. $13=N+6$ 19. $15-N=8$
5. $N=0+8$ 10. $N+2=11$ 15. $N-0=14$ 20. $8+N=18$

Checking subtraction. Every subtraction should be checked immediately. The best check is to add the subtrahend and difference. The sum should equal the minuend.

A drill for accuracy and speed in subtraction is given on page 516.

Exercise 5   Written

Copy the figures and subtract in each of the following. Check each result immediately by adding the subtrahend and difference.

1. 32,756	2. $28,485.34	3. $56,318.48	4. $35,405.56
4,254	2,670.49	3,908.69	5,826.37

5. 51,006	6. $75,800.00	7. $63,003.06	8. $20,220.20
4,936	24,847.58	46,606.87	15,738.49

REVIEW ASSIGNMENT 2 b

✔ *Be sure to check each calculation as soon as you complete it.*

1. Copy each sentence, replacing N with a numeral that makes the sentence true.

a $N + 6 = 15$ c $20 - N = 15$
b $12 + N = 20$ d $N - 7 = 18$

2. On the morning of August 10, Lorin Dunn's bank balance was $213.46. He deposited $86.14 during the day. At the end of the day his bank balance was $219.75. What was the amount that he withdrew from the bank during the day?

3. Fred Paige had on hand a quantity of fuel oil on September 10 that cost him $17.00. During the heating season he purchased additional oil costing $282.17. At the end of the season he had on hand a quantity of oil that cost him $21.50. What was the cost of the oil he used during the season?

4. Ann White is the owner of Ann's Hat Shop. At the close of the day, March 31, she took an inventory and found that she had hats on hand that cost $6,247.55. During April she purchased additional hats costing $3,354.65.

a What was the cost of the hats that she had available for sale during the month?

b After the close of business on April 30 she had on hand a stock of hats that cost $5,835.40. What was the cost of the hats sold during April?

5. The March sales of Paul Moore, owner of a stationery store, amounted to $15,942.18.

a What was his gross profit for the month if the goods he sold cost him $11,140.90?

b If the total operating expenses amounted to $3,716.34, what was his net profit (net income) for the month?

SECTION 3

Proving the Checkbook Balance

As a general rule the bank mails to each depositor a monthly report showing his deposits, his withdrawals, and the balance of his account. The depositor uses this report to check the accuracy of his own records and the accuracy of the report itself.

WHY DO THE CHECKBOOK AND BANK BALANCES DIFFER?

IS MY CHECKBOOK BALANCE CORRECT?

IS THE BANK RIGHT?

PART 3a The Reconciliation Statement

The bank statement. The monthly report that the bank sends to the depositor is called a *bank statement*. Shown below is the bank statement Robert Mason received from the Freedom National Bank early in October, covering his account for the month of September.

STATEMENT OF YOUR ACCOUNT

FREEDOM NATIONAL BANK
AKRON, OHIO

Robert Mason
48 Wabash Road
Akron, Ohio 44314

ACCOUNT NO. 406-56500

CHECKS		DEPOSITS	DATE	BALANCE
		BALANCE FORWARD	Sep 1 70	220.30
16.50			Sep 3 70	203.80
20.00	15.00		Sep 5 70	168.80
35.00	7.50		Sep 8 70	126.30
		189.65	Sep 12 70	315.95
69.50	20.40		Sep 17 70	226.05
		100.00	Sep 18 70	326.05
28.55	15.75	88.60	Sep 20 70	370.35
1.00 SC			Sep 29 70	369.35

CC CERTIFIED CHECK	EC ERROR CORRECTED	OD OVERDRAWN
CM CREDIT MEMO	LS LIST OF CHECKS	RT RETURNED ITEM
DM DEBIT MEMO	NC CHECK NOT COUNTED	SC SERVICE CHARGE

Bank statement for Robert Mason

The bank statement on page 19 shows among other things:

1. The balance at the beginning of the month.
2. The checks paid by the bank during the month.
3. The bank's service charge for the month.
4. The amounts deposited during the month.
5. The balance after each day's transactions.

Of the ten items in the "Checks" column, nine are checks that were paid by the bank. The item of $1.00 SC is the bank's service charge for handling the account for the month.

The reconciliation statement. On October 2, Robert Mason received the bank statement shown on page 19 together with the canceled checks paid by the bank during September.

The balance on the statement is $369.35. The balance shown on his last check stub for September was $346.65. The difference is caused by the service charge and the *outstanding checks*, that is, checks issued but not presented at the bank for payment.

To bring the two balances into agreement, Mason prepared the following reconciliation statement:

Robert Mason
Reconciliation Statement
September 30, 19 — —

Checkbook balance	$346.65	Bank statement balance		$369.35
Deduct		Deduct		
Service charge	1.00	Outstanding checks:		
		#257	$12.95	
		#258	10.75	23.70
Correct checkbook				
balance	$345.65	Available bank balance		$345.65

Reconciliation statement for Robert Mason

By examining the bank statement, Mason found the $1.00 service charge that had been subtracted on the bank statement but not on the check stubs. He therefore had to subtract $1.00 from the checkbook balance on the left side of the reconciliation statement to show the correct checkbook balance, $345.65.

By comparing the canceled checks with the check stubs, he found that check No. 257 for $12.95 and check No. 258 for $10.75 were outstanding. He therefore subtracted their sum, $23.70, from the bank statement balance on the right side to show the available bank balance of $345.65.

The available bank balance, $345.65, is the same as the correct checkbook balance, $345.65.

This process of bringing the bank statement balance and the checkbook balance into agreement with each other is called *reconciling the bank balance*. The statement showing the calculation of the reconciliation is called the *reconciliation statement*.

WHY IS MY BANK STATEMENT BALANCE LARGER THAN MY CHECKBOOK BALANCE?

Exercise 1   Written

Prepare a reconciliation statement for each of the following. Use your own name in the heading of Problems 1 through 4.

✓ *Be sure to check each calculation as soon as you complete it.*

	Date	Check-book Balance	Bank State-ment Balance	Service Charge	Outstanding Checks
1.	May 31	$222.90	$248.03	$1.30	No. 56, $18.45; No. 62, $7.98 Adjusted Balances, $221.60
2.	July 31	502.99	568.24	1.10	No. 21, $3.98; No. 23, $35.42; No. 25, $26.95
3.	Dec. 31	39.91	99.06	1.75	No. 73, $17.81; No. 75, $33.76; No. 76, $6.99; No. 77, $2.34
4.	April 30	633.39	740.04	2.20	No. 93, $3.48; No. 94, $7.79; No. 95, $95.60; No. 96, $1.98

5. Otto Waldo's checkbook balance of July 31 was $285.92. His July 31 bank statement showed a balance of $343.58. Checks outstanding were No. 485 for $29.55, No. 493 for $18.75, and No. 495 for $11.76. The bank service charge for July was $2.40.

REVIEW ASSIGNMENT 3a

1. Find the value of N in each of the following.

   a $N + 8 = 25$ **b** $N - 15 = 20$ **c** $5 \times N = 40$

2. Warren Hoffman's checkbook balance on July 31 was $542.13. For the same date, his bank statement for July showed a bank balance of $583.91. Included on the statement was a service charge of $1.56. Checks outstanding were: No. 110, $13.25; No. 114, $30.09. Prepare a reconciliation statement.

3. For the month of June, Owen Sinclair, who operates a men's wear store, had sales amounting to $12,536. The cost of the goods sold was $7,953. Operating expenses were $3,706. Find the gross profit and the net income (net profit) for the month.

4. Raymond Harrington, owner of a stationery store, took an inventory after the close of business on August 31 and found that he had on hand a stock of merchandise that cost $8,438. During September he purchased additional merchandise costing $6,217.

- **a** What was the cost of the merchandise that Harrington had available for sale during September?

- **b** Harrington took an inventory at the close of business on September 30 and found that the stock of merchandise on hand cost $9,113. What was the cost of the goods he sold during September?

5. Raymond Harrington, owner of the stationery store referred to in Problem 4, placed $75 in change in his cash register on the morning of September 30. At the close of the day, the register totals showed that he had taken in $313.42 and had paid out $11.81. Upon counting the money in the cash drawer, he found the amount to be $376.31.

- **a** Was this the correct amount that should have been in the cash drawer?

- **b** If not, was the cash over or short? How much?

PART 3b   Special Reconciliation Problems

◆ **Reconciliation statement of Ross Conroy.** Ross Conroy's bank statement for June showed a bank balance of $460.80 on June 30. His checkbook balance on that date was $460.20. Upon comparing the bank statement and canceled checks with his checkbook record, he found the following:

A service charge of $1.90 had been subtracted on the bank statement but not on the check stubs.

A check for $35, which he wrote and cashed at the bank on June 14, had not been recorded and subtracted on the stubs.

A deposit of $75 on June 20 was omitted on the check stubs.

Check No. 221 for $4.60 had been recorded on the stub as $6.40. This was $1.80 more than the correct amount.

Checks No. 234 and 235, totaling $25.70, were outstanding.

A deposit of $65 on June 30 was recorded in the checkbook but was deposited too late to appear on the bank statement.

I FORGOT TO RECORD A CHECK!

With this information, Mr. Conroy prepared the following reconciliation statement:

Ross Conroy

Reconciliation Statement

June 30, 19--

Checkbook balance		$460.20		Bank statement balance		$460.80
Deduct				Deduct		
Service				Outstanding checks:		
charge	$ 1.90			#234 $18.50		
Check not				#235 7.20	25.70	
recorded	35.00	36.90				
					$435.10	
		$423.30		Add		
Add				Deposit not recorded	65.00	
Deposit						
omitted	$75.00					
Amount on						
stub #221						
too large	1.80	76.80				
Correct check-						
book balance		$500.10		Available bank balance		$500.10

Reconciliation statement for Ross Conroy

The unrecorded service charge and the check written and cashed at the bank but not recorded in the checkbook caused the checkbook balance to be $36.90 more than the correct amount. The omitted deposit and the error on the stub of check No. 221 caused the checkbook balance to be $76.80 less than the correct amount.

Hence $36.90 was subtracted from the checkbook balance, and $76.80 was added to that result to give the correct checkbook balance, $500.10.

The outstanding checks caused the bank statement balance to be $25.70 more than the available bank balance. The late deposit on June 30 caused it to be $65 less. Therefore, $25.70 was subtracted from the bank statement balance, and $65 was added to that result to give the available bank balance, $500.10.

❷ Exercise **2**   Written

Find the available bank balance in each of the following problems. Set up your solution in a form like the right half of the reconciliation statement shown on page 23.

✔ *Be sure to check each calculation as you complete it.*

	Date	Bank Statement Balance	Outstanding Checks	Late Deposit not Recorded on Bank Statement
1.	Jan. 31	$546.06	$47.53; $7.47; $51.80; $1.15	$93.25 $531.36
2.	July 31	170.53	$4.25; $15.21; $7.99; $6.75	25.00
3.	Feb. 28	707.64	$35.27; $6.16; $24.99; $6.04	56.82

4. A bank statement of May 31 shows a balance of $909.33. A deposit of $91.07 on May 31 was made too late to appear on the statement. Checks No. 379 for $9.87, No. 384 for $4.75, No. 386 for $33.33, and No. 387 for $2.99 are outstanding.

❸ Exercise **3**   Written

Find the correct checkbook balance in each of the following six problems. Set up your solution in a form similar to the left half of the illustration on page 23. In Problems 1 through 5, use August 31 as the date of the checkbook balance.

	Check-book Balance	Omitted on Check-Stub Record			Other Adjustments
		Service Charge	Check for	Deposit of	
1.	$343.26	$ .80	$12.25	$ 25.50	Check No. 27 for $16.75 entered on stub as $17.65 $356.61
2.	827.05	2.40	19.95	30.00	Check No. 93 for $3.70 entered on stub as $7.30
3.	763.52	1.20	None	120.00	Check No. 63 for $35.20 entered on stub as $25.30
4.	400.21	1.65	12.99	None	Deposit of $25.00 entered twice in checkbook

5. Your last check stub for the month shows a balance of $123.63. Upon examining your bank statement, you find that there is a service charge of $2.76 which has not been entered in the checkbook. Also, you find that check No. 33 for $9.60 was shown on the stub as $6.90. What is the correct checkbook balance?

6. At the end of June, Rice's checkbook showed a balance of $259.83. An examination of the bank statement showed that a deposit of $89.90 had not been entered on the stubs, and that a check No. 43 for $9.58 had been entered on the stub as $9.00. What was the correct checkbook balance?

▶ **Exercise 4**   Written

Prepare a reconciliation statement for each of the following problems. Use the illustration on page 23 as a guide. In Problems 1 through 7, use February 28 as the dates of the balances, and use your own name in the heading of each statement.

✓*Be sure to check each calculation immediately.*

	Bank Statement Balance	Checkbook Balance	Service Charge	Outstanding Checks	Other Adjustments
1.	$737.92	$626.58	$1.65	$15.60; $1.99; $9.60; $45.80	$40 deposit omitted on check stub
2.	353.00	315.42	2.25	$27.16; $10.80; $5.67; $4.20	Deposit of $8 entered twice on stub
3.	428.01	318.83	1.20	$36.12; $20.50; $123.00; $5.76	$75 late deposit omitted on bank statement
4.	336.29	131.64	.90	$33.06; $5.29; $67.20	Deposit of $100 not recorded on check stub
5.	257.58	200.10	.70	$8.75; $30.18; $22.50	Check for $3.25 omitted on check stub
6.	995.86	859.69	None	$60.80; $42.76; $33.59	Check for $19.98 entered as $19 on check stub
7.	401.02	564.22	None	$12.05; $15.25; $1.90; $7.60	$200 late deposit omitted from bank statement

8. Gene Faber's checkbook balance on June 1 was $229.04. His bank statement for that date showed a balance of $211.82. Checks outstanding were No. 46 for $7.25, No. 47 for $6.98, and No. 49 for $29.95. A deposit of $60, mailed on May 31, had been received by the bank too late to be entered on the statement. There was a service charge slip for $1.40.

9. The balance in Iris Kem's checkbook on July 31 was $99.36. The bank statement of that date showed a balance of

$97.35. Checks outstanding were: No. 63 for $7.50; No. 65 for $5.49. It was found that a deposit of $15.00 had been entered twice in the checkbook by error.

10. On April 30, Neal's checkbook showed a balance of $506.21. His April bank statement showed a balance of $514.49 on the same date. With the statement there was a slip showing that Neal's account had been charged $18.75 for a U.S. Savings Bond purchased for him by the bank. Checks outstanding were: No. 337 for $14.85, No. 340 for $4.95, and No. 342 for $7.23.

REVIEW ASSIGNMENT **3 b**

✔ *Be sure to check each calculation as soon as you complete it.*

1. Find the value of N in each of the following.

a $10 + N = 17$ **c** $6 \times N = 48$ **e** $22 - N = 22$
b $25 - N = 5$ **d** $18 \div N = 3$ **f** $0 + N = 41$

2. Oliver Marshall's checkbook balance on June 30 was $694.28. His bank statement for June showed a balance of $758.49 on June 30. Included on the statement was a service charge of $1.37. Outstanding checks were: No. 169, $24.84; No. 184, $8.55; No. 188, $32.19. Prepare a reconciliation statement.

3. The total sales of a service station last month amounted to $22,542. The cost of goods sold was $16,908. Operating expenses were $3,607. What was the net profit for the month?

4. On November 1, Fred Hudson, owner of Hudson's Sport & Ski Shop, had on hand a stock of goods that cost $25,894. During November he purchased additional goods costing $9,768. On November 30 he had on hand a stock of goods that cost $26,825.

   a What was the cost of the goods he sold during November?

   b Hudson's sales for November amounted to $12,752. What was the amount of his gross profit for the month?

5. Castle, a snack bar owner, placed $80 in change in his cash register Tuesday morning. The register totals at the end of the day showed that he had taken in $234.70 and had paid out $27.95. By actual count, the money in the cash drawer at the end of the day was $287.10. How much was the cash over or short?

▶ **6.** Morgan's bank statement showed a balance of $681.60 on May 1. His checkbook balance was $762.50. Checks outstanding were: No. 88, $22.50; No. 94, $119.62; No. 95, $37.83. A deposit of $258.75, made by mail on April 29, had not been received by the bank in time to be added to the statement. There was a service charge of $2.10. Prepare a reconciliation statement.

UNIT Two

Buying Problems

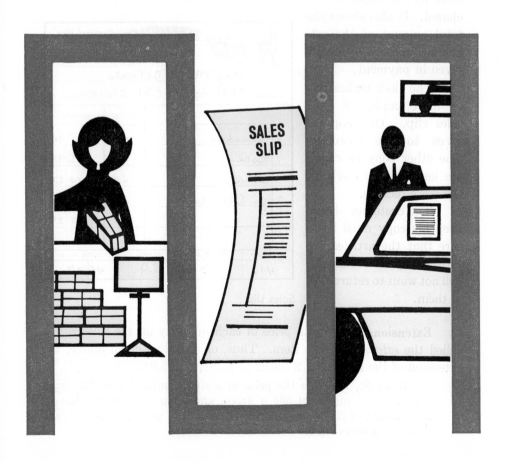

SECTION 4

Sales Slips

In many stores, when a customer makes a purchase, he is given a sales slip which serves as a record of the transaction. This sales slip also is evidence of the purchase if the customer should find later that an error has been made or that the goods must be returned.

PART 4a   Checking Calculations

Use of sales slips. The sales slip illustrated below shows the quantity, description, unit price, and total price for each article purchased. It also shows the total amount of the sale and the amount of money given in payment.

The clerk makes two or more copies of each sales slip. One copy is given to the customer. The other copy or copies are kept by the clerk for the store records.

The customer should keep his copy until he is sure that the articles are satisfactory and that he will not want to return any of them.

greenwood plaza elmore			
DATE 9/25/--			
SOLD TO Mrs. M. C. DeCarlo			
ADDRESS 36 Plainview St., Elmore			
		PRICE	AMOUNT
2	Slacks	7.97	15 94
1	Robe	6.95	6 95
3	Shirts	4.94	14 82
2	pr. Gloves	3.79	7 58
			45 29

NUMBER	CASH RECEIVED	CLERK	TOTAL SALE
416	50 00	L.9.	45 29

Sales slip

Extensions. The total price of each quantity on the sales slip is called the *extension* of the item. Thus, on the slip shown above, the extension of the first item, 2 slacks at $7.97, is $15.94.

At, or @, refers to the price of a single unit. Thus, "2 dozen eggs at 59¢" means *at* 59¢ *a dozen*, and "2 pounds of peaches @ 29¢" means *at* 29¢ *a pound*. But "2 pounds of peaches, 29¢," means that two pounds sell for 29¢.

Exercise 1   Oral

1. Give the extension for each of the following prices:

a 2 doz. eggs at 59¢
b 2 lb. peaches at 29¢
c 3 pkg. crackers at 41¢
d 4 cans tuna at 43¢

e 2 melons @ 49¢
f 3 bch. celery @ 42¢
g 3 jars pickles @ 33¢
h 5 bots. ketchup @ 35¢

2. Find the extended price for each article below:

0 6 pens at 2 for 29¢
   Think: 6 ÷ 2 = 3
        3 × 29¢ = 87¢
a 6 pkg. carrots at 2 for 33¢
b 8 cans peas @ 2 for 31¢

c 6 cans plums @ 3 for $1.00
d 9 bars soap @ 3 for 41¢
e 6 lemons at 2 for 15¢
f 4 cans soup @ 2 for 39¢
g 1 gal. salad oil at 52¢ a qt.

Exercise 2   Written

For each problem, list the items as they would appear on a sales slip. Show the unit price, extended price, and total sale.

1. Donna Jenkins buys at the Superway Market:

3 lb. stew beef at 79¢
2 doz. oranges at 67¢
2 lb. cheese at 89¢

5 lb. onions at 9¢
6 ears corn, 39¢
2 lb. butter at 79¢

2. The Fabrics Circus sells to Mrs. O. L. Greco:

3 yd. flannel @ $2.97
4 yd. corduroy @ $2.37
3 yd. velvet @ $4.49

4 yd. chintz, $2.76
3 zippers @ 49¢
6 spools thread @ 15¢

3. At the Naborhood Mart, Keith Loomis purchases:

3 lb. sausage @ 91¢
6 lb. apples @ 2 for 49¢

2 heads cabbage, 39¢
12 bars soap @ 4 for 29¢

4. Russo's Market sells the following to H. C. Marks:

5 lb. hamburger @ 75¢
2 lb. franks @ 84¢
3 lb. liver @ 59¢

3 boxes cake mix @ 41¢
3 bars of soap, 47¢
6 cans pet food @ 2 for 31¢

Counting change. Change is usually given in the fewest pieces possible. Thus, if you offer a $5 bill in payment of a purchase amounting to $2.73, your change ordinarily consists of 2 pennies, 1 quarter, and 2 one-dollar bills.

In giving you the change, the clerk first repeats the amount of the purchase, "$2.73." She then gives you 2 pennies, saying "$2.75"; then

1 quarter, saying "$3.00"; and then 2 one-dollar bills, saying "and two are $5.00."

Clerks sometimes make mistakes in counting, so you should always check the change they give you.

$2.75, $3.00, AND TWO ARE $5.00

Exercise **3**   Written

Make a copy of the form below. Complete the form by showing for each problem the number of pieces of each denomination given to the customer.   Proceed as in Problem 1.

Think: $5.37 and 3¢ are $5.40 (write 3 in the 1¢ column);
      and 10¢ are $5.50 (write 1 in the 10¢ column);
      and 50¢ are $6.00 (write 1 in the 50¢ column);
      and $4 are $10.00 (write 4 in the $1 column).

	Amount Received	Amount of Sale	Change 1¢	5¢	10¢	25¢	50¢	$1	$5
1.	$10.00	$5.37	3		1		1	4	
2.	1.00	.28							
3.	1.00	.59							
4.	5.00	2.17							
5.	10.00	3.49							
6.	1.00	.36							
7.	5.00	1.66							
8.	10.00	3.22							

REVIEW ASSIGNMENT **4** a

✓ *Don't forget. Check all calculations immediately.*

1. What numeral is represented by the letter in each of the following?

      a $N+12=40$ **c** $24-y=20$ **e** $N=12-0$
      b $x=0+9$ **d** $7\times z=56$ **f** $36\div r=4$

2. Subtract 34,769 from 72,002.

3. Paul Warner's checkbook balance on May 31 was $843.41. His May bank statement showed a balance of $913.72 on that date. The bank statement included a service charge amounting to $2.63 which had not been deducted in the checkbook. Outstanding checks were: No. 107, $42.18; No. 114, $7.47; No. 117, $23.29. Prepare a reconciliation statement.

4. Wednesday morning, Henry Cole, owner of Cole's Pastry Shop, placed $50 in change in his cash register. At the end of the day, there was $345.99 in the cash drawer. The register totals showed total receipts of $318.49 and paid-out totals of $22.75. By how much was the cash over or short?

5. Donald Gould makes the following deposit at his bank: 98 pennies, 21 nickels, 41 dimes, 16 quarters, 27 half dollars, 9 one-dollar bills, 7 five-dollar bills, 4 ten-dollar bills, 1 twenty-dollar bill, and checks for $35.64, $38.60, and $51.36. Find the amount of the deposit.

◖ **6.** On April 30, Ella Dorr's checkbook balance was $598.42. Her bank statement showed a balance of $432.29 on that date. One check, No. 212 for $84.82, was outstanding. A deposit of $250, made by mail, had not been received by the bank in time to be added to the statement. Recorded on the bank statement was a service charge of $.95. Prepare a reconciliation statement.

PART 4b Multiplication

Need for multiplication. When you buy two or more articles at a given price, you multiply to find the cost of the purchase. In solving other practical personal and business problems, you will frequently find it necessary to use multiplication.

Meaning of multiplication. Multiplication is a short way of adding two or more equal numbers. 3×5 is the same as $5 + 5 + 5$. You do not have to do the addition, because you have learned the multiplication table and know that $3 \times 5 = 15$.

When you multiply, two numbers are given — *multiplicand* and *multiplier*. You multiply the former by the latter. The result is the *product*. The multiplicand and multiplier are also called *factors* of the product.

		Check
Multiplicand (Factor)	35	24
Multiplier (Factor)	24	35
	140	120
	70	72
Product	840	840

Checking multiplication. Multiplication may be checked by going over the work or by reversing the factors and multiplying again.

Exercise 4   Written

Find the product in each of the following. Check the result by reversing the factors and multiplying again.

	1.	2.	3.	4.	5.
a	32	43	37	432	864
	26	25	38	214	357
b	59	57	39	264	579
	26	24	68	531	246

Principles of multiplication. You should keep the following principles in mind when you are using multiplication.

1. When you multiply two numbers, the order in which you multiply them does not affect the product. $5 \times 3 = 3 \times 5$.

This is the *commutative principle of multiplication*. In a problem such as finding the cost of 135 postage stamps at 8¢ each, this principle permits you to simplify the work by using .08 as the multiplier instead of 135.

You also use this principle when you check multiplication by reversing the factors.

2. Multiplication can be done on only two numbers at a time. When you have three or more numbers to multiply, the way you group the numbers does not affect the product. For example, $(3 \times 4) \times 5 = 3 \times (4 \times 5)$. This is the *associative principle of multiplication*.

You can use this principle at times to simplify calculations. For example, in finding the product of $79 \times 4 \times 25$, the work can be done mentally if the numbers are grouped this way: $79 \times (4 \times 25) = 79 \times 100 = 7,900$.

3. A number is not changed when it is multiplied by 1.   For this reason, 1 is called the *identity number for multiplication*.

4. When a number is multiplied by 0, the product is always 0. Thus, $0 \times 5 = 0$. This is the *zero principle of multiplication*.

Exercise 5   Oral

State the value of N in each of the number sentences given below.

1. $3 \times N = 5 \times 3$
2. $17 \times 4 = 4 \times N$
3. $(7 \times 5) \times 2 = 7 \times (N \times 2)$
4. $(5 \times 9) \times 2 = (5 \times N) \times 9$

5. $N = 1 \times 62$
6. $1 \times 1 = N$
7. $N = 0 \times 54$
8. $N \times 67 = 67$

9. $N = (5 - 5) \times 8$
10. $27 \times N = 0$
11. $1 \times N = 1$
12. $35 \times N = 0$

Exercise 6   Written

Show that the following are true. Use the method shown in the example at the right.

Example

$(3 \times 4) \times 5 = 3 \times (4 \times 5)$

$12 \times 5 = 3 \times 20$

$60 = 60$

1. $(5 \times 17) \times 2 = (5 \times 2) \times 17$
2. $(9 \times 25) \times 4 = 9 \times (25 \times 4)$
3. $(9 \times 75) \times 4 = 9 \times (75 \times 4)$
4. $15 \times (27 \times 2) = (15 \times 2) \times 27$

5. $(18 \times 75) \times 4 = 18 \times (75 \times 4)$
6. $(8 \times 17) \times 125 = (8 \times 125) \times 17$

REVIEW ASSIGNMENT 4 b

1. Find the value of N in each of the following.

a $N = 0 \times 7$ **c** $N = 1 \times 9$ **e** $N - 8 = 7$
b $12 \times N = 0$ **d** $16 \times N = 16$ **f** $6 \times N = 72$

2. The inventory of Sandra's Gift Shop was $8,425 on June 1 and $9,116 on June 30. Additional goods purchased in June cost $2,433. Find the cost of the goods sold in June.

3. A ticket seller at a summer theater had $35 in change in the cash box of the ticket-selling window at the start of a particular day. At the close of the day, when he was proving the cash, he found that he had sold 214 tickets at $1.35 each. What was the correct amount of money that should have been in the cash box at the close of that day?

4. A school cafeteria bought eight boxes of peanut bars at $1.80 a box, each box containing two dozen bars. All of the bars were sold at 10¢ each. What amount of gross profit did the cafeteria make on the eight boxes?

❍ 5. Fred Dover's bank statement of July 1 showed a balance of $742.16 in his account. Outstanding checks totaled $87.19. A deposit of $42.55 on June 30 was made too late to appear on the bank statement. What was Dover's correct available bank balance on July 1?

PART 4c Multiplication (continued)

Placing the decimal point in the product. The decimal point is placed in the product by pointing off from the right as many decimal places as there are in the multiplicand and multiplier.

In the following example, there are two places in both the multiplicand and multiplier; and, hence, four places in the product.

Example

Find the cost of 5.25 cartons of tile at $15.06 a carton.

Solution	Explanation	Check
$ 1 5.0 6	There are two decimal places in the multiplicand and two in the multiplier. Therefore, four places are pointed off from the right in the product.	5.2 5
5.2 5		$ 1 5.0 6
7 5 3 0		3 1 5 0
3 0 1 2		2 6 2 5 0
7 5 3 0		5 2 5
$ 7 9.0 6 5 0	**Ans.** *$79.07, to the nearest cent*	$ 7 9.0 6 5 0

Rounding numbers. When the final result is an amount in dollars and cents, as in the example given above, the amount is usually rounded to a whole number of cents.

The method of rounding varies in business practice. In some situations the amount is rounded to the nearest cent. In others, any fraction of a cent is treated as an additional cent.

To round a result to the nearest cent, drop the digits to the right of the cents place. If the first digit to the right of the cents place was 5 or more, add one to the cents digit. Thus,

$79.0650 = $79.07, rounded to the nearest cent
$43.9886 = $43.99, rounded to the nearest cent
$85.6349 = $85.63, rounded to the nearest cent

In solving the problems in this text, round the final results to the nearest cent except where directions are given to the contrary.

The same principle may be applied in cases where a number is to be rounded to the nearest hundred, the nearest thousand, or any other specified place.

Thus, 38,276, rounded to the nearest hundred, is 38,300; to the nearest thousand, it is 38,000, and so on.

Similarly, 8.9637, rounded to the nearest tenth is 9.0; to the nearest hundredth, it is 8.96; to the nearest thousandth, it is 8.964.

Likewise, 3,682, rounded to the first digit on the left, is 4,000; 6.34, rounded to the first digit on the left, is 6; .002658, rounded to the first nonzero digit on the left, is .003.

Exercise 7 Oral

1. Round each of the following as indicated to the

a Nearest cent: $6.1493; $9.5649; $23.2953; $50.9961

b Nearest tenth of a cent: $.0763; $.0776; $.2085

c Nearest tenth: 9.726; 6.362; 8.953

d Nearest hundredth: 2.417; .3973; .006

e Nearest tenth of a cent: 4.56¢; 2.97¢; 19.95¢; 20.949¢

f Nearest cent: $8.524; $3.586; $7.398; $9.499

2. Round each of the following to the nearest million, then to the nearest hundred thousand, to the nearest ten thousand, and to the nearest thousand.

a 43,575,149	**b** 3,733,485	**c** 17,028,732
d 28,083,736	**e** 5,294,550	**f** 9,549,791

3. Round each numeral to the first nonzero digit at the left.

a 545	**e** 1.893	**i** .0397	**m** $22.00	**q** $849.56
b 4,705	**f** 199.9	**j** .0055	**n** $35.46	**r** $751.22
c 7,876	**g** 6.065	**k** .0449	**o** $78.03	**s** $348.95
d 916	**h** 53.92	**l** .0239	**p** $41.99	**t** $172.36

Estimating the product. Either before or immediately after multiplying, you should estimate the product. To do this, round the multiplicand and multiplier to simpler numbers that you can multiply mentally. Then compare the exact product with the estimate to see whether the exact product is a reasonable answer.

For example, in the illustrative example on page 34, the multiplicand and multiplier may be rounded to $15 and 5, giving an estimated product of $75. The exact product, $79.0650, is close to $75 and is therefore a reasonable answer. Obviously, an exact product of $7.9065 or $756.7650 would be unreasonable and would indicate an error in multiplication or an error in pointing off in the product.

However, whenever the exact product appears to be unreasonable, the estimated product should be recalculated to make sure it is correct before assuming that the exact product is incorrect.

Exercise 8   Oral

How was each estimated answer found?

	Estimate		Estimate
1. $5.34 \times \$9.95$	\$50	4. 27.5×7.26	210
2. $9.6 \times \$15.20$	\$150	5. 22.3×96.72	2,200
3. $92 \times \$337$	\$27,000	6. $1,396 \times 579$	600,000

Exercise 9   Written

In each of the following, (1) estimate the product, (2) find the exact product, (3) check the exact product against the estimate, and (4) check the exact product by reverse multiplication.

	a	b	c	d
1.	3.881×438	$\$650.76 \times 29$	$\$16.55 \times 34.8$	736.2×99.9
2.	$1,305 \times 423$	$\$505.80 \times 75$	$\$97.35 \times 46.55$	453.6×48.08

REVIEW ASSIGNMENT 4 c

✔ *Estimate each product and check all calculations.*

1. What numeral is represented by the letter in each of the following?

a $8 + x = 21$ **c** $4 \times z = 56$ **e** $15 \times b = 15$

b $27 - y = 20$ **d** $k \div 3 = 12$ **f** $18 \times a = 0$

2. **a** Subtract 64,479 from 81,033.

   b Find the product of $3,604 \times 13.02$.

3. Julian Sinclair's checkbook balance on July 1 was \$452.11. His bank statement showed a balance of \$491.22 on that date. There was a service charge of \$1.84 which had not been deducted in his checkbook. Outstanding checks were: No. 81, \$31.18; No. 87, \$9.77. Prepare a reconciliation statement.

4. Tuesday a cashier had \$100 in change at the beginning of the day. At the end of the day, the cash register showed that \$742.18 had been received and \$27.59 paid out. There was \$814.22 in the cash drawer. By how much was the cash over or short?

5. A ticket seller at a school baseball game was given 250 seventy-five cent tickets and \$25 in cash for change. At the end of the game he returned 33 tickets and \$187.25 in cash.

   a What is the correct amount of cash he should have returned?

   b By what amount was his cash over or short?

6. How much will you pay for 18 cans of grapefruit sections which are priced at 3 cans for 79¢?

SECTION 5

Sales Slips and Taxes

Frequently the buyer must pay a local or state tax, or both, on an article or service he buys, generally 2% to 6% of the amount of the purchase.

This tax is collected by the seller and forwarded to the proper government agency.

I'D BUY IT, BUT I CAN'T AFFORD THE TAXES

PART 5a Sales Taxes

Local and state taxes. The tax imposed by a city, county, or state on a sale is called a *sales tax.* The sales slip below shows the price paid for a basketball priced at $10.95, plus a 3% sales tax amounting to $.33, calculated to the nearest cent.

$$.03 \times \$10.95 = \$.3285$$
$$= \$.33$$

Exercise 1 Oral

1. State the amount of the sales tax on:

a A camera priced at $25. Sales tax, 3%.

b A sweater priced at $9. Sales tax, 5%.

c A tent priced at $70. Sales tax, 6%.

d A rifle priced at $50. Sales tax, 4%.

GOLDEN'S SPORTS CENTER

greenwood plaza · elmore

DATE _Oct. 14_ 19 _ _

SOLD TO: _Glen Hayes_

ADDRESS: _104 Maple Street_

CLERK	AMT. REC'D	TERMS
_m_	_$15_	_Cash_

1	Basketball	10	95
	Sales tax, 3%		33
		11	28

Sales slip including taxes

2. How much is the sales tax on each item?

	Item	Price	Sales Tax			Item	Price	Sales Tax
a	Handbag	$ 7.00	3%		e	Typewriter	$90.00	3%
b	Jewelry	5.00	2%		f	Sportcoat	50.00	4%
c	Shoes	16.00	4%		g	Repairs	22.00	5%
d	Watch	40.00	6%		h	Automobile	$3,300	6%

Exercise 2   Written

Find the amount of the sales tax and the total sale for each of the following items:

	Amount of Sale	Sales Tax Rate	Sales Tax Amount	Total Sale			Amount of Sale	Sales Tax Rate	Sales Tax Amount	Total Sale
1.	$ 7.99	4%	$ .32	$8.31		6.	$ 3.95	2%		
2.	16.95	6%				7.	.89	4%		
3.	24.10	3%				8.	12.41	5%		
4.	39.50	5%				9.	65.49	3%		
5.	73.49	3%				10.	99.95	6%		

PART 5b   Multiplication (continued)

Multiplication by 10, 100, and 1,000.   To multiply by 10, 100, 1,000, and so on, move the decimal point in the multiplicand to the *right* as many places as there are zeros in the multiplier, annexing zeros if necessary.   Omit the decimal point in the result if the product turns out to be a whole number.   Thus,

$2.75 × 10 = $27.50   2.75 × 10 = 27.5
$2.75 × 100 = $275   2.75 × 100 = 275
$2.75 × 1,000 = $2,750   2.75 × 1,000 = 2,750

Exercise 3   Oral

Multiply each number by (a) 10, (b) 100, and (c) 1,000.

1.	.435	5.	14	9.	$2.49	13.	$.06	17.	25¢
2.	.64	6.	23	10.	$6.40	14.	$.08	18.	38¢
3.	3.5	7.	18	11.	$ .285	15.	$.47	19.	3¢
4.	.04	8.	20	12.	$ .375	16.	$.73	20.	9¢

Exercise 4   Oral

Multiply each number by (a) $10, (b) $100, and (c) $1,000.

1. .235	**5.** 4.36	**9.** .06	**13.** .35	**17.** 17
2. .45	**6.** 7.3	**10.** 2.45	**14.** 15.5	**18.** 3.8
3. .075	**7.** 15	**11.** .75	**15.** .035	**19.** .05
4. .05	**8.** 35	**12.** 22.4	**16.** .085	**20.** 1.46

Multiplication by a multiple of 10, 100, or 1,000. To multiply by a number such as 40, 400, or 4,000, first multiply by 4 and then by 10, 100, or 1,000, as the case may be.

For example, in multiplying .32 by 40:

1. First write 128, which is the product of .32 times 4, without a decimal point between the 1 and 2. Simply imagine that the decimal point is there.
2. Then to multiply 1.28 by 10, move the imaginary point one place to the right and mark a decimal point between the 2 and 8. The product of .32 × 40 is therefore 12.8.

Exercise 5   Mental

Write the product in each of the following. Perform the work mentally, writing the final result only.

1.	**2.**	**3.**	**4.**
a .52 × 30	3.3 × 200	40 @ $.41	80 @ 21¢
b .73 × 20	4.2 × 300	20 @ $.54	40 @ 25¢
c .31 × 60	5.1 × 400	70 @ $.31	60 @ 75¢
d 5.2 × 40	40 × .62	200 @ $.53	200 @ $1.25
e 4.3 × 30	30 × .73	400 @ $.52	17 @ $30
f 5.1 × 70	60 × .51	300 @ $.33	22 @ $200

REVIEW ASSIGNMENT 5 b

√ *Estimate each product and check all calculations.*

1. Find the value of N in each of the following.
   a $N + 15 = 40$ **b** $N - 9 = 6$ **c** $7 \times N = 63$

2. **a** From 10,131 subtract 8,286.
   b Multiply 203.06 by 1.08.

3. How much will you pay for two dozen cans of tomatoes priced at two cans for 59¢?

4. Goods bought at the Wallace Department Store are subject to a 4% sales tax. Find the total cost, including tax, of each of the following items:

a 1 pair of shoes, $19.45
b 6 pairs of socks at 3 pairs for $1.59
c 3 pairs of work pants at $5.89 each

5. A dealer buys pencils at 85¢ a dozen and sells them at 10¢ each. How much gross profit will the dealer make in buying and selling 15 dozen of these pencils?

6. A ticket seller at a school dance was given 250 75-cent tickets and $35 for change. At the end of the dance he returned 33 tickets and $197.85 in cash.

a What is the correct amount of cash he should have returned?
b Was the cash he returned over or short? How much?

7. Ann's Hat Shop bought 8 dozen misses' hats at $35 a dozen and paid $14.45 express charges on the shipment. The shop sold all of the hats at $4.45 each.

a What was the total cost of the 8 dozen hats?
b What was the store's gross profit on the entire lot?

The *total cost* is the purchase price of the hats plus the cost of the express charges. The *gross profit* is the total amount received for the hats minus the total cost.

PART 5c | Multiplication (concluded)

Multiplication of numbers containing end zeros. When there are end zeros on the right of the multiplicand or multiplier, or both, and the numbers are whole numbers, multiply only the numbers at the left of the end zeros. Annex to the product as many zeros as there are end zeros in both the multiplicand and the multiplier.

Examples

$$250 \times 705 = ?$$

$$
\begin{array}{r}
7\,0\,5 \\
2\,5\,0 \\
\hline
3\,5\,2\,5 \\
1\,4\,1\,0 \\
\hline
1\,7\,6,2\,5\,0
\end{array}
$$

$$5,500 \times 430 = ?$$

$$
\begin{array}{r}
4\,3\,0 \\
5\,5\,0\,0 \\
\hline
2\,1\,5 \\
2\,1\,5 \\
\hline
2,3\,6\,5,0\,0\,0
\end{array}
$$

Notice that the numbers which are to be multiplied in the two solutions above are arranged vertically in exactly the same manner as they would be if there were no end zeros.

End zeros at the right of the decimal point
have no effect upon the value of the numeral.
For example, 2.3, 2.30, and 2.300 all have the
same value. Therefore in multiplying with such
numerals as 2.30, 2.300, and 2.3000, the end
zeros at the right of the decimal point should be
ignored.

Example

$3,6\,0\,0 \times \$\,2.3\,0 = ?$

$\$\,2.3$
$3\,6\,0\,0$
$\overline{1\,3\,8}$
$6\,9$
$\overline{\$\,8\,2\,8\,0.0} = \$\,8{,}2\,8\,0$

Exercise 6   Written

Multiply in the manner explained on page 40 and above.

✓ *Estimate each product and check all calculations.*

	1.	**2.**	**3.**	**4.**
a	$234 \times 5{,}700$	640×2.105	$\$6.70 \times 56$	$7{,}600 \times \$4.68$
b	$3{,}500 \times 258$	$370 \times 2{,}600$	$350 \times \$2.36$	$\$89.50 \times 230$
c	$4{,}600 \times 490$	$\$13.50 \times 24$	$\$6{,}900 \times .02136$	$\$32{,}000 \times 2.06$

Multiplication by 1¢ and 10¢. To multiply by 1¢, or $.01, move
the decimal point in the multiplicand *two places to the left.*

To multiply by 10¢, or $.10, simply move the decimal point in the
multiplicand *one place to the left.*

135 postage stamps @ $.01 = $1.35

53 postage stamps @ $.10 = $5.30

Exercise 7   Oral

State the product in each of the following:

1. 450 lb. @ $.10	5. 72 gal. @ 10¢	9. 380 lb. @ 10¢
2. 218 lb. @ $.10	6. 134 lb. @ 10¢	10. 225 lb. @ 1¢
3. 635 ft. @ $.01	7. 1,520 lb. @ 1¢	11. 62.5 ft. @ $.10
4. 156 ft. @ $.01	8. 420 ft. @ 1¢	12. 37.5 lb. @ 10¢

Multiplication by a multiple of 1¢ or 10¢. To multiply by a
unit price such as $.03 or $.30, multiply mentally by 3 or 30, as the case
may be, and write the product. Then point off two places in the product
and prefix a dollar sign.

For example, to find the cost of 121 articles @ $.30:

1. Multiply 121 by 30 and write the product.   *3630*

2. Point off 2 places in 3630 and prefix a $.   *$36.30*

Exercise 8   Mental

Write the cost of each of the following:

	1.	2.	3.	4.
a	42 @ $.04	62 @ 6¢	53 @ $.30	65 @ 30¢
b	115 @ $.06	84 @ 5¢	34 @ $.20	45 @ 60¢
c	93 @ $.03	115 @ 3¢	62 @ $.40	230 @ 20¢
d	130 @ $.03	75 @ 7¢	160 @ $.90	90 @ 70¢
e	210 @ $.07	120 @ 8¢	230 @ $.80	75 @ 50¢

REVIEW ASSIGNMENT 5 c

✓*Be sure to estimate each product and check all calculations.*

1. Find the number represented by the letter in each of the following.

   a $15 + x = 22$ **b** $8 \times y = 88$ **c** $z = 1{,}600 - 938$

2. a Find the product of $40{,}700 \times 3{,}020$.

   b Multiply $4.30 by 1,600.

3. A record player is priced at $23.45 plus a sales tax of 5%. For what amount should you write a check to pay for the purchase of this record player?

4. A retailer pays $135.45 for a TV set. At what price should he sell it if he desires a gross profit of $34.50?

5. Dick Wells, owner of Dick's Hi-Fi Center, had an inventory of merchandise on August 1 of $26,130. His purchases during August amounted to $8,850. On August 31 his merchandise inventory was $28,460.

   a What was the cost of the goods he sold during August?

   b His sales for August totaled $9,310. How much was his gross profit for the month?

6. King's Variety Store buys golf pencils at $2.75 a gross (12 dozen) and sells them at the rate of 2 pencils for 5 cents. What is the store's gross profit on 12 dozen of these pencils?

7. The Dolly Grey Store purchased 100 dresses at $17.75 each. The store sold 70 of the dresses at $29.95 and the remainder at $24.95. What was the store's gross profit on the entire lot?

❯ **8.** On May 1, Culver's checkbook balance was $889.74. Upon preparing a reconciliation statement, he found that the same deposit of $15 had been entered twice in the checkbook; he had neglected to deduct a check he had written for $12.80; and a check for $19.30 had been entered as $13.90 in the checkbook. What was his correct available checkbook balance?

SECTION 6

Aliquot Parts on Sales Slips

Aliquot parts. In the sales slip below, the prices of the articles are exact fractional parts of $1. Thus, 50¢ is $\frac{1}{2}$ of $1.00; 25¢ is $\frac{1}{4}$ of $1.00; and 12$\frac{1}{2}$¢ is $\frac{1}{8}$ of $1.00.

Each of these prices is contained in $1 without a remainder. When one number is contained in another without a remainder, the first is known as an *aliquot part* of the second.

Thus, 50¢, 25¢ and 12$\frac{1}{2}$¢ are aliquot parts of $1, because each is contained in $1 without a remainder.

Since 50¢ is contained exactly two times in $1, then 50¢ is $\frac{1}{2}$ of $1. In this relationship, $1 is called the *base*; and $\frac{1}{2}$ is called the *fractional equivalent* of 50¢ in relation to the base. The fractional equivalent, $\frac{1}{2}$, expresses the part that 50¢ is of $1.

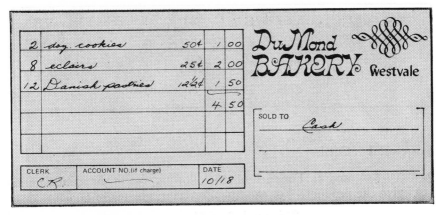

Sales slip using aliquot parts

Multiples of aliquot parts. Numbers that are convenient multiples of aliquot parts are also referred to as aliquot parts.

For example, 75¢ is 3 times 25¢. Since 25¢ is $\frac{1}{4}$ of $1, it follows that 75¢ is $\frac{3}{4}$ of $1.

Similarly, since 12$\frac{1}{2}$¢ is $\frac{1}{8}$ of $1, 37$\frac{1}{2}$¢ is $\frac{3}{8}$ of $1, 62$\frac{1}{2}$¢ is $\frac{5}{8}$ of $1, and 87$\frac{1}{2}$¢ is $\frac{7}{8}$ of $1.

Multiplication by an aliquot part. The unit price of an article may be an aliquot part of $1. When it is and several of the articles are being purchased, multiply by the fractional equivalent of the unit price instead of by the unit price itself.

Example

Find the cost of 16 yds. of nylon rope at 75¢ a yd.

Solution

$16 \times 75 = ?$

Since 75¢ is $\frac{3}{4}$ of $1, the problem becomes

$16 \times \frac{3}{4} \times \$1 = ?$

$16 \times \frac{3}{4} = 12$

$12 \times \$1 = \$12$ **Ans.**

RULE: To multiply a number by an aliquot part, multiply separately by the fractional equivalent and the base.

Table of aliquot parts of $1. The more commonly used aliquot parts of $1 are shown below.

50¢ = $\frac{1}{2}$	12$\frac{1}{2}$¢ = $\frac{1}{8}$	33$\frac{1}{3}$¢ = $\frac{1}{3}$	8$\frac{1}{3}$¢ = $\frac{1}{12}$
25¢ = $\frac{1}{4}$	37$\frac{1}{2}$¢ = $\frac{3}{8}$	66$\frac{2}{3}$¢ = $\frac{2}{3}$	6$\frac{2}{3}$¢ = $\frac{1}{15}$
75¢ = $\frac{3}{4}$	62$\frac{1}{2}$¢ = $\frac{5}{8}$	16$\frac{2}{3}$¢ = $\frac{1}{6}$	6$\frac{1}{4}$¢ = $\frac{1}{16}$
	87$\frac{1}{2}$¢ = $\frac{7}{8}$	83$\frac{1}{3}$¢ = $\frac{5}{6}$	

Exercise 1   Oral

$\frac{1}{4}$, $\frac{1}{2}$, and $\frac{3}{4}$. For each of the following, recite the solution and give the product. For example, for the problem, 48 @ 25¢:

25¢ equals $\frac{1}{4}$ of $1.

48 times $\frac{1}{4}$ equals 12.

12 times $1 equals $12.

1.	**2.**	**3.**	**4.**
a 12 @ 25¢	20 @ 50¢	12 @ 75¢	48 @ $.25
b 32 @ 25¢	26 @ 50¢	32 @ 75¢	28 @ 75¢
c 36 @ $.25	42 @ $.50	20 @ $.75	44 @ 25¢
d 20 @ $.25	34 @ $.50	48 @ $.75	36 @ $.75

Exercise 2 Oral

$\frac{1}{8}$, $\frac{3}{8}$, $\frac{5}{8}$, and $\frac{7}{8}$. Recite the solution and give the product for each.

ALIQUOT PARTS ARE HANDY
TOOLS OF ARITHMETIC

ALIQUOT PARTS

$33\frac{1}{3}$ $37\frac{1}{2}$

$8\frac{1}{3}$ $6\frac{1}{4}$

1.

a 80 @ $12\frac{1}{2}$¢
b 32 @ $.12\frac{1}{2}$
c 40 @ $.12\frac{1}{2}$
d 40 @ $37\frac{1}{2}$¢
e 48 @ $37\frac{1}{2}$¢
f 88 @ $.37\frac{1}{2}$

2.

a 16 @ $.62\frac{1}{2}$
b 56 @ $62\frac{1}{2}$¢
c 72 @ $62\frac{1}{2}$¢
d 24 @ $.87\frac{1}{2}$
e 88 @ $87\frac{1}{2}$¢
f 16 @ $.87\frac{1}{2}$

	3.	**4.**	**5.**	**6.**
a	96 @ $12\frac{1}{2}$¢	72 @ $.87\frac{1}{2}$	64 @ $37\frac{1}{2}$¢	112 @ $12\frac{1}{2}$¢
b	80 @ $62\frac{1}{2}$¢	48 @ $62\frac{1}{2}$¢	64 @ $.87\frac{1}{2}$	160 @ $.87\frac{1}{2}$
c	32 @ $.37\frac{1}{2}$	320 @ $.12\frac{1}{2}$	56 @ $.37\frac{1}{2}$	240 @ $62\frac{1}{2}$¢

Exercise 3 Oral

$\frac{1}{3}$, $\frac{2}{3}$, $\frac{1}{6}$, and $\frac{5}{6}$. Recite the solution and give the product for each.

	1.	**2.**	**3.**	**4.**
a	18 @ $33\frac{1}{3}$¢	54 @ $16\frac{2}{3}$¢	45 @ $33\frac{1}{3}$¢	69 @ $.66\frac{2}{3}$
b	33 @ $.33\frac{1}{3}$	30 @ $.16\frac{2}{3}$	66 @ $.16\frac{2}{3}$	60 @ $83\frac{1}{3}$¢
c	42 @ $33\frac{1}{3}$¢	60 @ $16\frac{2}{3}$¢	21 @ $.66\frac{2}{3}$	63 @ $66\frac{2}{3}$¢
d	24 @ $66\frac{2}{3}$¢	36 @ $83\frac{1}{3}$¢	54 @ $83\frac{1}{3}$¢	120 @ $.33\frac{1}{3}$
e	48 @ $.66\frac{2}{3}$	72 @ $.83\frac{1}{3}$	78 @ $.16\frac{2}{3}$	360 @ $83\frac{1}{3}$¢
f	27 @ $66\frac{2}{3}$¢	12 @ $83\frac{1}{3}$¢	96 @ $33\frac{1}{3}$¢	240 @ $.16\frac{2}{3}$

Exercise 4 Oral

$\frac{1}{12}$, $\frac{1}{15}$, and $\frac{1}{16}$. Recite the solution and give the product for each.

	1.	**2.**	**3.**	**4.**
a	48 @ $8\frac{1}{3}$¢	30 @ $6\frac{2}{3}$¢	64 @ $.06\frac{1}{4}$	84 @ $8\frac{1}{3}$¢
b	72 @ $8\frac{1}{3}$¢	75 @ $.06\frac{2}{3}$	24 @ $.08\frac{1}{3}$	320 @ $6\frac{1}{4}$¢
c	36 @ $.08\frac{1}{3}$	32 @ $6\frac{1}{4}$¢	80 @ $6\frac{1}{4}$¢	450 @ $.06\frac{2}{3}$
d	45 @ $6\frac{2}{3}$¢	48 @ $6\frac{1}{4}$¢	150 @ $.06\frac{2}{3}$	120 @ $8\frac{1}{3}$¢

REVIEW ASSIGNMENT 6

✔ *Be sure to estimate each product and check all calculations.*

1. Find the number represented by the letter in each of the following.

    a $n + 10 = 19$ **b** $9 \times c = 54$ **c** $24 \div s = 8$

2. a Subtract 2,694 from 8,103.

    b Find the product of $7,900 \times 260$.

    c Multiply $3.40 by 1,700.

3. According to his October bank statement, Owen King's bank balance on October 31 was $1,142.15. His checkbook balance on that date was $1,007.13. A service charge of $1.67 was reported on the bank statement. Outstanding checks were: No. 232, $98.84; No. 241, $37.85. Prepare a reconciliation statement.

4. Joan Palmer, proprietor of Joan Hair Stylists, placed a change fund of $60 in the cash register on the morning of October 5. At the end of the day there was $278.40 in the cash drawer. The register totals showed that $234.50 had been received and $15.75 paid out. How much was the cash over or short?

5. A ticket seller at a school football game was given 200 95-cent tickets and $25 in change. At the end of the game, he turned in 27 tickets and $189.65 in cash. Was his cash over or short? By how much?

6. A supermarket buys canned tomatoes at $2.65 a dozen cans and sells them at the rate of 2 cans for 53¢. What is the store's gross profit on the purchase and sale of 20 dozen cans?

7. Cooper's Archery Shop purchased 20 archery sets at $10.95 each and paid $4.55 express charges on the shipment. The shop sold all of the sets at $17.95 each. What was the shop's gross profit on the 20 archery sets?

8. Ned's Discount Center purchased 300 men's hats at $2.60 each and paid $15 for freight charges on the shipment. The store sold 260 of the hats at $3.95 each and closed out the remainder at $2.95 each. What was the store's gross profit on the 300 hats?

◑ **9.** Henry Crane's checkbook balance was $498.32 on March 31. Upon comparing his checkbook with the bank statement, Crane discovered the following discrepancies: A canceled check for $10.87 had not been recorded in the checkbook. A deposit of $35 had been entered twice in the checkbook. A canceled check for $68.20 had been recorded in the checkbook as $62.80. The bank had deducted a service charge of $1.70. Find the correct checkbook balance.

Figuring Unit Prices

A store often quotes two prices on the same article, one for a single unit and one for a group of two or more units. In the illustration at the right, the price of two cans of pears, 74¢, averages only 37¢ a can but the price of one can alone is 39¢. Prices are set this way to encourage the customer to buy the larger quantity. The wise buyer figures which purchase is best for his own needs. The larger quantity may or may not be the better buy for him at that time.

Price quotations of a grocery store

PART 7a Finding the Cost of One Unit

Finding a unit price from a group price. Cucumbers may be priced at 3 for 28¢. In such a case, the unit price is the group price divided by the number of units in the group. Any fraction in the result is counted as a whole cent. Thus, the price of one cucumber at 3 for 28¢ is 10¢, since 28¢ ÷ 3 is $9\frac{1}{3}$¢. The price of two is 2 × 10¢, or 20¢.

Exercise 1 Oral

Give rapidly the cost of a single unit of each item.

1. 4 bars of soap . . . . $.45
2. 3 cans of beets 37
3. 5 lbs. of onions 53
4. 10 fresh limes 63
5. 6 pears 32

6. 3 cans of soup . . . . $ .61
7. 4 cantaloupes 89
8. 3 cans of tomatoes. .95
9. 12 cans of cola 99
10. 3 pkg. of cereal . . . 1.00

Exercise 2   Written

For each of the following, find to the nearest cent the price per pound. For example, a 12-ounce (oz.) jar of jam is priced at $.43:

Cost per oz. is $\dfrac{\$.43}{12}$. Hence, cost per lb. is $16 \times \dfrac{\$.43}{12}$.

$$16 \times \frac{\$.43}{12} = \overset{4}{\cancel{16}} \times \frac{\$.43}{\underset{3}{\cancel{12}}} = \frac{\$1.72}{3} = \$.57\tfrac{1}{3}, \text{ or } \$.57 \; Ans.$$

1. A 10 oz. jar of instant coffee is sold at $1.45.
2. A 20 oz. can of popping corn sells for 39¢.
3. A 28 oz. jar of mince meat is priced at $.49.
4. A 30 oz. can of sliced pineapple costs you $.58.
5. A 15 oz. box of raisins is priced at 35¢.
6. A 3 oz. tube of hand cream is marked at $.74.
7. A 9 oz. can of peanuts is reduced to $.55.
8. A 7 oz. can of tuna fish is marked at 47¢.
9. A 5 oz. tube of tooth paste retails at 54¢.

PART 7b Division

Need for division. In finding the price of one unit when the price of a group is given, you divide by the number of units in the group. You will use division for solving many other problems, too.

Ways of indicating division. There are several common ways of indicating division. For example, if we wish to express by symbols that 15 divided by 3 is five, we may use any one of these forms:

$$15 \div 3 = 5 \qquad \frac{15}{3} = 5$$

$$\overset{5}{3)\overline{15}} \qquad 3)\overline{15} = 5 \qquad \overset{}{3)\underset{5}{\underline{15}}}$$

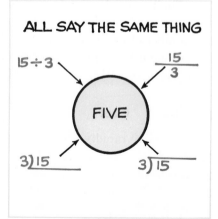

ALL SAY THE SAME THING

$15 \div 3$ → FIVE ← $\dfrac{15}{3}$

$3)\overline{15}$ → FIVE ← $3)\overline{15}$

In each case, 15 is the *dividend*, 3 is the *divisor*, and 5 is the *quotient*.

Inverse operations of multiplication and division. Division is the inverse operation of multiplication.

For example, if you start with 5 and multiply it by 3, you get 15. If you now divide 15 by 3, you get 5, which is the number you started with. Dividing by 3 "undoes" what was done by multiplying by 3. In other words, $(3 \times 5) \div 3 = 5$, or $\dfrac{3 \times 5}{3} = 5$.

Similarly, multiplication is the inverse operation of division. If you start with 15 and divide it by 3, you get 5. If you now multiply 5 by 3, you get 15, which is the number you started with. Multiplying by 3 "undoes" what you did by dividing by 3. That is to say, $(15 \div 3) \times 3 = 15$, or $\dfrac{15}{3} \times 3 = 15$.

Exercise 3   Oral

1. Using your knowledge of inverse operations, state the result of the operations in each of the following:

a $(6 \div 3) \times 3$	**f** $9 + 2 - 2$	**k** $x + 5 - 5$
b $(18 \div 9) \times 9$	**g** $(48 \times 37) \div 37$	**l** $(35 \times N) \div 35$
c $(8 \times 4) \div 4$	**h** $15 - 7 + 7$	**m** $(8 \times N) \div N$
d $(3 \times 9) \div 3$	**i** $(8 \div 4) \times 4$	**n** $(y \times 37) \div 37$
e $\dfrac{3 \times 9}{3}$	**j** $\dfrac{8}{4} \times 4$	**o** $\dfrac{12 \times b}{12}$

2. For each sentence below, state what number should be substituted for the question mark or letter to make the sentence true.

a $(N \div 3) \times 3 = 40$	**g** $(4 \times ?) \div 4 = 28 \div 4$
b $(? \div 7) \times 7 = 22$	**h** $(? \div 3) \times 3 = 13 \times 3$
c $(6 \times n) \div 6 = 32$	**i** $? + 8 - 8 = 25 - 8$
d $(? \times 7) \div 7 = 30$	**j** $(8 \times n) \div 8 = 96 \div 8$
e $(5 \times ?) \div 5 = 19$	**k** $(x \div 5) \times 5 = 7 \times 5$
f $\dfrac{5 \times ?}{5} = 19$	**l** $\dfrac{r}{3} \times 3 = 20 \times 3$

REVIEW ASSIGNMENT **7** b

✔ *Estimate each product and check all calculations.*

1. a Find the product of 8,100 × 620.
   b Find the cost of 2,140 lb. @ 12½¢.

2. At the Central Mart, men's shirts are priced at $3.45 each or 3 for $9.45. How much would a customer save by buying 3 shirts at one time rather than 3 shirts one at a time?

3. A fruit dealer bought 3 boxes of pears (100 pears to the box) at $8.25 a box. He sold the pears at the rate of 5 for 59 cents. What was his gross profit on the entire lot?

4. A retailer bought 3 crates of strawberries (16 quarts to the crate) at $7.25 a crate. He had to throw out 3 quarts that were spoiled. The remainder he sold at 69¢ a quart. What was his gross profit on the entire transaction?

5. Miss Pember, a cashier at an amusement park, had $45 in change in the cash box of the ticket-selling window at the start of a particular day. At the close of the day, when she was proving the cash, she found that she had sold 213 90-cent tickets and 92 45-cent tickets. What was the correct amount of money that should have been in the cash box at the close of the day?

PART **7c**   Division (continued)

Meaning of division. When you do multiplication, you are combining two factors to obtain a product. For example, when you combine the factors 3 and 5, you get a product of 15.

$$3 \times 5 = 15$$

We can state the way the factors and product are related in this way:

Factor × Factor = Product

or   **F × F = P**

When you do division, you are doing the inverse, or opposite, of multiplication. You are separating the product into the two factors. Thus, when you divide the product, 15, by the factor 3, you get the other factor, 5.

$$15 \div 3 = 5$$

We can state this relationship of the product and the factors in this way:

Product ÷ Factor = Factor

or   **P   ÷   F   =   F**

We therefore define division as the process of finding the other factor of a product when one factor and the product are known.

We think of the expression "15 ÷ 3" as asking us the question, "What number multiplied by 3 gives 15 as a product?" Since the answer is 5, we can say "15 ÷ 3 = 5."

In any division problem, the dividend represents a product. The divisor and quotient are the factors of that product.

Identifying the factors and product. In dealing with number sentences involving multiplication or division, you will find it helpful to identify the factors and product. This can be done by writing the appropriate letter, F or P, above each numeral or letter in the sentence. Observe the following examples.

$$\begin{array}{llll}
\text{F} \quad \text{F} \quad \text{P} & \text{F} \quad \text{F} \quad \text{P} & \text{P} \quad \text{F} \quad \text{F} & \text{P} \quad \text{F} \quad \text{F} \\
\textbf{1. } 3 \times 5 = 15 & \textbf{2. } 3 \times n = 15 & \textbf{3. } 15 \div 3 = 5 & \textbf{4. } n \div 3 = 5
\end{array}$$

Exercise 4   Oral

For each numeral or letter in each of the following, state whether the numeral or letter represents a factor or a product.

1. $8 \times 6 = 48$	**6.** $x \div 6 = 9$	**11.** $9 \times t = 45$
2. $12 \times 8 = 96$	**7.** $9 \times 6 = y$	**12.** $r \div 4 = 12$
3. $42 \div 7 = 6$	**8.** $7 \times n = 56$	**13.** $x = 12 \times 8$
4. $32 \div 2 = 16$	**9.** $26 \div 2 = b$	**14.** $n \div 5 = 12$
5. $4 \times 9 = n$	**10.** $n \div 8 = 4$	**15.** $36 = 3 \times a$

Exercise 5   Written

Copy each number sentence in Exercise 4. Above each numeral and letter, write F or P to show whether it represents a factor or a product.

Finding a missing product or missing factor of a product. In the sentences $3 \times 5 = N$ and $N \div 3 = 5$, the two factors are known; but the product, N, is missing. We find the value of the missing product, N, by multiplying 3×5. $N = 3 \times 5 = 15$.

In the sentences $3 \times N = 15$ and $15 \div N = 3$, the product, 15, and one factor, 3, are known. The other factor, N, is missing. To find the value of N, we apply the definition of division, and divide 15 by 3. $N = 15 \div 3 = 5$.

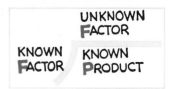

Remember, in any division problem, the dividend represents a product.

Exercise 6   Oral

1. For each of the following, state whether the missing number is a factor or a product.

a $13 \times 5 = x$ **e** $? \div 7 = 12$ **i** $10 = r \div 5$

b $9 \times a = 72$ **f** $z = 7 \times 105$ **j** $48 = 8 \times p$

c $? \times 5 = 60$ **g** $96 = a \times 12$ **k** $x \div 9 = 19$

d $96 \div 12 = n$ **h** $b = 108 \div 9$ **l** $7 \times ? = 84$

2. State the value of the missing number in each of the number sentences in Problem 1.

Exercise 7   Written

Copy each of the following. Over each numeral and letter, write F or P to show whether it represents a factor or a product. Then find the value of the missing number.

1. $16 \times n = 208$ **5.** $19 \times a = 513$

2. $x \div 17 = 21$ **6.** $r \div 13 = 26$

3. $136 \div y = 17$ **7.** $23 = 391 \div s$

4. $z = 391 \div 23$ **8.** $15 \times t = 195$

REVIEW ASSIGNMENT 7c

✓*Estimate each product and check all calculations.*

1. Copy each of the following. Over each numeral and letter, write F or P to show whether it represents a factor or a product. Then find the value of the missing number.

    a $25 \times n = 475$ **b** $x \div 19 = 34$ **c** $390 \div y = 26$

2. a Multiply 20.84 by 1,040.
    b Multiply $4.70 by 1,300.

3. A food store bought 10 crates of blueberries (16 baskets of berries to the crate) at $6.20 a crate. Six of the baskets spoiled and were thrown away. The remainder were sold at 55¢ a basket. What was the store's gross profit on the entire transaction?

4. Golf balls, regularly priced at 98¢ each, are reduced to 3 for $2.35 during a special sale. How much would you save by buying a dozen of these golf balls at the special sale price?

5. Weatherby, a retail vegetable dealer, bought 8 boxes of lettuce, 24 heads to the box, at $3.30 a box. He sold the lettuce at 2 heads for 39¢. What was his gross profit on the 8 boxes?

6. The Roberts Store purchased 80 dresses at $13.50 each and paid $15.60 transportation charges on the shipment. The store sold 68 of the dresses at $21.95 and the remainder at $17.50. What was the store's gross profit on the entire lot?

PART 7d Division (continued)

Principles of division. You should keep the following principles in mind when you are using division:

1. Dividing a number by 1 does not change the number. 1 is therefore called the *identity number* for division.

$$6 \div 1 = 6; \quad \frac{18}{3} \div 1 = \frac{18}{3}; \quad \frac{2 \times 3}{1} = 2 \times 3; \quad N \div 1 = N$$

2. Zero (0) can never be used as a divisor.

3. When a number (not 0) is divided by itself, the quotient is **1.**

$$6 \div 6 = 1; \quad N \div N = 1$$

4. When 0 is divided by a number (not 0) the quotient is 0.

$$0 \div 6 = 0; \qquad \frac{0}{6} = 0; \qquad 0 \div N = 0$$

5. The quotient is not changed if the dividend and divisor are multiplied by the same number (not 0).

$$\frac{24}{8} = 3; \quad \frac{24 \times 2}{8 \times 2} = \frac{48}{16} = 3; \quad \frac{24 \times 10}{8 \times 10} = \frac{240}{80} = 3$$

$$\frac{4.5}{.5} = \frac{4.5 \times 10}{.5 \times 10} = \frac{45}{5} = 9; \quad \frac{3.5}{.05} = \frac{3.5 \times 100}{.05 \times 100} = \frac{350}{5} = 70$$

6. The quotient is not changed if the dividend and divisor are divided by the same number (not 0).

$$\frac{24}{8} = 3; \quad \frac{24 \div 2}{8 \div 2} = \frac{12}{4} = 3; \quad \frac{24 \div 4}{8 \div 4} = \frac{6}{2} = 3$$

Exercise 8   Oral

1. State the answer in each of the following.

a $43 \div 1 =$ **d** $1 \times 52 =$ **g** $41 \times 0 =$ **j** $5 \div 5 =$

b $35 \div 35 =$ **e** $N \times 1 =$ **h** $8 \div 1 =$ **k** $N \div N =$

c $0 \div 51 =$ **f** $1 \times N =$ **i** $N \div 1 =$ **l** $1 \div 1 =$

2. For each sentence, state what number substituted for the letter will make the sentence true.

a $13 \div 1 = x$ **e** $k \div 1 = 37$ **i** $y = 0 \div 12$

b $x = 19 \div 19$ **f** $27 \div a = 1$ **j** $20 \times 0 = a$

c $0 \div 63 = n$ **g** $x \div 8 = 0$ **k** $15 \div x = 15$

d $17 \times 1 = x$ **h** $9 \times b = 9$ **l** $y \div 19 = 1$

Exercise 9   Written

Copy each of the following and complete the indicated operations.

1. $\dfrac{6.3}{.3} = \dfrac{6.3 \times 10}{.3 \times 10} =$

3. $\dfrac{5}{.25} = \dfrac{5 \times 100}{.25 \times 100} =$

5. $\dfrac{195}{15} = \dfrac{195 \div 5}{15 \div 5} =$

2. $\dfrac{48}{.12} = \dfrac{48 \times 100}{.12 \times 100} =$

4. $\dfrac{4.5}{.015} = \dfrac{4.5 \times 1,000}{.015 \times 1,000} =$

6. $\dfrac{216}{36} = \dfrac{216 \div 3}{36 \div 3} =$

Expressing the remainder as a fraction. In many division problems the division is not exact; hence there is a remainder.

For example, in the illustration at the right, there is a remainder of 10. This remainder may be expressed as a fractional part of the divisor by writing it over the divisor, 15. The fraction is $\frac{10}{15}$, which, reduced to lowest terms, is $\frac{2}{3}$.

The complete quotient is $8\frac{2}{3}$.

Example

$130 \div 15 = ?$

$$\begin{array}{r} 8\frac{2}{3} \\ 15\overline{)130} \\ 120 \\ \hline 10 \end{array} \quad \frac{10}{15} = \frac{2}{3}$$

Ans. $8\frac{2}{3}$

Checking division. Division may be checked by going over the work again. Also, it may be checked by multiplying the whole number in the quotient by the divisor and then adding the remainder. The result should equal the dividend.

$$\begin{array}{r} 15 \times 8 = 120 \\ + 10 \\ \hline 130 \end{array}$$

Thus, the division in the example above is checked as shown at the left. The quotient whole number, 8, times the divisor, 15, gives 120. 120 plus the remainder, 10, gives 130, which is the same as the dividend.

Exercise **10**   Written

In each of the following, divide and then check the division. Express any remainder as a fraction in lowest terms.

1. 1,872 ÷ 8	**5.** 2,975 ÷ 4	**9.** 413 ÷ 12
2. 4,077 ÷ 9	**6.** 4,533 ÷ 9	**10.** 675 ÷ 16
3. 2,244 ÷ 6	**7.** 2,637 ÷ 8	**11.** 558 ÷ 24
4. 2,156 ÷ 7	**8.** 1,749 ÷ 6	**12.** 1,230 ÷ 36

Locating the decimal point in the quotient when the divisor is a whole number. When the dividend contains a decimal and the divisor is a whole number, the decimal point in the quotient is placed directly above the decimal point in the dividend.

$$\frac{3.11}{8)24.88}$$

The illustration at the left indicates the division of 24.88 by 8. The decimal point in the quotient, 3.11, is placed directly above the decimal point in the dividend, 24.88.

Exercise **11**   Written

Perform each division and check the result:

1. 27.02 ÷ 7	**3.** 5.160 ÷ 8	**5.** 69.08 ÷ 22
2. 51.42 ÷ 6	**4.** 489.6 ÷ 9	**6.** 14.525 ÷ 35

Locating the decimal point in the quotient when the divisor contains a decimal. When the divisor contains a decimal, change the divisor to a whole number by multiplying both the dividend and the divisor by 10, 100, or 1,000, and so on. Then divide.

Example

Divide 35.1 by 2.25.

Solution	Explanation
$\dfrac{15.6}{2.25.)35.10.0}$ Ans. *15.6*	The decimal points in both the dividend and divisor are moved to the right two places to multiply both numbers by 100 and thereby make the divisor a whole number.

Multiplying both numbers by 100 does not change the value of the quotient.

The decimal point in the quotient is placed directly above the new position of the decimal point in the dividend.

Exercise 12   Written

Perform the division in each problem and check the result.

1. 2,160 ÷ 7.2	**5.** .65 ÷ 32.5	**9.** .125 ÷ .25
2. 21.6 ÷ .072	**6.** .18 ÷ 4.5	**10.** .125 ÷ .05
3. .216 ÷ .0072	**7.** .27 ÷ 13.5	**11.** .14 ÷ .04
4. .432 ÷ .0144	**8.** 5.32 ÷ 133	**12.** .01 ÷ .25

REVIEW ASSIGNMENT 7d

√*Estimate each product and check all calculations.*

1. Copy each of the following. Over each numeral and letter write F or P to show whether it represents a factor or a product. Then find the value of the missing number.

a $k \div 16 = 32$ **b** $45 \times m = 360$ **c** $35 = 490 \div a$

2. a Divide 98.28 by 27.   **b** Divide 26.6004 by 8.21.
c Multiply 802.1 by 3.07.
d Find the cost of 2,310 lb. @ 25¢.

3. A furniture dealer buys a china cabinet for $95. At what price should he sell it in order to make a gross profit of $75?

4. A food market buys 250 bags of potatoes at 68¢ a bag. At what price per bag should the store sell these potatoes in order to realize a gross profit of $45 on the entire lot?

5. A ticket seller for a school entertainment was given 200 75-cent tickets for adults, 300 50-cent tickets for students, and $15 in cash for change. After the entertainment, he returned 40 adult tickets and 28 student tickets, and $272 in cash. Was his cash short or over? How much?

6. On July 1, the merchandise inventory of the Warner Hardware store was $16,926. During the following three months, the store's sales were $23,435; and its purchases were $18,345. The inventory on September 30 was $18,113. What was the gross profit for the three months?

◐ 7. Spencer's checkbook balance on September 1 was $634.23. Upon preparing a reconciliation statement, Spencer found that his bank had made a service charge of $1.95; the same deposit of $30 had been entered twice in his checkbook; a check for $15 had been entered in the checkbook as $5; and he had neglected to deduct a check he had written for $25. What was his correct available checkbook balance?

SECTION 8

Large-Unit Prices

Many articles purchased in large quantities are priced by the *hundred* (C), the *thousand* (M), the *hundredweight* or *hundred pounds* (cwt.), or the *ton* (T). These include such articles as business envelopes and file cards, livestock feed, certain steel and wire products, brick, cement, lumber, coal, hay and other agricultural products.

PART 8a   Figuring with Large-Unit Prices

To find the cost of goods priced by the C, cwt., or M. First, divide the quantity by 100 or 1,000 to find the number of hundreds or thousands in the quantity. Then multiply by the unit price.

Example

Find the cost of 1,600 bricks at $54 per **M**.

Solution: *1,600 ÷ 1,000 = 1.6*
1.6 × $54 = $86.40 **Ans.**

To find the cost of goods priced by the ton (T). When the weight is given in pounds, divide the weight by 2,000, the number of pounds in one ton. Then multiply that number by the price per ton.

Example

Find the cost of 3,000 lb. of agricultural lime at $11.80 per **T**.

Solution: *3,000 ÷ 2,000 = 1.5 tons*
1.5 × $11.80 = $17.70 **Ans.**

In some cases where the price per ton is an even number, the solution can be shortened by dividing the quantity in pounds by 1,000 and then multiplying that result by half the price per ton.

Example

Find the cost of 3,300 lb. of cement at $24 per T.

Solution	Explanation
$3,300 \div 1,000 = 3.3$ $\$24 \div 2 = \$12$ $3.3 \times \$12 = \$39.60$ **Ans.**	Dividing 3,300 by 1,000 gives 3.3, the number of thousands of pounds in 3,300. Since the price per ton is $24, half of this price, or

$12, is the price of 1,000 pounds. The cost is therefore 3.3 × $12, or $39.60. This is easier than multiplying $24 by $1\frac{13}{20}$!

Exercise 1   Written

Find the cost of each of the following:

1. 275 bolts @ $2.60 per 100. $7.15
2. 450 lb. wire @ $18 per cwt.
3. 160 hooks @ $2.40 per C.
4. 250 boxes @ $2.30 per C.
5. 65 lb. @ $9.25 per cwt.
6. 3,460 cards @ $2.20 per M. $7.61

7. 375 rivets @ $12.50 per M.
8. 12,600 lb. @ $7.95 per ton.

                            $50.09

9. 3,280 lb. @ $15.35 per T.
10. 1,560 lb. @ $22 per ton.
11. 2,475 lb. @ $9.60 per T.
12. 375 fasteners at $6.20 per hundred.
13. 650 pounds of wire at $14.75 per hundredweight.
14. 1,870 blocks at $225 per thousand.
15. 3,800 pounds of fertilizer at $55 per ton.

PART 8b   Division (continued)

Division by 10, 100, and 1,000. To divide by 10, 100, 1,000, and so on, move the decimal point to the left in the dividend as many places as there are zeros in the divisor.

$$4,300 \div 10 = 430 \qquad 73.4 \div 10 = 7.34$$
$$286 \div 100 = 2.86 \qquad .56 \div 100 = .0056$$
$$8,400 \div 1,000 = 8.4 \qquad 62.8 \div 1,000 = .0628$$

Exercise 2   Mental

In each of the following, perform the division mentally by the method explained on page 58. Write the quotient only.

	1.	**2.**	**3.**	**4.**
a	2,300 ÷ 10	8.4 ÷ 10	60 ÷ 100	40 ÷ 1,000
b	64,000 ÷ 100	3,895.4 ÷ 1,000	500 ÷ 1,000	.05 ÷ 10
c	58,000 ÷ 1,000	3.9 ÷ 10	7 ÷ 100	9.06 ÷ 100

Exercise 3   Mental

Find the cost in each of the following. Make the calculations mentally and write only the answer.

1. 300 articles @ $12 per C.

2. 1,200 lb. @ $4 per cwt.

3. 135 articles @ $10 per C.

4. 140 lb. @ $.70 per cwt.

5. 2,000 articles @ $6 per M.

6. 2,750 ft. @ $100 per M.

7. 4,000 lb. @ $15 per T.

8. 6,000 lb. @ $12 per T.

9. 3,000 lb. @ $12 per T.

10. 1,550 lb. @ $20 per T.

REVIEW ASSIGNMENT 8 b

1. Find the missing number in each of the following.
   a $1.6 \times k = 56$ **b** $r \div 2.5 = 15$ **c** $.12 \times n = 48$

2. **a** Divide 22.505 by 35.   **b** Divide 10.325 by 41.3.
   c Find the cost of 645 bolts at $4.20 per 100.

3. On May 1, Ivan Day's bank balance was $511.15, and his checkbook balance was $487.32. The bank had deducted a service charge of $2.10, and the following checks were outstanding: No. 211, $18.52; No. 217, $7.41. Prepare a reconciliation statement.

4. Ellis Hale, owner of the Pine Hills Record Shop, had $65 in change in his cash register at the beginning of the day. At the end of the day there was $187.52 in the cash drawer. The register totals showed that he had taken in $132.50 during the day and had paid out $9.43. How much was the cash over or short?

5. The Bently Drug Store purchased 400 boxes of candy at 65¢ a box. The store sold 365 boxes at 98¢ a box. The remainder became unsalable because of spoilage and was thrown away. What was the store's gross profit on the entire transaction?

6. A sporting goods store buys 25 tennis rackets at $5.60 each and pays $2.50 transportation charges on the shipment. At what price should the store sell each racket in order to make a gross profit of $95 on the entire lot?

SECTION 9

Figuring Average Prices

If a person has purchased several articles of the same kind at different unit prices, he may wish to know the average price he has paid for them. This is one of the many ways a person may use the idea of averages in his everyday affairs.

PART 9a   Simple Averages and Weighted Averages

Figuring the average. A *simple average* is the quotient obtained by adding a series of numbers and dividing that sum by the number of items added.

Example

During last week Mrs. Gaylord purchased three boxes of cereal. She paid 37¢ for the first box, 38¢ for the second, and 42¢ for the third.

What average price per box did she pay for the three boxes of cereal?

Solution

$ .37
  .38
  .42

$1.17, cost of 3 boxes
$1.17 ÷ 3 = $.39, average
    price per box. **Ans.**

If the quantity at any given unit price is more than one unit, the average is computed as shown in the following example.

Example

During last week Mrs. Monroe purchased seven boxes of cereal as follows: 2 boxes @ 37¢; 1 box @ 38¢; and 4 boxes @ 42¢.

What average price per box did she pay for the seven boxes of cereal?

Solution

2 boxes @ $.37 = $ .74
1 box   @ $.38 =   .38
4 boxes @ $.42 = 1.68
7 boxes $2.80

$2.80 ÷ 7 = $.40 **Ans.**

As shown in the preceding example, if the quantity at a given price is more than one unit, multiply each unit price by the quantity at that price. Then divide the sum of these products by the sum of the quantities. Such an average is called a *weighted average*.

Exercise 1   Written

√*Be sure to estimate each product and check all calculations.*

1. Mrs. Lee purchased one dozen lemons at 89¢, a dozen at 93¢, and a third dozen at 97¢. What was the average cost per dozen? 93¢

2. A waiter's tips for five days were: $15.40; $16.20; $17.75; $16.50; $15.20. What was his average daily tip?

3. While on vacation, Ben Avery's gasoline purchases were: 10 gal. @ 32.4¢; 10 gal. @ 31.7¢; 8 gal. @ 33.5¢; 14 gal. @ 32¢. What average price per gallon, to the nearest tenth of a cent, did he pay for the gasoline? 32.3¢

4. A grass seed mixture contains 100 lb. of seed costing $.90 a lb., 70 lbs. costing $1.20 a lb., and 30 lbs. costing $1.60 a lb. What is the average cost per pound of the mixture?

5. Find the total sales for six weeks of a salesman whose weekly sales averaged $859.42.

6. On his first four weekly tests in mathematics, Cal's average grade was 86. On the fifth test his grade was 90 and on the sixth, 88. Find his average grade on the six tests.

Finding a missing item in a series. When one item in a series is missing, the problem is to find the value of the missing item.

Example

During one heating season, from September to June, a homeowner purchased 10 tons of coal at an average cost of $28.50 a ton. He paid $28.00 a ton for the first 6 tons, and $29.00 a ton for the next 3.

What was the price of the last ton?

Solution: $6 \times \$28.00 = \$168$ *amount paid for 6 tons*
   $3 \times \$29.00 = \underline{\quad 87}$ *amount paid for 3 tons*
   $\$255$ *amount paid for 9 tons*
   $10 \times \$28.50 = \$285$ *amount paid for 10 tons*
   $\$285 - \$255 = \$\ 30$ *amount paid for last ton*   **Ans.**

Exercise 2   Written

1. During one winter a homeowner purchased 8 tons of coal at an average cost of $26.20 per ton. He paid $26.10 per ton for the first 7 tons. What did he pay for the last ton? **$26.90**

2. During one spring, Mr. West bought 5 shrubs for his home at an average cost of $6.38. The first four cost $4.95, $5.50, $6.75, and $7.50. What was the cost of the fifth shrub?

AVERAGES ARE ALL AROUND US!

AVERAGE INCOME

BATTING AVERAGE

AVERAGE GRADES IN SCHOOL

AVERAGE WEIGHT

AVERAGE TEMPERATURE

AVERAGE DAILY SALES

3. A student allowed himself an average of $12 a month for certain expenses. For the first three weeks of February, he had spent $3.10, $3.45, and $3.30. What was the most he could spend in the fourth week and stay within his monthly allowance?

4. Jay has taken four tests in business mathematics with the following marks: 83, 85, 78, and 92. What mark must he get on the next test to average 85 for the five tests?

REVIEW ASSIGNMENT 9 a

✔ *Estimate each product and check all calculations.*

1. a Divide 34 by 23, correct to two decimal places.

b Find the cost of 462 bolts at $5.58 per 100.

c Multiply 346.8 by .008.   **d** Divide .8606 by 6.5.

2. On six consecutive tests, Robert's marks were 83, 78, 89, 87, 86, and 93, respectively. What was his average mark on the six tests?

3. A candy mix consisted of 40 pounds of candy costing 72¢ a pound and 20 pounds of candy costing $1.20 a pound. What is the average cost per pound of this candy mixture?

4. On the first four tests in business mathematics, Marion received marks of 78%, 85%, 92%, and 84%. What percent must she receive on the fifth test in order that her average may be 85% on the five tests?

5. A furniture store purchased 40 scatter rugs at $5.65 each and paid $8.10 for freight charges on the shipment. The store sold 30 of these rugs at $9.85 and the remainder at $6.95. What was the store's gross profit on the entire lot of rugs?

◉ **6.** A store buys bowling shoes at $5.70 a pair and sells them at $9.45 a pair. How many pairs will the store have to buy and sell in order to realize a gross profit of $150?

PART 9b Division (concluded)

Estimating the quotient. Either before or immediately after dividing, you should estimate the quotient to avoid an absurd answer to the problem.   To estimate the quotient, round the divisor to the first digit on the left; round the dividend to the nearest easy multiple of this approximate divisor; then divide.

Example

Find the exact and estimated quotients of 413 ÷ 7,375

Solution

Exact Quotient	Estimated Quotient
(The calculations that are necessary for this division are omitted.)	*Round the divisor, 7,375, to 7,000.*
$\dfrac{.056}{7375)413.000}$	*Round the dividend, 413, to 420, the nearest easy multiple of 7. 420 ÷ 7,000 = .42 ÷ 7 = .06, estimated quotient.*
.056 **Ans.**	

In the above example, .06 and .056 are not so much different as to indicate that .056 is an unreasonable answer.   In a case where one quotient is about ten or more times the other, one of them is not reasonable. The estimated quotient should be calculated again to make sure it is correct.   Then the exact quotient should be recalculated.

Study the following additional examples.

	Approximate Divisor	Approximate Dividend	Estimated Quotient
7,668 ÷ 42	40	8,000	200
4,608 ÷ 36	40	4,400	110
4,275 ÷ 25.9	30	4,200	140
*29 ÷ .072	70	28,000	400

---

*Before rounding, move the decimal points in the dividend and divisor to the right to change the divisor to a whole number if the divisor is less than 1.   Thus, 29 ÷ .072 becomes 29,000 ÷ 72.

Exercise 3   Oral

Explain how the estimated quotient was obtained in each of the following:

1. 1,769 ÷ 579 is about 3.   4. $7,120 ÷ 55 is about $120.

2. 538 ÷ 17 is about 30.   5. $491.70 ÷ 82 is about $6.

3. 832.6 ÷ 38.2 is about 20.   6. $7,762.40 ÷ 44 is about $200.

Exercise 4   Written

Estimate the quotient in each of the following.   Wherever it is possible, make the estimate mentally, without the aid of written calculations, writing the estimated quotient only.

	1.	2.	3.	4.
a	$2,126 ÷ 32 $70	$16,876 ÷ 513	3.64 ÷ 10.6	.3627 ÷ .23
b	$3,285 ÷ 43	26.3 ÷ 2.18	7.346 ÷ 8.75	6.45 ÷ .723
c	$2,848 ÷ 49	263.8 ÷ 2,354	21.44 ÷ 8.13	.26 ÷ .063

Division to a stated number of decimal places.   Problems involving the division of decimals usually require that the answers be given correct to a stated number of decimal places.   In such cases, the division must be carried one place further.   The quotient is then rounded to the number of places stated in the problem.

Example

Find the average cost per gallon of fuel oil, to the nearest *tenth* of a cent, if 431 gallons cost $73.98.

Solution	Explanation
$ .1716 431)$73.9800 **Ans. $.172 or 17.2¢**	Since the third decimal place is the position of the figure representing tenths of a cent, the answer is to be given correct to *three* decimal places.

The quotient is therefore carried to four places.   Since the last figure in the quotient is 6, the preceding figure is increased by 1.   Rounded to three decimal places, the quotient is $.172.

In cases where the answer is in dollars and cents, the final result is given to the nearest cent if the problem does not specify the number of decimal places in the answer.

Exercise **5**   Written

In each of the following problems (a) estimate the quotient, (b) perform the division and give the answer correct to the number of decimal places indicated, and (c) check the quotient.

1.	2.	3.
To 3 decimal places	To the nearest *hundredth*	To the nearest *tenth* of a cent
a 264.5 ÷ 2,345 .113	34.1 ÷ 2.13	$17.54 ÷ 504
b 7.438 ÷ 9.08	3.45 ÷ .412	$39.05 ÷ 304
c .3544 ÷ .22	45 ÷ .1312	$96.71 ÷ 412

End zeros in the divisor. Sometimes there are zeros at the end of the divisor and the divisor is a whole number. In such cases, strike off the end zeros and move the decimal point in the dividend to the left as many places as there are zeros struck off in the divisor. Then divide in the usual manner.

Example

What is the average cost per gallon of fuel oil, to the nearest tenth of a cent, if 1,800 gallons cost $315.95?

Solution	Explanation
$315.95 ÷ 1,800 = ? .17 55 18̸0̸0̸)3̸.15.95 $.176, or 17.6¢ **Ans.**	Striking off the end zeros in the divisor and moving the decimal point to the left two places in the dividend divides both the dividend and the divisor by 100. This does not change the value of the quotient.

Exercise **6**   Written

In each of the following problems (a) estimate the quotient, (b) perform the division and give the answer correct to the number of decimal places indicated, and (c) check the quotient.

1.	2.	3.
To 2 decimal places	To 3 decimal places	To 4 decimal places
a 276 ÷ 140 1.97	413 ÷ 11,800	291.5 ÷ 2,500
b 27.2 ÷ 510	880 ÷ 2,400	2,100 ÷ 8,200
c 340 ÷ 3,500	410 ÷ 7,400	191,300 ÷ 76,520,000

REVIEW ASSIGNMENT 9 b

  ✔*Estimate each product and quotient, and check all calculations.*

1. Find the missing number in each of the following.

a $.35 \times a = 210$ **b** $x - 42 = 85$ **c** $y \div 3.5 = 70$

2. a Multiply 9.64 by .08.   **c** Divide 662.2 by 43.
b Multiply 30,600 by 2,030.   **d** Divide .1089 by 4.5.
e Find the cost of 265 lb. of feed at $3.20 per cwt.
f Divide 16 by 21, correct to 3 decimal places.

3. On the first three tests in business mathematics, Ronald had marks of 77%, 92%, and 84%. What mark must he earn on the fourth test in order to have an average of 85% on the four tests?

4. A salted nut mixture consists of 30 lbs. of nut meats at 60¢ a pound, 15 lbs. at 90¢ a pound, and 5 lbs. at $1.30 a pound. What is the average cost per pound of this nut mixture?

5. The Hilton Fashion Shop purchased 40 car coats for $900. The shop sold 34 of them at $37.50 and the remainder at $29.50.
  a What was the shop's gross profit on the entire lot?
  b What was the shop's average gross profit per coat?

6. A school store buys 250 notebooks at $22.30 per 100, and pays $1.75 for transportation charges on the shipment. At what price should the store sell each of these notebooks in order to make a gross profit of $15 on the entire lot?

7. A grocer bought a crate of eggs (30 dozen) for $11.95. One dozen were broken and had to be thrown away. At what price per dozen must he sell the remainder in order to make a gross profit of $4 on the entire lot?

8. A ticket seller at a track meet was given 300 50-cent tickets, 250 80-cent tickets, and $25 in cash for change. After the meet, he returned 26 50-cent tickets, 32 80-cent tickets, and $335.90 in cash. Was his cash short or over? How much?

◗ **9.** A food store buys canned goods at $1.15 a dozen cans and sells them at 3 cans for 35¢. At that rate how many dozen cans must the store buy and sell to make a gross profit of $15?

◗ **10.** John Kirby's bank statement as of March 31 showed a bank balance of $1,236.45. His checkbook balance was $1,340.85. The checks outstanding were: No. 71, $17.80; No. 74, $32.10; No. 75, $27.60. A mail deposit of $142.20 was received by the bank too late to appear on the bank statement. There was a canceled check for $39.70 which Mr. Kirby had failed to record in his checkbook. Prepare a reconciliation statement.

UNIT Three

Special Buying Problems

SECTION 10

Buying Fractions of a Unit

The unit price of an article is often the price for some convenient unit of measure such as a dozen or a pound. If a fraction of such a unit is purchased, the cost is the product of the fraction and the unit price.

PART 10a | Fraction of a Dozen, Pound, or Yard

Finding the cost of a fraction of a unit. Suppose oranges are priced at 69¢ a dozen and you wish to purchase 8 oranges, or $\frac{2}{3}$ of a dozen. The cost would be computed by multiplying 69¢ by $\frac{2}{3}$.

Notice that the unit price, 69¢, is exactly divisible by 3, the denominator of the fraction. You therefore make that division first and then multiply the quotient by the numerator, 2. The calculations would be:

$$69¢ \div 3 = 23¢, \text{ cost of } \tfrac{1}{3} \text{ dozen}$$

$$2 \times 23¢ = 46¢, \text{ cost of } \tfrac{2}{3} \text{ dozen}$$

Buying a fraction of a unit

If the price were 74¢ instead of 69¢, you would multiply 74¢ by 2 and divide the product by 3. The method shown on page 68 would not be used here, because 74¢ is not exactly divisible by 3.

$$2 \times 74¢ = \$1.48, \text{ cost of 2 dozen}$$
$$\$1.48 \div 3 = 49\tfrac{1}{3}¢, \text{ or } 49¢, \text{ cost of } \tfrac{2}{3} \text{ dozen}$$

In some stores, any fraction of a cent is treated as an additional cent. In others, only a fraction equal to or greater than $\tfrac{1}{2}$ is treated as an additional cent. In the latter case, $49\tfrac{1}{3}¢$ is expressed as 49¢, and $49\tfrac{1}{2}¢$ as 50¢. Each is said to be expressed to the nearest cent.

In solving the problems in this text, express answers to the nearest cent except when directions are given to the contrary.

Exercise 1   Written

1. Jacquelin Clement buys the following fabrics:

   $\tfrac{3}{4}$ yd. terry cloth @ $1.28 $\tfrac{8}{9}$ yd. velveteen @ $3.51
   $\tfrac{5}{6}$ yd. hopsacking @ $1.98

   If she gives a $20 bill in payment, how much change does she receive?

2. What is the total cost of the following purchase?

   $\tfrac{7}{8}$ lb. steak @ $1.39 $\tfrac{5}{8}$ lb. cold cuts @ $1.21
   $\tfrac{3}{4}$ lb. cheese @ 29¢

3. Lucy Otis bought 27 inches of denim at 67¢ a yard.

   a What fraction of a yard did she buy?
   b What was the cost of the purchase?

4. A housewife buys 8 oranges priced at 71¢ a dozen.

   a What fraction of a dozen does she purchase?
   b What is the cost of her purchase?

5. Lamb chops weighing 14 oz. are priced at $1.79 a pound.

   a The quantity is what fraction of a pound?
   b What is the cost of these chops?

6. Mrs. Prior charged these purchases at the Corner Market:
   13 oz. beef liver @ 59¢ per lb.; 10 oz. bacon @ $1.09 per lb.;
   14 oz. pork chops @ 97¢ per lb.; 8 cantaloupe @ $1.13 per doz.
   What was the correct total of the sales slip, without tax?

PART 10b Common Fractions

Fractional numbers. In preceding sections, much of your work has been with whole numbers. These are the numbers 0, 1, 2, 3, 4, 5, and so on indefinitely.

When you figure the cost of $\frac{2}{3}$ of a dozen of oranges or $\frac{3}{4}$ of a pound of meat, you are dealing with what is called a fractional number.

A *fractional number* is the number obtained by dividing one number by another when the result is not a whole number. Thus, dividing 2 by 3 or 6 by 5 results in a fractional number, because the quotients, $\frac{2}{3}$ and $\frac{6}{5}$, do not represent whole numbers.

Fractions. A symbol such as $\frac{2}{3}$ or $\frac{6}{5}$ is called a *fractional numeral* or, briefly, a *fraction*. It is also called a *common fraction*.

A fraction consists of the numerals of a pair of numbers and indicates the division of one number by the other. The number represented above the line is called the *numerator* of the fraction. The number represented below the line is called the *denominator* of the fraction. The denominator may be any number except zero.

A fraction may be read in three ways. For example, the fraction $\frac{2}{3}$ may be read "two thirds," "two divided by three," or "two over three."

Uses of fractions. We use fractions as symbols or names for fractional numbers. Examples of such fractions are: $\frac{2}{3}$; $\frac{5}{8}$; $\frac{3}{4}$; $\frac{6}{5}$; $\frac{9}{2}$.

We may also use fractions as symbols or names for whole numbers. The following are examples; $\frac{2}{1}$; $\frac{4}{2}$; $\frac{9}{3}$; $\frac{12}{4}$; $\frac{28}{7}$.

Since any number divided by itself equals 1, we may use the fractions $\frac{1}{1}$, $\frac{2}{2}$, $\frac{3}{3}$, $\frac{4}{4}$, and so on, as symbols or names for the number 1.

Exercise 2 Oral

1. State which of the following fractions name whole numbers.

a $\frac{5}{12}$ **c** $\frac{8}{4}$ **e** $\frac{8}{3}$ **g** $\frac{7}{8}$ **i** $\frac{3}{1}$ **k** $\frac{7}{4}$ **m** $\frac{4}{5}$ **o** $\frac{8}{8}$

b $\frac{9}{5}$ **d** $\frac{12}{3}$ **f** $\frac{5}{6}$ **h** $\frac{6}{1}$ **j** $\frac{3}{2}$ **l** $\frac{4}{4}$ **n** $\frac{0}{4}$ **p** $\frac{1}{1}$

2. State which fractions in Problem 1 name fractional numbers.

3. State which of the fractions in Problem 1 are names for the number 1.

Exercise 3   Written

1. Write each of the following in the form of a fraction.

a $15 \div 5$ b $9 \div 7$ c $5 \div 6$ d $8 \div 8$ e $32 \div 35$

2. Write each of the following with a division sign ($\div$).

a $\frac{5}{8}$ b $\frac{9}{7}$ c $\frac{8}{4}$ d $\frac{6}{8}$ e $\frac{15}{16}$ f $\frac{385}{462}$ g $\frac{91}{90}$ h $\frac{90}{91}$

REVIEW ASSIGNMENT 10 b

✔*Estimate each product and quotient, and check all calculations.*

1. a Find the cost of 440 lb. nails at $21.15 per cwt.
b $6 \times n = 5$. Find the value of n.
c Divide 23 by 31, correct to 3 decimal places.
d Multiply 46.7 by .007.   e Divide 4,590 by 3,400.

2. Mrs. Bogart's budget provides an average of $30 a week for food for her family. During the current four-week period, she spent $33.50 for the first week, $26.75 for the second, and $31.25 for the third. What is the most she may spend on food for the fourth week and still stay within the budget?

3. A florist buys 50 dozen roses at $3.50 a dozen. He estimates that 5 dozen will become wilted and unsalable. At what price per dozen must he sell the remainder in order to make a gross profit of $140 on the entire lot?

4. A fruit dealer bought 5 crates of strawberries (16 baskets to the crate) at $6.85 a crate. He threw out 5 baskets that had spoiled and sold the remainder at 65¢ a basket. What was his gross profit on the entire lot?

5. Ben's Smoke Shop bought 20 boxes of cigars, each box containing 50 cigars, at $4.50 a box, and sold them at the rate of 2 cigars for 25¢. What was the store's gross profit on the 20 boxes?

6. For the month of September, egg sales of the Oakhill farm were as follows: 60 doz. @ 59¢; 80 doz. @ 63¢; 40 doz. @ 66¢; 70 doz. @ 57¢. Find to the nearest cent the average price per dozen the farm received for the September sales of eggs.

❥ 7. Miller's bank statement for June showed a bank balance of $784.33 on June 30. His checkbook balance was $861.15. A deposit of $98.85, mailed on June 29, was not recorded on the bank statement. A check for $25.48 had not been recorded in the checkbook. The outstanding checks were: No. 214, $15.63; No. 219, $31.88. Prepare a reconciliation statement.

PART | 10c | Common Fractions (continued)

The number line. The whole numbers, 0, 1, 2, 3, and so on, can be represented by points on a number line like the one below.

```
0       1       2       3       4       5
|       |       |       |       |       |  →
```

All points shown on the line are equal distances apart. The distance from 0 to 1, of any convenient length, is laid off first and is called the *unit length*. With this distance as a unit, points for the succeeding numbers are marked off. The distance from 0 to 1 is therefore 1 unit; from 0 to 2, it is 2 units; from 0 to 3, it is 3 units; and so on.

The line may be extended in the direction of the arrow to include as many number points as are desired.

Fractional numbers on the number line. Fractional numbers as well as whole numbers can be represented by points on the number line. Obviously, points representing fractional numbers will fall between those representing whole numbers.

On the number line above, the distances between the whole-number points have been divided into two and four equal parts. The distance from 0 to A is $\frac{1}{4}$ of the distance from 0 to 1, or $\frac{1}{4}$ of the unit length. From 0 to B, it is $\frac{2}{4}$, or $\frac{1}{2}$, of the unit length. From 0 to C, it is $\frac{3}{4}$ of the unit length.

From 0 to D, the distance is $\frac{4}{4}$, or $\frac{2}{2}$, of the distance from 0 to 1. That is, the distance is equal to one unit length. From 0 to E, it is $\frac{5}{4}$ of the distance from 0 to 1, or $\frac{5}{4}$ of one unit length. From 0 to H, it is $\frac{8}{4}$, or $\frac{4}{2}$, of the distance from 0 to 1, or two times one unit length.

Notice that each numeral represents the distance from 0 to a given point in terms of the distance from 0 to 1.

In a similar way, the unit length may be divided to show thirds, fifths, sixths, or any other divisions that are desired.

Facts shown by the number line. There are several facts to observe in studying the number line.

1. The denominator of a fraction shows the number of equal parts into which the unit length is divided. The numerator shows the number of these parts represented by the fraction.

2. When the numerator of a fraction is smaller than the denominator, the fraction names a number less than 1. The fractions $\frac{1}{4}$, $\frac{2}{4}$, $\frac{1}{2}$, and $\frac{3}{4}$, for example, name numbers less than 1.

3. When the numerator is greater than the denominator, the fraction names a number greater than 1. Examples are $\frac{5}{4}$, $\frac{6}{4}$, and $\frac{3}{2}$.

4. When the numerator and denominator are the same, the fraction names the number 1. Examples are $\frac{2}{2}$ and $\frac{4}{4}$. Each stands for the number 1 and represents one unit or a whole unit.

Since the unit length has been divided into halves and fourths, the fractions $\frac{2}{2}$ and $\frac{4}{4}$ mean that the whole consists of *two halves* or *four fourths*. Similarly, the whole may consist of *three thirds*, *five fifths*, *six sixths*, and so on.

Exercise 4   Oral

1. Select the fractions that name numbers less than 1.

a $\frac{3}{4}$ **c** $\frac{2}{5}$ **e** $\frac{5}{2}$ **g** $\frac{5}{8}$ **i** $\frac{3}{3}$ **k** $\frac{8}{3}$ **m** $\frac{3}{8}$ **o** $\frac{8}{4}$

b $\frac{5}{8}$ **d** $\frac{9}{10}$ **f** $\frac{10}{9}$ **h** $\frac{7}{7}$ **j** $\frac{12}{4}$ **l** $\frac{5}{1}$ **n** $\frac{1}{5}$ **p** $\frac{1}{1}$

2. From the list in Problem 1, select the fractions that name:
a The number 1.
b Numbers greater than 1.
c Whole numbers greater than 1.

3. State what numeral substituted for the question mark in each statement will make the statement true.

a 1 unit = ? sixths   **d** ? fourths = 3 units
b 2 units = ? thirds   **e** 4 units = ? halves
c 4 units = ? eighths   **f** ? fifths = 2 units

4. How many units are expressed by each of the following:
a 12 twelfths   **c** 12 thirds   **e** 20 fourths   **g** 7 sevenths
b 12 fourths   **d** 5 fifths   **f** 6 thirds   **h** 24 eighths

Multiplication of a fraction by a fraction. *To multiply two or more fractions, multiply the numerators to obtain the numerator of the product, and multiply the denominators to obtain the denominator of the product.* To illustrate,

$$\frac{2}{3} \times \frac{4}{5} = \frac{2 \times 4}{3 \times 5} = \frac{8}{15}$$

An expression like "$\frac{1}{2}$ of $\frac{3}{4}$" means the same as "$\frac{1}{2} \times \frac{3}{4}$." Hence, to find $\frac{1}{2}$ of $\frac{3}{4}$, multiply the two fractions.

Exercise 5   Oral

State as a fraction the product in each of the following:

	1.	2.	3.	4.	5.
a	$\frac{1}{3} \times \frac{1}{4}$	$\frac{2}{3}$ of $\frac{4}{8}$	$\frac{1}{2} \times \frac{2}{2}$	$\frac{2}{3} \times \frac{2}{2}$	$\frac{5}{1} \times \frac{3}{3}$
b	$\frac{1}{6}$ of $\frac{1}{3}$	$\frac{3}{8} \times \frac{5}{8}$	$\frac{1}{2} \times \frac{3}{3}$	$\frac{2}{3} \times \frac{3}{3}$	$\frac{3}{1} \times \frac{5}{5}$
c	$\frac{1}{3} \times \frac{1}{8}$	$\frac{7}{8} \times \frac{5}{6}$	$\frac{1}{2} \times \frac{4}{4}$	$\frac{3}{8} \times \frac{3}{3}$	$\frac{6}{1} \times \frac{4}{4}$

Equal fractions. You have already seen that $\frac{2}{2}$, $\frac{3}{3}$, $\frac{4}{4}$, and so on, are fractions that name the number 1. You also know that multiplying a number by 1 does not change the number.

Hence, we may write $\frac{1}{2} = \frac{1}{2} \times \frac{2}{2}$. This means that $\frac{1}{2}$ and $\frac{1}{2} \times \frac{2}{2}$ are names for the same fractional number. Completing the multiplication, we have,

$$\frac{1}{2} = \frac{1}{2} \times \frac{2}{2} = \frac{1 \times 2}{2 \times 2} = \frac{2}{4}$$

FRACTIONS THAT NAME THE SAME NUMBER ARE EQUAL TO EACH OTHER

Thus, $\frac{1}{2}$ and $\frac{2}{4}$ are names for the same fractional number, one half. Since they name the same number, they are called *equal fractions*. Other fractions equal to $\frac{1}{2}$ can be obtained by multiplying $\frac{1}{2}$ by $\frac{3}{3}$, $\frac{4}{4}$, $\frac{5}{5}$, and so on. The first three would be $\frac{3}{6}$, $\frac{4}{8}$, and $\frac{5}{10}$.

Stated briefly, we obtain an equal fraction if we multiply the numerator and denominator of a fraction by the same number.

Since division is the inverse of multiplication, we also obtain an equal fraction by dividing the numerator and denominator by the same number. Thus, $\dfrac{2}{4} = \dfrac{2 \div 2}{4 \div 2} = \dfrac{1}{2}$.

To summarize: If we multiply or divide both the numerator and denominator of a fraction by the same number, we obtain an equal fraction. The value of a fraction is not changed if the numerator and the denominator are multiplied or divided by the same number.

Turn now to the second number line on page 72. Notice that the equal fractions $\frac{1}{2}$ and $\frac{2}{4}$ are at the same point, B, as would be expected. If the unit length had been divided also into sixths, eighths, and tenths, other equal fractions falling at the same point would be $\frac{3}{6}$, $\frac{4}{8}$, and $\frac{5}{10}$.

Other points showing equal fractions are D, F, and H.

Exercise 6   Oral

1. For each fraction below, give the four equal fractions obtained by multiplying the numerator and denominator by 2, 3, 4, and 5.

a $\frac{3}{4}$ **b** $\frac{2}{5}$ **c** $\frac{6}{5}$ **d** $\frac{3}{8}$ **e** $\frac{1}{1}$ **f** $\frac{2}{1}$ **g** $\frac{4}{1}$ **h** $\frac{3}{10}$

2. For each fraction below, give the equal fraction obtained by dividing the numerator and denominator by the number indicated.

a $\frac{3}{18}$, by 3   **b** $\frac{15}{35}$, by 5   **c** $\frac{42}{48}$, by 6   **d** $\frac{15}{10}$, by 5   **e** $\frac{18}{6}$, by 6

3. Each of the following fractions is equal to $\frac{90}{45}$. State how each fraction can be obtained from $\frac{90}{45}$.

a $\frac{2}{1}$ **b** $\frac{10}{5}$ **c** $\frac{180}{90}$ **d** $\frac{30}{15}$ **e** $\frac{360}{180}$ **f** $\frac{6}{3}$ **g** $\frac{18}{9}$ **h** $\frac{270}{135}$

REVIEW ASSIGNMENT 10c

✔ *Be sure to estimate each product and quotient, and check all calculations.*

1. a Find the cost of 13,250 bricks at $58.40 per M.
b Divide 12 by 17, correct to 3 decimal places.
c Multiply 10,400 by 1,850.   **e** Divide 9,568 by 4,600.
d Multiply 208.3 by 6.97.   **f** Divide 3,586.72 by 11.6.

2. Rossman, a florist, placed $30 in change in his cash register on the morning of August 11. At the close of the day the register showed that $342.87 had been taken in and $28.76 paid out. The cash on hand in the money drawer at the end of the day was $344.26. Was the cash over or short? How much?

3. A hat shop bought 80 ladies hats at $6.85 each. The shop sold 71 of them at $11.95 and the remainder at $8.95. Find the shop's average profit per hat to the nearest cent.

4. $1.03 \times c = 41.2$. Find the value of c.

5. The merchandise inventory of Phil's Hobby Shop was $17,980 on July 1 and $19,140 on September 30. Sales for the three months were $22,340, and the purchases were $14,630. What was the store's gross profit for the three months?

▶ **6.** A clothier buys men's shirts at $39 a dozen and sells them at $4.95 each. How many shirts will he have to buy and sell in order to realize a gross profit of $85?

PART 10d   Common Fractions (continued)

Reducing a fraction to lowest terms. The numerator and denominator are called the *terms* of a fraction. Of two equal fractions, the one with the smaller numbers in the numerator and denominator is said to be expressed in *lower terms*. To express a fraction in lower terms, we therefore *divide* the numerator and denominator by the same number.

A fraction is said to be in *lowest terms* when no number except 1 will exactly divide both of its terms. Hence, to reduce a fraction to lowest terms, divide the numerator and denominator by the largest number that will exactly divide both of them. This number is called the *greatest common factor** of the terms.

1. $\dfrac{6}{16} = \dfrac{6 \div 2}{16 \div 2} = \dfrac{3}{8}$; or $\dfrac{\overset{3}{\cancel{6}}}{\underset{8}{\cancel{16}}} = \dfrac{3}{8}$ 2. $\dfrac{8}{12} = \dfrac{8 \div 4}{12 \div 4} = \dfrac{2}{3}$; or $\dfrac{\overset{2}{\cancel{8}}}{\underset{3}{\cancel{12}}} = \dfrac{2}{3}$

In a set of equal fractions, the fraction in lowest terms is regarded as the simplest name for the fractional number. Thus, $\frac{1}{2}$ is the simplest name for the fractional number represented by the fractions $\frac{1}{2}$, $\frac{2}{4}$, $\frac{3}{6}$, $\frac{4}{8}$, $\frac{5}{10}$, $\frac{6}{12}$, and so on.

Exercise 7   Oral

Reduce each fraction to lowest terms.

1. $\frac{6}{10}$, $\frac{7}{21}$, $\frac{5}{20}$, $\frac{27}{33}$ 3. $\frac{12}{18}$, $\frac{8}{16}$, $\frac{9}{21}$, $\frac{27}{36}$

2. $\frac{10}{15}$, $\frac{15}{18}$, $\frac{20}{24}$, $\frac{18}{27}$ 4. $\frac{18}{20}$, $\frac{6}{18}$, $\frac{5}{25}$, $\frac{25}{30}$

Reducing the product of fractions to lowest terms. The product of two or more fractions can be reduced to lowest terms by dividing the

*A factor of a number is a number which divides that number without a remainder.

numerators and denominators by the common factors before multiplying. For example:

$$\frac{6}{7} \times \frac{3}{4} \times \frac{11}{15} = \frac{\overset{3}{\cancel{6}}}{7} \times \frac{\overset{1}{\cancel{3}}}{\cancel{4}} \times \frac{11}{\underset{5}{\cancel{15}}} = \frac{33}{70}$$

Whenever an answer is a fraction, reduce it to lowest terms.

Exercise 8   Oral

State the product in each of the following:

	1.	2.	3.	4.	5.
a	$\frac{1}{3} \times \frac{3}{4}$	$\frac{3}{8}$ of $\frac{4}{25}$	$\frac{8}{9} \times \frac{1}{2}$	$\frac{1}{4} \times \frac{4}{1}$	$\frac{5}{8} \times \frac{4}{5}$
b	$\frac{1}{5} \times \frac{5}{16}$	$\frac{5}{8}$ of $\frac{8}{9}$	$\frac{1}{2}$ of $\frac{15}{16}$	$\frac{3}{4} \times \frac{5}{8}$	$\frac{2}{3} \times \frac{3}{2}$
c	$\frac{3}{5} \times \frac{2}{3}$	$\frac{12}{25} \times \frac{1}{4}$	$\frac{2}{5} \times \frac{5}{2}$	$\frac{5}{8} \times \frac{8}{5}$	$\frac{4}{9}$ of $\frac{3}{4}$

Exercise 9   Written

Find the product in each of the following:

	1.	2.	3.	4.	5.
a	$\frac{7}{24} \times \frac{36}{49}$	$\frac{3}{14}$ $\frac{11}{12}$ of $\frac{54}{77}$	$\frac{15}{49} \times \frac{42}{55}$	$\frac{27}{56} \times \frac{64}{81}$	$\frac{45}{56} \times \frac{35}{54} \times \frac{24}{25}$
b	$\frac{14}{27} \times \frac{9}{35}$	$\frac{15}{16}$ of $\frac{56}{65}$	$\frac{56}{63} \times \frac{36}{49}$	$\frac{16}{35} \times \frac{49}{68}$	$\frac{8}{15} \times 36 \times \frac{35}{24}$

Proper fractions and improper fractions. When the numerator
of a fraction is smaller than the denominator, the fraction is a *proper
fraction*. When the numerator is equal to or greater than the denomi-
nator, the fraction is an *improper fraction*. Thus, $\frac{3}{4}$, $\frac{5}{6}$, and $\frac{9}{10}$ are proper
fractions; and $\frac{5}{5}$, $\frac{9}{4}$, and $\frac{12}{7}$ are improper fractions.

Changing an improper fraction to mixed number form. Turn to the
second number line on page 72. Notice that the distance from 0 to point
I is 2 units plus $\frac{1}{4}$ of a unit, or $2\frac{1}{4}$ units. We could therefore label point I
$2\frac{1}{4}$. Point I is presently labeled $\frac{9}{4}$. This means that both $2\frac{1}{4}$ and $\frac{9}{4}$ are
names for the same fractional number.

The number represented by a numeral like $2\frac{1}{4}$, consisting of numerals for a whole number and a fraction, is called a *mixed number*.

When fractions are multiplied, the result may be an improper
fraction. Ordinarily, it should be changed to mixed number form. A
quick way to do this is to divide the numerator by the denominator.

$$\frac{9}{4} = 9 \div 4 = 2\frac{1}{4}$$

Exercise 10 Oral

State the mixed number or whole number that is equal to the improper fraction in each of the following.

1. $\frac{5}{3}$　　3. $\frac{9}{5}$　　5. $\frac{23}{5}$　　7. $\frac{16}{4}$　　9. $\frac{6}{4}$　　11. $\frac{20}{6}$

2. $\frac{7}{4}$　　4. $\frac{25}{8}$　　6. $\frac{6}{6}$　　8. $\frac{27}{3}$　　10. $\frac{10}{8}$　　12. $\frac{26}{8}$

Multiplication of a whole number and a fraction. Frequently, a fractional part of a pound, dozen, or other unit, is purchased at a unit price in even cents. To find the cost of the purchase, you multiply the price, which is a whole number, by the quantity, which is a fractional number.

To find the product in an expression such as $13 \times \frac{3}{8}$, the whole number may be thought of as $\frac{13}{1}$. The numerator of the product will be 13×3, or 39. The denominator will be 1×8, or 8. Hence the rule:

To find the product of a whole number and a fraction, multiply the numerator by the whole number, and divide by the denominator. Thus,

$$13 \times \frac{3}{8} = \frac{13 \times 3}{8} = \frac{39}{8} = 4\frac{7}{8}$$

The product can be reduced to lowest terms by dividing the whole number and the denominator of the fraction by a common factor, if there is one, before multiplying. To illustrate:

$$15 \times \frac{7}{12} = \overset{5}{\cancel{15}} \times \frac{7}{\underset{4}{\cancel{12}}} = \frac{35}{4} = 8\frac{3}{4}$$

With fractional numbers, as with whole numbers, multiplication is commutative. The multiplication of 15 by $\frac{7}{12}$ may therefore be expressed either as $\frac{7}{12} \times 15$ or $15 \times \frac{7}{12}$.

Exercise 11 Oral

State the product in each of the following:

	1.	2.	3.	4.	5.
a	$44 \times \frac{3}{4}$	$\frac{3}{4}$ of 80	$4 \times \frac{3}{8}$	$\frac{2}{3} \times 4$	$\frac{1}{12}$ of 8
b	$27 \times \frac{2}{3}$	$4 \times \frac{5}{24}$	$3 \times \frac{7}{9}$	$\frac{1}{4}$ of 9	$\frac{1}{16}$ of 6
c	$\frac{3}{8} \times 24$	$5 \times \frac{4}{25}$	$\frac{11}{12} \times 6$	$\frac{3}{4}$ of 7	$\frac{4}{9} \times 12$
d	$\frac{3}{4} \times 36$	$\frac{2}{15} \times 3$	$\frac{8}{15} \times 5$	$\frac{1}{15} \times 9$	$\frac{5}{12} \times 10$
e	$\frac{2}{5}$ of 20	$\frac{3}{16} \times 2$	$\frac{1}{3} \times 5$	$\frac{1}{32} \times 24$	$\frac{3}{10}$ of 8

REVIEW ASSIGNMENT **10** d

✔Don't fail to estimate each product and quotient, and check all of your calculations.

1. a Find the cost of 28,800 ft. of lumber at $145 per M.

b $16 \times p = 12$. Find the value of p.

c Divide $6.55 by 12, correct to the nearest cent.

d Multiply 13.4 by 4.06.   **e** Divide 84,448 by 2,080.

2. Eckert's checkbook balance on June 1 was $681.42. The bank statement he received on that date showed a balance of $785.22. Checks outstanding were as follows: $8.29; $69.43; $28.03. In addition, the bank had deducted a service charge of $1.95. Prepare a reconciliation statement.

3. The Sanders Men's Shop purchased 60 summer sportcoats at $24.25 each and marked them to sell at $39.50. Fifty-two were sold at that price and the remainder were closed out at $29.50. What was the store's gross profit on the 60 coats?

4. A fruit dealer buys 15 crates of strawberries (16 baskets to the crate) at $7.85 a crate. He estimates that 20 baskets will spoil and will have to be thrown away. At what price per basket, to the nearest cent, must he sell the remainder in order to make a gross profit of $35 on the 15 crates?

◗ **5.** On August 31, Clary's checkbook balance was $788.41. Upon comparing the bank statement with his checkbook, Clary found that a check for $12.60 had been recorded in the checkbook as $16.20 and that a deposit of $49.95 had not been recorded in the checkbook. What was his correct available checkbook balance?

PART | 10e | Common Fractions (continued)

Addition and subtraction of like fractions. Fractions, such as $\frac{2}{7}$ and $\frac{3}{7}$, which have the same denominator, are called *like fractions* and are said to have a *common denominator*.

Just as 2 pounds + 3 pounds = 5 pounds, so 2 sevenths + 3 sevenths = 5 sevenths.

$$\tfrac{2}{7} + \tfrac{3}{7} = \tfrac{5}{7}$$

Similarly, just as 7 dollars − 2 dollars = 5 dollars, so 7 ninths − 2 ninths = 5 ninths.

$$\tfrac{7}{9} - \tfrac{2}{9} = \tfrac{5}{9}$$

Hence, to add or subtract like fractions, add or subtract the numerators and write the result over the common denominator.

Exercise 12   Oral

1. State the sum in each of the following:

a $\frac{1}{5}+\frac{3}{5}$ **e** $\frac{1}{8}+\frac{3}{8}$ **i** $\frac{3}{8}+\frac{3}{8}$ **m** $\frac{3}{5}+\frac{3}{5}$ **q** $\frac{3}{4}+\frac{3}{4}$

b $\frac{2}{7}+\frac{4}{7}$ **f** $\frac{1}{9}+\frac{2}{9}$ **j** $\frac{2}{9}+\frac{4}{9}$ **n** $\frac{5}{7}+\frac{4}{7}$ **r** $\frac{5}{6}+\frac{3}{6}$

c $\frac{5}{9}+\frac{2}{9}$ **g** $\frac{1}{15}+\frac{2}{15}$ **k** $\frac{3}{10}+\frac{1}{10}$ **o** $\frac{2}{3}+\frac{2}{3}$ **s** $\frac{3}{8}+\frac{7}{8}$

d $\frac{2}{15}+\frac{11}{15}$ **h** $\frac{2}{12}+\frac{2}{12}$ **l** $\frac{8}{15}+\frac{2}{15}$ **p** $\frac{3}{5}+\frac{4}{5}$ **t** $\frac{11}{12}+\frac{5}{12}$

2. State the difference in each of the following:

a $\frac{6}{7}-\frac{2}{7}$ **d** $\frac{6}{7}-\frac{3}{7}$ **g** $\frac{7}{8}-\frac{3}{8}$ **j** $\frac{5}{8}-\frac{3}{8}$ **m** $\frac{9}{10}-\frac{5}{10}$

b $\frac{7}{9}-\frac{5}{9}$ **e** $\frac{7}{9}-\frac{4}{9}$ **h** $\frac{11}{12}-\frac{7}{12}$ **k** $\frac{5}{6}-\frac{1}{6}$ **n** $\frac{11}{16}-\frac{5}{16}$

c $\frac{7}{10}-\frac{4}{10}$ **f** $\frac{11}{12}-\frac{5}{12}$ **i** $\frac{11}{16}-\frac{7}{16}$ **l** $\frac{7}{8}-\frac{1}{8}$ **o** $\frac{11}{12}-\frac{3}{12}$

Raising a fraction to higher terms. Of two equal fractions, the one with the larger numbers in the numerator and denominator is said to be in *higher terms*. Hence, to raise a fraction to higher terms, *multiply* the numerator and denominator by the same number.

Suppose, for example, you are asked to express $\frac{2}{3}$ as an equal fraction with the denominator 12, or to express $\frac{2}{3}$ in terms of twelfths. You can state the problem in this manner: $\frac{2}{3} = \frac{?}{12}$.

Since the new denominator is 4 times the old denominator (4 × 3 = 12), the new numerator must be 4 times the old numerator, or 4 × 2, which is 8. The fraction equal to $\frac{2}{3}$ is therefore $\frac{8}{12}$. $\frac{2}{3} = \frac{8}{12}$.

Exercise 13   Oral

1. State the numeral that may be substituted for the question mark so that each sentence is a true statement.

a $\frac{1}{2}=\frac{?}{8}$ **d** $\frac{2}{3}=\frac{?}{15}$ **g** $\frac{5}{6}=\frac{?}{24}$ **j** $\frac{2}{3}=\frac{?}{9}$

b $\frac{3}{4}=\frac{?}{12}$ **e** $\frac{3}{8}=\frac{?}{24}$ **h** $\frac{3}{10}=\frac{?}{20}$ **k** $\frac{3}{4}=\frac{?}{16}$

c $\frac{1}{4}=\frac{?}{20}$ **f** $\frac{4}{5}=\frac{?}{20}$ **i** $\frac{5}{8}=\frac{?}{16}$ **l** $\frac{5}{6}=\frac{?}{18}$

2. Raise each fraction to higher terms as indicated.

a $\frac{1}{2}, \frac{2}{3}, \frac{3}{4}, \frac{5}{6}$ to 12ths   **d** $\frac{1}{8}, \frac{5}{6}, \frac{3}{4}, \frac{7}{12}$ to 24ths

b $\frac{1}{4}, \frac{3}{8}, \frac{1}{2}, \frac{3}{4}$ to 16ths   **e** $\frac{1}{4}, \frac{1}{9}, \frac{2}{3}, \frac{5}{12}$ to 36ths

c $\frac{1}{3}, \frac{4}{9}, \frac{1}{2}, \frac{5}{6}$ to 18ths   **f** $\frac{2}{7}, \frac{3}{4}, \frac{1}{2}, \frac{1}{14}$ to 28ths

Addition and subtraction of unlike fractions. Fractions that have different denominators are called *unlike fractions*. The fractions $\frac{2}{3}$ and $\frac{3}{4}$, for example, are unlike fractions because they do not have the same denominator.

To add $\frac{2}{3}$ and $\frac{3}{4}$, it is first necessary to replace them with equal fractions having the same denominator. For $\frac{2}{3}$, we can substitute $\frac{8}{12}$. For $\frac{3}{4}$, we can substitute $\frac{9}{12}$. The sum of $\frac{8}{12}$ and $\frac{9}{12}$ is $\frac{17}{12}$.

$$\frac{2}{3} + \frac{3}{4} = \frac{8}{12} + \frac{9}{12} = \frac{17}{12} = 1\frac{5}{12}$$

Unlike fractions are subtracted in a similar manner.

$$\frac{3}{4} - \frac{2}{3} = \frac{9}{12} - \frac{8}{12} = \frac{1}{12}$$

Least (smallest) common denominator. In adding and subtracting unlike fractions, the common denominator may be any number that is a multiple of the denominators. It is customary, however, to use the least common multiple of the denominators. Such a number is called the *least common denominator.*

A *multiple* of a number is the product of that number and a whole number. A *common multiple* of two or more numbers is a number that is a multiple of each. The *least common multiple* of two or more numbers is the smallest number that is a multiple of each.

In many cases the largest of the denominators is the least common denominator. When it is not, multiply it by 2, 3, 4, and so on, until a product is reached that is a multiple of the other denominators. This is the least common denominator.

Exercise 14   Oral

1. State the least common denominator of the fractions in each of the following:

a $\frac{3}{8}$, $\frac{1}{2}$ **d** $\frac{2}{3}$, $\frac{3}{4}$ **g** $\frac{3}{4}$, $\frac{1}{6}$ **j** $\frac{3}{4}$, $\frac{5}{8}$, $\frac{1}{16}$ **m** $\frac{1}{4}$, $\frac{3}{8}$, $\frac{1}{6}$

b $\frac{3}{4}$, $\frac{5}{12}$ **e** $\frac{5}{8}$, $\frac{2}{3}$ **h** $\frac{5}{6}$, $\frac{3}{8}$ **k** $\frac{2}{3}$, $\frac{1}{4}$, $\frac{5}{12}$ **n** $\frac{7}{10}$, $\frac{3}{4}$, $\frac{1}{2}$

c $\frac{7}{16}$, $\frac{3}{8}$ **f** $\frac{3}{4}$, $\frac{4}{5}$ **i** $\frac{3}{10}$, $\frac{1}{4}$ **l** $\frac{2}{3}$, $\frac{3}{4}$, $\frac{1}{2}$ **o** $\frac{5}{6}$, $\frac{1}{4}$, $\frac{3}{8}$

2. In each set of fractions given in Problem 1, express each fraction in terms of a fraction whose denominator is the same as the least common denominator of the fractions in that set.

3. State the sum in each of the following:

a $\frac{1}{4} + \frac{1}{8}$ **e** $\frac{1}{6} + \frac{5}{12}$ **i** $\frac{1}{4} + \frac{7}{8}$ **m** $\frac{3}{4} + \frac{3}{8}$ **q** $\frac{1}{2} + \frac{1}{12}$

b $\frac{1}{4} + \frac{3}{8}$ **f** $\frac{3}{8} + \frac{1}{16}$ **j** $\frac{1}{3} + \frac{5}{6}$ **n** $\frac{3}{4} + \frac{7}{8}$ **r** $\frac{1}{6} + \frac{1}{12}$

c $\frac{1}{3} + \frac{2}{9}$ **g** $\frac{3}{4} + \frac{1}{16}$ **k** $\frac{1}{2} + \frac{7}{12}$ **o** $\frac{3}{4} + \frac{7}{16}$ **s** $\frac{1}{4} + \frac{5}{12}$

d $\frac{1}{8} + \frac{3}{16}$ **h** $\frac{1}{2} + \frac{3}{4}$ **l** $\frac{1}{4} + \frac{15}{16}$ **p** $\frac{1}{3} + \frac{1}{6}$ **t** $\frac{1}{3} + \frac{5}{12}$

4. State the sum in each of the following:

a $\frac{2}{3} + \frac{5}{6}$ **d** $\frac{3}{4} + \frac{7}{12}$ **g** $\frac{1}{2} + \frac{1}{3}$ **j** $\frac{1}{6} + \frac{1}{8}$ **m** $\frac{2}{3} + \frac{1}{4}$

b $\frac{5}{6} + \frac{5}{12}$ **e** $\frac{2}{3} + \frac{7}{12}$ **h** $\frac{1}{4} + \frac{1}{5}$ **k** $\frac{1}{2} + \frac{2}{3}$ **n** $\frac{1}{4} + \frac{5}{6}$

c $\frac{1}{4} + \frac{11}{12}$ **f** $\frac{1}{3} + \frac{1}{4}$ **i** $\frac{1}{4} + \frac{1}{6}$ **l** $\frac{1}{3} + \frac{3}{4}$ **o** $\frac{1}{6} + \frac{3}{8}$

5. State the difference in each of the following:

a $\frac{3}{4} - \frac{1}{8}$ **e** $\frac{3}{4} - \frac{3}{16}$ **i** $\frac{5}{6} - \frac{1}{2}$ **m** $\frac{3}{4} - \frac{1}{2}$ **q** $\frac{2}{3} - \frac{1}{4}$

b $\frac{7}{8} - \frac{1}{16}$ **f** $\frac{2}{3} - \frac{1}{12}$ **j** $\frac{2}{3} - \frac{1}{6}$ **n** $\frac{1}{2} - \frac{1}{4}$ **r** $\frac{2}{3} - \frac{1}{3}$

c $\frac{5}{8} - \frac{1}{16}$ **g** $\frac{11}{12} - \frac{1}{3}$ **k** $\frac{2}{3} - \frac{5}{12}$ **o** $\frac{1}{2} - \frac{1}{3}$ **s** $\frac{11}{12} - \frac{1}{6}$

d $\frac{3}{4} - \frac{1}{16}$ **h** $\frac{15}{16} - \frac{1}{4}$ **l** $\frac{3}{4} - \frac{7}{12}$ **p** $\frac{2}{3} - \frac{1}{2}$ **t** $\frac{5}{6} - \frac{1}{3}$

REVIEW ASSIGNMENT 10e

✓*Estimate each product and quotient and check all calculations.*

1. a Find the cost of 5,720 lb. at $12.40 a ton.

b Divide $5.35 by 15, correct to the nearest cent.

c Multiply 37 by $\frac{3}{8}$.   **d** Divide 70.87 by 1.9.

2. A ticket seller at a basketball game was given 200 65-cent tickets, 150 95-cent tickets, and $15 in change. After the game, he returned 31 65-cent tickets, 43 95-cent tickets, and $226.85 in cash. Was his cash short or over? How much?

3. The Economy Mart bought a job lot of 130 pairs of tropical slacks for $700. The store sold 30 pairs at $8.95, 45 pairs at $7.45, and the remainder at $5.95. Find, to the nearest cent, the store's average gross profit per pair.

❷ **4.** Henry Allen's checkbook balance on April 1 was $490.31. In making a reconciliation statement he found that a check for $17.00 was recorded in the checkbook as $27.00, and that he had no record in his checkbook of a service charge of $1.55 and a deposit of $32.40. What was his correct checkbook balance?

SECTION 11

Purchases Involving Mixed Numbers

Sometimes the quantity purchased or the unit price is a mixed number. For example, a person may purchase $2\frac{3}{8}$ pounds of meat, or $3\frac{2}{3}$ dozen oranges. Or soup may be priced at $19\frac{1}{2}$¢ a can, pencils at $4\frac{5}{6}$¢ each, rope at $5\frac{1}{4}$¢ a foot, and so on. In all such cases, figuring the cost of the purchase involves multiplication with a mixed number.

PART 11a   Quantity or Price as a Mixed Number

Finding the cost when the quantity or the unit price is a mixed number. To find the cost when the quantity or the unit price is a mixed number, multiply the price or the quantity by each part of the mixed number separately, and then add the results.

If Warren Russel purchases $2\frac{3}{8}$ lbs. of bacon at 85¢, the cost would be figured as shown at the right.

$.85
$2\frac{3}{8}$
$8)\overline{255}$ $(3 \times 85 = 255)$
   $31\frac{7}{8}$ $(255 \div 8 = 31\frac{7}{8})$
   170 $(2 \times 85 = 170)$
$2.01\frac{7}{8}$, or $2.02, cost of purchase

Exercise 1   Written

✔ *Be sure to estimate each product and check all calculations.*

1. Sara Hull purchased the following fabrics:

$2\frac{2}{3}$ yd. muslin @ 53¢ **$1.41** $3\frac{1}{2}$ yd. flannel @ $2.97
$3\frac{1}{4}$ yd. gingham @ 65¢ $4\frac{5}{6}$ yd. tweed @ $3.85

What was the total cost of the purchase?

2. Mrs. Fortunato bought the following from a market:

$7\frac{3}{8}$ lb. ham @ 69¢ $1\frac{1}{4}$ lb. coldcuts @ 79¢

$4\frac{3}{4}$ lb. beef @ 87¢   5 cans tuna @ 2 for 65¢

How much change should she have received from a $20 bill given in payment?

3. What is the correct total cost of the following building materials: 32 feet of plywood at $20\frac{1}{8}$¢ per foot; 46 feet of pine at $36\frac{3}{4}$¢ a foot; 65 floor tiles @ $16\frac{1}{2}$¢ each; 75 feet of molding @ $9\frac{5}{8}$¢ a foot?

4. By planning ahead, Webb Dodge could have bought a single length of electric wire, 250 feet long, for $16.50. Instead, he bought four separate lengths, as follows: 150 feet @ $7\frac{3}{8}$¢; 50 ft. @ $7\frac{3}{4}$¢; 35 ft. @ $8\frac{1}{2}$¢; and 15 ft. @ $9\frac{1}{4}$¢. How much would he have saved by planning ahead?

PART 11b   Common Fractions (continued)

Multiplication of a whole number and a mixed number. To multiply a whole number by a mixed number, multiply by each part of the mixed number separately and add the results.

Example

a Multiply 35 by $9\frac{3}{8}$.   **b** Multiply $27\frac{5}{6}$ by 32.

Solution (a)	Explanation	Solution (b)

Solution (a)

35
$9\frac{3}{8}$
8)105
$13\frac{1}{8}$
315
$328\frac{1}{8}$ **Ans.**

Explanation

The solution at the left shows the process of multiplying a whole number by a mixed number. 35 is multiplied by $\frac{3}{8}$ by multiplying by 3 and dividing by 8. The result is $13\frac{1}{8}$, which is the first partial product. The whole numbers are then multiplied in the usual manner.

The solution at the right shows the process of multiplying a mixed number by a whole number. 32 is multiplied by $\frac{5}{6}$ by multiplying by 5 and dividing by 6. The result is $26\frac{2}{3}$, which is the first partial product in the solution. The whole numbers are then multiplied in the usual manner.

Solution (b)

$27\frac{5}{6}$
32
6)160
$26\frac{2}{3}$
54
81
$890\frac{2}{3}$ **Ans.**

Exercise 2   Written

Find the product in each of the following. Be sure to estimate each product and check all your calculations.

	1.	**2.**	**3.**	**4.**	**5.**
a	$33 \times 7\frac{1}{3}$	242	$72 \times 4\frac{5}{12}$	$25\frac{3}{8} \times 24$	$17 \times 4\frac{3}{4}$	$80\frac{3}{4}$	$60 \times 5\frac{3}{8}$
b	$45 \times 8\frac{3}{5}$		$40 \times 5\frac{3}{8}$	$14\frac{2}{5} \times 60$	$23 \times 3\frac{2}{3}$	$29\frac{3}{4} \times 15$

Addition of mixed numbers. Sometimes quantities expressed as mixed numbers must be added.

Example

Mrs. Fred Myers purchased three smoked hams weighing $7\frac{5}{8}$ pounds, $9\frac{7}{16}$ pounds, and $8\frac{3}{4}$ pounds.
What was the total weight of the hams she purchased?

Solution	Explanation
16ths	The L. C. D. (least common denominator) of the fractions is 16. The fractions are therefore changed to 16ths, and the numerators of the equal fractions are written in a column at the right. The numerators are added, and the sum, 29, is written as $\frac{29}{16}$.

$7\frac{5}{8}$ | 10
$9\frac{7}{16}$ | 7
$8\frac{3}{4}$ | 12

$24 + \frac{29}{16} = 25\frac{13}{16}$ **Ans.**

The whole numbers are added and their sum, 24, is then combined with the sum of the fractions, $\frac{29}{16}$, giving $25\frac{13}{16}$ $(24 + 1\frac{13}{16})$.

Exercise 3   Written

Find the sum in each of the following. Check all calculations.

1.	**2.**	**3.**	**4.**	**5.**	**6.**	**7.**	**8.**	**9.**	**10.**
$4\frac{1}{8}$	$6\frac{2}{3}$	$9\frac{3}{4}$	$3\frac{3}{4}$	$8\frac{3}{4}$	$7\frac{5}{6}$	$4\frac{2}{3}$	$\frac{1}{3}$	$8\frac{1}{2}$	$\frac{2}{3}$
$5\frac{1}{16}$	$4\frac{1}{2}$	$4\frac{2}{3}$	$8\frac{2}{3}$	$6\frac{1}{4}$	$9\frac{1}{8}$	$7\frac{5}{8}$	$2\frac{1}{4}$	$\frac{3}{4}$	$\frac{3}{4}$
$2\frac{3}{4}$	$7\frac{1}{6}$	$5\frac{5}{12}$	$6\frac{1}{2}$	$3\frac{2}{3}$	$3\frac{1}{2}$	$2\frac{1}{4}$	$4\frac{5}{6}$	$\frac{2}{5}$	$\frac{5}{6}$
$11\frac{15}{16}$									

REVIEW ASSIGNMENT 11b

1. **a** $32 \times p = 28$. Find the value of p.
   b Multiply 29 by $\frac{5}{8}$.   **c** Multiply 10,200 by 1,750.

2. A gift shop bought 15 novelty table lamps at \$7 each and paid \$4.25 for express charges on the shipment. At what average price each should the gift shop sell these lamps in order to make a gross profit of \$70 on the entire lot?

3. A store buys apricot nectar at $1.50 a dozen cans. The store sells it at the rate of 2 cans for 31¢. Find the store's average gross profit per can.

4. Florence received an average mark of 83 on her first four tests in business mathematics. What mark must she receive on the fifth test if she desires an average mark of 85 on these five tests?

5. A vegetable dealer buys 10 boxes of lettuce, 24 heads to the box, at $4.88 a box, delivered. He estimates that 20 heads will spoil and will have to be thrown away. At what price per head must he sell the remainder in order to make a gross profit of $15 on the 10 boxes?

◗ **6.** A men's shop buys athletic socks at $5.25 a dozen pairs and sells them at the rate of 2 pairs for $1.25. How many pairs of these socks will the shop have to buy and sell in order to make a gross profit of $45?

PART | **11c** | Common Fractions (continued)

Subtraction of mixed numbers. The subtraction of mixed numbers is performed in much the same manner as the addition of mixed numbers.

Example

Subtract $23\frac{5}{6}$ from $68\frac{3}{8}$.

Solution	Explanation

$$\begin{array}{c|c} & 24ths \\ \hline 7 & 33 \\ 6\overset{\scriptstyle 7}{\cancel{8}}\frac{3}{8} & \cancel{9} \\ 23\frac{5}{6} & 20 \\ \hline \end{array}$$

$44 + \frac{13}{24} = 44\frac{13}{24}$ **Ans.**

The L. C. D. of the fractions is 24. The fractions are therefore changed to 24ths, and the numerators of the equal fractions are written in the column at the right.

Since 20 twenty-fourths cannot be subtracted from 9 twenty-fourths, 24 twenty-fourths (or 1 unit) are borrowed and added to the 9 twenty-fourths, giving 33 as the new minuend in the column at the right.

Now 20 is subtracted from 33, leaving 13, which is written as $\frac{13}{24}$.

The whole numbers are subtracted. The difference, 44, is combined with the difference between the fractions, $\frac{13}{24}$, giving $44\frac{13}{24}$.

Exercise 4   Written

Perform the subtraction in each of the following. Show and check all the necessary calculations.

1.	2.	3.	4.	5.	6.	7.
$7\frac{3}{8}$	$9\frac{3}{16}$	$18\frac{2}{3}$	$16\frac{3}{4}$	$13\frac{5}{8}$	$8\frac{1}{6}$	$7\frac{1}{6}$
$3\frac{3}{4}$	$3\frac{5}{8}$	$5\frac{3}{4}$	$8\frac{5}{6}$	$7\frac{13}{16}$	$3\frac{1}{4}$	$3\frac{2}{3}$
$3\frac{5}{8}$						

8.	9.	10.	11.	12.	13.	14.
$18\frac{1}{4}$	$43\frac{1}{3}$	$25\frac{1}{4}$	$18\frac{3}{4}$	$8\frac{5}{12}$	$10\frac{3}{5}$	$9\frac{2}{5}$
$6\frac{3}{8}$	$8\frac{7}{8}$	$7\frac{1}{3}$	$10\frac{7}{8}$	$3\frac{2}{3}$	$4\frac{2}{3}$	$4\frac{3}{4}$

Expressing a mixed number as an improper fraction. Any mixed number such as $5\frac{3}{4}$ means $5 + \frac{3}{4}$. To change $5\frac{3}{4}$ to an improper fraction, we can change 5 to the improper fraction $\frac{5}{1}$ and then add the fractions $\frac{5}{1}$ and $\frac{3}{4}$.

Thus, $5 = \frac{5}{1} = \frac{5 \times 4}{1 \times 4} = \frac{20}{4}$. Since $5 = \frac{20}{4}$, then $5 + \frac{3}{4} = \frac{20}{4} + \frac{3}{4} = \frac{23}{4}$.

The improper fraction equal to $5\frac{3}{4}$ is therefore $\frac{23}{4}$.

As a short cut, there is the following rule: *Multiply the whole number by the denominator of the fraction, and to the result add the numerator. Then write this sum over the denominator of the fraction.* Thus,

$$5\frac{3}{4} = \frac{(5 \times 4) + 3}{4} = \frac{20 + 3}{4} = \frac{23}{4}$$

Exercise 5   Oral

State the improper fraction that is equal to each of the following.

	1.	2.	3.	4.	5.	6.
a	$1\frac{3}{4}$	$4\frac{2}{3}$	$12\frac{1}{2}$	$6\frac{7}{12}$	$4\frac{1}{15}$	$2\frac{15}{16}$
b	$2\frac{3}{8}$	$3\frac{5}{6}$	$5\frac{7}{8}$	$3\frac{9}{16}$	$2\frac{11}{12}$	$10\frac{5}{8}$

Multiplication of a mixed number by a mixed number. Sometimes both the quantity and the unit price are mixed numbers. Two methods of multiplying a mixed number by a mixed number are shown in the following example.

Example

Multiply $9\frac{1}{2}$ by $5\frac{2}{3}$.

Method 1. Change the mixed fractions to improper fractions and then multiply.

$$5\frac{2}{3} \times 9\frac{1}{2} = \frac{17}{3} \times \frac{19}{2} = \frac{323}{6} = 53\frac{5}{6}.\ \textbf{Ans.}$$

◗ *Method 2. Multiply separately the fraction and whole number in the multiplicand by the fraction and whole number in the multiplier, and add the results. This is often referred to as the* four-step method.

$$\begin{array}{l} 9\frac{1}{2} \\ 5\frac{2}{3} \\ \hline \frac{1}{3} \\ 6 \\ 2\frac{1}{2} \\ 45 \\ \hline 53\frac{5}{6} \end{array}$$

Step 1. $\frac{2}{3} \times \frac{1}{2} = \frac{1}{3}$
Step 2. $\frac{2}{3} \times 9 = 6$
Step 3. $5 \times \frac{1}{2} = 2\frac{1}{2}$
Step 4. $5 \times 9 = 45$

Ans.

Exercise 6 Written

√ *Be sure to estimate and check.*

1. In each of the following, change the mixed numbers to improper fractions and then multiply.

a $3\frac{1}{4} \times 2\frac{1}{2}\ 8\frac{1}{8}$ **c** $4\frac{1}{2} \times 2\frac{1}{4}$ **e** $4\frac{1}{8} \times 3\frac{1}{2}$ **g** $1\frac{1}{5} \times 2\frac{5}{8}$ **i** $5\frac{1}{4} \times 2\frac{1}{3}$
b $2\frac{1}{4} \times 4\frac{1}{5}$ **d** $3\frac{1}{5} \times 2\frac{1}{8}$ **f** $6\frac{1}{3} \times 4\frac{1}{4}$ **h** $3\frac{1}{5} \times 2\frac{1}{4}$ **j** $2\frac{3}{4} \times 1\frac{2}{3}$

◗ **2.** Find the product by the four-step method.

a $28\frac{1}{5} \times 5\frac{1}{4}\ 148\frac{1}{20}$ **c** $24\frac{1}{3} \times 6\frac{1}{2}$ **e** $28\frac{1}{3} \times 9\frac{1}{4}$ **g** $32\frac{1}{2} \times 14\frac{1}{4}$
b $39\frac{1}{4} \times 8\frac{1}{3}$ **d** $32\frac{1}{3} \times 9\frac{1}{2}$ **f** $56\frac{1}{6} \times 12\frac{1}{4}$ **h** $24\frac{2}{3} \times 6\frac{1}{2}$

REVIEW ASSIGNMENT 11c

1. a Divide $71.50 by 23, correct to the nearest cent.
b Multiply 28 by $\frac{5}{8}$.   **d** Add $12\frac{3}{4}$, $8\frac{1}{4}$ and $11\frac{5}{6}$.
c Multiply 52 by $3\frac{5}{8}$.   **e** Divide 78.12 by 42.

2. The inventory of Jan's Record Shop was $12,650 on May 1 and $11,345 on May 31. Additional merchandise purchased in May cost $4,385. Find the cost of the goods sold in May.

3. A fruit dealer bought ten boxes of pears (135 pears to the box) at $7.35 a box. He sold them at the rate of 5 pears for 39¢. What was his gross profit on the ten boxes?

4. For four weeks a salesman's sales averaged $1,130 a week. What must be his sales the fifth week in order that the weekly average may be $1,150 for the five weeks?

Finding Unit Prices

The quoted price of an article may be for a quantity expressed as a fraction or a mixed number. The price of salted nuts, for example, may be for an 8 oz. ($\frac{1}{2}$ lb.) can, or the price of candy may be for a $1\frac{1}{2}$ or $2\frac{1}{2}$ lb. box. The price of hair spray may be for a 14 oz. ($\frac{7}{8}$ lb.) pressure can. A toothpaste price may be for a 5 oz. ($\frac{5}{16}$ lb.) tube.

Frequently, you will want to compare the prices quoted for different fractional quantities of the same article to see which one represents the best buy.

To do this, you need to convert them to prices for a whole unit, such as one ounce, one pound, or one quart, as the case may be.

CORN Flakes
BRAND X
1¼ lb.
49¢

CORN FLAKES
BRAND Y
1½ lb.
56¢

WHICH IS THE BETTER BUY?

PART | 12a | Quantity a Fraction or a Mixed Number

Finding the unit price when the quoted price is for a fraction of a unit. We have seen in a preceding section that, when the quoted price is for two or more units, the buyer divides the price by the quantity to find the price of one unit. Thus,

$$\text{Price of 3 dozen} = \$1.59$$
$$\text{Price of 1 dozen} = \$1.59 \div 3 = \$.53$$

The same rule applies when the quoted price is for a fractional part of a unit. To find the unit price, the buyer would divide the quoted price by the fraction representing the quantity.

Example

The price of a pressure can containing 14 oz. ($\frac{7}{8}$ lb.) of hair spray is 57¢. What is the price of one pound?

Solution: *Price of $\frac{7}{8}$ lb. = 57¢*
Price of 1 lb. = 57 ÷ $\frac{7}{8}$ = 65$\frac{1}{7}$, or 65¢. **Ans.**

Explanation:

Since the cost of $\frac{7}{8}$ lb. is 57¢, the cost of 1 lb. is 57 ÷ $\frac{7}{8}$. To divide 57 by $\frac{7}{8}$, multiply 57 by $\frac{8}{7}$. Thus,
$$57 \div \tfrac{7}{8} = 57 \times \tfrac{8}{7} = \tfrac{456}{7} = 65\tfrac{1}{7}¢, \text{ or } 65¢. \textbf{ Ans.}$$

Exercise 1   Written

In each problem, find the unit price to the nearest cent.

1. Find the price per pound for each item given below.

Where the weight is in ounces, change it to a fraction of a pound before dividing. For example, 12 oz. = $\frac{12}{16}$, or $\frac{3}{4}$, lb.

	Weight	Con-tainer	Description	Price	Price per lb.
a	$\frac{1}{4}$ lb.	can	Black pepper	$ .49	$1.96
b	$\frac{3}{4}$ lb.	jar	Preserves	.37	
c	$\frac{5}{8}$ lb.	jar	Instant coffee	1.29	
d	6 oz.	jar	Mustard	.13	
e	12 oz.	jar	Peanut butter	.43	
f	4 oz.	pkg.	Nutmeats	.41	

2. Find the price per dozen for each article listed below. In each case change the quantity to a fraction of a dozen before dividing. For example, 9 articles = $\frac{9}{12}$, or $\frac{3}{4}$, dozen; and 15 articles = $\frac{15}{12}$, or $\frac{5}{4}$, dozen.

a Squash @ 2 for 29¢ $1.74
b Melons @ 3 for 99¢
c Pineapples @ 4 for $1.09

d Corn, 10 ears for 69¢
e Tangerines @ 8 for 44¢
f Oranges @ 20 for 95¢

Finding the unit price when the quoted price is for a quantity expressed as a mixed number. If the quoted price is for a quantity expressed as a mixed number, you would find the price of one unit by dividing the quoted price by the mixed number.

Example

If the price of a $1\frac{3}{4}$ lb. box of rice is 84¢, what is the price per pound?

Solution: *Price of $1\frac{3}{4}$ lb. = 84¢*
Price of 1 lb. = 84¢ ÷ $1\frac{3}{4}$ = 48¢. **Ans.**

Explanation:

Since the cost of $1\frac{3}{4}$ lb. is 84¢, the cost of 1 lb. is 84 ÷ $1\frac{3}{4}$. To divide 84 by $1\frac{3}{4}$, change $1\frac{3}{4}$ to $\frac{7}{4}$. Then multiply 84 by $\frac{4}{7}$. Thus, 84 ÷ $1\frac{3}{4}$ = 84 ÷ $\frac{7}{4}$ = 84 × $\frac{4}{7}$ = 48¢. **Ans.**

Exercise 2   Written

For each item, find the price per pound to the nearest cent. Change weights in pounds and ounces to mixed numbers representing pounds. Example: 2 lb. 10 oz. = $2\frac{10}{16}$, or $2\frac{5}{8}$, lb.

	Weight	Con-tainer	Contents	Price	Price per lb.
1.	$1\frac{1}{4}$ lb.	bot.	Ketchup	$ .27	22¢
2.	$1\frac{1}{2}$ lb.	can	Corned beef hash	.51	
3.	$5\frac{3}{4}$ lb.	can	Boiled ham	5.49	
4.	1 lb. 6 oz.	can	Spray starch	.33	
5.	1 lb. 13 oz.	can	Tomatoes	.30	
6.	2 lb. 8 oz.	box	Biscuit mix	.47	

REVIEW ASSIGNMENT 12 a

✔*In all of your written work, always estimate each product and quotient, and check all of your calculations.*

1. a Add $18\frac{2}{3}$, $9\frac{3}{4}$, and $8\frac{5}{6}$.   **c** Multiply $12\frac{1}{4}$ by $8\frac{1}{3}$.
b Subtract $9\frac{5}{8}$ from $16\frac{1}{3}$.   **d** Divide 2,890 by 34,000.
e Find the cost of 6,340 lb. at $25.60 a ton.

2. Find the value of n in each of the following.
a $n = 6,800 \times 270$ **b** $54 \times n = 45$ **c** $\frac{3}{4} \times 35 = n$

3. Find the average cost per pound of a grass seed mixture consisting of 25 pounds of seed at $1.05 a pound, 15 pounds at $1.55 a pound, and 10 pounds at $2.15 a pound.

4. Yesterday, Theodore Cummings, a pharmacist, started the day with a change fund of $40 in his cash register. At the end of the day there was $307.15 in the register, and the register totals showed receipts of $287.16 and paid outs of $19.48. By how much was the cash over or short?

5. A food store buys canned beans at $2.20 a dozen cans and sells them at the rate of 3 cans for 70¢. What is the store's average gross profit per can?

6. Henry the Hatter bought 15 dozen hats for $1,085. The shop sold 120 hats at $9.95 each, 40 at $7.95, and 20 at $5.95. Find, to the nearest cent, the shop's average gross profit per hat.

7. On June 30, Glenn Martin had a checkbook balance of $742.16. When he compared this balance with his bank statement he found that he had no record in his checkbook of a service charge of $1.45, a deposit of $37.50, and a check he had written for $9.15. What is his correct checkbook balance?

PART 12b Common Fractions (continued)

Reciprocals. Examine the two multiplications shown below at the right. Notice that the product in each case is 1.

When the product of two numbers is 1, each number is called the *reciprocal* of the other. Thus, in the illustration, $\frac{4}{3}$ is the reciprocal of $\frac{3}{4}$; and $\frac{3}{4}$ is the reciprocal of $\frac{4}{3}$. Likewise, 3 is the reciprocal of $\frac{1}{3}$; and $\frac{1}{3}$ is the reciprocal of 3.

Example
$\frac{3}{4} \times \frac{4}{3} = 1$
$\frac{1}{3} \times 3 = 1$

To obtain the reciprocal of any number, we interchange the numerator and denominator in the fraction representing the number. The reciprocal of $\frac{5}{8}$ is $\frac{8}{5}$; the reciprocal of $\frac{10}{8}$ is $\frac{8}{10}$; the reciprocal of 4 (thought of as $\frac{4}{1}$) is $\frac{1}{4}$.

Interchanging the numerator and denominator is often called *inverting the fraction*.

Division involving fractions. When the quoted price is for a fraction of a unit, you divide the price by the fraction to find the unit price.

To divide any number by a fraction or a whole number, multiply the dividend by the reciprocal of the divisor (or invert the divisor and multiply). Study these examples:

1. $5 \div \frac{2}{3} = 5 \times \frac{3}{2} = \frac{15}{2} = 7\frac{1}{2}$ **3.** $\frac{3}{5} \div 4 = \frac{3}{5} \times \frac{1}{4} = \frac{3}{20}$

2. $\frac{2}{5} \div \frac{3}{4} = \frac{2}{5} \times \frac{4}{3} = \frac{8}{15}$ **4.** $32 \div 4 = 32 \times \frac{1}{4} = 8$

The foregoing rule is a short cut which we derive from the longer method shown below.

$$\tfrac{2}{3} \div \tfrac{3}{4} = (\tfrac{2}{3} \times \tfrac{4}{3}) \div (\tfrac{3}{4} \times \tfrac{4}{3}) = (\tfrac{2}{3} \times \tfrac{4}{3}) \div 1 = \tfrac{2}{3} \times \tfrac{4}{3}$$

Notice that we start by multiplying both the dividend, $\tfrac{2}{3}$, and the divisor, $\tfrac{3}{4}$, by $\tfrac{4}{3}$ so that the divisor becomes 1. The final result shows that $\tfrac{2}{3} \div \tfrac{3}{4} = \tfrac{2}{3} \times \tfrac{4}{3}$, which means that dividing by a number is equal to multiplying by its reciprocal.

Exercise 3   Oral

State the quotient in each of the following:

	1.	2.	3.	4.	5.	6.
a	$1 \div \tfrac{1}{2}$	$\tfrac{1}{3} \div \tfrac{1}{3}$	$\tfrac{2}{5} \div \tfrac{2}{3}$	$\tfrac{3}{10} \div \tfrac{1}{3}$	$\tfrac{3}{3} \div 3$	$\tfrac{1}{3} \div 4$
b	$1 \div \tfrac{1}{3}$	$\tfrac{1}{4} \div \tfrac{1}{4}$	$\tfrac{3}{8} \div \tfrac{3}{5}$	$\tfrac{2}{9} \div \tfrac{1}{4}$	$\tfrac{4}{5} \div 4$	$\tfrac{1}{6} \div 4$
c	$2 \div \tfrac{1}{4}$	$\tfrac{2}{3} \div \tfrac{2}{3}$	$\tfrac{3}{5} \div \tfrac{3}{4}$	$\tfrac{1}{2} \div \tfrac{2}{3}$	$\tfrac{3}{4} \div 3$	$\tfrac{2}{5} \div 3$
d	$4 \div \tfrac{1}{3}$	$\tfrac{1}{2} \div \tfrac{1}{4}$	$\tfrac{3}{4} \div \tfrac{3}{8}$	$\tfrac{1}{3} \div \tfrac{3}{4}$	$\tfrac{5}{8} \div 5$	$\tfrac{3}{4} \div 5$
e	$2 \div \tfrac{2}{3}$	$\tfrac{1}{2} \div \tfrac{1}{6}$	$\tfrac{5}{8} \div \tfrac{5}{16}$	$\tfrac{1}{4} \div \tfrac{2}{5}$	$\tfrac{8}{11} \div 4$	$\tfrac{2}{3} \div 8$
f	$5 \div \tfrac{5}{8}$	$\tfrac{1}{3} \div \tfrac{1}{12}$	$\tfrac{2}{3} \div \tfrac{2}{9}$	$\tfrac{2}{3} \div \tfrac{3}{4}$	$\tfrac{12}{25} \div 3$	$\tfrac{3}{8} \div 6$
g	$\tfrac{1}{3} \div \tfrac{1}{2}$	$\tfrac{2}{3} \div \tfrac{3}{5}$	$\tfrac{8}{9} \div \tfrac{2}{9}$	$\tfrac{3}{4} \div \tfrac{4}{5}$	$\tfrac{8}{12} \div 4$	$24 \div 8$
h	$\tfrac{1}{4} \div \tfrac{1}{3}$	$\tfrac{3}{8} \div \tfrac{5}{8}$	$\tfrac{2}{7} \div \tfrac{6}{7}$	$\tfrac{3}{4} \div \tfrac{2}{1}$	$\tfrac{12}{15} \div 3$	$3 \div 18$
i	$\tfrac{1}{5} \div \tfrac{1}{4}$	$\tfrac{1}{4} \div \tfrac{3}{4}$	$\tfrac{2}{5} \div \tfrac{1}{2}$	$\tfrac{5}{6} \div \tfrac{3}{1}$	$\tfrac{1}{4} \div 5$	$8 \div 28$

Exercise 4   Written

Find the quotient in each of the following:

	1.	2.	3.	4.	5.
a	$5 \div \tfrac{3}{8}$ $13\tfrac{1}{3}$	$36 \div \tfrac{4}{5}$	$3 \div \tfrac{9}{10}$	$\tfrac{3}{8} \div \tfrac{5}{6}$ $\tfrac{9}{20}$	$\tfrac{8}{15} \div 12$ $\tfrac{2}{45}$
b	$14 \div \tfrac{5}{6}$	$24 \div \tfrac{3}{8}$	$8 \div \tfrac{6}{7}$	$\tfrac{2}{3} \div \tfrac{4}{5}$	$\tfrac{9}{10} \div 6$
c	$27 \div \tfrac{2}{3}$	$2 \div \tfrac{8}{9}$	$6 \div \tfrac{4}{5}$	$\tfrac{4}{15} \div \tfrac{5}{6}$	$\tfrac{4}{5} \div 10$

Division involving mixed numbers. Sometimes, in determining unit prices, the quantity or the unit price, or both, may be a mixed number. The division in such cases may be performed by changing each mixed number to an improper fraction and then proceeding with the division, To illustrate:

$$3\tfrac{1}{3} \div 1\tfrac{1}{2} = \tfrac{10}{3} \div \tfrac{3}{2} = \tfrac{10}{3} \times \tfrac{2}{3} = \tfrac{20}{9} = 2\tfrac{2}{9}$$

Exercise 5 Written

Find the quotients of the following:

	1.		2.		3.		4.	5.
a	$4\frac{3}{8} \div 5$	$\frac{7}{8}$	$6\frac{2}{3} \div 8$		$5 \div 6\frac{2}{3}$		$8\frac{3}{4} \div \frac{5}{6}$	$11\frac{3}{4} \div 1\frac{1}{4}$
b	$5\frac{3}{5} \div 7$		$8\frac{3}{4} \div 15$		$3 \div 4\frac{1}{2}$		$1\frac{1}{4} \div 8\frac{1}{3}$	$16\frac{1}{2} \div 3\frac{2}{3}$
c	$3\frac{3}{4} \div 4$		$2 \div 3\frac{1}{8}$	$\frac{16}{25}$	$2\frac{2}{5} \div 1\frac{1}{3}$	$1\frac{4}{5}$	$5\frac{1}{8} \div 6\frac{5}{6}$	$6\frac{5}{6} \div 5\frac{1}{8}$
d	$6\frac{3}{4} \div 9$		$4 \div 6\frac{2}{5}$		$1\frac{1}{4} \div 1\frac{2}{3}$		$1\frac{2}{3} \div 1\frac{1}{9}$	$32\frac{1}{2} \div 6\frac{1}{2}$

REVIEW ASSIGNMENT 12 b

1. a Add $18\frac{2}{3}$, $12\frac{1}{4}$, and $13\frac{5}{6}$. **c** Multiply $12\frac{1}{2}$ by $8\frac{1}{4}$

b Subtract $7\frac{1}{3}$ from $12\frac{1}{4}$. **d** Divide 94,080 by 28,000

e Divide \$24.50 by 18, correct to the nearest cent.

f $\frac{1}{5} \times w = 4$. Find the value of w.

2. For four weeks a salesman's sales were \$990, \$1,180, \$1,030, and \$1,140. What must be his sales the fifth week in order that the weekly average may be \$1,100 for the five weeks?

3. A salesman's average sales for 13 weeks were \$1,040 a week. What were his total sales for the 13 weeks?

4. A salesman's average sales for 9 weeks were \$980 a week. After computing that average, he worked 3 weeks, and his sales amounted to \$912, \$1,064, and \$868, respectively. Find his average weekly sales for the 12 weeks.

5. The Butler Store purchased 300 dresses at \$16 each. The store sold 80 of the dresses at \$29.95, 100 at \$24.95, and the remainder at \$19.95. What was the gross profit on the entire lot?

◗ **6.** Reynolds purchased 60 summer dresses at \$8.70 each and marked them to sell at \$13.50 each. At the end of the season, he has 8 dresses left. To what price each may he reduce these 8 dresses and still make a gross profit of \$250 on the entire lot?

PART 12c Ratio and Proportion

Meaning of ratio. Suppose your mathematics class consists of 8 girls and 12 boys. One way of comparing the two groups is to say that the number of girls is related to the number of boys as 8 is related to 12. A comparison expressed in this way is called a *ratio*. We say that the ratio of girls to boys is 8 to 12.

Since the number of girls is $\frac{8}{12}$ of the number of boys, we may use the fraction $\frac{8}{12}$ to express the ratio of girls to boys. When used this way, the fraction is read "8 to 12."

The ratio of boys to girls is 12 to 8; and we may express the ratio with the fraction $\frac{12}{8}$, which is read "12 to 8."

We may also express the ratio of 8 to 12 as $8 \div 12$ and 8:12, and the ratio of 12 to 8 as $12 \div 8$ and 12:8.

Exercise 6   Oral

1. In a class of 26 students, 15 are boys and 11 are girls. Give the ratio of:

a The number of boys to the number of girls.

b The number of girls to the number of boys.

c The number of boys to the total number of students.

d The number of girls to the total number of students.

2. A football team won 7 games and lost 5. State the ratio of games won to games played.

3. What is the ratio of 7 in. to 2 ft.? (Change the feet to inches.)

4. What is the ratio of 9 oz. to 3 lb.?

5. Out of his weekly earnings of $72, Fred saves $7. Give the ratio of the amount saved to the amount earned.

6. What is the ratio of: **a** 17¢ to 39¢. **b** $.27 to $.43

Expressing ratios in lowest terms. In a class consisting of 8 girls and 12 boys, the ratio of girls to boys is 8 to 12. A ratio, like a fraction, is changed to an equal ratio in lowest terms by dividing both terms by their greatest common fractor. Thus, the ratio 8 to 12, when reduced to lowest terms, becomes 2 to 3. The fraction $\frac{2}{3}$ expresses this ratio.

Exercise 7   Written

Write each ratio as a fraction in lowest terms.

1. 24 to 28 $\frac{6}{7}$ **4.** 4 oz. to 1 lb.   **7.** 3 yd. to 2 ft.

2. 10 in. to 24 in.   **5.** 1 hr. to 20 min.   **8.** 27 to 21

3. 5 in. to 5 ft. $\frac{1}{12}$ **6.** 2 lb. to 6 oz.   **9.** 44 to 16

Using ratios. If we are told that the ratio of girls to boys in a class is 2 to 3, the ratio tells us nothing about the number of girls and boys in the class. It does tell us that there are 2 girls for every 3 boys. That is, out of every five students, 2 are girls and 3 are boys. In other words, $\frac{2}{5}$ of the students are girls and $\frac{3}{5}$ are boys.

Hence, if we are told that there are 20 students in the class, we know that the number of girls is $\frac{2}{5}$ of 20, or 8. Similarly, the number of boys is $\frac{3}{5}$ of 20, or 12.

Exercise 8   Written

1. In a class of 35 students, the ratio of girls to boys is 2 to 3. How many girls are there in the class?   14

2. A salted-nut mixture is made up of 3 pounds of cashews to 5 pounds of peanuts. How many pounds of each are needed to make 40 pounds of the mixture?

In a ratio problem like this one and those below, check your results by adding the answers. The sum should equal the quantity or amount given in the problem. In this problem, the sum of the two answers should equal 40 pounds.

3. Jack and Jim worked together mowing and raking lawns and took in $13.50. Because Jack furnished the mower, they divided the money in a 5 to 4 ratio in favor of Jack. How much was each boy's share?

4. Two business partners divide their profits in a 1 to 4 ratio. Find each partner's share of a profit amounting to $8,400.

5. *A* and *B* are partners. How much does each receive if a profit of $13,000 is divided in a ratio of 7 to 3 in favor of *A*?

▶ **Meaning of proportion.** Reduced to lowest terms, the ratio $\frac{4}{6}$ becomes $\frac{2}{3}$; and the ratio $\frac{8}{12}$ also becomes $\frac{2}{3}$. Since $\frac{4}{6}$ and $\frac{8}{12}$ name the same ratio, $\frac{2}{3}$, we say they are equal; and we may write $\frac{4}{6} = \frac{8}{12}$. This statement, which expresses the equality of the two ratios, is called a *proportion*. It is read "4 is to 6 as 8 is to 12."

▶ **Rule of proportion.** If the numerator of one of the fractions in a proportion is multiplied by the denominator of the other, the result is a *cross product*. In the proportion $\frac{4}{6} = \frac{8}{12}$, the indicated cross products are 12×4 and 6×8. Notice that the cross products are equal; that is, $12 \times 4 = 48$ and $6 \times 8 = 48$. This is true in every proportion. Hence the *Rule of Proportion:*

In any proportion the cross products are equal.

◗ **Finding the missing term in a proportion.** The rule of proportion provides an easy way for finding the missing term in a proportion when only three of the terms are known.

Example

If 25 feet of wire weigh 15 pounds, what is the weight of 20 feet of the same kind of wire?

The ratio of the weights equals the ratio of the lengths.

Solution

Let N represent the missing weight.

Then $\dfrac{N}{15}$ is the ratio of the missing weight to the known weight.

And $\dfrac{20}{25}$ is the ratio of the length of the missing weight to the length of the known weight.

Equal ratios $\dfrac{N}{15} = \dfrac{20}{25}$

Cross products $25 \times N = 15 \times 20$

Missing factor $25 \times N = 300$

$N = 12$ **Ans. 12 pounds**

◗ **Exercise 9**   Written

1. 40 feet of wire rope weigh 26 pounds. What is the weight of 100 feet of the same kind of rope?   65 lbs.

2. A motorist drove 140 miles in 5 hours. At the same rate of speed, how far can he drive in 7 hours?
The ratio of the miles equals the ratio of the hours.

3. A certain car travels 105 miles on 6 gallons of gasoline. At this rate, how many gallons are needed for a 280-mile trip?
The ratio of the gallons equals the ratio of the miles.

4. On a trip of 175 miles, Green's driving time was 5 hours. At the same rate, what would be his driving time for a 245-mile trip?
The ratio of the hours equals the ratio of the miles.

5. Dick was paid $5.85 for working $4\frac{1}{2}$ hours. At the same rate, how much should he be paid for working 7 hours?
The ratio of the dollars equals the ratio of the hours.

6. At the rate of 8 yards for $70, what is the cost of 6 yards of carpeting? $52.50

7. A salesman was paid a commission of $20 for selling $250 worth of goods. What would be his commission on $350 of sales at the same rate of commission?

The ratio of the dollars of commissions equals the ratio of the dollars of sales.

8. A retailer sells for $40 an article that costs him $25. At the same rate, what would be his selling price of an article that costs him $35?

9. If 6 yards of cloth cost $5.25, what will 10 yards cost at the same rate?

10. If 9 yards of goods cost $7.50, how many yards can be bought, at the same rate, for $50?

REVIEW ASSIGNMENT **12** c

✓*Don't forget. In all written work, you are expected to estimate each product and quotient, and check all calculations.*

1. a Find the cost of 1,280 articles at 95¢ per C.
b Divide $172 by 35, correct to the nearest cent.
c Subtract $5\frac{1}{8}$ from $12\frac{1}{4}$.   **d** Multiply $16\frac{2}{3}$ by $9\frac{3}{4}$.

2. Find the value of y in each of the following.
a $\frac{1}{4} \times y = 8$ **b** $y = 31 \times \frac{7}{8}$ **c** $17 \div \frac{3}{4} = y$

3. Clinton Brooks had a checkbook balance of $642.11 on June 1 and a bank statement balance of $779.58. A service charge of $2.15 was reported on the bank statement. Outstanding checks were: $13.42; $46.50; $38.70; $41.00. Prepare a reconciliation statement.

4. A salesman's sales for 6 weeks averaged $936 a week. For the next two weeks his sales were $865 and $943, respectively. Find his average weekly sales for the 8 weeks.

5. A ticket seller for a school concert was given 200 75-cent tickets, 316 50-cent tickets, and $15 in change. He returned 67 75-cent tickets, 59 50-cent tickets, and $242.75 in money. Was the amount of money short or over? How much?

6. Two business partners divide their net income in a 5 to 3 ratio. Find each partner's share of a net income of $10,000.

The sum of the two answers should equal $10,000.

❯ **7.** A men's store bought 60 suits at $34.50 each and marked them to sell at $57.50. At the end of the season, 12 suits were left. To what price each may the store reduce the remaining suits and still make a gross profit of $1,200 on the 60 suits?

UNIT Four

Wage Income Problems

SECTION 13

Figuring Wage Income

The principal income of many people is the weekly wages they receive for work in a store, office, factory, or on a farm. Usually, they are paid by the hour for the number of hours worked or by the piece for the quantity produced. A worker should be able to check the calculation of the pay he receives to make sure it is correct.

YOUR SALARY INCREASE IS IN THIS WEEK'S PAY. BE SURE TO CHECK THE NEW AMOUNTS

PAYROLL CLERK

PART 13a   Straight Time and Overtime Wages

Hour-rate wages. When an employee is paid on an hour-rate basis, he is paid a definite amount for each hour he works. For example, if an employee works 40 hours during one week at the rate of $3.00 an hour, his earnings for the week are $120:

$$40 \times \$3.00 = \$120$$

Regular time and overtime. The number of hours for a regular day's or week's work is referred to as *regular time* or *straight time.*

The time an employee works in excess of the regular hours is *overtime.*

The wage rate per hour for overtime is usually one and one half times the regular rate. In such cases the employer is said to pay time and a half for overtime.

In some businesses *double time* (two times the regular rate) is paid for work on Sundays and holidays.

Figuring overtime wages and total wages. When time and a half is paid for overtime, the employee's overtime wages may be calculated in the following manner:

1. Multiply the regular hourly rate by $1\frac{1}{2}$ to find the overtime hourly rate. Do not round the result.

2. Multiply the overtime rate by the number of overtime hours.

The total wages is the sum of the regular-time wages and the overtime.

Example

The employees of the Fairfax Knitting Corporation are paid weekly on the basis of a 40-hour week with time and a half for overtime. Find the total wages earned in one week by Martin Cobane who works 45 hours and whose regular wage rate is $2.40 an hour.

Solution

Overtime wages

$45 - 40 = 5$ overtime hours

$ 2.40 regular rate

$\times 1\frac{1}{2}$

$ 3.60 overtime rate

$\times 5$

$18.00 overtime wages

Regular-time wages

$40 \times \$2.40 = \$96.00$

Total wages

$96.00 regular-time wages

18.00 overtime wages

$114.00 total wages **Ans.**

Exercise 1 Written

1. Find the overtime rate for each of the regular-time rates shown below. Time and a half is paid for overtime.

Regular rate $1.80 $2.32 $1.94 $1.85 $2.33 $3.27

Overtime rate $2.70

2. The Visutemp Instruments Company pays its employees on the basis of a 40-hour week with time and a half for overtime.

Find the total wages for each of the following employees:

	Name	Hour Rate	Hours Worked			Name	Hour Rate	Hours Worked
a	Joel Ames	$2.50	42	$107.50	e	Ted Hess	$2.90	49
b	Nell Downs	2.60	46		f	Hugh Kray	3.10	50
c	Carl Gallo	2.70	48		g	Amos Parry	3.30	47
d	Louis Hall	2.80	43		h	Paul Ring	3.40	52

3. Workers at Central Mills are employed on an eight-hour-a-day basis with time and a half for all time over 8 hours a day.

The hourly rates and the hours worked each day last week by six of the mill hands are shown in the following table.

Copy the table and complete it by showing for each employee his total regular-time hours, total overtime hours, and total wages for the week.

		Hours Worked						Total Hours		
	Name	M	T	W	T	F	Hour Rate	Regu-lar	Over-time	Total Wages
a	B. F. Banks	8	6	8	9	9	$2.40	38	2	$98.40
b	C. A. Cole	9	10	7	8	8	2.00			
c	W. O. Egan	8	9	9	8	10	2.50			
d	L. R. Getz	10	9	9	9	8	1.80			
e	G. C. Mott	6	10	8	7	8	2.30			
f	D. K. Ryan	11	8	8	7	10	2.80			

Exercise 2   Written

1. Last week, Owen Rand earned $149.20, $\frac{1}{8}$ of which was overtime earnings. How much were his overtime earnings?

2. Luke Tobin left his $2.40 an hour job at Ferris Gear, Inc. to work at Romco Foundry for $\frac{1}{4}$ more per hour. What rate was he paid at Romco?

3. Stuart Casey's wages for the week of October 23 were $105, of which $15 was overtime pay. What part of his wages was his overtime pay?

4. During the first week of July, Floyd Mann earned $120. During the second week he earned $140. What part more were his second week's earnings than his first week's earnings?

PART 13b Common Fractions (continued)

Problems in fractional relationships. The problems in Exercise 2 on this page are examples of four types of problems involving the fractional relationships of numbers. These four types of problems are:

1. To find a part of a number.
2. To find the number that is a certain part greater (or smaller) than a given number.
3. To find what part one number is of another number.
4. To find what part one number is greater (or smaller) than another number.

The method of solution for each of these four types of problems is explained and and illustrated below on the following pages.

To find a part of a number. To find a part of a given number, multiply the number by the fraction representing the part.

Example

What number is $\frac{3}{4}$ of 36?

Solution	**Explanation**

$\frac{3}{4} \times 36 = 27$ **Ans.**   An expression such as "$\frac{3}{4}$ of 36" means the same as "$\frac{3}{4} \times 36$."

Therefore, to find $\frac{3}{4}$ of 36, we multiply 36 by $\frac{3}{4}$.

Other expressions that mean the same as $\frac{3}{4}$ times 36 are "$\frac{3}{4}$ *as much as* 36," "$\frac{3}{4}$ *as great as* 36," "$\frac{3}{4}$ *as large as* 36," and "$\frac{3}{4}$ *as many as* 36." In each case the result would be obtained by multiplying 36 by $\frac{3}{4}$.

Exercise 3 Oral

State what the missing number is in each of the following:

1. ? is $\frac{3}{4}$ of 48.
2. ? is $\frac{2}{3}$ of 33.
3. $\frac{3}{4}$ of 40 is ?.
4. $\frac{3}{5}$ of 30 is ?.

5. $\frac{4}{5} \times 20$ is ?.
6. $\frac{3}{8} \times 32$ is ?.
7. $24 \times \frac{3}{4}$ is ?.
8. ? is $18 \times \frac{5}{6}$.

9. ? is $\frac{6}{5}$ of 15.
10. $\frac{5}{3} \times 18$ is ?.
11. ? is $\frac{7}{4} \times \$16$.
12. $\frac{4}{9}$ of 18 is ?.

13. ? is $\frac{7}{8}$ as large as 24.
14. ? is $\frac{2}{3}$ as much as $30.

15. ? is $\frac{5}{8}$ as great as $48.
16. ? are $\frac{5}{6}$ as many as 54.

To find the number that is a certain part greater (or smaller) than a given number. An expression such as "$\frac{1}{4}$ greater than 36" or "$\frac{1}{4}$ more than 36" means $\frac{1}{4}$ of 36 added to 36. Thus, the number that is $\frac{1}{4}$ greater than 36 is 45.

$$36 + \tfrac{1}{4} \text{ of } 36 = 36 + 9 = 45$$

Similarly, an expression such as "$\frac{1}{4}$ smaller than 36" or "$\frac{1}{4}$ less than 36" means $\frac{1}{4}$ of 36 subtracted from 36. Thus, the number that is $\frac{1}{4}$ smaller than 36 is 27.

$$36 - \tfrac{1}{4} \text{ of } 36 = 36 - 9 = 27$$

Exercise 4   Oral

State what the missing number is in each of the following:

1. ? is $\frac{1}{4}$ more than $24.
2. ? is $\frac{1}{6}$ greater than $36.
3. $\frac{1}{8}$ more than $32 is ?.
4. ? is $\frac{1}{5}$ larger than 25.
5. $28 plus $\frac{1}{4}$ of itself is ?.

6. ? is $\frac{1}{6}$ smaller than $36.
7. ? is $\frac{1}{3}$ less than $30.
8. $\frac{1}{4}$ less than $28 is ?.
9. ? is $\frac{1}{7}$ smaller than 21.
10. $32 minus $\frac{1}{8}$ of itself is ?.

11. $30 increased by $\frac{1}{6}$ of itself equals?.
12. $30 decreased by $\frac{1}{6}$ of itself equals?.

To find what part one number is of another number. To find what part one number is of another, express the relationship of the numbers in the form of a fraction. For the numerator, write the number representing the part. For the denominator, write the number representing the whole with which the part is compared. Reduce the resulting fraction to its lowest terms.

Example

27 is what part of 36?

Solution	Explanation
$\frac{27}{36} = \frac{3}{4}$ Ans.	27 is the number representing the part. 36 is the whole, or the number with which 27 is to be com-
Check	pared. Therefore the fraction $\frac{27}{36}$, or $\frac{3}{4}$, expresses
$\frac{3}{4}$ of 36 = 27	what fractional part 27 is of 36.

When a number is compared with a number larger than itself, the result is less than 1. When it is compared with itself, the result is equal to 1. When it is compared with a number smaller than itself, the result is more than 1. Thus,

30 is $\frac{5}{6}$ of 36 $(\frac{30}{36} = \frac{5}{6})$

30 is the whole of $(1 \times)$ 30 $(\frac{30}{30} = 1)$

30 is $\frac{6}{5}$ of 25 $(\frac{30}{25} = \frac{6}{5})$

Exercise 5   Oral

1. 5 is what part of 12? 9? 8? 6? 4? 3? 2?
2. 8 is what part of 15? 13? 11? 9? 7? 5? 3?
3. 12 is what part of 36? 24? 16? 7? 5? 9? 8?
4. What part of 12 is 3? 4? 11? 13? 17? 15? 16?

REVIEW ASSIGNMENT   13 b

√*Arithmetic errors in business can be costly. Make it a habit to check all answers to make sure they are correct.*

1. **a** Add $2\frac{1}{3}$, $4\frac{1}{6}$, and $3\frac{1}{2}$.   **c** Divide $5\frac{1}{3}$ by $\frac{3}{4}$.
   b Divide 19 by $\frac{3}{8}$.   **d** What amount is $\frac{3}{8}$ of $1,400?
   e $196 increased by $\frac{1}{4}$ of itself equals what amount?
   f Divide $43.50 by 17, correct to the nearest cent.

2. Fox works on a 40-hour-week basis at $2.70 an hour with time and a half for overtime. Last week he worked 45 hours. What were his total earnings for the week?

3. The regular factory hours of the Hirsch Corporation are 8 hours a day for a 5-day week. Time and a half is paid for time worked in excess of 8 hours on any day. During one week, Grover Conklin worked the following number of hours:

Mon., 7; Tues., 8; Wed., 10; Thurs., 10; Fri., 9

Conklin's regular hourly rate of pay is $2.90. What were his total earnings for the week?

4. **a** A salary of $415 a month is equal to how much a year?
   b A salary of $5,112 a year is equal to how much a month?
   c $77.50 a week is equal to how much a year?
   d $4,290 a year is equal to how much a week?

5. Ashby and Wells, two business partners, divide their net profit in the ratio of 3 to 2 in favor of Ashby. Find the amount of each partner's share of a net profit of $13,540.

The sum of the two answers should equal $13,540.

6. Find the missing number in each of the following:
   a $\frac{2}{3} \times n = 18$ **b** $r = 79.98 \div 18.6$ **c** $s - 23 = 35$

◐ 7. A retailer bought some men's shirts at $2.40 each and marked them to sell at $3.98. At that price he sold 40 shirts the first week. In order to increase sales, he reduced the price to $3.48. As a result, he sold 75 shirts the second week.

a During which week did he make the larger gross profit?
b How much larger was his gross profit that week?

Deduction from Wages

An employer is usually required to make certain deductions from an employee's wages.

These include deductions for income and social security taxes, insurance, hospital care, and any other deductions authorized by the employee.

The employee's net pay, after all deductions have been made, is often referred to as his *take-home pay.*

PART 14a Figuring Take-Home Pay

Income tax withholding tables. The deduction for the federal income tax is called the *withholding tax.* The employer determines the amount to withhold from tables supplied by the government. A portion of a table for deductions from a weekly payroll follows:

INCOME TAX WITHHOLDING TABLE
MARRIED PERSONS—WEEKLY PAYROLL PERIOD

And the wages are —		And the number of withholding exemptions claimed is —										
At least	But less than	0	1	2	3	4	5	6	7	8	9	10 or more
		The amount of income tax to be withheld shall be —										
100	105	16.40	13.80	11.30	8.70	6.50	4.50	2.50	.60	0	0	0
105	110	17.30	14.80	12.20	9.70	7.30	5.30	3.20	1.30	0	0	0
110	115	18.30	15.70	13.20	10.60	8.10	6.00	4.00	2.00	.10	0	0
115	120	19.20	16.70	14.10	11.60	9.00	6.80	4.70	2.70	.80	0	0
120	125	20.20	17.60	15.10	12.50	10.00	7.50	5.50	3.50	1.50	0	0
125	130	21.10	18.60	16.00	13.50	10.90	8.40	6.20	4.20	2.20	.40	0
130	135	22.00	19.50	17.00	14.40	11.90	9.30	7.00	5.00	3.00	1.10	0
135	140	23.00	20.50	17.90	15.40	12.80	10.30	7.70	5.70	3.70	1.80	0
140	145	24.00	21.40	18.90	16.30	13.80	11.20	8.70	6.50	4.50	2.50	.60
145	150	24.90	22.40	19.80	17.30	14.70	12.20	9.60	7.20	5.20	3.20	1.30

The amount of the withholding tax depends upon the employee's wages, whether he is married or single, and the number of exemptions he claims. An employee may claim one exemption for himself, one for his wife (or husband), and one for each dependent.

Using the withholding table. To find the amount of the tax, first read down the wages column at the left until the appropriate wage-bracket line is reached. Then read across to the column headed by the number of exemptions claimed.

For example, if an employee's wages are $102 and he claims 3 exemptions, the tax is found on the first line of the table in the column headed "3." The amount is $8.70.

If his wages are $115 and he claims 5 exemptions, the tax is on the fourth line in the column headed "5." The amount is $6.80.

Exercise 1 Oral

Using the withholding tax table on page 106, state the withholding tax for each of the following:

	Total Wages	Exemptions		Total Wages	Exemptions		Total Wages	Exemptions
1.	$100.00	2	7.	$124.00	5	13.	$115.00	1
2.	105.00	2	8.	125.10	2	14.	130.00	0
3.	110.00	2	9.	134.60	5	15.	146.50	3
4.	120.00	2	10.	140.05	1	16.	124.00	9
5.	120.00	4	11.	109.86	5	17.	140.00	10
6.	103.00	1	12.	135.10	7	18.	148.75	6

Finding the FICA tax. The tax for social security is levied under the Federal Insurance Contributions Act and is known as the *FICA tax* or *social security tax.** This tax is 4.8% of the first $7,800 of the employee's annual wages. Thus, for a person whose salary is $124.50 a week, or $6,474 a year, the tax each week is $5.98.

.048 × $124.50 = $5.976, or $5.98 to the nearest cent.

Shown on the next page are portions of a social security tax table supplied by the government to aid employers in figuring the FICA taxes.

*The tax rate may be changed from time to time. The one used here is the rate that was in force when this book was published.

SOCIAL SECURITY EMPLOYEE TAX TABLE—4.8 PERCENT

Wages		Tax to be withheld	Wages		Tax to be withheld	Wages		Tax to be withheld
At least	But less than		At least	But less than		At least	But less than	
117.61	117.82	5.65	123.86	124.07	5.95	128.03	128.23	6.15
117.82	118.03	5.66	124.07	124.28	5.96	128.23	128.44	6.16
118.03	118.23	5.67	124.28	124.48	5.97	128.44	128.65	6.17
118.23	118.44	5.68	124.48	124.69	5.98	128.65	128.86	6.18
118.44	118.65	5.69	124.69	124.90	5.99	128.86	129.07	6.19
118.65	118.86	5.70	124.90	125.11	6.00	129.07	129.28	6.20
118.86	119.07	5.71	125.11	125.32	6.01	129.28	129.48	6.21
119.07	119.28	5.72	125.32	125.53	6.02	129.48	129.69	6.22
119.28	119.48	5.73	125.53	125.73	6.03	129.69	129.90	6.23
119.48	119.69	5.74	125.73	125.94	6.04	129.90	130.11	6.24

The table shows that a wage of $125 is in the "At least $124.90 but less than $125.11" wage bracket, and that the tax on amounts in this bracket is $6.00. This means that the tax on any amount from $124.90 through $125.10 is $6.00. The tax on $125.11 is $6.01.

Exercise 2   Oral

Using the social security tax table above, state the FICA tax on the following wages:

1. $117.61   4. $118.00   7. $124.06   10. $128.64

2. $117.80   5. $118.75   8. $125.55   11. $129.10

3. $117.82   6. $123.86   9. $128.25   12. $130.00

Exercise 3   Written

1. Copy and complete the following table. Use the tables on pages 106 and 108 for determining the income and FICA taxes.

On line f, the sum of the income tax and FICA totals should equal the total deductions. The sum of the total net wages and the total deductions should equal the total wages.

	Name	Ex-emp-tions	Total Wages	Deductions			Net Wages
				Income Tax	FICA Tax	Total	
a	Bosco, A. Y.	2	$119.00	$14.10	$5.71	$19.81	$99.19
b	Camp, M. C.	4	$125.20				
c	Drew, B. L.	5	$119.47				
d	Engel, S. J.	3	$128.75				
e	Ford, R. O.	6	$130.00				
f	Totals						

2. Calculate the FICA tax at 4.8% on the indicated wages of each of the employees listed below.

a Holt, $120.00 $5.76   **b** Knox, $85.00   **c** Miles, $136.00

3. Snyder is employed on the basis of a 40-hour week at $3.40 an hour with time and a half for overtime. Last week he worked 44 hours. Deductions from his earnings totaled $43.76. How much was his take-home pay?

4. Taft is employed on a 40-hour week basis at $3.00 an hour with time and a half for overtime. During a recent week he worked 48 hours.

From his total earnings, $7.49 was deducted for the FICA tax, $16.10 for withholding taxes, $1.00 for United Appeal donation, and $2.25 for group insurance.

What amount did Taft receive as take-home pay?

5. Keefe works on an 8-hour day basis at $3.20 an hour with time and a half for overtime. During a recent week he worked the following number of hours:

Mon., 9; Tues., 8; Wed., 10; Thurs., 7; Fri., 10

His employer deducted $7.14 for FICA tax, $12.20 for withholding tax, and $6.25 for savings bonds. How much did Keefe receive as take-home pay?

REVIEW ASSIGNMENT **14**a

1. a Multiply 47 by $\frac{2}{3}$.   **c** Divide $4\frac{1}{2}$ by $\frac{3}{8}$.

b Multiply $16\frac{1}{3}$ by $12\frac{1}{2}$.   **d** Divide 12 by $3\frac{3}{4}$.

e Divide 14 by 19, correct to the nearest hundredth.

f $312 decreased by $\frac{1}{4}$ of itself gives what amount?

2. Gaynor is paid $3.08 an hour for a 40-hour week with time and a half for overtime. Last week he worked 45 hours. Total deductions from his earnings were $24.47. What amount did Gaynor receive as take-home pay?

3. During one week in March, Hicks had total earnings of $165.40. At the rate of 4.8%, what amount was deducted for FICA taxes?

4. On five tests in biology, Bob had an average mark of 62. What mark must he receive on the sixth test in order to have an average mark of 65 on all six tests?

5. For the first four months of the year the sales of the Greylock Gift Shop averaged $4,186.10 a month. For June and July the sales were $4,218.72 and $3,994.12, respectively. What were the store's average monthly sales for the six months?

6. a A salary of $585 a month is equivalent to how much a year?

b How much a week?

7. Find the missing number in each of the following:

a $\frac{3}{5} \times y = 30$ **b** $28 \times r = 24$ **c** $10 + x = 35$

PART 14b   Common Fractions (continued)

To find what part one number is greater (or smaller) than another number. To find what part one number is greater (or smaller) than another number, first subtract the smaller from the larger to find the number representing the part. Then write this number as the numerator of a fraction whose denominator represents the number with which the part is to be compared. Reduce the resulting fraction to its lowest terms.

Example

30 is what part greater than 24?

Solution	Explanation
$30 - 24 = 6$ $\frac{6}{24} = \frac{1}{4}$ **Ans.** **Check** $24 + (\frac{1}{4} \times 24) =$ $24 + 6 = 30$	30 is 6 greater than 24. 6 is therefore the number representing the part. The expression "greater than 24" means that 24 is the whole, or the number with which the part, 6, is to be compared. Therefore the fraction $\frac{6}{24}$, or $\frac{1}{4}$, expresses the part of 24 by which 30 is greater than 24.

Example

24 is what part smaller than 30?

Solution	Explanation
$30 - 24 = 6$ $\frac{6}{30} = \frac{1}{5}$ **Ans.** **Check** $30 - (\frac{1}{5} \times 30) =$ $30 - 6 = 24$	24 is 6 smaller than 30. 6 is therefore the number representing the part. The expression "smaller than 30" means that 30 is the whole, or the number with which the part, 6, is to be compared. Therefore the fraction $\frac{6}{30}$, or $\frac{1}{5}$, expresses the part of 30 by which 24 is smaller than 30.

Exercise 4 Oral

State what the missing number is in each of the following:

1. 15 is what part more than 14? 13? 11? 10? 12? 9?

2. 20 is what part less than 30? 25? 24? 22? 50? 35?

3. What part more than 12 is 13? 17? 19? 14? 16? 15?

4. What part smaller than 15 is 14? 13? 11? 10? 12? 9?

5. 14 equals 10 increased by what part of itself?

REVIEW ASSIGNMENT 14 b

✓*In business, incorrect answers are worthless. Form the habit of checking all your work to make sure it is correct.*

1. a Divide 23 by $\frac{2}{3}$.   **c** Divide 15 by $1\frac{2}{3}$.

   b Divide $6\frac{2}{3}$ by $\frac{4}{5}$.   **d** Divide $1\frac{3}{5}$ by $1\frac{1}{3}$.

   e $216 is what part greater than $180?

   f $225 is what part less than $270?

2. a A salary of $591.50 a month is equal to how much a year?
   b How much a week?

3. Clark is employed on an 8-hour day basis, with time and a half for time worked in excess of 8 hours. His regular hourly rate of pay is $2.78. Last week he worked the following hours:

Mon., 8; Tues., 8; Wed., 6; Thurs., 10; Fri., 10

Find Clark's total earnings for the week.

4. An employee whose gross earnings were $123.34 had 4.8% deducted for FICA tax, $17.60 for withholding tax, and $2.45 for insurance. Find this employee's take-home pay for the week.

5. A stationer's merchandise inventory was $16,843 on October 1 and $17,355 on December 31. Sales for the quarter were $21,466, and the purchases were $13,927. Find the gross profit for the quarter.

6. Two business partners, Davis and Cook, share their net income in the ratio of 2 to 1, with the larger share going to Davis. Find each partner's share of a net income of $19,395.

7. Find the missing number in each of the following:

   a $t \times 56 = 40$ **b** $\frac{5}{6} \times a = 60$ **c** $14 = 350 \div x$

❽ **8.** A store reduced the price of women's gloves from $3.45 a pair to $2.95. As a result, sales increased from 6 pairs a day to 20 pairs. The gloves cost the store $2.25 a pair. What was the store's increase in daily gross profit?

SECTION | 15

Special Wage Problems

The special wage problems considered in this section are:

1. Figuring an employee's wage time and earnings from his timecard record.

2. Figuring an employee's wages when payment is made on a piece-rate basis.

PART | 15a | Timecard Records and Piece-Rate Wages

Use of time clock and timecard. With timecards, a time clock is used to stamp each employee's card. The card shows arriving and leaving time for regular morning and afternoon hours, and for overtime.

The timecard record of R. Boyd for the week ending October 9 is shown at the right.

Boyd works a $7\frac{1}{2}$-hour day, from 8 a.m. to 12 noon and from 1 p.m. to 4:30 p.m.

NO. 67 NAME R. Boyd			PAY PERIOD ENDING Oct. 9, 19--	
HOURS	RATE	AMOUNT	DEDUCT	EXEMPTIONS
R.T. 36	R.T. 3.00	R.T. 108.00	W.T. 10.90	4
				TOTAL
O.T. 4	O.T. 4.50	O.T. 18.00	F.I.C.A. 6.05	EARNINGS 126.00
TOTAL 40		TOTAL 126.00	INS. 1.26	DEDUCTIONS 22.90
			BONDS 4.69	BALANCE DUE
				103.10

days							hours
1	≤807	≤1202	≤1250	≤433			7¾
2	₱755	₱1156	₱104	₱429			6¾
3	≥756	≥1200	≥1255	≥431			7½
4	₣744	₣1203	₣127	₣435			7
5	⁴758	⁴1201	⁴1258	⁴430	⁴459	⁴903	11¼
6							
7							
	IN	OUT	IN	OUT	IN	OUT	40
	MORNING		AFTERNOON		EVENING		

Timecard

Figuring wage time and earnings from the timecard. The number of hours that Boyd worked each day is shown in the lower half of the timecard, in the column at the right.

This time is credited in hours and full quarter hours. Time less than a quarter hour is not credited. No time credit is given for arriving early or leaving late.

Thus, on Monday, on Boyd's timecard, 8:07 was treated as 8:15; 12:02 as 12:00; 12:50 as 1:00; and 4:33 as 4:30. Boyd was therefore credited with $7\frac{1}{4}$ hours for Monday.

On Tuesday, 7:55 was treated as 8:00; 11:56 as 11:45; 1:04 as 1:15; and 4:29 as 4:15. He was therefore credited with $6\frac{3}{4}$ hours for Tuesday. Other times were treated in similar fashion.

The payroll clerk recorded on the upper half of the card the hours, rates, earnings, deductions, and balance due.

Exercise 1   Oral

Assume that regular hours are from 8 a.m. to 12 noon and from 1 p.m. to 5 p.m. Time less than $\frac{1}{4}$ hour is not credited. State the number of hours credited for each of the following:

In	Out		In	Out		In	Out
1. 7:58	12:00	**5.**	12:55	5:04	**9.**	1:05	3:46
2. 8:00	12:06	**6.**	12:44	4:55	**10.**	9:20	11:59
3. 7:50	12:08	**7.**	1:03	5:03	**11.**	1:50	4:45
4. 8:11	12:05	**8.**	12:56	4:10	**12.**	8:27	12:02

Exercise 2   Written

1. Guy Macy's working day is from 8 a.m. to 12 noon and from 12:30 p.m. to 4:30 p.m. His hourly wage is $2.80 and he is paid time and a half for overtime after 4:30. Time less than $\frac{1}{4}$ hour is not credited, but three minutes are allowed without penalty for late arrival or early departure. His timecard for a week is shown below at the left. Find his total earnings.

NAME	Guy Macy					
	MORNING		AFTERNOON		EVENING	
	IN	OUT	IN	OUT	IN	OUT
M	8⁰⁰	12⁰²	12³¹	4³⁰		
TU	7⁵⁸	11⁵³	12²⁸	4³⁴		
W	7⁵⁶	12⁰¹	12³¹	4³⁵		
TH	7⁵⁹	12⁰⁰	12³²	4³¹	5⁰⁰	8⁰²
FR	7⁵⁷	11⁵⁸	12⁴²	4⁰⁰		

NAME	Earl Flagg					
	MORNING		AFTERNOON		EVENING	
	IN	OUT	IN	OUT	IN	OUT
M	7⁵⁹	12⁰¹	1⁰⁰	4⁵⁵		
TU	7⁵⁵	12⁰⁰	12⁵⁵	5⁰⁰	6⁰⁰	10⁰⁰
W	7⁵⁸	12⁰³	12⁵⁸	4³⁰		
TH	8⁰⁰	12⁰⁴	1⁰⁰	4⁴²		
FR	8⁰⁴	12⁰²	12⁵⁷	4⁰⁰		

2. Earl Flagg's working hours are from 8 a.m. to 12 noon and from 1 p.m. to 5 p.m. His hourly wage is $3.60, with time and a half for time after 5 p.m. Time less than $\frac{1}{4}$ hour is not credited, but three minutes are allowed without loss of time for late arrival or early departure. His timecard for a week is shown above at the right. Find his total earnings for the week.

Piece-rate wages. In some factories a worker is paid a certain amount for each article he produces. These articles are called *pieces*, and the worker is said to be working on a *piece-rate* basis.

Example

The Eagle Electronics Corporation pays on a piece-rate basis. In one of the departments of the factory the rate is 60¢ a piece. Ralph Bond completed the following number of pieces during the last week of October: Mon. 44; Tues. 48; Wed. 40; Thurs. 42; Fri. 46. What was the amount of his total earnings for the week?

Solution

44 + 48 + 40 + 42 + 46 = 220, number of pieces
220 × $.60 = $132.00, total earnings   **Ans.**

Exercise 3   Written

✔ *Aim for 100% accuracy. Check every calculation immediately.*

1. For each person, find total pieces and total earnings.

Name	Number of Pieces					Total Pieces	Rate per Piece	Total Earn- ings
	M	T	W	T	F			
a Olson, D.C.	31	33	29	35	32	160	$.70	$112.00
b Riley, L. E.	26	24	27	29	22		.90	
c Roth, H. A.	27	30	29	26	28		.75	
d Swan, C. V.	35	38	34	37	36		.67	
e York, R. O.	42	41	40	37	40		.62½	

2. The four workers listed below are paid by the number of dozen pieces produced. For each worker, find how many dozens he produced, and his total wages for the week.

Name	Number of Dozen					Total Dozen	Rate per Dozen	Total Wages
	M	T	W	T	F			
a Baxter, L.	7	8	8	9	8	40	$3.05	$122.00
b Conrad, R.	7	8	7	$8\frac{4}{12}$	$7\frac{10}{12}$		3.24	
c Furbeck, M.	8	6	6	$6\frac{8}{12}$	$7\frac{5}{12}$		3.60	
d Mooney, C.	6	5	$6\frac{9}{12}$	$6\frac{7}{12}$	7		3.75	

3. In one department of Mojet Corporation, pieceworkers are paid according to the following daily production schedule:

80 pieces or less, 30¢ each
Next 10 pieces, 35¢ each
All over 90 pieces, 40¢ each

On one day last week, nine workers produced the number of pieces indicated below. Find each worker's earnings for the day.

a Gibbs 72 $21.60   **d** Longo 85 $25.75   **g** Page 92 $28.30

b Hanes 75   **e** Masci 88   **h** Russo 94

c Irwin 80   **f** Novak 90   **i** Vogel 91

REVIEW ASSIGNMENT **15 a**

1. a Divide $1\frac{2}{3}$ by $\frac{5}{8}$.   **b** Divide $1\frac{1}{9}$ by $1\frac{2}{3}$.

c $152 is what part smaller than $228?

d Divide 4 by 11, correct to the nearest thousandth.

2. Waterman, a factory worker, is paid $.18$\frac{2}{3}$ for each acceptable piece he completes. During a recent week he completed the following number of pieces:

Monday   162   Wednesday 174   Friday 168
Tuesday   158   Thursday   169

Twenty-one pieces were not accepted. What were Waterman's total earnings for the week?

3. Alfred obtained marks of 87, 90, 98, and 82 on four consecutive tests. What mark must he obtain on his fifth test in order to have an average mark of 90 for all five tests?

4. Alger, a store owner, had $25 in change in his cash register at the beginning of the day. The register totals at the end of the day showed that he had taken in $410.32 and had paid out $53.19. The amount in the cash drawer at the end of the day was $382.38. How much was the cash over or short?

5. A salesman's average sales for the first 11 months of the year are $4,485 a month. What must be the amount of his sales for the next month in order that his average monthly sales for the 12 months may be $4,550?

6. A salary of $461.50 a month is equal to how much a week?

7. The Victor Carpet Center purchased a job lot of 80 scatter rugs for $801.50. The store sold 10 of the rugs at $25.50 each, 30 at $18.75 each, and the remainder at $12.95 each. Find, to the nearest cent, the store's average gross profit per rug.

8. Find the missing number in each of the following:

a $7 \times ? = 245$ **b** $\frac{3}{4} \times z = 48$ **c** $27 = a \div 9$

9. Dolan's checkbook balance on March 1 was $951.21. In making a reconciliation statement, he found that a check for $13 was recorded in the checkbook as $18, and that he had no record in his checkbook of a service charge of $1.85 and a canceled check for $17.82. Find his correct checkbook balance.

PART 15b   Common Fractions (concluded)

Additional types of problems involving fractional relationships. In Sections 13 and 14 you worked with four types of problems involving fractional relationships (see page 103). The problems in Exercise 4, below, are examples of two additional types of problems. They are:

5. To find the whole when a part is known.

6. To find the whole when an amount that is a part greater (or smaller) than the whole is known.

Exercise 4   Written

1. Oliver Baker's overtime earnings last week amounted to $13.75, which was $\frac{1}{8}$ of his total earnings.

a What was the amount of his total earnings for the week?

b What was the amount of his regular-time earnings?

2. Lew Regan's total earnings for the second week in November were $84.90, which was $\frac{1}{5}$ more than his earnings for the first week. How much did he earn for the first week?

3. Mary Snyder's total earnings during the second week in November were $89.60, which was $\frac{1}{8}$ less than her earnings during the first week. How much did she earn during the first week?

Important principles of fractional relationships. In the statement "60 is $\frac{2}{3}$ of 90," 60 is compared with 90; and the fraction $\frac{2}{3}$ expresses the comparison. 90 is the number with which 60 is compared, or the number on which the comparison is based. 90 is therefore referred to as the *base*, and the fraction $\frac{2}{3}$ is said to be *based* on 90.

The word "of" as used here means multiplication. That is, "$\frac{2}{3}$ of 90" indicates "$\frac{2}{3}$ *times* 90." Since 90 is the *base*, the number representing the base is multiplied by the fraction.   The important principle you should remember is this: *The number representing the base, and only that number, may be multiplied by the fraction.*

The number representing the base is usually indicated by the number, expressed or implied, which follows immediately the expression indicating multiplication — such as "of," "as much as," "greater than," "less than," "smaller than," etc.

In each of the following, 90 is the base, since it follows immediately the expression indicating multiplication. 90 may therefore be multiplied by the fraction in finding the unknown number.

? is $\frac{2}{3}$ *as much as* 90.   ? is $\frac{2}{3}$ *greater than* 90.

$\frac{2}{3}$ *as much as* 90 is ? .   ? is $\frac{2}{3}$ *smaller than* 90.

In the problems given below, however, the *unknown number* is the base, because the space representing the missing number follows immediately the expression indicating multiplication.   Therefore, the known number, 30, may not be multiplied by the fraction, because 30 *does not represent the base.*

30 is $\frac{3}{4}$ *as much as* ? .   30 is $\frac{2}{3}$ *greater than* ? .

$\frac{2}{3}$ *as much as* ? = 30.   30 is $\frac{2}{3}$ *smaller than* ? .

The method of solving problems like the four above is explained in the topic beginning at the bottom of this page and in the discussion on pages 118 and 119.

⬤ **Exercise 5**   Oral

In each of the following state whether the given whole number should or should not be multiplied by the fraction.

1. ? is $\frac{2}{5}$ as much as 20.   6. $\frac{2}{3}$ of ? is $48.

2. 18 is $\frac{2}{3}$ as much as ?.   7. $\frac{3}{5}$ of $45 is ?.

3. 24 is $\frac{3}{4}$ as much as ?.   8. ? is $\frac{1}{3}$ greater than 30.

4. ? is $\frac{4}{5}$ of $40.   9. 20 is $\frac{1}{4}$ greater than ?.

5. $45 is $\frac{3}{5}$ of ?.   10. $\frac{2}{5}$ of ? equals 50.

⬤   **To find the whole when a part is known.** When the value of a fractional part of a number is known and it is desired to find the value of the whole, the problem is one of finding the number on which the given fraction is based. It is simply a problem of finding the missing factor when the other factor and the product are known.

Example

45 is $\frac{3}{5}$ of what number?

The problem tells us that, if a certain unknown number is multiplied by $\frac{3}{5}$, the product is 45. Stated briefly:

$$\begin{array}{ccc} \text{F} & \text{F} & \text{P} \\ \frac{3}{5} \times \text{the original number} & = & 45 \end{array}$$

We see at once that $\frac{3}{5}$ is one of the factors of 45, and that the other factor is the original number, which is unknown. You have learned on page 52 that the missing factor can always be found by dividing the product by the known factor. In the foregoing problem the product is 45, and the known factor is $\frac{3}{5}$. Hence the missing factor is 45 divided by $\frac{3}{5}$.

Solution: $\frac{3}{5} \times$ *the original number* $= 45$
The original number $= 45 \div \frac{3}{5} = 75$ **Ans.**

Check: $\frac{3}{5} \times 75 = 45$

> ### Exercise 6   Oral

State what the missing number is in each of the following:

1. 20 is $\frac{2}{5}$ of ?.
2. $\frac{2}{5}$ of ? is \$10.
3. $\frac{3}{5}$ of 45 is ?.
4. ? $\times \frac{3}{4}$ is \$36.
5. $\frac{4}{5} \times$ \$20 is ?.
6. 60 is $\frac{4}{3}$ of ?.

7. 30 is $\frac{2}{5}$ as much as ?.
8. ? is $\frac{3}{4}$ as much as \$24.
9. 18 is $\frac{2}{3}$ as large as ?.
10. ? is $\frac{5}{4}$ of \$40.
11. 8 is $\frac{1}{5}$ of ?.
12. $\frac{3}{4}$ of ? is $\frac{2}{3}$ of \$18.

13. A number 5 times as large as 4 is $\frac{1}{3}$ as large as ?.
14. A number $\frac{1}{3}$ as large as 45 is $\frac{3}{5}$ of ?.

> **To find the whole when an amount that is a part greater (or smaller) than the whole is known.** You have heard or seen an expression such as "15 is $\frac{1}{4}$ greater than another number" or "15 is $\frac{1}{4}$ more than another number." It means that 15 is the result of *adding* $\frac{1}{4}$ of the unknown number to the unknown number.

Similarly, an expression such as "15 is $\frac{1}{4}$ smaller than another number" means that 15 is the result of *subtracting* $\frac{1}{4}$ of the unknown number from the unknown number.

In these cases, the problem of finding the unknown number is one of finding the number on which the given fraction is based. This is a problem of finding the missing factor when the other factor and the product are known.

Example

What number increased by $\frac{1}{4}$ of itself equals 15?

The problem tells us that, if $\frac{1}{4}$ of a certain unknown number is added to that number, the sum is 15. In other words,

The unknown number $+ \frac{1}{4}$ of the unknown number $= 15$

(1) Since the increase is $\frac{1}{4}$ *of the unknown number*, it follows that the unknown number represents the base, or the whole, and that it is divided into *fourths*. The unknown number is therefore $\frac{4}{4}$ of itself.

(2) The increase is $\frac{1}{4}$ of the unknown number.

(3) The unknown number *plus* the increase is therefore $\frac{5}{4}$ of the unknown number. This sum, according to the problem, is equal to 15.

Solution: $\frac{4}{4} \times$ *the number* $=$ *the number*
$\underline{+ \frac{1}{4} \times \textit{the number} = \textit{the increase}}$
$\frac{5}{4} \times$ *the number* $=$ *the number* $+$ *the increase* $= 15$

$\textit{The number} = 15 \div \frac{5}{4} = 12$ **Ans.**

Check: $12 + (\frac{1}{4} \text{ of } 12) = 12 + 3 = 15$

Example

What number decreased by $\frac{1}{4}$ of itself equals 15?

The problem tells us that, if $\frac{1}{4}$ of a certain unknown number is subtracted from that number, the difference is 15. Thus,

The unknown number $- \frac{1}{4}$ of the unknown number $= 15$

Solution: $\frac{4}{4} \times$ *the number* $=$ *the number*
$\underline{- \frac{1}{4} \times \textit{the number} = \textit{the decrease}}$
$\frac{3}{4} \times$ *the number* $=$ *the number* $-$ *the decrease* $= 15$

$\textit{The number} = 15 \div \frac{3}{4} = 20$ **Ans.**

Check: $20 - (\frac{1}{4} \text{ of } 20) = 20 - 5 = 15$

❯ Exercise **7**   Oral

State what the missing number is in each of the following:

1. 24 is $\frac{1}{3}$ larger than ? .   3. 45 is $\frac{2}{3}$ more than ? .

2. 36 is $\frac{1}{4}$ less than ? .   4. $\frac{1}{6}$ less than ? is $60.

5. ? increased by $\frac{3}{4}$ of itself equals $28.

6. 60 is ? decreased by $\frac{1}{5}$ of itself.

7. A number 3 times as large as 4 is $\frac{1}{3}$ less than ? .

❯ **Review of problems involving fractional relationships.** In the last two sections you have studied six different general types of problems involving fractional relationships. The two exercises that follow provide review practice in solving each of these types of problems.

❯ **Exercise 8**   Oral

State what the missing number is in each of the following:

1. ? is $\frac{2}{3}$ as large as 12.
2. ? is $\frac{1}{4}$ more than 32.
3. 36 is $\frac{3}{4}$ as large as ? .
4. 20 is $\frac{1}{4}$ larger than ? .
5. $\frac{3}{2}$ of ? equals 36.
6. 60 is $\frac{1}{3}$ less than ? .
7. 48 is $\frac{1}{3}$ larger than ? .
8. $\frac{5}{3}$ of 15 is ? .
9. 24 is $\frac{3}{8}$ of ? .

10. 60 is $\frac{1}{4}$ less than ? .
11. 36 is $\frac{1}{2}$ larger than ? .
12. $\frac{1}{5}$ less than ? is 40.
13. ? is $\frac{3}{4}$ larger than 36.
14. $\frac{1}{4}$ more than ? is 60.
15. ? is $\frac{1}{4}$ smaller than 80.
16. $\frac{5}{3}$ of ? equals 30.
17. 28 is $\frac{3}{7}$ less than ? .
18. $\frac{2}{3}$ of ? equals 36.

19. 36 diminished by $\frac{1}{3}$ of itself equals ? .
20. ? diminished by $\frac{1}{3}$ of itself equals 36.
21. 12 is what part of 15?
22. 24 is what part more than 20?
23. What part less than 36 is 30?
24. What part more than 10 is 12?
25. What part more than 12 is 16?
26. 40 is what part less than 44?

❯ **Exercise 9**   Written

Find the missing number in each of the following:

1. $4.80 is $\frac{3}{4}$ of ? .
2. $14.70 is $\frac{2}{3}$ of ? .
3. $\frac{5}{7}$ of ? equals $5.60.
4. $5.20 is $\frac{3}{5}$ more than ? .
5. $8.80 is $\frac{3}{8}$ more than ? .
6. $\frac{4}{5}$ more than ? is $1.80.
7. $32.48 is $\frac{1}{8}$ less than ? .

8. $\frac{3}{10}$ less than ? is $4.20.
9. ? is $\frac{5}{6}$ more than $1.92.
10. $\frac{5}{8}$ of $4.80 equals ? .
11. ? is $\frac{1}{3}$ less than $9.72.
12. $\frac{7}{8}$ of ? equals $3.36.
13. ? is $\frac{1}{4}$ more than $8.40.
14. $4.20 is $\frac{3}{5}$ of ? .

15. $2,500 is what part of $3,000?
16. What part of $20 is $7.50?
17. 75¢ is what part of $9.00?
18. 33 is what part more than 27?
19. What part more than $4.80 is $7.80?
20. $20 is what part less than $22.50?
21. What part less than $15 is $12.75?

REVIEW ASSIGNMENT **15 b**

✔*Aim for 100% accuracy in all of your work.   Check every calculation immediately to detect any minor errors in computation. Estimate each product and quotient to verify the placement of the decimal point in the result and to reveal any gross errors in multiplication and division.*

1. a Multiply 51 by $\frac{5}{6}$.   **c** Divide 21 by $\frac{5}{8}$.

   b Multiply $9\frac{1}{4}$ by $8\frac{2}{3}$.   **d** Divide $7\frac{1}{5}$ by $2\frac{1}{4}$.

   e Divide 3 by 13, correct to the nearest thousandth.

   f $272 increased by $\frac{1}{4}$ of itself gives what amount?

2. Find the total earnings of Bickford, who in one week works 40 hours regular time and 7 hours overtime, if he receives $2.68 an hour for regular time, and time and a half for overtime.

3. Coleman, whose gross earnings in one week were $137.28, had 4.8% deducted for social security, $15.40 for federal income tax, $.30 for disability insurance, and $3.25 for hospital insurance. What was Coleman's take-home pay for the week?

4. Using the tables on pages 106 and 108, determine the income tax and FICA tax that should be deducted from the week's wages of each of the employees given below.

   a D. Crosby: $125.00 total wages; 3 exemptions.

   b O. French: $119.06 total wages; 1 exemption.

   c C. Slocum: $129.75 total wages; 2 exemptions.

5. A salary of $94.35 for a 37-hour week is equal to what hourly rate of pay?

6. A salary of $400 a month is equal to how much a week, to the nearest cent?

7. The Kimball Sales Corporation keeps a record of the sales of its salesmen. Irwin's average weekly sales for the first 10 weeks of the year were $3,427.75. His sales for the 11th and 12th weeks were $4,132.20 and $3,777.50, respectively. What were Irwin's average weekly sales for the 12 weeks?

8. $\frac{3}{4} \times w = 42$. Find the missing number.

▶ **9.** What amount increased by $\frac{1}{4}$ of itself gives $220?

▶ **10.** A retailer bought 100 coats at $46.50 each and marked them to sell at $75. At the end of the season, 20 of the coats were still unsold, and he decided to close them out in a special sale. To what price can he reduce these 20 coats and still make a gross profit of $2,450 on the entire lot?

SECTION 16

Family Cash Record Summaries

You have already seen, in the illustrations and problems of Section 1, how monthly records of personal cash receipts and personal cash payments are sometimes kept. When such records are used, it is customary to transfer the column totals to a monthly summary sheet at the end of each month. At the end of the year, the columns of the monthly summary are totaled. The information in the summary is helpful for reviewing the financial activities of the past year and for budgeting expenditures of the next year.

PART 16a Monthly Summary

Monthly cash record summary of the Santori family. Illustrated below is the monthly summary for the Santori family. Their record of classified cash payments for a month is shown in Problem 2 on page 5.

MONTHLY SUMMARY

MONTH	RECEIPTS		PAYMENTS		CLASSIFICATION OF PAYMENTS											
					FOOD		CLOTHING		HOUSING		OPERATING		DEVELOPMENT		SAVINGS	
January	705	65	685	48	174	68	70	15	120	00	145	20	105	45	70	00
February	705	65	693	10	169	40	95	75	120	00	136	75	96	20	75	00
November	724	30	701	19	175	34	62	35	130	00	147	86	100	64	85	00
December	724	30	715	28	185	35	81	25	130	00	150	03	108	65	60	00
	8,542	40	8,494	87	2,124	60	928	30	1,480	00	1,781	25	1,285	72	895	00

After entering the December figures, Mr. Santori totaled and ruled the summary sheet to show the total receipts and payments for the year.

Exercise 1   Written

1. Keith Spencer receives a monthly take-home pay of $600. His expenditures last month were as follows:

Food..... $150	Housing... $105	Development.. $75
Clothing.. 90	Operating.. 120	Savings....... 60

Find what fractional part of his income was spent for each item. The sum of the results should be 1.

2. Last year the Berne family spent $\frac{3}{10}$ of its income for food, $\frac{1}{5}$ for rent, $\frac{3}{20}$ for clothing, and $\frac{1}{4}$ for other items. The remainder was saved. What fractional part of the income was saved?

3. Craft, a householder, estimates that his total cash income for the coming year will amount to $6,400. He plans to budget it as shown below. Find the dollar amounts that he will budget for each expenditure. The sum of the results should be $6,400.

Food..... $\frac{1}{4}$	Housing... $\frac{3}{16}$	Development.. $\frac{1}{8}$
Clothing.. $\frac{1}{8}$	Operating.. $\frac{7}{32}$	Savings....... $\frac{3}{32}$

4. Ives, a single man, has a quarterly cash income of $1,200. He plans to spend it as shown below. Find the amount he plans to spend for each item. The sum of the results should be $1,200.

Board and room.. $\frac{11}{25}$	Operating..... $\frac{9}{50}$	Savings.. $\frac{4}{25}$
Clothing......... $\frac{2}{25}$	Development.. $\frac{7}{50}$	

PART 16b   Decimal Fractions

Meaning of decimals. The preceding problems dealt with amounts expressed in dollars and cents. One dollar consists of 100 cents. Any given number of cents is therefore that number of hundredths of a dollar. Thus, 67 cents is $\frac{67}{100}$ of a dollar. Since 67 ÷ 100 = .67, we may refer to 67 cents as .67 of a dollar, or $.67.

Both $\frac{67}{100}$ and .67 are numerals that name the same fractional number. A numeral like .67 is called a *decimal numeral* or, briefly, a *decimal*. It is also called a *decimal fraction*.

A decimal is just another way of naming a fractional number when the fraction has a denominator of 10, 100, or 1,000, etc. Such a fraction is changed to the decimal form by dividing the numerator by the denominator. For example:

$$\frac{1}{10} = 1 \div 10 = .1 \qquad\qquad \frac{79}{100} = 79 \div 100 = .79$$

$$\frac{1}{100} = 1 \div 100 = .01 \qquad\qquad \frac{79}{1,000} = 79 \div 1,000 = .079$$

Exercise 2   Mental

Write each of the following in the form of a decimal fraction:

	1.	2.	3.	4.	5.	6.	7.
a	$\frac{35}{100}$	$\frac{9}{10}$	$\frac{68}{100}$	$\frac{19}{1,000}$	$\frac{1}{100}$	$\frac{8}{1,000}$	$\frac{237}{10,000}$
b	$\frac{159}{1,000}$	$\frac{89}{1,000}$	$\frac{1}{10}$	$\frac{5}{1,000}$	$\frac{3}{1,000}$	$\frac{6}{100}$	$\frac{1}{10,000}$

Facts about decimals. The following facts about decimals are important to keep in mind.

1. Any common fraction can be changed to a decimal by dividing the numerator by the denominator. For example:

$$\tfrac{1}{4} = 1 \div 4 = .25 \qquad\qquad \tfrac{2}{3} = 2 \div 3 = .66\tfrac{2}{3}$$
$$\tfrac{5}{8} = 5 \div 8 = .625 \qquad\qquad \tfrac{13}{4} = 13 \div 4 = 3.25$$

2. The fractions $\frac{9}{10}$, $\frac{90}{100}$, and $\frac{900}{1,000}$ are equal fractions. Since $\frac{9}{10} = \frac{90}{100} = \frac{900}{1,000}$, then $.9 = .90 = .900$. In other words, we may annex zeros to a decimal without changing the number it represents. Thus, $.25 = .250 = .2500$, and $3.25 = 3.250 = 3.2500$.

3. Any whole number can be expressed in decimal form by annexing a decimal point and as many zeros as are desired. Thus, $23 = 23.0 = 23.00 = 23.000$, and so on.

4. Decimals are useful because we can often substitute them for common fractions to make calculations easier. For example, it is easier to add $5.65 and $1.75 than $5\tfrac{13}{20}$ and $1\tfrac{3}{4}$.

5. It is often easier to compare fractions if they are expressed as decimals. It is easy to see that $\tfrac{5}{9}$ represents a larger number than $\tfrac{7}{13}$ if $\tfrac{5}{9}$ is expressed as .556 and $\tfrac{7}{13}$ as .538.

Changing a common fraction to a decimal. As you have seen above, a fraction is changed to an equal decimal by dividing the numerator by the denominator.

Example

Change $\tfrac{3}{8}$ to its equal decimal form.

Solution	Explanation
.375 **Ans.** $8)\overline{3.000}$	The numerator, 3, is divided by the denominator, 8, until there is no remainder.

In many cases the division does not end. No matter how far the quotient is extended, there will always be a remainder. In such cases it is necessary to specify the number of places in the quotient.

Example

Find the decimal equivalent of $\frac{3}{7}$ to 3 decimal places

Solution	Explanation
$\underline{.4285}$ $7)\overline{3.0000}$ **Ans.** *.429*	The quotient is carried to 4 decimal places and is then rounded at the third decimal place.

Example

Change $\frac{3}{7}$ to a decimal of four places of exact value.

Solution	Explanation
$\underline{.4285\frac{5}{7}}$ **Ans.** $7)\overline{3.0000}$	The division is carried to 4 decimal places. Since the *exact* decimal equivalent is required, the remainder, 5, is retained and is written in the common-fraction form, $\frac{5}{7}$. The exact decimal equivalent is $.4285\frac{5}{7}$.

Exercise 3   Written

1. Find the decimal equivalent of each of the following fractions to *three* decimal places: (a) $\frac{6}{7}$; (b) $\frac{8}{9}$; (c) $\frac{11}{12}$; (d) $\frac{8}{11}$; (e) $\frac{3}{14}$.

2. Change each of the following fractions to a decimal of *two places* of *exact* value: (a) $\frac{7}{9}$; (b) $\frac{6}{11}$; (c) $\frac{7}{12}$; (d) $\frac{5}{13}$; (e) $\frac{11}{14}$.

3. Find the decimal equivalent of each of the following fractions to the nearest hundredth: (a) $\frac{4}{9}$; (b) $\frac{5}{12}$; (c) $\frac{4}{13}$; (d) $\frac{7}{11}$; (e) $\frac{9}{14}$.

REVIEW ASSIGNMENT 16b

1. a Add $2\frac{3}{4}$, $6\frac{1}{2}$, $3\frac{2}{3}$.   **b** Divide $3\frac{3}{5}$ by $\frac{2}{3}$.

c Divide 5 by 17, correct to the nearest thousandth.

d \$162 increased by $\frac{2}{3}$ of itself equals what number?

e What amount equals \$216 decreased by $\frac{3}{8}$ of itself?

2. An office worker is paid \$86.25 for a $37\frac{1}{2}$-hour week. What is his hourly rate of pay?

3. Using the tables on pages 106 and 108, find the income tax and FICA tax that should be deducted from the gross earnings of the three employees listed below.

a L. Dwyer: $129.69 gross earnings; 4 exemptions.

b B. Knapp: $119.47 gross earnings; 2 exemptions.

c R. Lyons: $124.27 gross earnings; 1 exemption.

4. Partners Beck and Lyle share profits in the ratio of 5 to 4, respectively. The partnership profit for the year is $15,390. What is the amount of each partner's share of this profit?

5. $\frac{3}{4} \times ? = \$288$. Find the missing number.

❯ **6. a** $\frac{5}{6}$ of what amount equals $240?

b What amount increased by $\frac{1}{3}$ of itself gives $192?

❯ **7.** A dress that cost $13.50 had been selling for $22.50 at the rate of 12 dresses per day. During a special sale, the price was reduced to $19.50, and sales increased to 20 dresses per day. Did the daily gross profit increase or decrease, and how much?

PART 16c Decimal Fractions (concluded)

Multiplication by .1, .01, and .001. As you saw on page 34, when you multiply numbers represented by decimals, you place the decimal point in the product by pointing off to the left.

Hence, when the multiplier is .1, .01, or .001, and so on, rewrite the multiplicand, and move its decimal point to the *left* as many places as there are decimal places in the multiplier. Prefix zeros if necessary. The result is the product. Thus,

$$64.5 \times .01 \ = .645 \qquad \$8.50 \times .1 \ \ = \$ \ .85$$
$$.04 \times .1 \ \ = .004 \qquad \$ 164 \times .01 \ = \$1.64$$
$$35 \times .001 = .035 \qquad \$2,450 \times .001 = \$2.45$$

Exercise 4   Mental

In each of the following, perform the multiplication mentally by the method explained above. Write the product only.

	1.	**2.**	**3.**	**4.**
a	34.9 × .1	424 × .001	7.3 × .001	$372 × .01
b	73.4 × .01	573 × .001	.82 × .1	$4,560 × .01
c	5.8 × .1	819 × .1	6 × .01	$930 × .001
d	62.9 × .01	36 × .01	30 × .001	$38.40 × .1

Changing a decimal to a common fraction. To change a decimal to an equal common fraction, omit the decimal point and write the digits as the numerator of a fraction. For the denominator, write 1 followed by as many zeros as there are decimal places in the decimal. Reduce the fraction to lowest terms. For example:

$$.75 = \frac{75}{100} = \frac{3}{4} \qquad .125 = \frac{125}{1,000} = \frac{1}{8} \qquad 1.4 = \frac{14}{10} = \frac{7}{5}$$

▶ Sometimes the fraction is a complex fraction,* like $\frac{14\frac{2}{3}}{100}$. When it is, multiply the numerator and denominator by the denominator of the fraction in the numerator. Reduce the resulting fraction to lowest terms. Thus,

$$.14\tfrac{2}{3} = \frac{14\frac{2}{3}}{100} = \frac{14\frac{2}{3} \times 3}{100 \times 3} = \frac{44}{300} = \frac{11}{75}$$

Exercise 5   Written

Change each of the following decimals to its equal common fraction in lowest terms.

	1.	2.	3.	4.	▶5.	▶6.	▶7.
a	.37 $\tfrac{37}{100}$	.48	.085	.1875	.02$\tfrac{3}{4}$	.11$\tfrac{2}{3}$	.043$\tfrac{3}{4}$
b	.85	.025	.064	.0375	.03$\tfrac{1}{3}$	.73$\tfrac{1}{3}$	.833$\tfrac{1}{3}$

▶ **Division by .1, .01, and .001.** As you saw on page 55, when the divisor is a decimal, you move the decimal points in both the dividend and divisor to the right as many places as are needed to make the divisor a whole number.

Hence, when the divisor is .1, .01, or .001, and so on, rewrite the dividend and move its decimal point to the *right* as many places as there are decimal places in the divisor. Annex zeros if necessary. The result is the quotient. Thus,

$$645 \div .1 \ = 6,450 \qquad \$14.16 \div .1 \ = \$141.60$$
$$.0275 \div .01 \ = 2.75 \qquad \$8.50 \div .01 \ = \$850$$
$$9.3 \div .001 = 9,300 \qquad \$15.25 \div .001 = \$15,250$$

*A *complex fraction* is one whose numerator or denominator, or both, is a fraction or a mixed number.

▷ **Exercise 6** Mental

In each of the following, perform the division mentally by the method explained at the bottom of page 127. Write the quotient only.

	1.	2.	3.	4.
a	2.45 ÷ .1	.409 ÷ .001	47 ÷ .1	$.39 ÷ .01
b	.065 ÷ .01	3.4 ÷ .1	.7 ÷ .01	$8.00 ÷ .1
c	.0083 ÷ .001	3.79 ÷ .01	5.67 ÷ .001	$3.46 ÷ .001
d	.365 ÷ .01	63 ÷ .01	2.4 ÷ .01	$2.73 ÷ .001

REVIEW ASSIGNMENT **16** c

1. a Subtract $9\frac{7}{8}$ from $12\frac{2}{3}$.   **b** Divide 18 by $2\frac{1}{4}$.

c Express $\frac{3}{7}$ as a decimal to the nearest hundredth.

d $582 decreased by $\frac{1}{3}$ of itself gives what amount?

e What number is equal to 216 increased by $\frac{3}{8}$ of itself?

2. Your employer has been paying you twice a month at the rate of $455 a month. He now decides to change to a weekly payroll. At the same rate, how much should you receive per week?

3. On April 30, E. I. Lake's balance on his bank statement was $824.21. His checkbook balance was $689.30. The bank had deducted a service charge of $2.15. Checks for $32.15 and $104.91 were outstanding. Prepare a reconciliation statement.

4. For the first 11 months of the year a salesman's sales averaged $8,435 a month. What must be the amount of his sales for the next month in order that his monthly average for the year may be $8,500?

5. A dress shop paid $1,950 for 150 dresses. The shop sold 75 of the dresses at $22.50, 50 at $19.50, and the remainder at $15.00. Find the shop's average gross profit per dress.

6. $\frac{3}{8} \times n = \$192$. Find the missing amount.

▷ **7. a** What amount increased by $\frac{1}{5}$ of itself equals $450?

b What amount decreased by $\frac{1}{4}$ of itself equals $396?

▷ **8.** On October 31, William Chandler had a checkbook balance of $286. When he compared this balance with his bank statement, he found that he had no record in his checkbook of a service charge of $1.45, a deposit of $17, and a check he had written for $8.14. What was his correct checkbook balance?

Family Budget Problems

A budget is a plan for the spending of one's income. The amount allowed, or allocated, for each class of expenditure is often expressed as a percent of the income.

PART 17a | Allocating Income

The Hagen family budget. The chart below shows how the Hagen family spent its income of $6,000 last year. The percents were found by dividing each expenditure by the total cash income. Thus, the percent spent for food, 25%, was found by dividing $1,500 by $6,000.

$$\$1,500 \div \$6,000 = .25, \text{ or } 25\%$$

On the basis of these expenditures, next year's estimated income of $6,500 can be budgeted by multiplying $6,500 by each percent. The budget for food, for example, would be $1,625.

$$25\% \times \$6,500 = .25 \times \$6,500 = \$1,625$$

TOTAL CASH INCOME — $6,000
100%

Food	Cloth-ing	Housing	Operating	Develop-ment	Sav-ings
$1,500	$660	$1,080	$1,260	$900	$600
25%	11%	18%	21%	15%	10%

Exercise 1   Written

1. The estimated cash income of the Kern family for the current year is $5,000. The budget allowances for the year are:

Food . . . . $1,400   Housing . . . $ 900   Development . $600
Clothing .   650   Operating . 1,050   Savings 400

What percent of the income is budgeted for each item? The sum of the results should be 100%.

2. The Reed family expects cash income of $5,600 for next year. They budget according to the chart on page 129.

Find the amount that they allow for each kind of expenditure. The sum of the six amounts should be $5,600.

LET'S TRY TO SAVE MORE THIS YEAR

PART 17b Percents

Meaning of percent. *Percent* means "per hundred," "by the hundred," or "out of a hundred." It indicates the comparison, or ratio, of some number to 100. Hence, any ratio in which the second term, or denominator of the fraction representing the ratio, is 100 may be expressed as a percent. Thus 25 to 100, or 25/100, may be expressed as 25%; and 25% may be expressed as 25 to 100, or 25/100.

Since 25% = 25/100, and 25/100 = .25, then 25% = .25; and we may say that percent also means "hundredths." Hence, 25% may be expressed as .25, and .25 as 25%.

When a ratio is a fraction with a denominator of 1, 2, 4, 5, 10, 20, 25, or 50, the fraction may be changed to an equal fraction with the denominator 100 by raising it to higher terms. This new fraction may then be expressed as a percent. For example:

$$\frac{1}{4} = \frac{1 \times 25}{4 \times 25} = \frac{25}{100} = 25\%$$

When the denominator is not one of the numbers mentioned above, we use a different method for changing the fraction to a percent. This method will be explained later.

The important point to notice at this time is that $\frac{1}{4}$, .25, and 25% are all numerals representing the same number, one fourth, and are therefore equal to one another.

Exercise 2   Written

1. Express each ratio as a fraction, and then express the fraction as a percent. Use this form: 35 to 100 = $\frac{35}{100}$ = 35%.

a 45 to 100	**e** $33\frac{1}{3}$ to 100	**i** 200 to 100	**m** $\frac{3}{4}$ to 100
b 59 to 100	**f** 100 to 100	**j** 225 to 100	**n** .9 to 100
c $12\frac{1}{2}$ to 100	**g** 125 to 100	**k** $\frac{1}{2}$ to 100	**o** .3 to 100
d $6\frac{1}{4}$ to 100	**h** 150 to 100	**l** $\frac{2}{3}$ to 100	**p** .7 to 100

2. Express each fraction as an equal fraction with the denominator 100. Then express the new fraction as a percent.

Example: $\frac{3}{4} = \frac{3 \times 25}{4 \times 25} = \frac{75}{100} = 75\%$

a $\frac{1}{2}$ **c** $\frac{5}{10}$ **e** $\frac{3}{25}$ **g** $\frac{7}{10}$ **i** $\frac{13}{50}$ **k** $\frac{2}{1}$

b $\frac{1}{10}$ **d** $\frac{2}{5}$ **f** $\frac{7}{50}$ **h** $\frac{6}{25}$ **j** $\frac{1}{1}$ **l** $\frac{4}{1}$

3. Express each percent as a fraction with the denominator 100. Then divide the numerator by the denominator, expressing the result as a decimal or a whole number.

Examples: $12.5\% = \frac{12.5}{100} = .125$ $200\% = \frac{200}{100} = 2$

a 23% **c** 10% **e** 100% **g** 300% **i** 400% **k** 4.5%

b 44% **d** 75% **f** 230% **h** 350% **j** 37.5% **l** 9.2%

4. Multiply each of the following by 1 expressed as $\frac{100}{100}$. Then express the resulting fraction as a percent.

Example: $.25 = .25 \times \frac{100}{100} = \frac{25}{100} = 25\%$

a $.56$ **c** $.125$ **e** $.06$ **g** $.12\frac{1}{2}$ **i** 1.25 **k** 1

b $.83$ **d** $.375$ **f** $.032$ **h** $.16\frac{2}{3}$ **j** 1.74 **l** 3

REVIEW ASSIGNMENT **17 b**

1. a Multiply $12\frac{2}{3}$ by $6\frac{1}{2}$.   **b** Divide $7\frac{1}{5}$ by $2\frac{1}{4}$.
c 28 is what percent of 112?
d Express $\frac{5}{7}$ as a decimal, to the nearest hundredth.
e Express .12 as a common fraction in lowest terms.

2. a A salary of $87 a week is equal to how much a year?
b How much a month?

3. A salary of $115 for a 38-hour week is equal to what hourly rate of pay, to the nearest cent?

4. Kern works on an 8-hour day basis, at $2.54 an hour, with time and a half for overtime. During a recent week he worked the hours shown below. What were his total earnings for the week?
Mon., $7\frac{1}{2}$; Tues., 8; Wed., $6\frac{1}{2}$; Thurs., 10; Fri., 8

5. Kern's employer (Problem 4) deducted 4.8% of Kern's total earnings for social security, $11.30 for federal income tax, and $4.28 for other items. What was Kern's net pay for the week?

❯ **6.** Bacon's checkbook balance on July 1 was $811.16. In making a reconciliation statement, he found that a check for $17 was recorded in the checkbook as $12, and that he had no record in his checkbook of a service charge of $2.15 and a deposit of $37.79. Find Bacon's correct checkbook balance.

PART 17c   Percents (continued)

Changing a decimal or a whole number to a percent. As shown in Problem 4 of Exercise 2 on page 131, a decimal or whole number may be changed to a percent in this manner: Multiply the number by 1, expressed as 100/100, to change the number to a fraction with the denominator 100. Then express the fraction as a percent. Thus,

$$.135 = .135 \times \frac{100}{100} = \frac{13.5}{100} = 13.5\%$$

Since .135 = 13.5%, the foregoing process is the same as multiplying .135 by 100 and annexing a percent sign. Hence the short-cut rule: *Move the decimal point two places to the right and annex a percent sign.*

$.25 = 25\%$ $.16\frac{2}{3} = 16\frac{2}{3}\%$ $2 = 200\%$

$.006 = .6\%$ $1.75 = 175\%$ $.3 = 30\%$

Exercise 3   Oral

Express each of the following as a percent.

1. .46	**4.** .7	**7.** .235	**10.** $.12\frac{3}{4}$	**13.** 4.56	**16.** 4
2. .08	**5.** .1	**8.** .079	**11.** $.37\frac{1}{3}$	**14.** 2.20	**17.** 1
3. .01	**6.** .5	**9.** .0036	**12.** $3.41\frac{1}{2}$	**15.** 1.00	**18.** 3

Changing a fraction to a percent. As you have seen on page 130, a fraction with a denominator of 1, 2, 4, 5, 10, 20, 25, or 50 may be changed to a percent by changing it to an equal fraction with the denominator 100, and then expressing the latter fraction as a percent. For example:

$$\frac{4}{5} = \frac{4 \times 20}{5 \times 20} = \frac{80}{100} = 80\%$$

In all other cases, change the fraction to a decimal and then express the decimal as a percent. Thus,

$$\tfrac{3}{14} = 3 \div 14 = .21\tfrac{3}{7} = 21\tfrac{3}{7}\%$$

In the foregoing example, $\frac{3}{14}$ was changed to a two-place decimal of *exact value*. Usually the division is carried to a stated number of places of *approximate value*.

Example

Express $\frac{1}{17}$ as a percent, to the nearest *tenth* of a percent.

Solution	Explanation
$.058 \frac{14}{17}$ $17)\overline{1.000}$ **Ans.** *5.9%*	Dividing 1 by 17 to three decimal places gives .058, with a remainder that is $\frac{14}{17}$ of the divisor. Since $\frac{14}{17}$ is greater than $\frac{1}{2}$, the quotient is rounded to .059.

Hence, $\frac{1}{17} = .059 = 5.9\%$, to the nearest *tenth* of a percent.

Exercise 4   Written

1. Find the percent that is equal to each of the following fractions. Carry the division to a two-place decimal of exact value.

a $\frac{1}{16}$ **b** $\frac{4}{15}$ **c** $\frac{15}{16}$ **d** $\frac{5}{32}$ **e** $\frac{9}{64}$

2. Find to the nearest *tenth* of a percent the percent that is equal to each of the following fractions:

a $\frac{1}{15}$ **b** $\frac{5}{16}$ **c** $\frac{17}{18}$ **d** $\frac{9}{32}$ **e** $\frac{7}{64}$

To find what percent one number is of another. To find what percent one number is of another, divide the one by the other and then express the quotient as a percent.

Example

9 is what percent of 16?

Solution	Explanation
$.56\frac{1}{4} = 56\frac{1}{4}\%$ $16)\overline{9.00}$ **Ans.**	9 represents the part, and 16 represents the whole with which the part is to be compared. Therefore the fraction $\frac{9}{16}$ expresses the relationship of 9 to 16. Dividing 9 by 16 gives $.56\frac{1}{4}$, which equals $56\frac{1}{4}\%$.

Check: $56\frac{1}{4}\%$ of $16 = .56\frac{1}{4} \times 16 = 9$

Before dividing, the fraction expressing the relationship of the numbers should be reduced to lowest terms if this will make the division easier. Thus, to find what percent 15 is of 35 the solution would be:

$$\tfrac{15}{35} = \tfrac{3}{7} = 3 \div 7 = .42\tfrac{6}{7} = 42\tfrac{6}{7}\%$$

Any number is 100% of itself. The fact that any number is 100% of itself may be readily demonstrated by solving the problem, "25 is what percent of 25?" Since the fraction $\tfrac{25}{25}$ expresses the fractional relationship of 25 to 25,

$$\tfrac{25}{25} = 25 \div 25 = 1 = 100\%$$

When a number is compared with a number larger than itself, the result is *less than* 100%. When it is compared with itself, the result is *equal to* 100%. When it is compared with a number smaller than itself, the result is *more than* 100%. Thus,

$$24 \text{ is } 80\% \text{ of } 30, \text{ since } \tfrac{24}{30} = \tfrac{4}{5} = 80\%$$
$$24 \text{ is } 100\% \text{ of } 24, \text{ since } \tfrac{24}{24} = 1 = 100\%$$
$$24 \text{ is } 120\% \text{ of } 20, \text{ since } \tfrac{24}{20} = \tfrac{6}{5} = 120\%$$

Exercise 5 Oral

State what the missing percent is in each of the following:

1. 10 is ? % of 20.
2. 12 is ? % of 36.
3. $8 is ? % of $32.
4. $10 is ? % of $25.
5. ? % of 10 is 7.
6. ? % of 30 is 6.
7. ? % of $24 is $8.
8. ? % of $50 is $40.
9. 20 is ? % of 30.
10. 20 is ? % of 20.
11. 20 is ? % of 10.
12. 20 is ? % of 5.
13. 20 is ? % of 2.
14. ? % of 6 is 12.
15. ? % of 7 is 28.
16. $24 is ? % of $20.

Exercise 6 Written

Find the missing percent in each of the following:

1. 45 is ? % of 180.
2. 84 is ? % of 240.
3. ? % of $1,400 is $63.
4. ? % of $192 is $12.
5. $4.80 is ? % of $60.
6. ? % of $180 is $22.50.
7. $8 is ? % of $120.
8. $19 is ? % of $3.80.
9. ? % of $8.25 is $33.
10. $5\tfrac{1}{3}$ is ? % of 16.

REVIEW ASSIGNMENT **17**c

1. **a** Multiply 16 by $\frac{3}{4}$.   **b** Divide 16 by $\frac{3}{4}$.

c 90 is what percent of 225?

d Express .0125 as a percent.

e Express $\frac{4}{15}$ as a percent, to the nearest tenth of a percent.

2. A keypunch operator works each day, Monday through Friday, from 9:00 a.m. to 5:00 p.m., with an hour out for lunch. Last week she worked full time at $2.95 an hour. What were her total earnings for the week?

3. **a** A salary of $112.50 a week is the same as how much a year?

b How much a month?

4. Ruth Nelson, a typist, is paid a salary of $93.60 a week for a 40-hour week, with time and a half for overtime.

a $93.60 for a 40-hour week is equal to how much an hour?

b What is Ruth's rate of pay for each overtime hour?

5. Last week, Ruth Nelson (Problem 4) worked 47 hours. What were her total earnings for the week?

6. A clerk who is paid $461.50 a month is now to be paid weekly. How much should she receive each week?

7. Find the missing amount in each of the following:

a $.35 \times r = \$28$ **b** $\frac{3}{4} \times p = \$204$

⬣ 8. **a** 126 is equal to what number increased by $\frac{1}{6}$ of itself?

b What amount decreased by $\frac{2}{5}$ of itself gives $4.50?

PART **17d** Percents (continued)

Changing a percent to a decimal. In finding a percent of a number, you often need to change the percent to a decimal before multiplying. For example, in Problem 2 on page 130, to find the amount budgeted for clothing, you had to change 11% to .11.

You have learned on page 132 that a decimal may be changed to a percent by moving the decimal point two places to the right and annexing a percent sign. Thus, .187 = 18.7%.

By reversing the process, a percent may be changed to a decimal. Hence, to change a percent to a decimal, *move the decimal point two places to the left in the percent and drop the percent sign.*

Study the following examples:

$18.7\% = .187$ $16\frac{3}{4}\% = .16\frac{3}{4}$ or $.1675$ $100\% = 1$

$1\frac{2}{3}\% = .01\frac{2}{3}$ $\frac{3}{4}\% = .00\frac{3}{4}$ or $.0075$ $135\% = 1.35$

$\frac{2}{3}\% = .00\frac{2}{3}$ $6\frac{7}{8}\% = .06\frac{7}{8}$ or $.06875$ $200\% = 2$

Exercise 7   Mental

For each of the following percents write the equal decimal or whole number, as the case may be.

	1.	2.	3.	4.	5.	6.
a	35%	3.4%	.8%	345%	$133\frac{1}{3}\%$	$2\frac{2}{3}\%$
b	79%	4.7%	.3%	200%	$29\frac{1}{2}\%$	$6\frac{3}{8}\%$
c	36.5%	6%	100%	1,000%	$41\frac{2}{3}\%$	$\frac{1}{3}\%$
d	23.4%	1%	150%	$137\frac{1}{2}\%$	$3\frac{1}{4}\%$	$\frac{3}{4}\%$

To find a percent of a number. In Problem 2 on page 130 you had to find 11% of $5,600. Since "percent" means "hundredths," the expression "percent of" means "hundredths of," or "hundredths times." Hence, to find a percent of a number, multiply the number by the decimal equivalent of the percent. Thus,

$$11\% \text{ of } \$5,600 = .11 \times \$5,600 = \$616$$

When the result is to be obtained mentally, it is usually easier to multiply by the number in the percent and then point off in the product. For example, in finding 8% of 345, write the product of 8×345, which is 2,760, and then point off two places, giving 27.60.

Exercise 8   Mental

In each of the following, do the multiplication without the aid of written calculations. Write the answers only.

	1.	2.	3.	4.
a	3% of $800	7% of $120	30% of $33	55% of $50
b	5% of $400	2% of $480	70% of $41	90% of $91
c	9% of $200	100% of $68	20% of $54	1% of $726
d	15% of $50	200% of $220	80% of $76	2% of $2,030
e	4% of $180	500% of $106	3% of $207	105% of $600
f	6% of $110	60% of $90	1% of $325	110% of $80

Multiplication by aliquot parts of 100%. When one factor is an aliquot part of 100%, the work can usually be shortened by using the fraction that is equal to the percent. In Problem 2 on page 130, for example, you had to find 25% of $5,600 in order to find the amount budgeted for food. Since 25% equals $\frac{1}{4}$, the product can be found more quickly by multiplying $5,600 by $\frac{1}{4}$ than by .25. Thus,

$$25\% \text{ of } \$5,600 = \frac{1}{4} \text{ of } \$5,600$$
$$= \$1,400$$

The fractional equivalents of some of the more frequently used percents are given below. These percents and their fractional equivalents should be memorized.

HERE COME THOSE ALIQUOT PARTS AGAIN!

$50\% = \frac{1}{2}$	$20\% = \frac{1}{5}$	$12\frac{1}{2}\% = \frac{1}{8}$	$33\frac{1}{3}\% = \frac{1}{3}$	$8\frac{1}{3}\% = \frac{1}{12}$
$25\% = \frac{1}{4}$	$40\% = \frac{2}{5}$	$37\frac{1}{2}\% = \frac{3}{8}$	$66\frac{2}{3}\% = \frac{2}{3}$	$6\frac{1}{4}\% = \frac{1}{16}$
$75\% = \frac{3}{4}$	$60\% = \frac{3}{5}$	$62\frac{1}{2}\% = \frac{5}{8}$	$16\frac{2}{3}\% = \frac{1}{6}$	
	$80\% = \frac{4}{5}$	$87\frac{1}{2}\% = \frac{7}{8}$	$83\frac{1}{3}\% = \frac{5}{6}$	

Exercise 9   Oral

Using the fraction that is equal to the percent, find:

1. 50% of $56;   of $46.
2. 25% of $28;   of $72.
3. 75% of $36;   of $40.
4. $12\frac{1}{2}$% of $24;   of $64.
5. 20% of $20;   of $45.
6. $37\frac{1}{2}$% of $48;   of $96.
7. 40% of $30;   of $55.
8. $62\frac{1}{2}$% of $16;   of $88.
9. $87\frac{1}{2}$% of $40;   of $80.
10. 80% of $15;   of $60.
11. $33\frac{1}{3}$% of $27;   of $51.

12. 60% of $25;   of $40.
13. $66\frac{2}{3}$% of $39;   of $75.
14. $16\frac{2}{3}$% of $18;   of $90.
15. $83\frac{1}{3}$% of $54;   of $66.
16. $8\frac{1}{3}$% of $84;   of $72.
17. $6\frac{1}{4}$% of $80;   of $32.
18. $12\frac{1}{2}$% of $32;   of $56.
19. 25% of $44;   of $64.
20. 40% of $35;   of $40.
21. 75% of $28;   of $52.
22. 20% of $15;   of $60.

Exercise **10**   Written

Multiply as indicated in each of the following problems. Use the fraction that is equal to the percent wherever this will make the solution easier. Notice that $125\% = 1\frac{1}{4}$; $166\frac{2}{3}\% = 1\frac{2}{3}$; etc.

	1.	**2.**	**3.**
a	45% of $1,600	20% of $305.40	125% of $88
b	80% of $5,800	25% of $628	$166\frac{2}{3}\%$ of $36.75
c	30% of $2,900	$33\frac{1}{3}\%$ of $822	$62\frac{1}{2}\%$ of $1,272
d	3% of $1,467	37.6% of $400	106% of $805
e	6% of $1,840	$4\frac{1}{2}\%$ of $1,600	$187\frac{1}{2}\%$ of $16.40
f	$16\frac{2}{3}\%$ of $540	$5\frac{1}{2}\%$ of $1,200	$8\frac{1}{3}\%$ of $4,020

Changing a percent to a common fraction. A percent may be changed to a common fraction by two different methods.

Method 1. Drop the percent sign and write the number as the numerator of a common fraction with the denominator 100. Then reduce the fraction to lowest terms. To illustrate:

$$8\% = \tfrac{8}{100} = \tfrac{2}{25} \qquad 140\% = \tfrac{140}{100} = \tfrac{14}{10} = \tfrac{7}{5}, \text{ or } 1\tfrac{2}{5}$$

▶ If the common fraction is in complex form, multiply the numerator and denominator by the denominator of the fraction in the numerator. Then reduce the resulting simple fraction to lowest terms. To illustrate:

$$4\tfrac{1}{2}\% = \frac{4\frac{1}{2}}{100} = \frac{4\frac{1}{2}\times 2}{100\times 2} = \frac{9}{200} \qquad \tfrac{2}{3}\% = \frac{\frac{2}{3}}{100} = \frac{\frac{2}{3}\times 3}{100\times 3} = \frac{2}{300} = \frac{1}{150}$$

▶ *Method 2. Change the percent to a decimal and then change the decimal to a common fraction in its lowest terms.* For example:

$$4.5\% = .045 = \tfrac{45}{1,000} = \tfrac{9}{200} \qquad 115\% = 1.15 = 1\tfrac{15}{100} = 1\tfrac{3}{20}$$

Exercise **11**   Mental

Express each of the following percents as a common fraction in its lowest terms or as a mixed number, as the case may be.

	1.	**2.**	**3.**	**4.**	**5.**	**6.**	▶ **7.**	▶ **8.**
a	3%	6%	44%	90%	60%	125%	.3%	.6%
b	17%	14%	5%	70%	25%	150%	.7%	.5%
c	31%	4%	15%	40%	75%	175%	1.3%	1.5%
d	2%	12%	45%	80%	50%	250%	.2%	2.5%

◢ Exercise **12**   Written

Change the percents to common fractions in lowest terms.

1. $1\frac{1}{4}\%$ $\frac{1}{80}$ 3. $17\frac{1}{2}\%$ 5. $30\frac{2}{3}\%$ 7. $9\frac{1}{6}\%$ 9. 26.4%

2. $1\frac{1}{2}\%$ 4. $26\frac{2}{3}\%$ 6. $3\frac{1}{8}\%$ 8. 17.5% $\frac{7}{40}$ 10. 5.8%

REVIEW ASSIGNMENT **17** d

1. a What amount is 32% of $85?

b Express $\frac{5}{9}$ as a decimal, to the nearest hundredth.

c Express .16 as a common fraction in lowest terms.

d Express .0235 as a percent.

e Express $\frac{7}{13}$ as a percent, to the nearest tenth of a percent.

2. A typist works each day for a five-day week, Monday through Friday, from 8:30 a.m. to 5:00 p.m., with one hour out for lunch, and receives $2.35 an hour. What are her gross earnings for one week if she works full time?

3. A bookkeeper is paid a salary of $133 for a 38-hour week, with time and a half for overtime. Last week she worked 43 hours.

a What is her hourly rate of pay for regular time?

b What is her hourly rate of pay for overtime?

c What were her gross earnings for last week?

4. Two business partners, Fisher and Lance, divide their net income in a ratio of 9 to 7 in favor of Fisher. Find the amount of each partner's share of a net income of $15,200.

5. A store's merchandise inventory was $19,338 on April 1 and $17,741 on June 30. If the sales for the quarter were $23,112 and the purchases $13,497, what was the store's gross profit?

6. Find the missing amount in each of the following:

a $.085 \times d = \$357.$ **b** $\frac{2}{3} \times c = \$330.$

✔ *Are you forming the habit of always estimating each product and quotient, and checking all calculations immediately?*

◢ **7. a** $216 equals what amount increased by $\frac{1}{8}$ of itself?

b What amount decreased by $\frac{1}{4}$ of itself equals $16.80?

◢ **8.** Shoes that cost a shoe store $10.50 a pair had been selling at $18.95 at the rate of 20 pairs a day. During a special sale, the price was reduced to $16.45, and the sales increased to 35 pairs a day. By how much was the daily profit increased or decreased by reducing the price?

GENERAL REVIEW

1. On May 31, E. J. Reed's bank balance was $763.14, and his checkbook balance was $720.08. The bank had deducted a service charge of $1.65. Checks for $19.78, $10, and $14.93 were outstanding. Prepare a reconciliation statement.

2. Yesterday, a cashier started the day with $32.50 in change. At the end of the day, the cash register totals showed that $432.13 had been taken in and $4.19 paid out. There was $460.16 in the cash drawer. How much was the cash over or short?

3. On both Monday and Tuesday, Eleanor received a mark of 85% in mathematics. On Wednesday, Thursday, and Friday she received marks of 75%, 90%, and 80%, respectively, in the same subject. What was her average mark for the five days?

4. In four consecutive weeks a salesman's earnings were $98, $119, $103, and $112, respectively. How much must he earn the fifth week in order to average $110 a week for the five weeks?

5. Fred Caldwell had an income of $4,500 in one year. He spent $2,184 for board and room, $258 for clothing, $689 for automobile expenses, and $784 for other items. He saved the remainder. What percent of his income did he save?

6. Cook works on a 40-hour week basis at $3.10 an hour with time and a half for overtime. Last week he worked 47 hours. His employer deducted 4.8% for social security and $16.10 for withholding tax. What was Cook's take-home pay for last week?

7. For the first week of March, Ott, a factory worker, had gross earnings of $129.69. He claims five exemptions. Using the tables on pages 106 and 108, find the income tax and FICA tax that were deducted from Ott's gross earnings.

8. Hendry, a radio dealer, buys 48 sets at $15 each. He sells 25 of them at $25 each, 20 at $20 each, and the remainder at $15 each. What is the average gross profit per set which Hendry makes on the entire transaction, to the nearest cent?

▶ **9.** A women's apparel store purchased 150 dresses at $18 each and marked them to sell at $29.95. Near the end of the season, 28 dresses remain unsold. What is the lowest price each, to the nearest cent, to which the store can reduce these 28 dresses and still make a gross profit of $1,500 on the entire lot?

▶ **10.** On May 1, Otto Hahn's bank statement showed a balance of $462.50. His checkbook balance was $554.63. Checks were outstanding for $118.28 and $60.34. A deposit of $268.75, made by mail on April 30, had been received by the bank too late to be entered on the statement. There was a service charge of $2.00. Prepare a reconciliation statement.

UNIT Five

Commission Income Problems

SECTION 18

Figuring Commissions

Many businesses pay their salesmen a commission rather than a fixed salary. The commission may be a certain amount for each article sold, or it may be a percent of the dollar value of the sales. Goods that are difficult to sell may carry a higher commission rate than goods that are easily sold. Extra commission may be paid for selling slow-moving merchandise. Some businesses pay both a salary and a commission. In any case, commission is an incentive to the salesman to increase his sales effort.

IT'S HORRIBLE - BUT I GET MORE COMMISSION FOR SELLING IT!

PART 18a   Salesmen's Commissions

Straight commission. When a salesman is paid only a commission, he is said to work on a *straight commission* basis.

To find amount of the commission when the rate is based on quantity sold. When the rate of commission is an amount for each article sold, the number of articles is multiplied by the rate to find the commission.

Rate of Commission × Quantity Sold = Commission

Example

Lois King, a high school student, sells greeting cards in her spare time. She is paid a straight commission of 25¢ on each box of cards that she sells. During November she sells 84 boxes of cards.

What is the amount of her commission?

Solution: *$.25 × 84 = $21, commission*

To find amount of the commission when the rate is based on value of sales. When the rate of commission is expressed as a percent, it is based on the dollar value of the sales. The amount of the sales is the base, so it is multiplied by the rate to find the commission.

Rate of Commission × Sales = Commission

Example

A salesman, Milton Porter, is paid a straight commission of 7% on his sales. During October his sales amount to $8,500.
What is the amount of his commission?

Solution: *.07 × $8,500 = $595, commission*

Exercise 1   Oral

What is the amount of the commission in each of the following?

	Quantity	Commission on Each		Sales	Rate of Commission
1.	140 brushes	20¢	4.	$2,500	6%
2.	180 pans	40¢	5.	$6,000	3%
3.	200 lamps	75¢	6.	$3,200	$12\frac{1}{2}$%

Salary and commission. A salesman may be paid a salary plus a commission. The commission may be a percent of his total sales, or a percent of his sales above a fixed amount known as his *quota*.

Example

Brian Quinn, a salesman in the Voss Appliance Store, is paid $70 a week, plus 6% on sales in excess of $900. Last week his sales amounted to $1,700.
What were his total earnings for the week?

Solution: *Salary*   = *$ 70*
                   Commission   =   *48 (6% of $800)*
                   Total earnings   *$118*

Exercise 2   Written

1. Grimm, a shoe salesman, is paid a commission of 8% on all sales. His sales last week totaled $1,781.25. What was his total commission for the week? $142.50

2. Grace Lorner, a salesperson, is paid a salary of $82.50 a week, plus a 2% commission on all sales. During one week her sales were $1,457.50. What were her total earnings for the week?

3. Rita Kiley, a salesclerk, receives a salary of $64 a week and a commission of 1% on all sales. Last week her sales were $902.65. What were her total earnings for the week?

4. Jack Otis, a salesman, receives a salary of $400 a month and a commission of 10% on sales in excess of a monthly quota of $2,500. His total sales last month were $7,351.60. What were his total earnings for the month? $885.16

5. A salesgirl receives a weekly salary of $72, plus $\frac{3}{4}$% commission on all sales. During the first week of December her sales were $880. What were her total earnings for the week?

REVIEW ASSIGNMENT **18a**

1. a Express .18 as a common fraction in lowest terms.
b Express 45% as a decimal.
c Express 13% as a common fraction.
d What amount is equal to $96 increased by $\frac{3}{4}$ of itself?
e $378 decreased by $\frac{1}{6}$ of itself gives what amount?
f $198 is what part greater than $165?

2. During one week, Cordiner sold 64 aluminum windows at $19.25 each. His commission rate was 20% of sales. How much commission did he earn on his sales for that week?

3. Roth, a salesman, is paid a salary of $125 a week plus 2% commission on all sales. Last week his sales totaled $2,467. What were his total earnings for last week?

4. A salesman receives a salary of $92.50 a week plus 5% of all sales in excess of a weekly quota of $1,200. During a recent week his sales totaled $1,874. What were his gross earnings for that week?

5. Your employer has been paying you twice a month at the rate of $325 a month. He now decides to change to a weekly payroll. At the same rate, how much should you receive per week?

6. A salary of $94.50 a week is equal to how much a month?

7. $52 = .65 × s. Find the missing amount.

▶ **8. a** $255 is $\frac{3}{5}$ of what amount?
b $528 equals what amount increased by $\frac{3}{8}$ of itself?
c $33 equals what amount decreased by $\frac{1}{3}$ of itself?

PART **18b** Percents (continued)

To find 1%, 10%, 100%, or 1,000% of a number. In Problem 3 at the top of page 144 you had to find 1% of $902.65. In Problem 4, you had to find 10% of $4,851.60. In other types of percentage problems you will have to find 100% or 1,000% of a number.

The decimals or whole numbers equal to 1%, 10%, 100%, and 1,000% are as follows:

$$1\% = .01 \qquad 100\% = \ \ 1$$
$$10\% = .1 \qquad 1,000\% = 10$$

To find 1%, 10%, 100%, or 1,000% of a number, move the decimal point in the number the same as you would to multiply by .01, .1, 1, or 10, as the case may be. Thus,

To Find	Multiply	By Moving the Decimal Point	Answer
1% of 125	125 × .01	2 places to the *left*	1.25
10% of 125	125 × .1	1 place to the *left*	12.5
100% of 125	125 × 1	no change	125
1,000% of 125	125 × 10	1 place to the *right*	1,250

Exercise **3**   Mental

In the following problems, perform the multiplication mentally. Write the answers only. Where the answer contains a fraction of a cent, give the result to the nearest cent.

	1.	**2.**	**3.**
a	1% of $60	100% of $28	10% of $242
b	1% of $85	100% of $6.70	10% of $3.84
c	10% of $94	1,000% of $43	10% of $27.25
d	10% of $33	1,000% of $15	1% of $64.45

Fractional parts of 1%. Commission rates are sometimes expressed as fractions of a percent, such as $\frac{1}{4}\%$, $\frac{1}{2}\%$, $\frac{2}{3}\%$. Thus, in Problem 5 at the top of page 144 the rate is $\frac{3}{4}\%$, and you had to find $\frac{3}{4}\%$ of $880 in order to obtain the commission.

A percent such as $\frac{3}{4}\%$ means "$\frac{3}{4}$ of 1%"; and $\frac{3}{4}\%$ of $880 means "$\frac{3}{4}$ of 1% of $880." To find $\frac{3}{4}\%$ of $880, first find 1% of $880 and then take $\frac{3}{4}$ of the result; or you may first find $\frac{3}{4}$ of $880 and then take 1% of that result.

Example

$$\tfrac{3}{4}\% \text{ of } \$880 = ?$$

Solution 1	Solution 2
1% of $\$880 = \$8.80$	$\tfrac{3}{4}$ of $\$880 = \$660$
$\tfrac{3}{4}$ of $\$8.80 = \$6.60$	1% of $\$660 = \$6.60$

◐ A fraction of a percent may be expressed in decimal form by first changing the common fraction to a decimal fraction and then changing the resulting percent to a decimal. For example,

$$\tfrac{3}{4}\% = .75\% = .0075$$

◐ When the fraction is one like $\tfrac{2}{3}$, $\tfrac{1}{6}$, or $\tfrac{4}{9}$, where the numerator is not exactly divisible by the denominator, drop the percent sign and then prefix two zeros and a decimal point. Thus,

$$\tfrac{2}{3}\% = .00\tfrac{2}{3}$$

Exercise 4   Oral

How much is:

1. $\tfrac{1}{4}\%$ of $\$1,600$? of $\$400$? of $\$3,600$? of $\$2,800$? of $\$820$?

2. $\tfrac{1}{2}\%$ of $\$600$? of $\$240$? of $\$860$? of $\$66.40$? of $\$42.40$?

3. $\tfrac{1}{8}\%$ of $\$3,200$? of $\$5,600$? of $\$8,800$? of $\$480$? of $\$800$?

4. $\tfrac{1}{10}\%$ of $\$3,000$? of $\$500$? of $\$1,000$? of $\$200$? of $\$166$?

Exercise 5   Mental

In each of the following problems perform the multiplication mentally. Write only the product.

	1.	2.	3.
a	25% of $\$3,200$	$\tfrac{1}{3}\%$ of $\$900$	$\tfrac{3}{8}\%$ of $\$72$
b	$\tfrac{1}{4}$ of $\$3,200$	$\tfrac{1}{8}\%$ of $\$720$	$\tfrac{1}{2}\%$ of $\$32$
c	$\tfrac{1}{4}\%$ of $\$3,200$	$\tfrac{1}{5}\%$ of $\$500$	$\tfrac{2}{5}\%$ of $\$30$
d	$\tfrac{1}{2}$ of $\$2,400$	$\tfrac{3}{4}\%$ of $\$400$	$\tfrac{3}{4}\%$ of $\$48$
e	$\tfrac{1}{2}\%$ of $\$2,400$	$\tfrac{2}{3}\%$ of $\$900$	$\tfrac{2}{3}\%$ of $\$45$

◉ Exercise **6**   Mental

Express each of the following as a percent. In each case, express the fractional part of 1% in the form of a common fraction. For example, the answer to **1-a** should be written as $\frac{3}{4}\%$.

	1.	**2.**	**3.**	**4.**	**5.**
a	.0075	.085	$.00\frac{1}{3}$	.00375	.0875
b	.0625	.005	.00125	$.0033\frac{1}{3}$	.00875
c	.0025	.002	.004	$.00\frac{2}{3}$	$.0066\frac{2}{3}$

REVIEW ASSIGNMENT **18** b

1. a $\frac{1}{3}\%$ of $855 is what amount?

b $75 is what percent of $250?

c Express 45% as a decimal.

d Express 27% as a common fraction.

2. Russell is paid $425 a month and $1\frac{1}{2}\%$ commission on all sales. His sales for the month of August were $12,842. What were his gross earnings for the month?

3. Lola Rogers, a salesclerk, is paid a weekly salary of $77.50 and a commission of 3% on all weekly sales in excess of $950. During the week of October 14, her sales amounted to $1,641. What were her total earnings for the week?

4. A salary of $4,537 a year is equal to how much a week?

5. A salary of $123.75 a week is equal to how much a month?

6. Beck works on an 8-hour basis at $3.36 an hour with time and a half for overtime. During a recent week he worked the hours shown below. What were his gross earnings for the week?

Mon., 9; Tues., 8; Wed., $6\frac{1}{2}$; Thurs., 9; Fri., $9\frac{1}{2}$

7. $54 = .72 \times c$. Find the missing amount.

◉ **8. a** $324 is $\frac{3}{4}$ of what amount?

b Express $\frac{1}{4}$ of 1% as a decimal.

c $30 equals what amount decreased by $\frac{1}{5}$ of itself?

◉ **9.** Gifford's checkbook balance on November 1 was $842.11. In making a reconciliation statement he found that a check for $12 was recorded in the checkbook as $21, that a check for $27 was recorded as $22, and that he had no record in his checkbook of a service charge of $2.15 and a deposit of $37.91. Find Gifford's correct checkbook balance.

SECTION 19

Graduated Commissions

Sometimes a salesman is paid a graduated commission. Under this plan, the rate of commission increases as the sales volume increases. For example, the rate may be 2% on all sales up to $10,000; 3% on the next $5,000; and 4% on all sales over $15,000.

PART 19a   Figuring Graduated Commissions

Computing the total commission. Under a graduated commission plan, the total commission is the sum of the commissions obtained by applying the individual rates to the proper sales amounts.

Example

Shaw, a salesman, is paid 10% commission on the first $700 of weekly sales and 15% on all sales in excess of $700. Last week his sales were $900. What was his commission?

Solution: *$900 − $700 = $200, excess sales*
.10 × $700 = $ 70, commission on first $700
.15 × $200 =   30, commission on excess
                  $100, total commission

Exercise 1   Written

1. Find the total commission in each of the following:

	Total Sales	Commission
a	$7,500	4% on first $6,000; 5% on excess over $6,000 $315
b	750	10% on first $400; 15% on excess over $400
c	825	8% on first $850; 12% on excess over $850
d	9,450	6% on first $6,500; 7% on next $6,500
e	6,920	10% on all sales, plus 5% on excess over $6,000

2. Prescott is paid 6% commission on the first $15,000 of monthly sales and 8% on all sales in excess of $15,000. His sales were $14,500 in June and $18,200 in July. What was his total commission for the two months? $2,026

3. Nancy Green sells cosmetics. She is paid a weekly commission of 60 cents each on the first 60 units sold, 75 cents each on the next 40, and $1.00 on any additional units sold. Last week she sold 107 units. What was her total commission for the week?

IT'S WORTH THE EXTRA EFFORT!

GET SELLING!!!
COMMISSION – SALES

4%	$1,000
3%	$750
2%	$500
BASE	SALARY

4. A salesman, Donald Wade, earned commissions of $440 in May and $550 in June. What percent greater was his June commission than his May commission?

5. Neil Cline's commission for June was $660 and for July, $528. His July commission was what percent smaller?

PART 19b Percents (continued)

Types of problems involving percent relationships. A percent, you have seen, is another way of expressing the ratio or fractional relationship of two numbers. There are six types of problems in percent relationships, corresponding with the six types of problems in fractional relationships that you studied in Sections 13 and 14. The six types of problems in percent relationships are as follows:

1. To find a percent of a number.
2. To find a number that is a given percent greater (or smaller) than a known number.
3. To find what percent one number is of another.
4. To find the percent that one number is greater (or smaller) than another.
5. To find a number when a given percent of it is known.
6. To find a number when an amount that is a given percent greater (or smaller) than the number is known.

The methods of solving problems indicated as Types 1 and 3 have been explained in Section 17. The principles and methods involved in Types 2, 4, 5, and 6 are discussed in this and the next two sections.

To find the percent that one number is greater (or smaller) than another. In Problem 4 on page 149, you had to find the percent that the June commission was greater than the May commission. In Problem 5, you had to find the percent that the July commission was smaller than the June commission.

To find the percent that one number is greater (or smaller) than another number, first subtract the smaller from the larger to find the number representing the part. Then divide this number by the number representing the whole, or the base, and express the result as a percent.

Example

30 is what percent greater than 24?

Solution	Explanation
$30 - 24 = 6$	30 is 6 greater than 24. 6 is therefore the number representing the part. The expression "greater than 24" means that 24 is the
$\frac{6}{24} = \frac{1}{4} = 25\%$ **Ans.**	number with which the part, 6, is to be com-

pared. Therefore $\frac{6}{24}$ expresses the relationship of 6 to 24. $\frac{6}{24} = \frac{1}{4} = 25\%$. Hence, 25% expresses the percent by which 30 is greater than 24.

Check: $24 + 25\%$ of $24 = 24 + 6 = 30$

Example

24 is what percent smaller than 30?

Solution	Explanation
$30 - 24 = 6$	24 is 6 smaller than 30. 6 is therefore the number representing the part. The expression "smaller than 30" means that 30 is the
$\frac{6}{30} = \frac{1}{5} = 20\%$ **Ans.**	number with which the part, 6, is to be com-

pared. Therefore the fraction $\frac{6}{30}$ expresses the relationship of 6 to 30. $\frac{6}{30} = \frac{1}{5} = 20\%$. Hence, 20% expresses the percent by which 24 is smaller than 30.

Check: $30 - 20\%$ of $30 = 30 - 6 = 24$

Exercise 2   Oral

State the missing percent in each of the following:

1. $5 is ? % more than $4.
2. $6 is ? % more than $5.
3. ? % more than $10 is $13.
4. $4 is ? % less than $5.
5. $3 is ? % less than $4.
6. ? % less than $10 is $7.
7. $8 is ? % more than $6.
8. $8 is ? % less than $10.
9. ? % more than $16 is $20.
10. 35 is ? % more than $30.
11. ? % less than $25 is $20.
12. ? % more than $24 is $32.

13. $24 is ? % less than $32.
14. $44 is ? % more than $40.
15. $7 is ? % less than $10.
16. $7 is ? % of $10.
17. $6 is ? % less than $8.
18. $6 is ? % of $8.
19. $5 is ? % more than $4.
20. $5 is ? % of $4.
21. $6 is ? % more than $5.
22. $6 is ? % of $5.
23. $10 is ? % of $5.
24. $15 is ? % of $5.

25. $15 is ? % more than $5.
26. ? % more than $10 is $25.
27. ? % of $10 is $25.
28. $12 is ? % more than $6.

REVIEW ASSIGNMENT 19 b

1. a $56 is what percent of $160?
b Express $\frac{3}{7}$ as a decimal, to the nearest thousandth.
c Express $\frac{9}{14}$ as a percent, to the nearest tenth percent.
d Express 19% as a common fraction.
e $96 increased by what percent of itself gives $120?
f $450 decreased by what percent of itself gives $270?

2. Larkin, a salesman, is paid a commission of 10% on all sales, and an additional commission of 4% on all sales in excess of $4,500 per month. Last month Larkin's sales totaled $6,285. What were his total earnings for the month?

3. Linda Clement is employed as a salesclerk with a base salary of $79.50 a week, plus $1\frac{1}{2}$% of all sales in excess of a weekly quota of $1,200. What would be her total earnings in a week in which her total sales were $2,245?

4. Nash receives a salary of $135 a week and Pitts a salary of $565.50 a month.
a Which one receives the larger weekly salary?
b How much larger is his salary per week?
c How much larger is his salary per month?

5. Dick's average mark on 5 successive tests in science was 87. After computing that average, he had 3 more tests in the same subject and obtained marks of 88, 92, and 89 respectively. Find his average mark for the 8 tests.

PART | 19c | Percents (continued)

To find a number that is a given percent greater (or smaller) than a known number. An expression such as "25% greater than 16" or "25% more than 16" means "25% of 16 *added* to 16"; that is, 16 + 25% of 16. The result is 16 + 4, or 20.

An expression such as "25% smaller than 16" or "25% less than 16" means "25% of 16 *subtracted* from 16"; that is, 16 − 25% of 16. The result is 16 − 4, or 12.

Example

16 *increased* by 25% of itself equals what number?

"16 increased by 25% of itself" means "*add* 25% of 16 to 16." The desired number therefore equals the known number, 16, *plus* the amount of the increase, 25% of 16. That is,

16 + 25% of 16 = the desired number.

Solution: 16 = *the known number*
            25% of 16 =   4 = *the increase*
                                    ———
                              20 = *the desired number*   **Ans.**

Example

16 *decreased* by 25% of itself equals what number?

"16 decreased by 25% of itself" means "*subtract* 25% of 16 from 16." The desired number is therefore equal to the known number, 16, *minus* the decrease, 25% of 16. Thus,

16 − 25% of 16 = the desired number.

Solution: 16 = *the known number*
            25% of 16 =   4 = *the decrease*
                                    ———
                              12 = *the desired number*   **Ans.**

Exercise 3   Oral

What amount is:

1. 10% more than $300?
2. 10% greater than $400?
3. 10% as much as $400?
4. 10% less than $300?
5. 10% smaller than $200?
6. 1% larger than $200?
7. $500 decreased by 20%?
8. $40 increased by 10%?

9. $60 diminished by $33\frac{1}{3}$%?
10. 30% larger than $40?
11. 25% less than $24?
12. 2% more than $500?
13. 20% smaller than $60?
14. 200% more than $20?
15. 100% more than $5?
16. $4 increased by 200%?

Percent increase or decrease. In personal or business affairs it is often desirable to compare quantities or amounts that apply to two periods of time. For example, a householder may want to compare his total food expenses for this month with the total for last month, or a salesman may want to compare his sales and commission in one month with those of a former month.

When comparisons of this kind are made, the percent of increase or decrease is often calculated. The amount for the earlier period is used as the base for comparison.

Example

For the month of August the total food expenses of the Leroy Owens family were $126 and for July, $140.

What was the percent increase or decrease in food expenses?

Solution:	Explanation

$140 − $126 = $14, decrease
$\frac{\$14}{\$140} = \frac{1}{10} = 10\%$

Ans. *10% decrease*

Check: $140 − 10% of $140 =
$140 − $14 = $126

The comparison must be based on the amount for July, because July is the earlier month. Since the expense for August is smaller than for July, the difference between the two amounts represents a decrease. The decrease, $14, is divided by $140, the expense for July, to find the percent decrease.

Exercise 4   Written

1. Roberta Paley saved $315 last year and $375 the year before. What was the percent increase or decrease in savings? 16%

2. For a special sale the price of a tire was dropped to $24.20 from $27.50. What was the percent decrease in price?

3. Fabric that sold for $5.50 a yard three years ago now sells for $7.15 a yard. What is the percent increase or decrease in price?

4. Last year, Morgan's weekly gasoline bill averaged $4.05. The year before, it averaged $3.60. By what percent did it increase or decrease?

5. A salesman sold $9,250 worth of goods in May and $8,510 worth in June. Find the percent increase or decrease in sales.

REVIEW ASSIGNMENT 19c

✔ *Try to make it a matter of habit always to estimate each product and quotient, and to check all calculations immediately.*

1. a $18 increased by 35% of itself gives what amount?
b $3.50 decreased by 16% of itself gives what amount?
c $20 increased by what percent of itself equals $23.60?
d $200 decreased by what percent of itself equals $170?
e Express 6% as a common fraction in lowest terms.

2. A salesman increased his weekly sales from $2,250 in one week to $2,610 in the next week. What was the percent increase?

3. A salesclerk is paid $73.50 a week and a commission of $1\frac{1}{2}$% on all sales. Her sales last week were $1,428. What was the amount of her total earnings for the week?

4. Watson, a salesman, is paid a commission of 10% on all sales, and an additional commission of 4% on all sales in excess of $1,200 per week. Last week Watson's sales amounted to $1,720. What were his gross earnings for that week?

5. Hart's salary is $422.50 a month. Alden's is $105 a week.
a Which one's salary is the greater, and how much greater per month?
b How much greater per week?

6. 95% × n = $228. Find the missing amount.

❯ **7.** Express $\frac{3}{4}$% as a decimal.

❯ **8.** A men's store bought suits at $39.50. At a retail price of $59.50, the store's sales averaged 15 suits a day. During a special sale, the price was reduced to $53.50, and the sales increased to 25 suits a day. By how much was the daily profit increased or decreased by reducing the price?

Commission Rates

In the preceding commission problems, you had to find the amount of the commission. The commission rate and amount of sales were known.

There are others, however, in which you have to find the commission rate; and still others, the amount of the sales. These problems are explained in this section.

PART 20a   Figuring Commission Rates and Sales

To find the rate of commission on sales. Since the rate is always based on the sales, the sales represent the base, or the whole, and the amount of commission represents the part. The problem is therefore one of finding what percent the commission is of the sales. Hence the percent, or rate of commission, may be found by dividing the commission by the sales.

$$\text{Rate of Commission} = \text{Commission} \div \text{Sales}$$

$$\text{Rate of Commission} = \frac{\text{Commission}}{\text{Sales}}$$

Example

For selling goods amounting to $4,000 a salesman received $200. What percent commission did he receive?

Solution 1	Solution 2
$4,000)$\overline{\$200}$ = .05 = 5% **Ans.**	$\frac{\$200}{\$4,000} = \frac{1}{20} = 5\%$ **Ans.**

Exercise 1   Written

1. Find the rate of commission in each of the following:

	Sales	Commission			Sales	Commission	
		Amount	Rate			Amount	Rate
a	$3,200	$224	7%	c	$1,400	$175	
b	$ 120	$ 18		d	$1,800	$ 63	

2. An agent who sells subscriptions for a magazine that costs $6.00 a year receives a commission of $1.80 on each annual subscription. What percent commission does he receive?

3. A salesman is paid a salary of $500 a month plus a commission on all sales. Last month his sales amounted to $9,000. His salary and commission together amounted to $680.

a How much commission was he paid?

b What rate of commission was he paid?

4. On sales of $7,200 a salesman's commission is $88. This is what percent on sales in excess of $5,000, the salesman's quota?

▷ **To find the amount of the sales when the amount of commission and rate of commission are known.** In certain cases you will want to find the amount of sales a salesman must make in order to earn a stated amount of commission.

Example

A company offers to pay a salesman a commission of 5%. How many dollars' worth of goods must he sell in one week in order that his commission for the week may be $120?

The rate of commission is always based on the sales. Therefore the 5% given in the problem means "5% of the sales" or "5% times the sales." The $120 is the amount of the commission. The problem therefore tells us that 5% of the sales is equal to $120. In other words,

$$5\% \times Sales = \$120$$

$120 is the product, and 5% is one of the factors of $120. The other factor is Sales, which is unknown. This factor can be found by dividing the product, $120, by the known factor, 5%.

Solution: $5\% \times Sales = \$120$
$Sales = \$120 \div 5\%$
$= \$120 \div .05 = \$2,400.$ **Ans.**

Check: Rate of Commission × Sales = Commission
$5\% \times \$2,400 = .05 \times \$2,400 = \$120$

Note that the $120 in the example should *not* be multiplied by the rate of commission, 5%, because the rate is based on the sales. *This means that only the number representing the sales may be multiplied by the 5%.* The $120 represents the amount of the commission, not the amount of the sales.

In every commission problem, the amount of the commission is the product of the sales and the commission rate.

Rate of Commission $\times$ Sales = Commission

The rate of commission and the sales are the factors, and the commission is the product. If the commission and the rate of commission are given, the unknown factor (Sales) may be found by dividing the product (Commission) by the known factor (Rate of Commission).

Sales = Commission $\div$ Rate of Commission

or

$$\text{Sales} = \frac{\text{Commission}}{\text{Rate of Commission}}$$

⬤ **Exercise 2**   Written

1. A salesman, Jerry Vale, is paid a commission of 7% on all sales. How many dollars' worth of goods must he sell in one month to earn $945 commission? $13,500

2. A saleswoman's commission is 5%. How many dollars' worth of goods must she sell to earn $625?

3. A salesman receives a salary of $400 a month and a commission of 3% on all sales. What must be the amount of his sales in a month so that his total monthly income will be $700?

4. At a weekly salary of $70, plus 4% commission on all sales, what minimum weekly sales are necessary to earn $100 a week?

5. Ray Welch receives a weekly salary of $90 with a 5% commission on all sales over $1,200 a week. What must be his total weekly sales if his total weekly income is to be $140?

REVIEW ASSIGNMENT **20**a

1. a $27 is what percent of $180?

b $27 increased by 42% of itself equals what amount?

c $175 decreased by what percent of itself equals $161?

d Express 16% as a common fraction in lowest terms.

2. An agency sold 1,420 trucks last year and 1,136 the year before. Find the percent increase or decrease.

3. Carner's sales last month totaled $6,150. His total earnings for the month were $844, of which $475 was his monthly salary. What percent commission was he paid?

4. Two business partners, Emery and Dole, divide their net profit in a ratio of 7 to 5 in favor of Dole. Find the amount of each partner's share of a net profit of $19,500.

5. A sales girl receives a weekly salary of $75 plus a commission of 5% on all sales in excess of $1,250 a week. During two consecutive weeks her total sales were $1,175 and $1,641, respectively. What were her total earnings for the two weeks?

6. Grover works each day, Monday through Friday, from 8:30 a.m. to 5:00 p.m., with one-half hour out for lunch, and is paid $2.88 an hour. What were his total earnings last week if he worked full time except for $2\frac{1}{2}$ hours lost on Monday?

7. $72\% \times z = \$39.60$. Find the missing amount.

▶ **8. a** $\frac{2}{5}$ of what amount is equal to $36.50?

   b Express $\frac{1}{8}\%$ as a decimal.

▶ **9.** A salesman's commission is 5% on all sales. To earn $135 commission, what must be the amount of his sales?

PART 20b | Percents (continued)

▶ **Important principle of percent relationships.** The rules of fractional relationships, which you studied on page 116, apply also to percents.

In the expression "16 is 20% of 80," 16 is the part. 80 is the whole with which 16 is compared, or the number on which the comparison is based. It is therefore referred to as the *base*; and the percent, 20%, is said to be *based* on 80.

The number that represents the base, and only the number that represents the base, may be multiplied by the percent.

The number representing the base is usually the number which follows immediately the expression that indicates multiplication — such as "times," "of," "greater than," etc.

In each of the following, 60 is the base since it follows immediately the expression that indicates multiplication. 60 may therefore be multiplied by the percent.

  ? is 25% *as large as* 60.   ? is 25% *smaller than* 60.

  25% *of* 60 is ? .   25% *more than* 60 is ? .

In the problems given below, however, the *unknown number* is the base, because the space that represents the missing number follows immediately the expression that indicates multiplication. Therefore the known number, 60, may *not* be multiplied by the percent, because 60 *does not represent the base.*

60 is 25% *as large as* ? .   60 is 25% *smaller than* ? .

25% *of* ? *equals* 60.   60 is 25% *greater than* ? .

Problems like these four cannot be solved by multiplying the known number by the percent.

▶ Exercise **3**   Oral

In each of the following, state whether the known number may or may not be multiplied by the percent to find the correct answer.

1. ? is 25% of 16.   6. ? is 60% as great as 90.
2. 18 is 30% of ? .   7. $75 is 45% as great as ? .
3. $40 is 20% of ? .   8. 55 is 20% times ? .
4. ? is 70% of $50.   9. ? is 20% times 55.
5. $20 is 80% of ? .   10. 10% of ? equals 90.

▶ To find a number when a given percent of it is known.

When the value of a given percent of a number is known and you want to find what that number is, the problem is one in finding the number on which the given percent is based. This is a problem in finding the unknown factor when the other factor and the product are known.

Example

48 is 12% of what number?

The problem tells us that 12% of a certain unknown number is equal to 48. Thus,

12% × the unknown number = 48

48 is the product, and 12% is one of the factors of 48. The other factor is the unknown number. This factor can be found by dividing the product, 48, by the known factor, 12%.

Solution: *12% × the unknown number = 48*

The unknown number = 48 ÷ 12%

= 48 ÷ .12 = 400 **Ans.**

Check: 12% × 400 = .12 × 400 = 48

▶ Exercise **4**   Written

Find the missing amount in each of the following:
1. $15\% \times ? = \$60$ $400
2. $18\% \times ? = \$36$
3. 29% of ? is $95.70
4. $5.39 is 35% of ? .
5. 46% of $184 is ? .

6. $5.46 is 21% of ? .
7. ? is 53% of $106.
8. $65\% \times ?$ is $24.70.
9. $81 = 45\% \times$? .
10. $11.20 is 35% of ? .

▶ Exercise **5**   Oral

1. What is 1% of an amount:

a If 2% of the amount is $4? $10? $18? $64? $150?

b If 3% of the amount is $6? $15? $36? $60? $120?

c If 9% of the amount is $27? $54? $180? $360? $72?

d If $\frac{1}{2}\%$ of the amount is $4? $10? $18? $64? $150?

e If $\frac{1}{5}\%$ of the amount is $10? $25? $40? $2? $15?

2. What is 100% of an amount:

a If 1% of the amount is $2? $18? $60? $1? $120?

b If 2% of the amount is $4? $10? $18? $64? $150?

c If 5% of the amount is $20? $35? $150? $350? $45?

d If $\frac{1}{2}\%$ of the amount is $4 $10? $1? $150? $2?

e If $\frac{1}{4}\%$ of the amount is $2? $5? $1? $4? $10?

▶ Exercise **6**   Oral

Find the missing amount in each of the following:
1. $5 is 1% of ? .
2. $2 is 1% of ? .
3. $36 is 6% of ? .
4. $20 is 5% of ? .
5. 3% of ? is $24.
6. $18 is 9% of ? .
7. $14 is 2% of ? .
8. 1% of ? is $3.
9. $9 is 1% of ? .
10. $4 is $\frac{1}{2}\%$ of ? .
11. $8 is $\frac{1}{2}\%$ of ? .
12. $1 is $\frac{1}{4}\%$ of ? .

13. $\frac{1}{5}\%$ of ? is $3.
14. $\frac{2}{5}\%$ of ? is $8.
15. $9 is $\frac{3}{4}\%$ of ? .
16. $10\% \times ? = \$34.
17. $30\% \times ? = \$27.
18. $40 is 25% of ? .
19. ? is 25% of $40.
20. $30 is 75% of ? .
21. $16\frac{2}{3}\%$ of ? is $30.
22. $60 is 100% of ? .
23. $60 is 200% of ? .
24. $60 is 300% of ? .

REVIEW ASSIGNMENT **20**b

1. **a** $\frac{3}{8}\%$ of $1,720 is what amount?

   b $48 is what percent of $150?

   c $3.50 increased by what percent of itself equals $4.48?

   d Express 36% as a common fraction in lowest terms.

2. Cecil Chase, a salesman, is employed on a salary-plus-commission basis. His total earnings for last year amounted to $13,700, of which $6,500 represented his guaranteed annual salary. If his total sales last year amounted to $144,000, what percent commission did he receive?

3. A salesman's sales for January of this year were $6,090. For January of last year his sales were $7,250. Find the percent of increase or decrease in his January sales.

4. Vernon Anderson, a factory worker, is employed at $3.36 an hour for an 8-hour day with time and a half for overtime. During a recent week, he worked the hours shown below. What were Anderson's gross earnings for the week?

Monday	9 hr.	Wednesday	$7\frac{1}{2}$ hr.	Friday	9 hr.
Tuesday	8 hr.	Thursday	9 hr.		

5. Harold Butler had salary and commission for last week totaling $172.20. His employer deducted 4.8% for social security, $19.90 for withholding tax, and $3.25 for insurance. What was Butler's net pay for the week?

6. Bullis, a salesman, receives a monthly salary of $450, a 5% commission on all sales, and an additional 2% on all monthly sales in excess of $4,500. His sales for May were $6,280. What were his total earnings for May?

7. Riley's sales for the Potter Company for March, April, and May were $6,275, $4,960, and $7,425, respectively. He is paid a salary of $550 a month and commission of 6% on that part of his sales in excess of $5,000 for any one month. What was the amount of Riley's total earnings for the three months?

8. 45% × s = $90. Find the missing amount.

   ❯ 9. **a** $3.24 is 72% of what amount?

   b Express $\frac{2}{5}\%$ as a decimal.

   ❯ 10. If a salesman is paid $80 a week plus a commission of 3% on all sales, what must be the amount of his sales each week in order that his total weekly income may be $125?

SECTION 21

Agents' Commissions

A person who is in business for himself, acting as an *agent* for others, usually receives some form of commission in payment for his services. The person for whom the agent acts is known as the *principal*.

PART 21a Figuring the Net Proceeds

Commission and expenses of an agent. A real estate agent may be engaged by the owner of a dwelling house to find a buyer and to complete the sale of the property. The agent usually receives a stated percent of the sale price in payment for his services. He may also be paid for legal expenses, transfer taxes, and other expenses in connection with the sale. The net amount left for the principal, after deducting the agent's commission and expenses, is the *net proceeds*.

A collection agent, who collects unpaid bills owed to business firms or individuals, usually receives a percent of the amount collected. He may also be reimbursed for some expenses in making the collection.

To find the amount of the agent's commission. The rate of commission of a selling agent is based on the sale price of the property sold. Hence, the amount of the commission is the product of the rate and the sale price.

Rate of Commission × Sale Price = Commission

Thus, if a house and lot are sold for $16,000 through an agent who charges 5% commission, the commission would be:

.05 × $16,000 = $800, commission

The commission of a collection agent is the product of the rate and the amount collected.

Rate of Commission × Amount Collected = Commission

To find the net proceeds received by the principal. The net proceeds is the amount received by the principal, after deducting the agent's commission and any allowable expenses incurred in connection with the transaction.

Sale Price − (Commission + Expenses) = Net Proceeds

or

Amount Collected − (Commission + Expenses) = Net Proceeds

Example

A. L. Gage, a collection agent, collected an outstanding bill of $500 for Mack & Co. He charged 40% commission and $25 for expenses. What net proceeds did the company receive?

Solution

Amount collected		*$500*
Deductions:		
Commission 40%		
of $500	*$200*	
Expenses	*25*	*225*
Net proceeds		*$275*

In cases where the agent's commission is the only deduction, the formula for the net proceeds would be:

Sale Price − Commission = Net Proceeds

or

Amount Collected − Commission = Net Proceeds

Exercise 1   Written

1. Find the commission, total deductions, and net proceeds in each of the following:

	Sale Price or Amount Collected	Commission Rate	Commission Amount	Agent's Expenses	Total Deductions	Net Proceeds
a	$15,650	6%	$ 939.00	None	$ 939.00	$14,711.00
b	340	35%		None		
c	22,800	5%	1,140.00	$125.50	1,265.50	21,534.50
d	980	40%		25.75		
e	32,900	6%		164.50		

2. Bill Bedell, a real estate agent, sold a house for Eugene Lerner for $19,500 and charged 6% commission. What net proceeds did Lerner receive? $18,330

3. A real estate agent sold a house for $25,200. How much did the original owner receive if the agent charged 5% for commission and $115.50 for expenses?

4. Victor Baum gave an agency accounts amounting to $740 to collect. The agency collected 60% of the accounts and charged $33\frac{1}{3}$% for collecting. How much did Baum receive?

❷ **5.** In collecting $900 for H. L. Powers, an agency charged 50% on the first $300, 35% on the next $200, and 25% on the excess over $500. How much did Powers receive?

❷ **To find the sale price or amount collected when the amount of the net proceeds and the rate of commission are known.** If the net proceeds and the rate of commission are known, and you want to find the sale price or amount collected, the problem is one in finding the number on which the given rate is based.

Example

A collection agent remitted $350 to his principal after deducting 30% for collecting an account. What was the amount collected?

The commission is 30% *of the amount collected.* The problem therefore tells us that, if 30% of the amount collected is subtracted from the amount collected, the difference is $350. Thus,

Amount Collected − 30% of Amount Collected = $350

(1) The amount collected is the base, or whole, and is therefore 100% of itself, or 100% *of the amount collected.*

(2) The commission is 30% *of the amount collected.*

(3) Subtracting (2) from (1) gives 70% *of the amount collected,* which represents the net proceeds, $350.

Solution: $\quad 100\% \times amount\ collected = Amount\ collected$
$\quad\quad \underline{-30\% \times amount\ collected = Commission}$
$\quad\quad\ \ 70\% \times amount\ collected = Net\ proceeds\ (\$350)$
$\quad\quad\quad\quad\quad Amount\ collected = \$350 \div 70\%$
$\quad\quad\quad\quad\quad\quad\quad\quad\quad\quad = \$350 \div .7 = \$500$

Ans.

Check: Amount Collected − Commission = Net Proceeds
$\quad\quad \$500 − 30\%\ of\ \$500 = \$500 − \$150 = \$350$

● Exercise **2**   Written

1. An agent sent his principal $115.50 after deducting 45% for collecting an account. What was the amount collected? $210

2. Bardin sold a house and lot through Melton Realtors who charged 5% commission. His net proceeds were $14,820. What was the sale price of the house and lot?

3. Home Realty, Inc. charges 6%. They sold a house and remitted $11,562 to the former owner. What was the price of the house?

4. A collection attorney, who charges 35% for collecting overdue accounts, collected an account and remitted $243.75 to his client. How much did he collect?

5. What should be the sale price of a house and lot in order that the owner may realize $27,730 on the sale after paying the real estate agent a commission of 6%?

● Exercise **3**   Written

1. A real estate agent's commissions were $714 for the month of July. This amount was 15% less than his June earnings. How much did he earn in June? $840

2. In the month of September a collection agent's commissions totaled $858, which was 12% below the total for August. What were his total commissions for August?

3. Leon Hyde sold his own house and lot for $13,275, which was 10% less than his asking price. What was his asking price?

4. A real estate agent was able to sell a piece of property for $23,100, which was 5% more than the owner's asking price. What was the asking price? $22,000

5. A real estate agent's total commission for November amounted to $891, which was an 8% increase over the October amount. What was the October amount?

REVIEW ASSIGNMENT **21a**

1. a $225.50 is what percent less than $275?
b $60 is what percent of $24?
c $165 is what percent greater than $120?
d Express $3\frac{1}{2}\%$ as a decimal.

2. A real estate agent sold an apartment house for $82,500. What were the original owner's net proceeds from the sale if the agent charged 6% commission and $346 for expenses?

3. An agency collected 75% of a claim of $1,400 and charged 35% for its services. How much commission did the agency receive?

4. On April 1, the merchandise inventory of the Cushing Furniture Store was $47,483. During the following three months, the store's sales were $66,071, and its purchases were $39,642. The inventory on June 30 was $45,985. What was the store's gross profit for the three months?

5. Last year, C. O. Fox, salesman, received a monthly salary of $475 and a commission on all sales. What rate of commission did he receive on last year's sales of $98,300 if his total earnings for the year, including both salary and commission, were $10,615?

6. Pupil registration in the Wakefield school was 784 last year and 896 the year before. What was the percent increase or decrease in pupil registration?

7. $35\% \times p = \$84$. Find the missing amount.

8. a $15.86 is 65% of what amount?

b Express 1.2% as a common fraction in lowest terms.

c Express 3.45 as a mixed number in simplest form.

d Express $1\frac{3}{4}$ as a decimal.

9. A real estate broker, who charges 5% commission, received $920 for selling a house and lot. What was the selling price of the property?

10. Barry wishes to sell a piece of property at a price that will bring him at least $14,500 after deducting the real estate agent's commission of 5%. What is the lowest price, to the nearest multiple of $10, at which he may sell the property and still realize not less than $14,500?

PART | 21b | Percents (concluded)

To find a number when an amount that is a given percent greater (or smaller) than the number is known. The expression "30 is 25% greater than another number" means that 30 is the result of *adding* 25% of the unknown number to the unknown number.

In the same way, "30 is 25% smaller than another number" means that 30 is the result of *subtracting* 25% of the unknown number from the unknown number.

In such cases, the problem of finding the unknown number is one in finding the number on which the given percent is based. This is a problem in finding the missing factor of a product when the product and the other factor are known.

Example 1

What number increased by 30% of itself equals 26?

The problem tells us that, if 30% of a certain unknown number is added to that number, the sum is 26. Thus,

The unknown number + 30% of the unknown number = 26

(1) The unknown number is the base, or whole, and is therefore 100% of itself, or 100% *of the unknown number*.

(2) The increase is 30% *of the unknown number*.

(3) Adding (2) to (1) gives 130% *of the unknown number*, which is equal to 26.

Solution: *100% × the number = the number*
    +30% × the number = the increase
    130% × the number = the number + the increase
                = 26
        The number = 26 ÷ 130%
                = 26 ÷ 1.3 = 20   **Ans.**

Check: 20 + 30% of 20 = 20 + 6 = 26

Example 2

What number decreased by 30% of itself equals 14?

The problem tells us that if 30% of a certain unknown number is subtracted from that number, the difference is 14. Thus,

The unknown number − 30% of the unknown number = 14

Solution: *100% × the number = the number*
    −30% × the number = the decrease
    70% × the number = the number − the decrease
                = 14
        The number = 14 ÷ 70%
                = 14 ÷ .7 = 20   **Ans.**

Check: 20 − 30% of 20 = 20 − 6 = 14

▶ **Exercise 4**   Written

Find the missing amount in each of the following:

1. ? + 45% of itself = $3,190. $2,200
2. ? + 4% of itself = $31.20.
3. ? increased by 18% of itself equals $885.
4. $24.91 = ? increased by 6%.
5. $369 is 64% greater than ? .
6. $123 is 50% more than ? .
7. ? plus 25% of itself gives $160.

▶ **Exercise 5**   Written

Find the missing amount in each of the following:

1. ? − 15% of itself = $7,820. $9,200
2. ? − 4% of itself = $312.
3. ? decreased by 40% of itself equals $33.60.
4. $11.22 = ? decreased by 15%.
5. $638 is 45% less than ? .
6. ? minus $16\frac{2}{3}$% of itself gives $10.80.
7. $12.30 is $33\frac{1}{3}$% smaller than ? .

▶ **Review of percentage problems.** Exercise 6 provides a review of the six types of problems in percent relationships.

▶ **Exercise 6**   Oral

State the missing amount in each of the following:

1. ? is 60% as much as $30.
2. ? is 25% more than $40.
3. 20 is ? % of 80.
4. $36 is ? % more than $30.
5. 50 is ? % less than 60.
6. 9 is 25% of ? .
7. $20 is 25% more than ? .
8. 24 is 25% less than ? .
9. $48 is $33\frac{1}{3}$% more than ? .
10. 12 is 20% of ? .
11. 24 is ? % more than 20.
12. ? is 6% of $30.
13. 20% more than 40 is ? .
14. $30 is ? % of $50.
15. $20 is ? % more than $15.
16. 25% less than $20 is ? .
17. 12 is $33\frac{1}{3}$% more than ? .
18. 40% less than $20 is ? .
19. $24 is 75% as much as ? .
20. ? is 30% of $200.
21. $10 is ? % less than $50.
22. 9 is ? % of 3.
23. 150% of ? is $18.
24. 10 is ? % of 5.

REVIEW ASSIGNMENT **21**b

    1. a $\frac{3}{4}$% of $192 is what amount?

    b .326 equals what percent?

    c $245 is what percent greater than $210?

    d $3.50 is what percent smaller than $5.25?

    e $8.75 increased by 36% of itself equals what amount?

    f $27.50 decreased by 28% of itself equals what amount?

    g Express $1\frac{1}{2}$% as a decimal.

    2. A collection agency collected 60% of a debt of $635 for Everett Lawrence and charged 32% for making the collection. What amount of money did the agency remit to Mr. Lawrence?

    ✓*By now, if you have faithfully acted upon these frequent reminders, it has become a habit for you to estimate each product and quotient and to check calculations immediately. This habit, as perhaps you have already observed, is your most effective aid in achieving 100% accuracy.*

    3. A real estate agent sold a house and lot for Bartholomew for $29,200. The agent deducted 5% for his commission and $93.65 for expenses. What amount did Bartholomew receive as net proceeds of the sale?

    4. Foster is employed as a salesman for a real estate agency. Yesterday, Foster sold a house for $39,500. The agency's commission was 5% of the selling price. Foster was paid 45% of the agency's commission. How much did Foster receive?

    5. Which salary offer is the better and how much better per month, an offer of $90 a week or an offer of $380 a month?

    ◗ **6. a** $13.30 is 35% of what amount?

    b $41.25 is 10% more than what amount?

    c What amount decreased by 10% of itself gives $31.50?

    ◗ **7.** A collection agent remitted $187 to his principal after deducting 32% for collecting an account. What was the amount collected?

GENERAL REVIEW

    1. a Express $\frac{6}{7}$ as a decimal, to the nearest thousandth.

    b Express .34 as a common fraction in lowest terms.

    c Express .356 as a percent.

    d Express $\frac{5}{14}$ as a percent, to the nearest tenth of a percent.

2. On September 1, Gordon Reynolds had a checkbook balance of $431.20 and a bank statement balance of $546.10. A service charge of $1.55 was reported on the bank statement. The following checks were outstanding: $21.25; $32.70; $18.50; $44.00. Prepare a reconciliation statement.

3. This morning, a cashier started the day with $30 in change. At the end of the day, the cash register totals show that $641.13 has been taken in and $7.65 paid out. There is $663.77 in the cash drawer. How much is the cash over or short?

4. This year the pupil registration in the Northfield school is 729. Last year it was 675. What is the percent increase or decrease in registration?

5. Last year, Wilbur Thornton, a salesman, had sales totaling $77,500. His sales this year are expected to increase 16% over last year. What are Thornton's expected sales for this year?

6. For the last eight weeks of last year, Perry's average sales were $1,448 a week. For the first three weeks of the present year, his sales amounted to $1,660, $2,088, and $1,564, respectively. Find his average weekly sales for the eleven weeks.

7. Stiles, a salesman, receives a monthly salary of $400 and a commission on all sales. Last year his total earnings, including salary and commission, were $9,580. His sales for the year were $95,600. What percent commission did he receive?

8. A salesman receives $435 a month salary, 3% commission on all sales, and an additional $\frac{1}{2}$% on sales in excess of $8,000 in any single month. His sales in July were $9,850. Find his total earnings for the month.

► **9. a** $720 is $4\frac{1}{2}$% of what amount?

b $2.52 is 5% more than what amount?

c What amount decreased by 15% of itself gives $21.25?

► **10.** A salesman receives a salary of $525 a month and a commission of $2\frac{1}{2}$% on all sales. What must be the amount of his sales each month in order that his total monthly income may be $850?

► **11.** Alger's bank statement showed a bank balance of $971.63 as of August 31. His checkbook balance was $957.20. Checks were outstanding for $31.16, $14.73, and $24.90. Among the canceled checks was one for $21.36 that Alger had not recorded in his checkbook. A deposit of $35, mailed on August 31, had been received by the bank too late to appear on the bank statement. Prepare a reconciliation statement.

UNIT Six

Personal Finance Problems

SECTION 22

Borrowing on a Note

When someone borrows money, he is usually required by the lender to sign a promissory note. If the note specifies that interest is to be paid, it is known as an *interest-bearing note*.

PART 22a   Finding Amount Due at Maturity

Using a promissory note. Alan Marsh was a college student. On February 1, 1971, Alan borrowed $800 from his aunt, Ruth Lee, to finish his senior year. In exchange for the loan, Alan signed the following note and gave it to his aunt.

$ 800 00   Albany, New York, February 1   19 71

One year   AFTER DATE ✓   PROMISE TO PAY TO

THE ORDER OF Ruth Lee

Eight Hundred no/100   DOLLARS

PAYABLE AT his home

VALUE RECEIVED WITH INTEREST AT   6   %

No. ---   DUE Feb. 1, 1972   Alan Marsh

Interest-bearing note

In the above note, $800 is the *face* or *principal*. February 1, 1971, is the *date of the note*. One year is the *time*. Ruth Lee, to whom the note is payable, is the *payee*. Alan Marsh, who signed the note, is the *maker*. The *due date*, or *date of maturity*, is February 1, 1972, which is one year from February 1, 1971. The *rate of interest* is 6 percent.

When the note is paid, the payee writes "Paid" across the face, followed by the date and his signature, and returns the note to the maker.

To find the interest on a loan for one year. In the note on page 172, Alan Marsh promises to repay the $800 "with interest at 6%." This means "with interest at the rate of 6% a year."

Since Alan borrows the $800 for exactly one year, the interest he will pay is 6% of $800. The calculation of interest would therefore be:

$$\text{Interest for 1 year} = \$800 \times .06 = \$48$$

The total amount Alan must pay on the date of maturity is the face of the note, $800, plus the interest, $48, which is $848.

To find the interest on a loan for a period other than one year. The interest on a loan is in proportion to the time. For $\frac{1}{4}$ of a year, the interest is $\frac{1}{4}$ of the interest for 1 year; for $1\frac{1}{2}$ years, it is $1\frac{1}{2}$ times the interest for 1 year; and so on.

Thus, on a loan of $400 for $2\frac{1}{2}$ years at 5%, the interest for $2\frac{1}{2}$ years would be as follows;

$$\text{Int. for 1 yr.} = \$400 \times .05 = \$20$$
$$\text{Int. for } 2\frac{1}{2} \text{ yr.} = 2\frac{1}{2} \times \$20 = \$50$$

If the time is given in months, each month is usually considered to be $\frac{1}{12}$ of a year. Thus, the interest for 8 months, for example, would be $\frac{8}{12}$, or $\frac{2}{3}$, of the interest for 1 year.

Exercise 1   Written

1. Find the interest and the total due at maturity in each of the following:

	Face of Note	Time	Rate	Interest	Total Due at Maturity
a	$350	2 yr.	6%	$42.00	$392.00
b	500	3 yr.	7%		
c	450	$1\frac{1}{2}$ yr.	5%		
d	240	3 mo.	7%	$4.20	$244.20
e	375	4 mo.	4%		
f	600	10 mo.	6%		

2. Vincent Tully borrowed $3,500 to start a television repair business. He repaid the principal, with 6% interest, $2\frac{1}{2}$ years later. How much did he repay? $4,025

3. In order to pay an emergency hospital bill, Adam Ludwig borrowed $675 at 5% from a business associate. He repaid the loan 8 months later. How much did he have to pay?

4. To pay his taxes on time and avoid a penalty, Joe Ross borrows $580 on a 9-month note bearing interest at $6\frac{1}{2}\%$. What total amount must he pay on the date of maturity?

REVIEW ASSIGNMENT **22** a

1. a 4% of $242.50 is what amount?

b 1.3 equals what percent?

c $35 is what percent of $140?

d $18 is what percent of $15?

e Express $4\frac{1}{2}\%$ as a decimal.

f Express 18.5% as a decimal.

2. What is the interest on $6,600 for $1\frac{1}{2}$ years at 5%?

3. Walker, who claims 4 exemptions, has gross earnings of $129.37 in one week. Using the tables on pages 106 and 108, find the withholding tax and social security that should be deducted from his gross earnings.

4. Which is the better salary offer and how much better per month, a salary of $575 a month or a salary of $135 a week?

5. A real estate broker sold a house and lot for Dumont for $28,200 and charged 5% for his commission and $165 for expenses. What was Dumont's net proceeds from the sale of the property?

6. Berry is employed at $3.20 an hour for a 40-hour week with time and a half for overtime. Last week he worked $45\frac{1}{2}$ hours. His employer deducted 4.8% for social security and $16.10 for withholding tax. What was Berry's net pay for last week?

7. $45\% \times a = \$144$. Find the missing amount.

8. a $455 is $3\frac{1}{2}\%$ of what amount?

b What amount decreased by 10% of itself equals $76.50?

c $448 equals what amount increased by $\frac{3}{4}$ of itself?

9. A salesman's commission is 5% on all sales. How many dollars' worth of goods must he sell in order to earn $9,750?

PART 22b Interest

Nature of interest. *Interest* is the amount paid for the use of another person's money. It is an expense to the borrower and an income to the lender.

Terms used in interest. If you borrow $1,000 for a year's time at 6%, you pay interest amounting to $1,000 × .06, or $60.

The amount borrowed, $1,000, is the *principal*. The percent, 6%, is the *rate of interest*, or *rate*. The time for which you borrow the money, one year, is the *time*. The $60 you pay for the use of the $1,000 is the *interest*. The sum of the principal and interest, $1,060, is the *amount*.

Unless otherwise stated, the rate of interest is **always an** *annual rate*. It states what percent of the principal is charged for the use of the money for *one year*.

Interest formulas. The principal multiplied by the rate gives the interest for one year.

Principal × Rate = Interest for 1 year

Interest for a period other than one year is found by multiplying the interest for 1 year by the time in years.

Principal × Rate × Time = Interest

Thus, the interest on $1,000 at 6% for 3 years is $180:

$$\$1,000 \times .06 \times 3 = \$180$$

For a period equal to $\frac{1}{5}$ of a year, the interest would be $12:

$$\$1,000 \times .06 \times \tfrac{1}{5} = \$12$$

Exercise 2   Oral

State the interest on:

1. $500 @ 6% for 1 yr.
2. $100 @ 6% for 4 yr.
3. $300 @ 6% for $\frac{1}{2}$ yr.
4. $200 @ 6% for $1\frac{1}{2}$ yr.
5. $400 @ 6% for $\frac{1}{4}$ yr.

6. $700 @ 5% for 1 yr.
7. $300 @ 7% for 2 yr.
8. $200 @ $5\frac{1}{2}$% for 1 yr.
9. $100 @ $4\frac{1}{2}$% for 2 yr.
10. $200 @ 7% for $1\frac{1}{2}$ yr.

Interest for periods of time expressed in days or months. To make interest calculations simple when the time is in days or months, it is common practice to use a 360-day year. The 360-day year, known as the *commercial year*, consists of 12 months of 30 days each.

Under this plan, the interest for 30 days is $\frac{30}{360}$, or $\frac{1}{12}$, of the interest for 1 year; the interest for 60 days is $\frac{60}{360}$, or $\frac{1}{6}$, of the interest for 1 year; and so on.

Thus, since 72 days is $\frac{72}{360}$, or $\frac{1}{5}$, of a year, the computation of the interest on $1,000 at 6% for 72 days will be:

$$\$1,000 \times .06 \times \tfrac{1}{5} = \$60 \times \tfrac{1}{5} = \$12, \text{ int. for 72 da.}$$

Similarly, since 4 months is $\frac{4}{12}$, or $\frac{1}{3}$, of a year, the interest on $900 at 6% for 4 months will be:

$$\$900 \times .06 \times \tfrac{1}{3} = \$54 \times \tfrac{1}{3} = \$18, \text{ int. for 4 mo.}$$

Exercise 3   Written

Find the interest to the nearest cent on:

1. $375 @ 6% for 60 da.
2. $435 @ 2% for 3 mo.
3. $255 @ 7% for 90 da.
4. $380 @ 5% for 6 mo.
5. $230 @ 4% for 4 mo.

6. $460 @ 3% for 120 da.
7. $670 @ 4% for 1 mo.
8. $750 @ 6% for 36 da.
9. $500 @ 5% for 5 mo.
10. $620 @ $4\tfrac{1}{2}$% for 180 da.

To find the rate of interest. If the interest for 1 year and the principal are known, the rate of interest can be found by dividing the interest by the principal.

$$\textbf{Rate of Interest} = \frac{\textbf{Interest for 1 yr.}}{\textbf{Principal}}$$

If the interest given in the problem is for a period other than a year, first find how much the interest would be for one year. Then divide this interest by the principal.

For example, David Hutton paid $15 interest on a loan of $1,000 for 90 days. The interest charge of $15 for 90 days ($\tfrac{1}{4}$ of a year) is equal to a charge of $60 for one year (4 × $15 = $60, or $15 ÷ $\tfrac{1}{4}$ = $60). Hence the rate of interest he paid was 6%.

$$\frac{\$60}{\$1,000} = .06 = 6\%$$

Exercise **4**   Written

Find the rate of interest in each of the following:

Principal	Time	Interest		Principal	Time	Interest
1. $800	30 da.	$4.00 6%		6. $800	3 mo.	$8.00
2. $300	60 da.	$2.50		7. $90	10 mo.	$4.50
3. $200	90 da.	$3.50		8. $180	8 mo.	$8.40
4. $180	2 mo.	$1.20 4%		9. $240	9 mo.	$8.10
5. $360	6 mo.	$5.40		10. $120	15 mo.	$9.00

REVIEW ASSIGNMENT **22 b**

1. a 1.7 equals what percent?
b $40 is what percent of $25?
c Express $5\frac{1}{2}\%$ as a decimal.

2. R. E. Boyer paid $7.50 interest on a loan of $900 for 60 days. What rate of interest did he pay?

3. Find the interest on $800 for 1 year and 6 months at 7%.

4. Barnes and Wallace share profits in the ratio of 3 to 4, respectively. The partnership profits for the year amount to $17,850. What is the amount of Wallace's share of the profits?

5. Judith Culver, a secretary, is paid a yearly salary of $5,330. This is equal to how much a week?

6. Alice Sears works each day from 8:30 a.m. to 4:30 p.m., Monday through Friday, with one hour out for lunch. She is paid $2.95 an hour. What were her gross earnings last week if she worked full time except for $1\frac{1}{2}$ hours lost on Wednesday?

7. The Rolf Collection Agency collected 60% of an outstanding bill of $815 owed to the Shay Sales Company and charged 35% commission. What was the amount of the check remitted to the Shay Sales Company?

8. a $45 is $7\frac{1}{2}\%$ of what amount?
b $5.32 is 5% less than what amount?

9. A real estate broker, who charges 5% commission, received $835 for selling a piece of property. What was the selling price of the property?

10. A collection agent remitted $208 to Johnson & Co. after deducting 36% for collecting a bill. What was the amount collected?

SECTION 23

Borrowing on a Note (concluded)

Usually, a promissory note shows on its face the due date or date of maturity of the note. On the note on page 172, for example, the due date is shown on the last line, and is February 1, 1972.

PART 23a Determining the Date of Maturity

Determining the date of maturity when the time is in months. When the time is given in months, the date of maturity is found by counting the number of months from the date of the note. The date of maturity is the same date in the month of maturity as the date of the note, provided the month of maturity has such a date. If it does not, the date of maturity is the last date in the month of maturity.

Example

Find the date of maturity of a 3-month note dated March 28.

Solution	Explanation
March 28 + 3 mo. = *June 28* **Ans.** *June 28*	The date of the note is March 28. The month of maturity is June, the third month after March. The date of maturity is therefore June 28.

Example

Find the date of maturity of a 3-month note dated March 31.

Solution	Explanation
March 31 + 3 mo. = *June 30* **Ans.** *June 30*	The date of the note is March 31. The month of maturity is June, the third month after March. Since there is no such date as June 31, the date of maturity is June 30, the last date in June.

Exercise 1   Oral

State the date of maturity on each of the following notes:

Date	Time		Date	Time		Date	Time
1. April 7	1 mo.		**4.** Aug. 31	1 mo.		**7.** Jan. 31	3 mo.
2. May 21	3 mo.		**5.** Aug. 31	2 mo.		**8.** Nov. 30	2 mo.
3. Oct. 3	2 mo.		**6.** Aug. 31	3 mo.		**9.** Nov. 30	3 mo.

Determining the date of maturity when the time is in days. When the time is expressed in days, the date of maturity is found by counting, from the date of the note, the number of days stated in the time.

Example

Find the date of maturity of a 90-day note dated March 28.

Solution	Explanation
90 da.	3 da. are left in March after March 28, the date
March 3	of the note. Subtract 3 da. from 90 da., leaving
87	87 da. to carry forward through April.
April 30	Subtract 30 da. for April, leaving 57 da. to carry
57	forward through May.
May 31	Subtract 31 da. for May, leaving 26 da. to carry
June 26	forward into June. The date of maturity is
Ans. *June 26*	therefore June 26.

The accuracy of the subtraction in the foregoing solution may be checked by adding the number of days used in each of the four months. Thus, 3 da. in March + 30 da. in April + 31 da. in May + 26 da. in June = 90 da., the time of the note.

Exercise 2   Written

Find the date of maturity of each of the notes indicated below.

Date	Time		Date	Time		Date	Time
1. Aug. 4	90 da. 11/2		**4.** July 5	60 da.		**7.** Nov. 18	75 da.
2. May 9	60 da.		**5.** Jan. 12	45 da.		**8.** Sept. 7	90 da.
3. Oct. 21	90 da.		**6.** April 3	80 da.		**9.** Mar. 1	30 da.

REVIEW ASSIGNMENT 23a

1. a Express 1.5 as a percent.

b $45 is what percent of $120?

c Express $2\frac{1}{2}\%$ as a decimal.

2. a Express 37.5% as a decimal.

b Find the due date of a 90-day note dated May 17.

c Find the due date of a 3-month note dated May 31.

3. A 60-day note for $375, dated March 8, bears interest at 6%. Find the due date and the amount due at maturity.

4. Burg borrowed $1,350 for 18 months at 5% interest. What was the total amount of interest he paid during the 18 months?

5. The cost of the interest on a loan of $900 for 60 days is $10.50. What is the annual interest rate on this loan?

PART 23b Interest (continued)

The 60-day method of calculating interest at 6%. Sixty days, or 2 months, is $\frac{1}{6}$ of a 360-day year. If the interest rate is 6% for a year, then the rate for 60 days is $\frac{1}{6}$ of 6%, which is 1%.

To find the interest on any sum of money for 60 days at 6%, multiply the principal by .01.

Since 6 days is $\frac{1}{10}$ of 60 days, the interest for 6 days is .001 of the principal. Also, since 600 days is 10 times 60, the interest for 600 days is .1 of the principal.

Hence, we have the following rules:

To find the interest at 6% on any sum of money for:

6 da.,	point off	3	places in the principal	
60 da.,	" "	2	" " "	"
600 da.,	" "	1	" " "	"
6,000 da.,	" "	no	" " "	"

Exercise 3 Oral

State the interest at 6% on:

1.	**2.**	**3.**
a $650 for 6 da.	$190 for 2 mo.	$740 for 6 da.
b $480 for 60 da.	$182 for 6,000 da.	$523 for 600 da.
c $1,300 for 6 da.	$435 for 60 da.	$280 for 60 da.
d $350 for 600 da.	$156 for 2 mo.	$995 for 6,000 da.

To find interest for multiples of 6, 60, or 600 days. When the number of days is a multiple of 6, 60, or 600 days, multiply the interest for 6, 60, or 600 days by 2, 3, or 4, etc., as the case may be.

Example

Find the interest at 6% on $482.50 for 18 days.

Solution	Explanation
$.4825 = int. for 6 da. 3 × $.4825 = $1.4475 **Ans. $1.45**	Since 18 days is 3 times 6 days, the interest for 18 days is 3 times the interest for 6 days.

Exercise **4**   Oral

State the interest at 6% on:

	1.	**2.**	**3.**
a	$250 for 12 da.	$130 for 180 da.	$90 for 42 da.
b	$400 for 18 da.	$120 for 36 da.	$80 for 360 da.
c	$800 for 24 da.	$500 for 48 da.	$450 for 1,200 da.
d	$350 for 120 da.	$110 for 240 da.	$110 for 1,800 da.

To find interest for aliquot parts of 6, 60, or 600 days. When the number of days is an aliquot or fractional part of 6, 60, or 600 days, multiply the interest for 6, 60, or 600 days, as the case may be, by the fraction that represents the part.

Example

Find the interest on $861.20 for 15 da. at 6%.

Solution	Explanation
$8.612 = int. for 60 da. $\frac{1}{4}$ × $8.612 = $2.153 **Ans. $2.15**	Since 15 days is $\frac{1}{4}$ of 60 days, the interest for 15 days is $\frac{1}{4}$ of the interest for 60 days.

FRACTIONAL PARTS OF 6, 60, AND 600 DAYS

	$\frac{1}{10}$	$\frac{1}{6}$	$\frac{1}{5}$	$\frac{1}{4}$	$\frac{1}{3}$	$\frac{1}{2}$	$\frac{2}{3}$	$\frac{3}{4}$	$\frac{5}{6}$
6 da.		1			2	3	4		5
60 da.	6	10	12	15	20	30	40	45	50
600 da.	60	100	120	150	200	300	400	450	500

Exercise 5   Oral

State the interest at 6% on:

1. $1,200 for 1 da.   **7.** $350 for 12 da.   **13.** $360 for 50 da.

2. $900 for 2 da.   **8.** $280 for 15 da.   **14.** $72 for 100 da.

3. $840 for 3 da.   **9.** $270 for 20 da.   **15.** $55 for 120 da.

4. $1,800 for 4 da.   **10.** $320 for 30 da.   **16.** $80 for 150 da.

5. $2,400 for 5 da.   **11.** $210 for 40 da.   **17.** $120 for 200 da.

6. $240 for 10 da.   **12.** $160 for 45 da.   **18.** $140 for 300 da.

REVIEW ASSIGNMENT 23 b

1. a Express 2.1 as a percent.

b $255 is what percent of $170?

c Express $4\frac{1}{4}$% as a decimal.

d Express 15.8% as a decimal.

e Find the due date of a 6-month note dated October 31.

f Find the due date of a 90-day note dated March 15.

2. Wilkins borrowed $450 for 18 months at $6\frac{1}{2}$% interest. What was the total interest he paid during that time?

3. A 120-day, 6% note for $585, is dated June 29.

a Find the due date.

b What will be the amount due at maturity?

4. Last year, the population of Montrose was 27,000. The year before, it was 22,500. What was the percent increase or decrease in the population of Montrose?

5. Greer, a salesman, was paid a monthly salary of $650 and a commission on all sales. His sales last year were $41,750; and his total earnings, including both salary and commission, were $11,140. What rate of commission did he receive?

6. A real estate broker sold some property for Sinclair for $32,750. The broker charged 5% for his commission and $177.55 for expenses. What net proceeds did Sinclair receive?

7. a 75% of what amount is equal to $3.60?

b $25.44 is 4% less than what amount?

c What amount increased by $\frac{2}{5}$ of itself gives $1.05?

8. A used-car salesman, who receives 8% commission, earned $108 on the sale of a car. What was the selling price of the car?

Borrowing from a Bank

A person in need of additional funds usually borrows from an organization that makes a business of lending money. Banks, credit unions, and loan companies are common examples of such businesses.

PART 24a   Borrowing from a Commercial Bank

Giving a note for a short-term loan. A commercial bank may lend money to a person who has a checking account at the bank. If the person is well known at the bank, has a good reputation, owns property, and has a regular income, he can usually obtain a loan by signing a promissory note.

An individual applying at a bank for a loan

The majority of such loans are made for only short periods of time, usually not exceeding 90 days, and are therefore known as *short-term loans*.

Discounting the note. When a bank makes a short-term loan, it usually requires the borrower to pay the interest at the time the loan is granted.

Since the interest is paid in advance, the borrower's note does not bear interest. Such a note is known as a *non-interest-bearing note.*

The following illustration shows the non-interest-bearing note Raymond Benson signed in obtaining a 60-day loan at the National Commercial Bank, Cincinnati, Ohio.

```
$ 625.00                    Cincinnati, Ohio                 May 21, 19--

  Sixty days                                   AFTER DATE     I      PROMISE TO PAY TO

THE ORDER OF National Commercial Bank

  Six Hundred Twenty-five----------------------------------------DOLLARS

PAYABLE AT National Commercial Bank

VALUE RECEIVED WITH INTEREST AT ------%

No. 342    DUE  July 20, 19--              Raymond Benson
```

Non-interest-bearing note

The bank collects the interest by deducting it from the face of the note. The amount the borrower receives is the face of the note less the interest.

Interest collected in advance in this manner is called *bank discount.* The rate of interest charged by the bank is referred to as the *rate of discount,* or *discount rate.* The amount of money that the borrower receives is called the *proceeds.* The loan in such cases is said to be granted, or obtained, by *discounting* the borrower's note.

If the rate of discount at the National Commercial Bank is 6%, the bank discount on Raymond Benson's note, shown above, would be $6.25. This is the interest on $625 for 60 days.

The proceeds he receives would be $618.75, as shown by the following calculations:

Face of note	$625.00
Discount	6.25
Proceeds	$618.75

On July 20, the date of maturity, Raymond Benson will discharge the debt by paying the bank $625, the amount of the face of the note.

Exercise 1   Written

Find the proceeds and due date of each of the following notes. Each note was discounted on the same day as the date of the note.

	Date of Note	Face	Time	Discount Rate	Proceeds	Due Date
1.	July 26	$ 750	60 da.	6%	$742.50	Sept. 24
2.	Sept. 3	1,620	60 da.	6%		
3.	Jan. 16	546	30 da.	6%		
4.	Mar. 6	1,240	30 da.	6%		
5.	June 22	2,355	20 da.	6%		
6.	Dec. 26	1,430	15 da.	6%		

REVIEW ASSIGNMENT **24**a

1. a 2 equals what percent?

b $4\frac{1}{2}\%$ of $328 is what amount?

c $2.40 is what percent of $7.20?

d $1,125 is what percent of $375?

e Express $3\frac{1}{4}\%$ as a decimal.

f Express 33.4% as a decimal.

g Find the due date of a 4-month note dated April 30.

2. On March 25, W. E. Scott discounted at the bank at 6% his 60-day non-interest-bearing note for $325, dated March 25.

a What are the proceeds of the note?

b What is the date of maturity of the note?

c What amount must Scott pay the bank at maturity?

3. A 90-day, 6% note for $925.50 is dated October 8.

a Find the due date.

b What will be the amount due at maturity?

4. What is the rate of interest charged on a loan of $720 for 90 days if the amount of the interest charge is $8.10?

5. What is the interest on $400 for 15 months at $5\frac{1}{2}\%$?

6. Last month, Don Jackson's sales amounted to $5,700. He estimates this month's sales will run 15% more than last month's. What are the estimated sales for this month?

7. Crowley, a salesman, is paid a salary of $425 a month, a 4% commission on all sales, and an additional commission of 1% on all monthly sales in excess of $12,500. His sales for June were $15,150. What were his total earnings for the month?

PART 24b | Interest (continued)

To find interest for any number of days — 1-day method. If the number of days is not an aliquot part or multiple of 6, 60, or 600 days, the interest may be found by the 1-day method.

Under this method, the interest for 6 days is divided by 6, giving the interest for 1 day. This result is then multiplied by the number of days in the problem.

Example

Find the interest on $246 for 53 da. at 6%.

Solution: $.246 = int. for 6 da.

$.246 ÷ 6 = $.041, int. for 1 da.

53 × $.041 = $2.173, int. for 53 da. **Ans. $2.17**

If the interest for 6 days is not evenly divisible by 6, it will be shorter to multiply the interest for 6 days by the number of days and then divide that product by 6.

Example

Find the interest on $635 for 23 days at 6%.

Solution: $.635 = interest for 6 days

23 × $.635 = $14.605

$14.605 ÷ 6 = $2.434   **Ans. $2.43**

Exercise 2   Written

Find the interest at 6% on:

1. $180 for 70 da. $2.10	**7.** $430 for 70 da. $5.02
2. $540 for 80 da.	**8.** $725 for 80 da.
3. $420 for 90 da.	**9.** $334 for 22 da.
4. $660 for 35 da.	**10.** $800 for 38 da.
5. $1,320 for 11 da.	**11.** $400 for 76 da.
6. $390 for 64 da.	**12.** $800 for 52 da.

◑   **To find interest for any number of days — 60-day method.**   The 60-day method can be used to find the interest for any number of days by combining the interest for various aliquot parts of 6, 60, or 600 days.

◑   **Combinations involving 6 days and aliquot parts of 6 days.**   Frequently used combinations of 6 days and aliquot parts of 6 days are:

7 da. = 6 + 1	9 da. = 6 + 3	13 da. = 6 + 6 + 1
8 da. = 6 + 2	12 da. = 6 + 6	14 da. = 6 + 6 + 2

Example

Find the interest at 6% on $1,352.80 for 67 days.

Solution	Explanation
$13 \| 5280 = int. for 60 da.*$	67 da. = 60 da. + 6 da. + 1 da.
6) 1 | 3528 = int. for 6 da.	Write the interest for 60 da.
2255 = int. for 1 da.	Draw a vertical line to take the
$15 \| 1063 = int. for 67 da.$	place of the decimal point. Write
	the interest for 6 da. Divide the
Ans. $15.11	interest for 6 da. by 6 to find the
	interest for 1 da. Add the interest

for 60 da., 6 da., and 1 da. to find the interest for 67 da.

*All calculations should be carried correct to 4 decimal places to insure accuracy in the cents column. The final result is rounded to the nearest cent.

◑ **Exercise 3**   Oral

State the interest at 6% on:

1. $180 for 7 da.	**5.** $300 for 8 da.	**9.** $420 for 7 da.
2. $150 for 8 da.	**6.** $660 for 7 da.	**10.** $2,400 for 9 da.
3. $260 for 9 da.	**7.** $8,000 for 9 da.	**11.** $2,700 for 8 da.
4. $300 for 7 da.	**8.** $900 for 8 da.	**12.** $2,400 for 7 da.

◑ **Exercise 4**   Written

Find the interest at 6% on:

1. $440 for 67 da.	**5.** $844 for 7 da.	**9.** $727 for 12 da.
2. $650 for 68 da.	**6.** $925 for 8 da.	**10.** $898 for 13 da.
3. $734 for 69 da.	**7.** $769 for 9 da.	**11.** $519 for 14 da.
4. $395 for 68 da.	**8.** $685 for 7 da.	**12.** $608 for 13 da.

REVIEW ASSIGNMENT **24b**

1. a 3 is equal to what percent?
b What amount is $3\frac{1}{2}\%$ of $184?
c $31.25 is what percent of $12.50?
d Find the due date of a 4-month note dated July 31.
e Find the interest at 6% on $1,142 for 7 days.

2. On July 22, C. J. Park discounted at the bank at 6% his 60-day non-interest-bearing note for $650, dated July 22.

a What are the proceeds of the note?
b What is the due date?

3. A 90-day, 6% note for $248.85 is dated April 30.
a Find the date of maturity.
b What will be the amount due at maturity?

4. A father willed his estate of $49,500 to his two sons in the ratio of 8 to 7. How much did each son receive?

5. An agency collected 85% of a debt of $400 for Gerald Williamson and charged 45% for making the collection. What amount did the agency remit to Mr. Williamson?

▶ **6. a** $37.40 is 15% smaller than what amount?
b Express 5.38 as a mixed number in simplest form.

PART **24c** Interest (continued)

▶ **Combinations of 60 days and an aliquot part of 60 days.** The following are the most frequently used combinations of 60 days and an aliquot part of 60 days.

| 66 da. = 60 + 6 | 72 da. = 60 + 12 | 80 da. = 60 + 20 |
| 70 da. = 60 + 10 | 75 da. = 60 + 15 | 90 da. = 60 + 30 |

▶ Exercise **5**   Oral

State the interest at 6% on:

1. $350 for 66 da.	**5.** $210 for 80 da.	**9.** $84 for 70 da.
2. $420 for 70 da.	**6.** $160 for 90 da.	**10.** $180 for 90 da.
3. $150 for 72 da.	**7.** $250 for 72 da.	**11.** $160 for 75 da.
4. $320 for 75 da.	**8.** $360 for 80 da.	**12.** $480 for 90 da.

◐ Exercise **6** Written

Find the interest at 6% on:

1. $1,265 for 66 da.   **5.** $1,584 for 90 da.
2. $1,723 for 70 da.   **6.** $775 for 70 da.
3. $895 for 75 da.   **7.** $2,540 for 90 da.
4. $1,645 for 80 da.   **8.** $4,145 for 75 da.

REVIEW ASSIGNMENT **24**c

1. a 1.7 equals what percent?

b 4 equals what percent?

c $.90 is what percent of $2.40?

d $5\frac{1}{2}\%$ of $150 equals what amount?

e Find the interest at 6% on $835.50 for 70 days.

f Express $4\frac{3}{4}\%$ as a decimal.

g Express 135% as a decimal.

2. On May 19, Walter Ross obtained a loan at the Essex National Bank by discounting his 60-day note for $545, dated May 19. The discount rate was 6%.

a What was the amount of the proceeds Mr. Ross received?

b On what date did the note come due for payment?

3. A 30-day note for $450, bearing interest at 6%, is dated July 12.

a What is the due date of the note?

b What is the amount due on the due date?

4. On June 1, Maxon's merchandise inventory was $13,455. Purchases for the month were $9,768. On June 30, the inventory was $12,535. Find the cost of goods sold in June.

5. Herman's sales last year totaled $65,000. His total earnings for the year were $10,950, of which $6,400 was his yearly salary. What percent commission was he paid?

6. Gloves that formerly sold for $3.75 a pair sell now for $4.50. What is the percent increase or decrease in the price?

◐ **7. a** $197.80 is 115% of what amount?

b Express 4.248 as a mixed number in simplest form.

◐ **8.** A salesman's commission rate is 15%. What dollar amount of goods must he sell in order to earn $2,700?

◐ **9.** Hoffman pays his salesclerks a weekly salary of $75, plus a commission of 4% on all sales over $600. What must be the total sales for a clerk to earn $90 in one week?

SECTION 25

Borrowing on Collateral

A bank may require a borrower to pledge some kind of property as a guarantee that the loan will be repaid. The pledged property is called *collateral*. Collateral is often required for a large loan or for a loan to a person whose credit is not well established.

PART 25a   Demand Loans

Collateral notes. A note secured by collateral is called a *collateral note*. Common forms of collateral are stocks, bonds, and life insurance policies. When the loan is repaid, the collateral is returned to the borrower.

Demand notes. Ordinary bank loans are payable at the end of fixed periods of time, such as 30, 60, or 90 days. Collateral loans, however, are often payable "on demand." Such a loan is a *demand loan*, and the note is a *demand note*. The note is interest bearing. Interest is usually payable monthly or quarterly.

DEMAND NOTE

$ 1,000.00   June 15, 19--

On demand_____ I _____ promise to pay to West End State Bank _____
or order, at the Banking House of said Bank in current funds One Thousand --------- DOLLARS
with interest at the rate of _____ 6% _____ per annum, for value received, having deposited with said Bank as
collateral security 40 shares Am. T & T common stock _____

which I hereby authorize said Bank or its President or Cashier to sell without notice at public or private sale at the option of said Bank or of its President or Cashier, in case of the nonperformance of this promise applying the net proceeds the payment of this note, including interest, and accounting to me for the surplus, if any. In case of deficiency I promise to pay to said Bank the amount thereof forthwith after such sale with legal interest, and it is hereby AGREED and UNDERSTOOD that if recourse is had to the collaterals, any excess of collaterals upon this note shall be applicable to any other note or claim held by said Bank against me, and in case of any exchange of, or addition to the collaterals above named, the provisions of this note shall extend to such new or additional collaterals. And if this note is placed in the hands of an attorney at law for collection, or has to be sued on, I agree to pay ten per cent attorney's fees and all expenses incurred in its collection, same to be taxed up in judgment. If collaterals are sold the said Bank is authorized to bid on same at any outside party.

No. _____ 9 _____   Robert C. Paulson
                                                By _____

Demand note

A demand loan is payable when the bank demands payment. The borrower, however, may repay the loan any time before the demand is made. A demand loan is convenient for the borrower when he does not know exactly how long he will need the money.

In the illustration on page 190, Robert Paulsen borrowed $1,000 from West End State Bank on June 15. On that date, he signed the note payable to the bank, on demand. The note bears interest at 6%.

This note is also a collateral note. It states on the face that Paulsen has deposited stock which can be sold by the bank if he does not pay the note when the bank demands payment.

To find the amount due on the date of settlement of a demand note. The amount due is the face of the note plus interest on the face from the date of the note (or date of last interest payment) to the date of settlement. So, the amount due on August 14 in payment of the 6% note for $1,000, dated June 15, would be $1,010.

Face of note	$1,000
Interest on $1,000 — June 15 to Aug. 14 (60 days)	10
Amount due on August 14	$1,010

To find the number of days between two dates. In finding the amount due on the date of settlement of a demand note, you need to find the number of days between two dates.

Example

Find the exact number of days from April 9 to July 7.

Solution		Explanation
	30	Since there are 30 days in April, there are 21 days
	− 9	left in April after April 9 (30 − 9 = 21). There
April	21	are 31 days in May, 30 in June, and 7 in July.
May	31	Adding 21, 31, 30, and 7 gives 89, the number of
June	30	days from April 9 to July 7.
July	7	
Ans.	89	

Exercise 1 Written

1. Find the number of days from:

a Oct. 7 to Jan. 10 95   c Mar. 9 to May 9   e Sept. 3 to Nov. 29

b Oct. 23 to Dec. 17   d May 15 to Aug. 5   f Jan. 12 to Feb. 21

2. For each of the demand notes shown below, find the number of days for which interest is charged, the amount of the interest at 6%, and the total amount due on the date of settlement.

	Face of Note	Date of Note	Date of Settlement		Face of Note	Date of Note	Date of Settlement
a	$824 80 da.	Mar. 3 $10.99 int.	May 22 $834.99 due	e	$1,020	April 27	July 3
b	975	June 10	Sept. 8	f	545	July 15	Sept. 28
c	426	Oct. 21	Dec. 29	g	1,495	Dec. 5	Feb. 9
d	750	Nov. 4	Jan. 13	h	1,640	Sept. 14	Nov. 25

3. Elmer Blake borrowed $930 on his 6% interest-bearing demand note dated May 2. If he paid the note and interest on the following July 11, what amount did he pay? $940.85

4. Roy Coe borrowed $3,600 on his 6% interest-bearing demand note dated November 20. On the following January 27, he settled the note. What amount was due on January 27?

5. A demand note for $1,800, dated March 27, with interest at 6%, was settled in full on June 9. What was the amount due on the date of settlement?

REVIEW ASSIGNMENT 25 a

1. a 1.25 equals what percent?
b 1 equals what percent?
c What amount is $1\frac{1}{2}\%$ of $164?
d $15 is what percent of $135?
e 30% of $19.50 is what amount?
f $\frac{3}{8}$ equals what percent?
g Express 115% as a decimal.
h Express $3\frac{3}{4}\%$ as a decimal.
i Find the number of days from March 28 to June 1.
j Find the interest at 6% on $1,381.70 for 8 days.

2. A demand note for $875, dated August 10, was settled in full on October 24, with interest at 6%. What was the amount due on the date of settlement?

3. If the interest on a loan of $5,850 for 90 days is $87.75, what is the rate of interest?

4. A student obtained marks of 98, 82, 90, and 87 on four tests given recently. What mark must he obtain on his fifth test in order to have an average of 90 for all five tests?

5. Burns sold a piece of property through a real estate broker. The sale price was $21,700. The broker charged $137.25 for expenses and 5% commission. What net amount did Burns receive from the sale of the property?

⊙ **6. a** $22.44 is 12% smaller than what amount?

  b Express 2.432 as a mixed number in simplest form.

  c $36 is $\frac{4}{3}$ of what amount?

PART 25b Mortgages

Real estate mortgages. A person who owns his home can usually obtain a loan by signing a note, sometimes called a *bond*, and giving the lender a *mortgage* on the property. The mortgage serves as security for the repayment of the loan. It gives the lender the right to take possession of the property if payments are not made according to the agreement.

WELCOME TO OUR MORTGAGED HOME

Payment of the interest and principal. Mortgages generally run from 10 to 25 or 30 years with interest payable monthly, quarterly, or semiannually.

If periodic payments to reduce the principal are not required, the full amount of the loan is due for payment at maturity. Most mortgages, however, require a payment against the principal on each interest date so that the loan will be repaid gradually over the life of the mortgage. In such cases, the interest due on any interest date is based upon the unpaid balance of principal in force since the last interest payment.

Assume, for example, that a 6% mortgage of $5,000 requires the quarterly payment of interest and a payment of $100 on the principal. The quarterly interest will be based on an unpaid balance of $5,000 for the first quarter, $4,900 for the second, $4,800 for the third, and so on.

Exercise 2   Written

1. A mortgage of $4,800 requires a quarterly payment of $80 on the principal. Find the amount of the unpaid balance in force during the first, second, third, fourth, and fifth quarters.

$4,800 $4,720

2. A mortgage of $5,000 requires a semiannual payment of $125 on the principal. Find the amount of the unpaid balance in force during the first, second, and third semiannual periods.

3. Find the semiannual interest on each of the following:

a $5,657 @ 6% $169.71   **b** $2,480 @ 5%   **c** $4,940 @ 7%

To find the interest due on an interest date of a mortgage, take $\frac{1}{2}$ of the interest for one year if the interest is payable semiannually, $\frac{1}{4}$ if payable quarterly, or $\frac{1}{12}$ if payable monthly.

4. Find the quarterly interest on each of the following:

a $3,425 @ 6%   **b** $1,975 @ 7%   **c** $4,350 @ 5%

5. On March 1, Nelson Kellogg placed a $2,000 mortgage at 6% on his home. He agreed to pay the interest quarterly with a payment of $50 on the principal. What total amount will he pay on (a) June 1, (b) September 1, and (c) December 1?

$80 $79.25

6. Ellen Holt placed a $4,800 mortgage at 7% on her home. She agreed to pay interest quarterly, with a payment of $100 on the principal. What amount was she required to pay at the end of (a) the first, (b) the second, and (c) the third quarters?

REVIEW ASSIGNMENT 25b

1. a 60% of $82.40 is what amount?

b What amount is $4\frac{1}{4}$% of $360?

c Express 125% as a decimal.

d Express $2\frac{3}{4}$% as a decimal.

e Find the number of days from April 3 to June 18.

f Find the interest at 6% on $842.60 for 75 days.

2. A demand note for $1,300, dated March 22, bearing interest at 6%, was settled in full on May 29. What was the amount due on the date of settlement?

3. An 80-day note for $315.65, dated May 1, bears interest at 6%.

a Find the due date of the note.

b Find the amount due at maturity.

4. Find the interest on $1,680 for $2\frac{1}{2}$ years at $5\frac{1}{2}$%.

5. B. E. Cooper gave an agency an account amounting to $375 to collect. The agency collected 60% of the amount and charged 40% for collecting. How much did Cooper receive?

6. Scott works on an 8-hour day basis, at $2.65 an hour, with time and a half for overtime. During one week he worked the hours shown below. Find his gross earnings for the week.

Mon., 8; Tues., 7; Wed., $9\frac{1}{2}$; Thurs., $10\frac{1}{2}$; Fri., 10

◗ **7. a** What amount decreased by $7\frac{1}{2}\%$ of itself gives $52.91?
b $186 is $\frac{3}{2}$ of what amount?
c Express 3.275 as a mixed number in simplest form.

◗ **8.** A salesman was paid a commission of $935 for selling a house and lot. His commission was figured at the rate of 5%. What was the selling price of this house and lot?

PART 25c Interest (continued)

◗ **Combinations of aliquot parts of 60 days and 6 days.** There are many combinations that may be made with aliquot parts of 60 days and 6 days. The following examples are suggestive:

16 da. = 10 + 6	27 da. = 15 + 6 + 6	37 da. = 30 + 6 + 1
21 da. = 15 + 6	36 da. = 30 + 6	40 da. = 20 + 20

Example

Find the interest at 6% on $469.75 for 19 days.

Solution	Explanation
6)$4 | 6975 *int. for 60 da.*	19 da. = 10 + 6 + 3
7829 *int. for 10 da.*	Write the interest for 60 da. Since
2) | 4698 *int. for 6 da.*	the number of days in the problem
2349 *int. for 3 da.*	is less than 60, draw a line under the
$1 | 4876 *int. for 19 da.*	interest for 60 da. to indicate that it

is not to be added to the subsequent

Ans. $1.49

interests.

Divide the interest for 60 da. by 6 to find the interest for 10 da. Move the decimal point one place to the left in the interest for 60 da. to find the interest for 6 da. Divide the interest for 6 da. by 2 to find the interest for 3 da. Add the interest for 10 da., 6 da., and 3 da. to find the interest for 19 da.

▶ **Exercise 3**   Written

Find the interest at 6% on:

1.	2.	3.
a $356 for 16 da.	$228 for 37 da.	$432 for 29 da.
b $467 for 21 da.	$602 for 38 da.	$616 for 49 da.
c $951 for 27 da.	$344 for 40 da.	$522 for 72 da.
d $743 for 26 da.	$736 for 46 da.	$230 for 76 da.
e $690 for 32 da.	$504 for 52 da.	$392 for 81 da.
f $543 for 36 da.	$184 for 19 da.	$608 for 86 da.

REVIEW ASSIGNMENT **25** c

1. a 70% of $28.30 is what amount?
b What amount is $3\frac{1}{4}$% of $160?
c Express 110% as a decimal.
d Find the number of days from May 10 to September 15.
e Find the interest at 6% on $762.14 for 16 days.

2. A 6% demand note for $825, dated June 1, was paid in full on August 9. What was the amount of the payment?

3. A cashier had $50 in change at the beginning of the day. At the close of the day, the cash register totals showed that $462.77 had been taken in and $35.41 paid out. The cash in the money drawer at the close of the day was $476.36. By how much was the cash over or short?

4. For the first four months of the year, the sales of the Winton Grocery averaged $85,488 a month. For the next two months, the sales were $96,744 and $79,704, respectively. What were the average monthly sales for the six months?

5. Fred Crandall is paid a commission of 8% on all sales. In addition, he receives a commission of 3% on all sales in excess of $900 per week. Last week Crandall's sales amounted to $1,565. What were his total earnings for the week?

▶ **6. a** $585 is 4% of what amount?
b $360 is $\frac{5}{4}$ of what amount?
c $25.76 is 15% more than what amount?

▶ **7.** A salesman is paid $90 a week, plus 10% commission on that part of sales in excess of $800 per week. If he wishes to earn $150 next week, what must be his total sales for the week?

▶ **8.** A collector sent his principal $255 after deducting 32% for collecting a bill. What was the amount of the bill collected?

SECTION 26

Borrowing from a Credit Union or Finance Company

Credit unions and consumer finance companies have been organized to make loans to persons of limited means who have not built up an acceptable credit rating at any bank. Loans by these organizations are repaid in installments, usually monthly. Such loans are called *installment loans*, or *consumer loans*, to distinguish them from single-payment loans, which are payable in one amount at the end of the loan period. For many persons, an installment loan is easier to repay than a single-payment loan.

PART 26a   Figuring the Finance Charge

Finance charge of a credit union. A *credit union* is a lending organization made up of persons who have something in common, such as the same occupation. Thus, the teachers in a certain city may form a credit union. Each member is required to purchase at least one share in the organization, ordinarily priced at $5 a share. The money the credit union receives from the sale of the shares is loaned to members who wish to borrow.

When a loan is made, the borrower receives the face amount of the loan. This amount is repaid in equal monthly installments. At the end of each month, the borrower pays the installment that is due. He also pays one month's interest on the unpaid balance that has been in force during the month. The highest interest rate charged by credit unions is 1% a month. This is equal to 12% a year.

The amount the borrower receives on the date of the loan is known as the *amount financed*. The interest he pays is called a *finance charge*.

Schedule of installment payments. Shown below is a schedule of monthly payments of interest and principal on a loan of $200 granted by a credit union to one of its members. The loan was repaid in four monthly payments of $50 each, plus 1% interest on the unpaid balance.

$200 LOAN REPAID IN 4 MONTHLY INSTALLMENTS WITH INTEREST AT 1% ON UNPAID BALANCES

End of —	Unpaid Balance	Finance Charge: 1% of Unpaid Balance	Payment on Principal	Total Payment
1st month	$200.00	$2.00	$50.00	$52.00
2d month	150.00	1.50	50.00	51.50
3d month	100.00	1.00	50.00	51.00
4th month	50.00	.50	50.00	50.50
Total		$5.00	$200.00	$205.00

The finance charge due at the end of each month was 1% of the corresponding unpaid balance. The total payment was the finance charge plus the $50 payment on the principal.

Exercise 1   Written

1. For each loan, prepare a schedule of monthly payments of interest and principal like the one shown above.

	Amount Financed	Monthly Repayment Plan		
		Number of Payments	Payment on Principal	Finance Charge on Unpaid Balance
a	$100	4	$25	1% Total $102.50
b	150	5	30	1%
c	240	6	40	$\frac{3}{4}$%
d	400	5	80	$\frac{1}{2}$%

2. Koy borrowed $175 from a credit union and repaid it in five monthly payments of $35 plus interest at 1% on the unpaid balance.

   a What was the total finance charge on the loan? $5.25

   b What was the total amount he paid the credit union?
                                                         $180.25

3. A member borrows $360 from his credit union, agreeing to repay it in six equal monthly payments plus a finance charge of .8% a month on the unpaid balance. What will be the total finance charge?

Finance charge of a finance company. A consumer finance company is in business to make a profit by lending money to anyone who can meet its credit requirements. Most finance companies and many credit unions use repayment plans in which the total payment each month is the same amount. This method of payment is called the *level payment plan*.

For example, in the case of one finance company, a loan of $100 for 12 months is repaid in twelve monthly payments of $9 each. The total of these payments is 12 × $9, or $108. Since the amount financed is $100, the finance charge is $108 − $100, or $8.

Exercise 2   Written

1. For each of the following loans, find the total amount paid to the finance company and the finance charge on the loan.

	Amount of Loan	Monthly Payments		Total Paid	Finance Charge
		Number	Amount		
a	$800	24	$40.27	$966.48	$166.48
b	100	6	18.20		
c	300	12	28.65		
d	400	18	26.95		
e	500	24	25.90		

2. Walter Howes can borrow $350 from a consumer finance company and repay it in 9 monthly payments of $42.95 each. How much will the finance charge cost him? $36.55

3. If a loan of $700 is repaid in 24 monthly payments of $35.88 each, how much is the finance charge?

REVIEW ASSIGNMENT 26 a

1. **a** 135% of $95 is what amount?
   b What amount is 12½% of $18.80?
   c Express 95½% as a decimal.
   d Find the number of days from August 24 to November 6.
   e Find the interest at 6% on $809.75 for 19 days.

2. Proctor borrowed $200 from a consumer finance company. He repaid the loan in 6 monthly payments of $36.20 each. What was the amount of the finance charge?

3. Milton Fuller, a salesman, made sales last year totaling $84,500. His sales this year are expected to run 18% ahead of last year. What are Fuller's expected sales for this year?

4. Three years ago an office employee was receiving an annual salary of $5,000. On January 1 of each year since that time, he has received a 10% increase. What is his present salary?

5. Ormsby works from 9:00 a.m. to 5:30 p.m. each day, Monday through Friday, with one hour out for lunch. What were his gross earnings last week at $3.65 an hour if he worked full time except for $2\frac{1}{2}$ hours lost on Monday?

❷ **6.** $65.34 is 35% more than what amount?

❷ **7.** Roberts works on an 8% straight-commission basis. How many dollars' worth of goods must he sell in order to earn $450?

❷ **8.** A real estate agent was paid $685 for selling a house and lot. What was the selling price of the property if the commission was figured at the rate of 5%?

PART 26b Interest (continued)

❷ **Combinations using parts of aliquot parts of 60 days.** Frequently the interest for a given number of days can be built up by finding the interest for an aliquot part of 60 days and adding to that amount an aliquot part of itself. For example:

11 da. = 10 + 1 ($\frac{1}{10}$ of 10)	25 da. = 20 + 5 ($\frac{1}{4}$ of 20)
22 da. = 20 + 2 ($\frac{1}{10}$ of 20)	35 da. = 30 + 5 ($\frac{1}{6}$ of 30)
23 da. = 20 + 2 ($\frac{1}{10}$ of 20) +	41 da. = 30 + 10 ($\frac{1}{3}$ of 30) +
1 ($\frac{1}{2}$ of 2)	1 ($\frac{1}{10}$ of 10)

Example

Find the interest at 6% on $897.50 for 11 days.

Solution	Explanation
6)8 | 9750 = int. for 60 da.	11 da. = 10 da. + 1 da.
$1 | 4958 = int. for 10 da.	Since 10 da. is $\frac{1}{6}$ of 60 da., the interest for 10 da. is the interest
| 1496 = int. for 1 da.	for 60 da. divided by 6.
$1 | 6454 = int. for 11 da.	Since 1 da. is $\frac{1}{10}$ of 10 da., the interest for 1 day is found by
Ans. $1.65	moving the decimal point 1 place to the left in the interest for 10 da., or by shifting the figures one place to the right.

❯ Exercise **3**   Written

Find the interest at 6% on:

1.	2.	3.
a $432 for 11 da.	$304 for 51 da.	$516 for 44 da.
b $744 for 31 da.	$768 for 22 da.	$720 for 50 da.
c $636 for 41 da.	$529 for 23 da.	$345 for 17 da.
d $543 for 43 da.	$855 for 28 da.	$688 for 25 da.
e $867 for 47 da.	$486 for 33 da.	$277 for 35 da.
f $390 for 49 da.	$252 for 34 da.	$894 for 71 da.
g $985 for 45 da.	$125 for 39 da.	$464 for 82 da.

REVIEW ASSIGNMENT **26**b

1. a What amount is 140% of $65?
b $2\frac{1}{4}$% of $300 is what amount?
c $12\frac{1}{2}$% of $4.16 equals what amount?
d .0436 is equal to what percent?
e Find the number of days from June 4 to October 7.
f Find the interest at 6% on $1,341.75 for 11 days.

2. Winston can borrow $250 from a consumer finance company and repay it in 18 monthly payments of $17.25 each. What will be the cost of the finance charge on the loan?

3. A 6% note for $275, dated April 22, was paid in full on June 29. What was the amount of the June 29 payment?

4. Find the due date and the amount due at maturity on a 75-day, 6% note for $1,655, dated August 15.

5. Interest amounting to $5.25 is charged on a loan of $900 for 30 days. What rate of interest is charged on this loan?

6. Horner, a salesman, receives a monthly salary of $550 and a commission on all sales. Last year his total sales were $73,750; and his total earnings, including both salary and commission, were $12,500. What percent commission was he paid?

❯ **7. a** $35.75 is 30% more than what amount?
b $37.29 is 45% less than what amount?
c $9.36 is $\frac{4}{3}$ of what amount?

❯ **8.** A salesman is paid $450 a month and a commission of 5% on sales in excess of $8,000 in any month. What must be the total of his sales for one month in order that his total earnings for the month may be $750?

SECTION 27

Borrowing from Other Agencies

Installment loans may also be obtained from personal loan departments of commercial banks and from industrial banks.

PART 27a Figuring the Installment Payments

Borrowing from the personal loan department of a commercial bank. At some banks the borrower receives the face amount of the loan, which is the amount financed. Interest is figured on this amount at a stated annual rate for the time the loan is to run. The total of the amount financed and the interest, or finance charge, is repaid in equal monthly installments.

Example

You wish to borrow $300 and repay it in six monthly installments. The personal loan department of a local bank will make the loan under the agreement that you pay interest on that amount at the yearly rate of 6% and that you repay the total of the face amount and the interest in six equal monthly installments.
 a What will be the total of your payments to the bank?
 b What will be the amount of each monthly payment?

Solution

(a) *Amount financed* $300.00
     Finance charge: Int. @ 6% on $300 for 6 mo.   9.00
     Total payments $309.00 **Ans.**
(b) *$309.00 ÷ 6 = $51.50* **Ans.**

At many banks the loan is made on a discount basis, and the borrower receives the face amount less the interest. If the loan above were handled this way, you would receive $300 − $9, or $291. The monthly payments would be $300 ÷ 6, or $50. The finance charge is the interest, $9. The amount financed is the proceeds, $291.

Borrowing from an industrial bank. Loans by industrial banks are usually made on the discount basis. Usually there is a service charge in addition to the interest. The sum of the interest and service charge represents the finance charge. This sum is deducted from the face amount, and the borrower receives the proceeds. Repayment of the face amount is made in weekly or monthly installments.

Exercise 1   Written

1. Each loan shown below was obtained at the personal loan department of a bank. Interest at the given annual rate was added to the face, and the total was paid in equal monthly payments. For each loan, find the amount of each monthly payment.

	Face of Loan	Interest— Yearly Rate	Terms of Payment of Total Principal and Interest
a	$300	6%	12 equal monthly payments $26.50
b	450	6%	12 equal monthly payments
c	200	6%	8 equal monthly payments
d	400	6%	10 equal monthly payments

2. Pitkin obtained a bank loan on his note for $450 and agreed to repay $450 in 15 equal monthly payments. The bank deducted in advance 15 months' interest at the rate of 6%.

   a What was the amount of the finance charge on this loan?

   b What proceeds did Pitkin receive? $416.25

3. Flynn obtained a bank loan on his note for $276 and agreed to repay $276 in 12 equal monthly payments. The bank deducted 12 months' interest at 6% and a service charge of $7.92.

   a What was the amount of the finance charge on this loan?

   b What proceeds did Flynn receive?

   c What was the amount of each monthly payment?

Figuring the finance charge per $100 of amount financed. To comply with the laws on installment loans, the lender has to figure the finance charge per $100 of amount financed. Dividing the finance charge by the amount financed gives the finance charge per $1. Multiplying that quotient by 100 gives the charge per $100. (The expression "FC/100" is often used as a symbol for "finance charge per $100 of amount financed.")

$$\text{Finance Charge per \$100 of Amount Financed} = \frac{\text{Finance Charge}}{\text{Amount Financed}} \times 100$$

Some persons prefer to multiply first and then divide, using the modified formula,

$$\frac{\text{Finance Charge per \$100}}{\text{of Amount Financed}} = \frac{\text{Finance Charge} \times 100}{\text{Amount Financed}}$$

Thus, if the finance charge is \$35.42 on a loan of \$235, the finance charge per \$100 of amount financed is \$15.07, as shown below.

$$\frac{\$35.42 \times 100}{235} = \frac{\$3,542}{235} = \$15.072, \text{ or } \$15.07$$

Exercise 2   Written

1. Find the finance charge per \$100 of amount financed.

	Amount Financed	Finance Charge			Finance Charge	Amount Financed
a	\$300	\$ 65.10 \$21.70	d		\$44.20	\$680
b	\$400	\$129.75	e		\$81.50	\$250
c	\$500	\$113.62	f		\$70.00	\$930

2. Carson borrowed \$750 from a consumer finance company and repaid it in 30 monthly payments of \$32.70 each.

a What was the finance charge on the loan?

b What was the amount financed?

c What was the finance charge per \$100 of amount financed?

3. Hiller obtained a loan at his bank by signing a note for \$400 and agreeing to repay that amount in 12 equal monthly payments. The bank deducted in advance 12 months' interest at the yearly rate of $7\frac{1}{2}\%$.

a What was the finance charge on the loan?

b What was the amount financed?

c What was the finance charge per \$100 of amount financed?

Determining the annual percentage rate. To comply with the laws on installment loans, the lender must tell the borrower what annual percentage rate is charged on the loan. *Annual percentage rate* means, in effect, the annual interest rate represented by the finance charge.

Calculating the annual percentage rate involves the use of a complicated formula. Tables, however, have been prepared with which the lender can easily find the rate. Two sections of the tables are shown at the top of page 205.

In the tables, the annual percentage rate for any loan is determined by the number of monthly payments and the finance charge per \$100 of the amount financed.

ANNUAL PERCENTAGE RATE TABLE FOR MONTHLY PAYMENT PLANS

Number of Payments	ANNUAL PERCENTAGE RATE										
	$10\frac{3}{4}\%$	11%	$11\frac{1}{4}\%$	$11\frac{1}{2}\%$	$11\frac{3}{4}\%$	12%	$12\frac{1}{4}\%$	$12\frac{1}{2}\%$	$12\frac{3}{4}\%$	13%	$13\frac{1}{4}\%$
	FINANCE CHARGE PER $100 OF AMOUNT FINANCED										
6	3.16	3.23	3.31	3.38	3.45	3.53	3.60	3.68	3.75	3.83	3.90
12	5.92	6.06	6.20	6.34	6.48	6.62	6.76	6.90	7.04	7.18	7.32
18	8.73	8.93	9.14	9.35	9.56	9.77	9.98	10.19	10.40	10.61	10.82
24	11.58	11.86	12.14	12.42	12.70	12.98	13.26	13.54	13.82	14.10	14.38
30	14.48	14.83	15.19	15.54	15.89	16.24	16.60	16.95	17.31	17.66	18.02

Number of Payments	ANNUAL PERCENTAGE RATE										
	$24\frac{1}{2}\%$	$24\frac{3}{4}\%$	25%	$25\frac{1}{4}\%$	$25\frac{1}{2}\%$	$25\frac{3}{4}\%$	26%	$26\frac{1}{4}\%$	$26\frac{1}{2}\%$	$26\frac{3}{4}\%$	27%
	FINANCE CHARGE PER $100 OF AMOUNT FINANCED										
6	7.27	7.34	7.42	7.49	7.57	7.64	7.72	7.79	7.87	7.95	8.02
12	13.76	13.91	14.05	14.20	14.34	14.49	14.64	14.78	14.93	15.07	15.22
18	20.50	20.72	20.95	21.17	21.39	21.61	21.83	22.05	22.27	22.50	22.72
24	27.49	27.79	28.09	28.39	28.69	29.00	29.30	29.60	29.90	30.21	30.51
30	34.72	35.10	35.49	35.88	36.26	36.65	37.04	37.43	37.82	38.21	38.60

Assume, for example, that the finance charge per $100 for a 6-payment loan is $3.40. In the table, read across on the 6-payment line to the value nearest $3.40. This is $3.38 in the $11\frac{1}{2}\%$ column. The annual percentage rate for this loan is therefore $11\frac{1}{2}\%$.

If the finance charge per $100 falls half way between two adjacent columns, use the higher percentage rate. For example, on the 6-payment line, $3.64 is half way between $3.60 in the $12\frac{1}{4}\%$ column and $3.68 in the $12\frac{1}{2}\%$ column. Hence, $12\frac{1}{2}\%$ is selected as the rate represented by $3.64.

Exercise 3　Written

Use the tables above for finding the annual percentage rate.

1. Find the annual percentage rate.

	No. of Payments	FC/100			No. of Payments	FC/100	
a	6	$ 3.62	$12\frac{1}{4}\%$	h	12	$14.27	$25\frac{1}{2}\%$
b	6	3.65		i	18	20.65	
c	12	6.30		j	24	29.15	
d	18	10.50		k	18	22.61	
e	24	12.90		l	30	36.00	
f	30	16.75		m	24	28.84	
g	6	7.45		n	12	14.86	

2. Wallace borrowed $300 which he repaid in **12 monthly** payments of $26.75 each.

   a What was the finance charge on this loan?

   b What was the finance charge per $100 of amount financed?

   c What was the annual percentage rate? $12\frac{3}{4}\%$

3. Sue Lee borrowed $250. She repaid the loan in 18 monthly payments of $17 each.

   a What was the finance charge per $100 of amount financed?

   b What was the annual percentage rate?

4. Gray repaid a loan of $500 in 30 monthly payments of $22.60 each. Find the annual percentage rate on this loan.

REVIEW ASSIGNMENT 27a

1. a What amount is 115% of $72?

   b $16\frac{2}{3}\%$ of $32.70 equals what amount?

   c Give the decimal equivalent of $94\frac{1}{4}\%$.

   d Find the interest on $704.81 for 22 days at 6%.

2. You can borrow $300 from a consumer finance company and pay it back in 24 monthly payments of $16.15 each. How much is the finance charge on this loan?

3. On a loan of $350 there was a finance charge of $24.52. The total of the loan and finance charge was repaid in 12 equal monthly payments.

   a What was the finance charge per $100 of amount financed?

   b What was the annual percentage rate? (Use the tables on page 205.)

4. Miller borrowed $450 at his bank for 12 months. The bank charged 6% interest on the loan. Miller repaid the total of the loan and interest in 12 equal monthly payments. What was the amount of each payment?

5. A real estate agent sold some property for Roberts for $35,650. How much did Roberts receive if the agent deducted $4\frac{1}{2}\%$ for his commission and $243.75 for expenses?

▶ **6.** Benson's checkbook balance on March 1 was $816.52. In making a reconciliation statement, he found that he had no record in his checkbook of a deposit of $35 and a check he had written for $15.35. He also found that a deposit of $20 had been entered twice in his checkbook and that a check for $42.30 had been recorded as $24.30. What was his correct checkbook balance?

PART 27b Interest (continued)

To find interest at 6% for any number of months. Interest is proportional to the time. For example, 1 month is $\frac{1}{2}$ of 2 months. The interest for 1 month is therefore $\frac{1}{2}$ times the interest for 2 months. Similarly, since 3 months is $1\frac{1}{2}$ times 2 months, the interest for 3 months is $1\frac{1}{2}$ times the interest for 2 months. Likewise, the interest for 4 months is 2 times the interest for 2 months; and so on.

Thus, since the interest on $300 at 6% for 2 months is $3,

Int. on $300 at 6% for 1 mo. $= \frac{1}{2} \times \$3.00 = \$1.50$

Int. on $300 at 6% for 3 mo. $= 1\frac{1}{2} \times \$3.00 = \$4.50$, etc.

Exercise 4 Oral

State the interest at 6% on:

1. $225 for 2 mo.   4. $150 for 4 mo.   7. $80 for 7 mo.
2. $340 for 1 mo.   5. $200 for 5 mo.   8. $70 for 5 mo.
3. $100 for 3 mo.   6. $120 for 8 mo.   9. $130 for 1 mo.

❯ **Interchanging the principal and the time expressed in days.** In computing interest, the principal and the time in days may be interchanged without affecting the result. For example, at 6%, the interest on $30 for 600 days and the interest on $600 for 30 days are the same amount, $3.

This principle can often be applied to simplify interest calculations. For example, the interest at 6% on $800 for 116 days can be computed easily by finding the interest on $116 for 800 days, as shown below.

```
3 )$11 | 6000  = int. for 600 da.        Hence, the interest on $800
     3 | 8667  = int. for 200 da.        for 116 days is $15.47.
    15 | 4667  = int. for 800 da.
       |
```

❯ Exercise 5 Oral

State the interest at 6% on:

1. $600 for 87 da.   6. $240 for 61 da.   11. $300 for 44 da.
2. $60 for 125 da.   7. $1,800 for 22 da.   12. $900 for 26 da.
3. $6,000 for 35 da.   8. $12,000 for 19 da.   13. $3,000 for 82 da.
4. $600 for 46 da.   9. $30 for 140 da.   14. $200 for 69 da.
5. $6,000 for 45 da.   10. $90 for 220 da.   15. $15 for 208 da.

⊙ **Exercise 6**   Written

Find the interest at 6% on:

1. $800 for 142 da.   6. $70 for 136 da.   11. $2,400 for 97 da.
2. $900 for 133 da.   7. $30 for 162 da.   12. $120 for 145 da.
3. $700 for 115 da.   8. $15 for 155 da.   13. $180 for 129 da.
4. $80 for 127 da.   9. $1,200 for 110 da.   14. $240 for 107 da.
5. $90 for 153 da.   10. $1,800 for 139 da.   15. $3,000 for 81 da.

REVIEW ASSIGNMENT 27 b

1. **a** Find 142% of $13.
   b How much is $16\frac{2}{3}\%$ of $45.90?
   c Express $96\frac{3}{4}\%$ as a decimal.
   d $2.25 is what percent less than $3.00?
   e Find the number of days from April 10 to July 5.
   f Find the interest on $387.35 for 67 days at 6%.

2. Rex Brown can borrow $175 from his local bank and repay it in 12 monthly payments of $15.45 each. What is the amount of the finance charge on this loan?

3. On a loan of $375 there will be a finance charge of $83.25. The sum of the loan and the finance charge are to be repaid in 18 equal monthly payments.
   a What is the finance charge per $100 of amount financed?
   b What is the annual percentage rate on this loan? (Use the tables on page 205.)

4. You wish to borrow $270 at your bank for 12 months. The bank will charge 6% interest and will require you to repay the total of the loan and the interest in 12 equal monthly payments. What will be the amount of each payment?

5. A salesman sold $825 worth of goods on Monday and $924 worth on Tuesday. What was the percent increase or decrease in his sales?

⊙ 6. **a** $5.40 is $4\frac{1}{2}\%$ of what amount?
   b $17.94 is 15% more than what amount?

⊙ 7. A saleslady is paid $72.50 a week plus a commission on all sales in excess of $1,100 in any single week. Last week her total sales amounted to $1,830, and her total earnings for the week were $83.45. What rate of commission did she receive?

SECTION 28

Installment Buying

Automobiles, television sets, record players, washing machines, furniture, clothing, and many other articles are often purchased on the installment plan. This method of buying is known also as the deferred payment or time payment plan.

PART 28a | Figuring Finance Charges and Installment Payments

Finance charge. The installment price of an article is usually higher than the cash price. In pricing an article for installment sale, the merchant adds a finance charge to the cash price. The purpose of this charge is to pay the merchant for interest on his money and to cover the extra cost of doing business on an installment basis.

If there are no other charges, the finance charge is the amount by which the installment price exceeds the cash price.

Installment payments. At the time of purchase, the installment purchaser may be required to make a *down payment* of part of the installment price. He is also required to sign an installment contract in which he agrees to pay the unpaid balance in a series of payments at stated intervals, usually monthly or weekly.

Example

A chair in a furniture store bears a cash price of $50. The install-
ment terms are $10 down and $4.50 a month for 10 months.
  a What is the installment price of the chair?
  b How much is the finance charge?
  c By what percent does the installment price exceed the cash
  price?

Solution	Explanation
Down payment $10.00 *Installments* — 10 × $4.50 45.00 *(a) Installment price* $55.00 *Cash price* $50.00 *(b) Finance charge* $ 5.00 (c) $\dfrac{\$\,5.00}{\$50.00} = 10\%$, *excess of in-* *stallment price over* *cash price.*	(a) The installment price is the sum of the down payment and the installment payments. (b) The finance charge is the difference between the install-ment price and the cash price. (c) The percent of excess is the finance charge divided by the cash price.

Exercise 1   Written

Find (a) the installment price, (b) the finance charge, and
(c) the percent by which the installment price exceeds the cash
price in each of the following:

	Article	Cash Price	Installment Terms
1.	Color TV	$400	$60 down; $31 a month for 12 months (a) $432 (b) $32 (c) 8%
2.	Floor Polisher	90	$15 down; $3 a week for 28 weeks
3.	Power Mower	175	$20 down; $11 a month for 16 months
4.	Dryer	250	$35 down; $13.75 a month for 18 months

Exercise 2   Written

1. Find the missing item in each of the installment terms.

	Article	Install-ment Price	Installment Terms	
a	Carpeting	$320	$50 down; $18 a month for ? months	15 mos.
b	Jewelry	150	$25 down; $2.50 a week for ? weeks	
c	Recorder	70	$10 down; ? a month for 8 months	$7.50
d	Camera	50	$ 5 down; ? a week for 15 weeks	

2. A record player can be purchased for $11 down and $8.25 a month for 12 months. What is the installment price of this record player?

3. A radio that sells for $40 cash may be purchased for $5.50 down and $2.75 a month for 14 months. By what percent does the installment price exceed the cash price?

4. A washer can be bought for $225 by paying $45 as a down payment and the balance in equal monthly payments of $7.50 each. How many months will it take the installment buyer to pay for this washer?

5. A watch can be bought for $85 by paying $10 down and the balance in 12 equal monthly payments. What will be the amount of each payment?

Finding the annual percentage rate. When you buy an article on the installment plan, you are really borrowing money from the merchant. The amount borrowed is the cash price or the cash price minus the down payment, if a down payment is required. In any case, the amount borrowed is the amount financed.

The finance charge is the price you are paying for the use of the merchant's money. The annual percentage rate, represented by this finance charge, is found by means of tables, in the way explained on page 205 for an installment loan. A section of the tables is shown at the top of page 212.

Example

The cash price of a tape recorder is $220. The installment price is $269; terms, $20 down and $8.30 a month for 30 months.

What annual percentage rate does the installment buyer pay for the use of the merchant's money?

Solution and Explanation

(1) $269 − $220 = $49, the finance charge

(2) $220 − $20 = $200, the amount of the merchant's money the buyer is using, which is the amount financed.

(3) $49 ÷ $200 = $24.50, the finance charge per $100 of amount financed.

(4) In the tables on page 212, on the 30-payment line, the value nearest $24.50 is $24.55, in the $17\frac{3}{4}\%$ column. The annual percentage rate is therefore $17\frac{3}{4}\%$.

ANNUAL PERCENTAGE RATE TABLE FOR MONTHLY PAYMENT PLANS

Number of Payments	ANNUAL PERCENTAGE RATE										
	$15\frac{3}{4}\%$	16%	$16\frac{1}{4}\%$	$16\frac{1}{2}\%$	$16\frac{3}{4}\%$	17%	$17\frac{1}{4}\%$	$17\frac{1}{2}\%$	$17\frac{3}{4}\%$	18%	$18\frac{1}{4}\%$
	FINANCE CHARGE PER $100 OF AMOUNT FINANCED										
6	4.64	4.72	4.79	4.87	4.94	5.02	5.09	5.17	5.24	5.32	5.39
12	8.74	8.88	9.02	9.16	9.30	9.45	9.59	9.73	9.87	10.02	10.16
18	12.93	13.14	13.35	13.57	13.78	13.99	14.21	14.42	14.64	14.85	15.07
24	17.22	17.51	17.80	18.09	18.37	18.66	18.95	19.24	19.53	19.82	20.11
30	21.62	21.99	22.35	22.72	23.08	23.45	23.81	24.18	24.55	24.92	25.29

Exercise 3   Written

Use the tables above in finding the annual percentage rate.

1. Find the annual percentage rate.

	Item	Cash Price	Installment Terms
a	Range	$225	$25 down; $18.20 a month for 12 months $16\frac{1}{2}\%$
b	Rug	150	$30 down; $11.00 a month for 12 months
c	Freezer	400	$40 down; $17.70 a month for 24 months
d	Desk	90	$5.75 a month for 18 months
e	Camera	150	$7.35 a month for 24 months

2. An outboard motor can be purchased for $270 cash or with 30 monthly payments of $11.10 each. What annual percentage rate is paid by the installment purchaser? 17%

3. The cash price of a watch is $95. The credit terms are $15 down and $5.05 a month for 18 months. What annual percentage rate is represented by the finance charge?

4. A motor boat can be bought for $340 cash or for $50 down and $11.90 a month for 30 months. What annual percentage rate is paid by the installment purchaser of this boat?

REVIEW ASSIGNMENT 28 a

1. a Express $105\frac{1}{2}\%$ as a decimal.
b $2.45 is what percent greater than $2.10?
c What amount is $62\frac{1}{2}\%$ greater than $44?
d Find the interest at 6% on $800 for 141 days.

2. The cash price of a chair was $120. Mrs. Wells purchased it for a down payment of $12 and 12 monthly payments of $9.80. By what percent does this installment price exceed the cash price?

3. Phelps is buying a television set on the installment plan for a total price of $295. He made a down payment of $25 and is paying the balance in equal monthly installments of $15 each. How many months will it take him to pay for the set?

4. Mrs. Frasier purchases some dining room furniture on the installment plan for a total cost of $415.50 by paying $37.50 down and the balance in 12 equal monthly payments. What will be the amount of each monthly payment?

5. Barcom borrowed $350 from his credit union and repaid the loan in 20 monthly payments of $19.15. How much was the finance charge?

6. The cash price of an air conditioner is $150. The installment price is $170.10, payable in 18 equal monthly payments. What annual percentage rate is paid by the installment purchaser? (Use the table on page 212.)

❿ **7.** A collection agent sent Preston Sales Company $182 after deducting 35% for collecting an account. What was the amount of the bill the agent collected?

PART 28b Interest (concluded)

To calculate interest at rates other than 6%. First find the interest at 6%. Then change that result by one of the following methods:

Method 1. (a) *Take an aliquot part of the interest at 6%, or* (b) *add or subtract an aliquot part of the interest at 6%.*

Use this method for such rates as 1% ($\frac{1}{6}$ of 6%), $1\frac{1}{2}$% ($\frac{1}{4}$ of 6%), 2% ($\frac{1}{3}$ of 6%), 7% (6% + $\frac{1}{6}$ of 6%), 5% (6% − $\frac{1}{6}$ of 6%), and so on.

Example

Find the interest on $960 for 20 days at 5%.

Solution	Explanation
3)$9.60 = *int. for 60 da. @ 6%*	Dividing the interest at 6%
6)$3.20 = *int. for 20 da. @ 6%*	by 6 gives the interest at 1%.
.533 = *int. for 20 da. @ 1%*	Subtracting that amount from
$2.667 = *int. for 20 da. @ 5%*	the interest at 6% gives the
Ans. $2.67	interest at 5%.

Method 2. *Multiply the interest at 6% by the given rate, and then divide that product by 6.*

The interest on $960 for 20 days at 6% is $3.20. 5 × $3.20 = $16. $16 ÷ 6 = $2.666, or $2.67. This result, $2.67, is the same as the answer obtained at the bottom of page 213 by Method 1.

This method, as a rule, is used only for rates such as $2\frac{1}{2}$%, $3\frac{1}{4}$%, and so on, which do not represent easy aliquot parts of 6%.

Exercise **4**   Written

Find the interest on:

1. $672 for 40 da. @ 3%
2. $726 for 45 da. @ 2%
3. $696 for 70 da. @ $1\frac{1}{2}$%
4. $748 for 80 da. @ 1%
5. $425 for 22 da. @ 7%
6. $380 for 36 da. @ 5%
7. $573 for 15 da. @ $7\frac{1}{2}$%

8. $630 for 75 da. @ $4\frac{1}{2}$%
9. $546 for 50 da. @ 8%
10. $872 for 25 da. @ 5%
11. $765 for 70 da. @ 4%
12. $864 for 20 da. @ $2\frac{1}{2}$%
13. $488 for 30 da. @ $3\frac{1}{2}$%
14. $400 for 33 da. @ $4\frac{1}{4}$%

● **To calculate interest mentally when the rate is a fractional part of 6%.** Multiply the interest at 6% by the fractional equivalent of the given rate. Thus, since 4% is $\frac{2}{3}$ of 6%, the interest on $360 for 60 days at 4% is $\frac{2}{3}$ of $3.60, or $2.40.

The more commonly used fractional equivalents are:

1% = $\frac{1}{6}$ of 6%	2% = $\frac{1}{3}$ of 6%	$4\frac{1}{2}$% = $\frac{3}{4}$ of 6%
$1\frac{1}{2}$% = $\frac{1}{4}$ of 6%	3% = $\frac{1}{2}$ of 6%	5% = $\frac{5}{6}$ of 6%
	4% = $\frac{2}{3}$ of 6%	

● Exercise **5**   Oral

State the interest on:

1. $660 for 60 da. @ 5%
2. $240 for 20 da. @ $4\frac{1}{2}$%
3. $120 for 15 da. @ 4%

4. $400 for 3 mo. @ 3%
5. $180 for 2 mo. @ 2%
6. $200 for 30 da. @ $1\frac{1}{2}$%

REVIEW ASSIGNMENT **28b**

1. **a** $1.50 is what percent less than $2.40?
   b What amount is $16\frac{2}{3}$% greater than $507.90?
   c $9.60 is what percent greater than $7.20?
   d Find the interest at 6% on $900 for 157 days.

2. Lake can buy a camera for $75 cash or on the installment plan by paying $5 down and making 10 monthly payments of $7.60 each. By what percent does the installment price exceed the cash price?

3. Mrs. Ahrens bought a refrigerator on the installment plan for $435. She was required to make a down payment of $75 and pay the balance in equal monthly payments of $15 each. How many months will it take her to pay for the refrigerator?

4. Hall buys a typewriter on the installment plan for $280, including finance charges. He makes a down payment of one-fourth of the purchase price, the balance to be paid in 8 equal monthly payments. What will be the amount of each payment?

5. The cash price of a snow blower is $320. On the deferred payment plan, it is priced at $384, payable in 24 equal monthly payments. What is the annual percentage rate under the deferred payment plan? (Use the table on page 212.)

◐ 6. A real estate agent who charges 5% commission received $3,245 for selling a piece of property. What was the selling price of this property?

GENERAL REVIEW

1. a Add $8\frac{1}{2}$, $3\frac{5}{6}$, $11\frac{1}{3}$, and $15\frac{3}{4}$.   **d** Divide $32\frac{1}{2}$ by $6\frac{1}{2}$.
  b Subtract $22\frac{5}{8}$ from $52\frac{1}{2}$.   **e** Multiply 804.25 by 7.2.
  c Multiply $12\frac{1}{4}$ by $8\frac{1}{3}$.   **f** Divide 80.006 by 73.4.

2. Borden's checkbook balance on October 31 was $339.11. His bank statement showed a balance of $394.62 on that date. There was a service charge of $1.74 which had not been deducted in the checkbook. Checks were outstanding for $41.32, $3.18, and $12.75. Prepare a reconciliation statement.

3. The Rainbow Luggage Shop had a merchandise inventory of $24,924 on September 1 and an inventory of $24,553 on September 30. Sales for September amounted to $10,389 and purchases, $6,555. What was the store's gross profit for the month?

4. A salesman earned $92, $106, $88, and $102 each week for four weeks. What amount will he need to earn the fifth week in order to have a final average sales for five weeks of $95?

5. A salted-nut mixture is made up of peanuts and cashews in the ratio of 3 to 2, respectively. How many pounds of each are needed to make a 45-pound mixture?

6. An agency that charges 40% commission collected 75% of a debt of $344 for Leroy Baxter. How much did Mr. Baxter receive from the agency?

7. A bank will lend Morton $360 for nine months at 6% interest, the total of the loan and interest to be repaid in 9 equal monthly payments. Find the amount of each payment.

8. Last year, the student enrollment at the Jefferson High School was 1,800. This year, the enrollment increased to 2,100. At the same rate of growth from this year to next year, what enrollment can be expected next year at Jefferson High?

9. What rate of interest is charged if the interest on a single-payment loan of $900 for 30 days is $5.25?

10. On November 8, Mr. Bowen borrowed $900 for 80 days at 6%. He repaid the loan when it came due for payment.

  a What was the total amount of money that Mr. Bowen repaid?

  b On what date did Mr. Bowen repay the loan?

11. A 6% demand note for $475, dated June 15, was paid in full on August 29. What was the amount of the payment?

12. Dewey is employed on the basis of an 8-hour day, at $2.70 an hour, with time and one-half for overtime. During a recent week, he worked the following hours:

Mon., 8; Tues., 6; Wed., 8; Thurs., 9; Fri., 10.

From Dewey's total earnings, 4.8% was deducted for FICA taxes. In addition, $13.20 was deducted for federal withholding tax and $1.75 for state withholding tax. What net amount did Dewey receive as take-home pay?

◗ **13.** Carver's bank statement for July showed a bank balance of $384.11 on July 31. His checkbook balance on the same date was $329.63. There was a service charge of $1.42 reported on the statement. Upon comparing the canceled checks with the check stubs, Carver found that checks for $13.27, $29.41, and $8.22 were outstanding. One of the canceled checks for $12.00 had been entered on the check stub as $17.00. Prepare Carver's reconciliation statement.

◗ **14.** Farley, a salesman, is paid a regular monthly salary of $495, plus a commission on all sales in excess of $9,500 in any single month. Last month his total sales were $15,500 and his total earnings $945. What percent commission was he paid?

◗ **15.** A salesman earned $9,000 last year on an 8% straight-commission basis. What was the amount of his sales last year?

◗ **16.** A saleslady is paid a salary of $80 a week and a commission of 4% on all sales in excess of $900 in any single week. What must be the total of her sales for one week in order that her total earnings for the week may be $100?

UNIT Seven

Savings and Investment Problems

Savings Accounts

A common way of keeping savings is in an account at a savings bank. The money the bank receives from depositors is invested by the bank in government bonds, real estate mortgages, and other high-grade securities. These investments earn an income for the bank. Out of this income, the bank pays interest to the depositors for the use of their money.

PART 29a | Finding Interest and New Bank Balances

Savings passbook. When a person opens a savings account, he is given a passbook in which the bank records his deposits, withdrawals, interest earned, and the balance after each transaction.

Shown at the right is the passbook record of Evan R. Day's account at the Seneca Savings Bank.

Notice that a deposit or interest item is added to the preceding balance, and that a withdrawal is subtracted.

SENECA SAVINGS BANK				
IN ACCOUNT WITH		Evan R. Day		
Date	With-drawal	Deposit	Interest	Balance
Jan. 2		500.00		500.00
May 8		100.00		600.00
June 5	150.00			450.00
July 1			11.25	461.25
July 1		80.00		541.25

Exercise 1 Written

In each of the following problems, rule a form similar to the passbook form shown above. Complete it by recording the transactions and the balance of the account after each transaction.

1. Jan. 2, deposit, $400; April 1, interest, $5; April 1, deposit, $100; July 1, interest, $6.31; July 1, withdrawal, $60. $451.31

2. Jan. 2, deposit, $600; April 5, deposit, $200; May 6, withdrawal, $150; July 1, interest, $12.00; Aug. 9, withdrawal, $175.

3. June 30, balance, $563.25 (enter in Balance column only);
July 1, interest, $14.08; Nov. 4, withdrawal, $375; Jan. 2, interest,
$5.05; Jan. 8, withdrawal, $35; Feb. 7, deposit, $84.50.

Interest on savings accounts.   Interest is added to the amount
on deposit at stated intervals, usually semiannually or quarterly.

In one year there are two semiannual interest periods or four
quarterly periods. The interest for one period is figured in the following
manner:

Divide the annual interest rate by the number of interest periods in one year (2 or 4) to find the rate for one period.   Then
multiply the principal by the latter rate.

As a rule, interest is figured on whole dollars only.   If you have
$35.89 on deposit, the interest would be figured on $35.

Example

If interest is paid at the rate of 5% a year, what is the interest
for one semiannual period on $120.95?

Solution: $5\% \div 2 = 2\frac{1}{2}\%$, *interest rate per period*

$2\frac{1}{2}\%$ *of* $120 = $3.00, *interest for one semiannual period*

$3.00 **Ans.**

Exercise 2   Written

1. Find the semiannual savings-bank interest on:

a $376.85 at 5% a year $9.40   **d** $755.42 at 5% a year
b $648.98 at 4% a year   **e** $509.65 at 5% a year
c $432.76 at 5% a year   **f** $864.88 at $4\frac{1}{2}\%$ a year

2. Find the quarterly savings-bank interest on:

a $844.50 at 5% a year $10.55   **d** $412.96 at 5% a year
b $684.70 at 4% a year   **e** $784.85 at 4% a year
c $528.80 at 5% a year   **f** $342.15 at 5% a year

Calculating interest and new balances.   At the end of each semiannual or quarterly interest period, the interest due is added to the
present balance. The new balance is the principal on which interest is
calculated for the new interest period.

Example

On January 2, Eric Lund deposited $425 in a savings bank that pays 4% interest and adds the interest on April 1, July 1, October 1, and January 2 of each year. If he made no withdrawals, how much did he have on deposit on July 1?

Solution

Jan. 2 Deposit..................................	*$425.00*
April 1 Quarterly interest, 1% of $425..............	*4.25*
April 1 New balance.............................	*$429.25*
July 1 Quarterly interest, 1% of $429..............	*4.29*
July 1 New balance.............................	*$433.54* **Ans.**

The illustration at the right shows the entries in Lund's passbook from Jan. 2 to July 1.

IN ACCOUNT WITH			*Eric Lund*	
Date	With-drawal	Deposit	Interest	Balance
Jan. 2		*425.00*		*425.00*
April 1			*4.25*	*429.25*
July 1			*4.29*	*433.54*

Exercise 3 Written

Prepare the solution of each of the following problems in the form of a passbook record similar to the one shown above.

1. On January 2, Remy deposited $600 in a savings bank that pays 5% interest a year and adds the interest on April 1, July 1, October 1, and January 2 of each year. If he made no withdrawals, how much did he have on deposit on the following January 2?
$630.56

2. In Problem 1, how much interest did the account earn for Remy during the year?

3. Platt deposited $900 in a savings bank on January 2. The bank pays 4% interest per year and adds interest to depositors' accounts on January 2, April 1, July 1, and October 1. If Platt made no withdrawals, what total amount of interest did the bank account earn for him during the first year?

4. A savings bank pays 5% interest and adds the interest quarterly on January 2, April 1, July 1, and October 1. Barr deposited $820 on January 2. If he made no withdrawals, what was his total interest for the first nine months?

5. On July 1, Gates deposited $1,400 in a savings bank that pays 4% interest a year and adds the interest on January 2, April 1, July 1, and October 1. If he made no withdrawals, how much did he have on deposit on the following July 1?

6. The Maxville Savings Bank pays interest at the rate of 5% a year and adds the interest on January 2 and July 1. Judd deposited $400 in the bank on January 2. How much did he have on deposit a year later if he made no withdrawals?

● Exercise **4**   Written

Prepare the solution for each of the following problems in the form of a passbook record similar to the one shown on page 220.

1. A savings bank pays 4% interest a year, adding the interest on January 2, April 1, July 1, and October 1. Morse deposited $200 on April 1 and $145 on July 1. How much did he have on deposit on October 1 if he made no withdrawals? $350.47

On July 1, figure and enter the interest on $200 before entering the July 1 deposit.

On October 1, figure and enter the interest on $347, which is the balance after entering the July 1 deposit.

2. A savings bank pays 5% interest a year and adds interest on January 2, April 1, July 1, and October 1. On July 1, Plummer deposited $500. On October 1, he made an additional deposit of $300. If he made no withdrawals, how much did he have in the bank on the following January 2?

3. A savings bank pays 5% interest a year, adding the interest on January 2, April 1, July 1, and October 1. R. A. Gobel deposited $800 on April 1 and withdrew $170 on July 1. How much did he have on deposit on October 1?

On July 1, figure and enter the interest on $800 before entering and subtracting the July 1 withdrawal.

On October 1, figure and enter the interest on $640, which is the balance obtained after subtracting the July 1 withdrawal.

●   Interest on minimum balances.

Banks differ in their methods of determining what amount shall draw interest when deposits or withdrawals are made between interest dates.

One method is to pay interest on the smallest balance on deposit during the period. This figure is the smallest amount in the balance column of the passbook record for the period between interest dates.

For example, the Milton Savings Bank pays 4% interest a year, adding the interest on January 2, April 1, July 1, and October 1. In the account at the right the smallest balance from April 1 to June 30 was $624.37. The interest for the period was therefore 1% of $624, or $6.24.

The smallest balance from July 1 to September 30 was $510.61. The interest for the period was therefore 1% of $510, or $5.10.

MILTON SAVINGS BANK				
IN ACCOUNT WITH		*Bruce Edison*		
Date	With-drawal	Deposit	Interest	Balance
April 1				*624.37*
May 29		*200.00*		*824.37*
July 1			*6.24*	*830.61*
July 5	*320.00*			*510.61*
Oct. 1			*5.10*	*515.71*

▶ **Exercise 5   Written**

Prepare the solution for each of the following problems in the form of a passbook record similar to the one shown above. Assume that interest is paid on the smallest balance on deposit.

1. The Plaza Savings Bank pays 4% a year, adding the interest on January 2, April 1, July 1, and October 1. On April 1, Eli Hoff had on deposit a balance of $482.73, including interest to date. He withdrew $150 on May 11 and deposited $200 on June 2. How much did he have on deposit on July 1? **$536.05**

2. A savings bank pays 5% interest a year, adding the interest on January 2, April 1, July 1, and October 1. Hal Valley deposited $900 on April 1. He withdrew $175 on May 1 and $75 on June 11. How much did he have on deposit on July 1?

3. The Center Savings Bank pays interest quarterly on January 2, April 1, July 1, and October 1 at the rate of 4% a year. On April 1, Kyle Toomey had on deposit a balance of $654.18, including interest to date. He deposited $125 on May 20, deposited $200 on June 19, and withdrew $300 on July 12. How much did he have on deposit on October 1?

REVIEW ASSIGNMENT **29** a

1. a $42 is what percent less than $112?

b What amount is $66\frac{2}{3}\%$ greater than $196.50?

c Express $112\frac{1}{4}\%$ as a decimal.

d Find the interest at 7% on $815.52 for 26 days.

2. On January 2, Ballard deposited $450 in a savings bank that pays 4% interest per year, payable quarterly. Interest was added to Ballard's account on April 1 and July 1. What total amount did he have on deposit on July 1?

3. Mr. Grover purchased a new car on a time payment plan. The cash price was $2,800. He made a down payment of $900 and paid the balance, plus a finance charge of $284, in 30 equal monthly payments. What was the amount of each monthly payment?

4. A loan of $280 was repaid in 12 equal monthly payments of $26.75 each. Find the annual percentage rate on this loan. (Use the tables on page 205.)

5. a $67.50 is 10% of what amount?

b Express 2.5% as a common fraction in lowest terms.

6. On April 1, Garrison deposited $520 in a savings bank that pays 4% interest per year, payable quarterly. On July 1, he made an additional deposit of $185. Interest was added to his account on July 1 and October 1. What total amount did he have on deposit on October 1?

PART 29b   Compound Interest

Nature of compound interest. If an amount of money remains on deposit in a savings account, interest at the end of each interest period is added to the principal. This sum then becomes the new principal on which interest for the next period is calculated. When interest is added in that manner at regular intervals, it is said to be compounded.

Interest may be compounded annually, semiannually, or quarterly. The total obtained at the end of the last interest period is called the *compound amount*. The total accumulated interest is called the *compound interest*. It is the difference between the original principal and the compound amount.

Compound interest tables. When compound interest is to be figured for several interest periods, a compound interest table similar to the one given below can be used. This table shows the compound amount of $1 for various rates and interest periods.

COMPOUND INTEREST TABLE FOR $1

Periods	1%	1¼%	2%	3%	4%	5%	6%
1	1.010000	1.012500	1.020000	1.030000	1.040000	1.050000	1.060000
2	1.020100	1.025156	1.040400	1.060900	1.081600	1.102500	1.123600
3	1.030301	1.037971	1.061208	1.092727	1.124864	1.157625	1.191016
4	1.040604	1.050945	1.082432	1.125509	1.169859	1.215506	1.262477
5	1.051010	1.064082	1.104081	1.159274	1.216653	1.276282	1.338226
6	1.061520	1.077383	1.126162	1.194052	1.265319	1.340096	1.418519
7	1.072135	1.090850	1.148686	1.229874	1.315932	1.407100	1.503630
8	1.082857	1.104486	1.171659	1.266770	1.368569	1.477455	1.593848
9	1.093685	1.118292	1.195093	1.304773	1.423312	1.551328	1.689479
10	1.104622	1.132271	1.218994	1.343916	1.480244	1.628895	1.790848
11	1.115668	1.146424	1.243374	1.384234	1.539454	1.710339	1.898299
12	1.126825	1.160755	1.268242	1.425761	1.601032	1.795856	2.012197
13	1.138093	1.175264	1.293607	1.468534	1.665074	1.885649	2.132928
14	1.149474	1.189955	1.319479	1.512590	1.731676	1.979932	2.260904
15	1.160969	1.204829	1.345868	1.557967	1.800944	2.078928	2.396558

For example, in the column headed 4%, the amount of $1 compounded annually at 4% for 5 years (5 periods) is $1.216653. For a principal of $500, the amount would be 500 × $1.216653, which is $608.3265, or $608.33.

The compound interest is $608.33 − $500, or $108.33.

Exercise 6   Written

Using the compound interest table, find the compound amount and the compound interest in each of the following:

	Prin-cipal	Rate	Time	Com-pounded	Compound Amount	Compound Interest
1.	$1,000	5%	10 years	Annually	$1,628.90	$628.90
2.	500	4%	6 years	Annually		
3.	600	2%	8 years	Annually		
4.	900	3%	12 years	Annually		
5.	1,200	6%	15 years	Annually		
6.	800	5%	13 years	Annually		

❯ **Interest compounded semiannually and quarterly.** If the interest is compounded semiannually, use the figure in the table for twice the given number of annual periods and one-half of the rate. If compounded quarterly, use the figure for four times the number of annual periods and one-fourth of the rate.

● **Exercise 7**   Written

Find the compound amount and compound interest, using the compound interest table.

	Principal	Rate	Time	Compounded	Compound Amount	Compound Interest
1.	$2,000	6%	5 years	Semiannually	$2,687.83	$687.83
2.	900	4%	4 years	Semiannually		
3.	1,000	5%	3 years	Quarterly	$1,160.76	$160.76
4.	800	4%	2 years	Quarterly		
5.	3,500	5%	2½ years	Quarterly		

● **Establishing a special-purpose savings fund.** A person sometimes finds it desirable to have one or more savings accounts for special purposes and deposit a fixed amount in each account every month.

For example, suppose after graduating from high school you want to make monthly savings out of your regular earnings so as to have $2,000 at the end of five years for traveling. Assume that you will place the savings in a bank that pays 4% interest, compounded quarterly. From the following table you can determine how much you must deposit each month.

Monthly Investment Needed to Produce $1,000 Interest Compounded Quarterly				
Time	4%	5%	6%	7%
5 yr.	$15.05	$14.70	$14.40	$13.95
10 yr.	6.80	6.45	6.10	5.80
15 yr.	4.10	3.75	3.45	3.15
20 yr.	2.75	2.45	2.20	1.95

On the "5 yr." line in the "4%" column, you find "$15.05." This is the amount you must deposit each month in order to have $1,000 in the account at the end of five years. Since you want a fund of $2,000, your monthly deposit must be 2 × $15.05, or $30.10.

At $30.10 a month, your total deposits over the five years will amount to 5 × 12 × $30.10, which is $1,806. The difference between $2,000 and $1,806 is $194. This amount represents the compound interest your deposits will earn for you over the five-year period.

► Exercise 8   Written

1. How much must I deposit each month in a savings bank that pays 5% interest, compounded quarterly, in order to have $1,000 in the bank at the end of 15 years? $3.75

2. How much must be deposited monthly at 4%, compounded quarterly, in order to have a fund of $2,000 at the end of 10 years?

3. How much must you invest each month at an annual interest rate of 6%, compounded quarterly, in order to receive $3,000 at the end of 20 years?

4. a In Problem 3 what will be the total of your actual cash investment for the 20 years? $1,584
   b What amount of compound interest will your cash investment earn for you over the 20-year period? $1,416

5. For each of the following, find (i) the amount to be invested each month in order to reach the indicated investment goal, (ii) the actual total cash investment, and (iii) the total of the compound interest earned by the cash investment.

	Investment Goal	Years	Annual Interest Rate*	(i)	(ii)	(iii)
a	$1,000	10	5%	$6.45	$774	$226
b	$1,000	20	4%			
c	$1,000	10	6%			
d	$2,000	5	4%			
e	$3,000	5	5%			
f	$5,000	20	7%			

*Compounded quarterly

6. Mr. Zeller wishes to have a fund of $15,000 available at the end of 20 years. How much must he invest each month at 5%, compounded quarterly, in order to achieve this goal?

7. Mr. Graham wishes to have $8,500 available at the end of ten years for his son's college education. How much must he deposit in the savings bank each month in order to have a fund of $8,500 at the end of 10 years if the bank pays 4% interest, compounded quarterly?

REVIEW ASSIGNMENT **29b**

1. a What amount is $33\frac{1}{3}\%$ of $25.26?

b $1\frac{1}{2}\%$ of $1,360 equals what amount?

c $240 is what percent less than $288?

d $29.40 increased by 25% of itself equals how much?

e $2.25 is what percent greater than $1.80?

f Find the interest on $1,800 for 134 days at 6%.

2. On April 1, Silberg deposited $300 in the West End Savings Bank which pays 5% interest per year, compounded quarterly. Interest was added to his account on July 1 and October 1. What total amount did Silberg have on deposit on October 1?

3. Mr. Ross obtained a loan of $540 for 18 months at his bank. To the amount of the loan, the bank added 18 months' interest at 6%. Ross repaid the total in 18 equal monthly payments. What was the amount of each payment?

4. Find the missing amount or amounts in each of the following. Assume that the current FICA tax is 4.8%.

	Name	Ex- emp- tions	Total Earn- ings	Deductions				Net Pay
				FICA Tax	Fed. In. Tax	State In. Tax	Insur- ance	
a	Cole, F.	2	$98.00	$4.70	$10.60	$2.15	$2.35	
b	Hicks, J.	1		4.42	13.50	2.70	1.25	$70.13
c	Paris, N.	1	88.00		12.80	2.55	1.25	

5. The cash price of an electronic organ is $550. It can be purchased on the installment plan by making 24 monthly payments of $27.50 each. What annual percentage rate is charged under the installment plan? (Use the table on page 212.)

6. a $23.22 is 35% more than what amount?

b Express .8% as a common fraction in lowest terms.

7. On January 2, Trainor deposited $600 in a bank that pays 5% interest per year, compounded quarterly. On July 1, he made an additional deposit of $250. Interest was added to his account on April 1, July 1, and October 1. What total amount did Trainor have on deposit on October 1?

8. A salesgirl is paid $75.00 a week plus a commission on all sales in excess of $950 in any single week. Her total sales last week amounted to $1,450. Her total earnings were $97.50. What percent commission was she paid?

Buying Life Insurance

Purpose of life insurance. The primary purpose of life insurance is to protect one's dependents against financial loss in the event of his death. Most types of life insurance also have a cash value that increases from year to year. A person can withdraw this amount if he discontinues his insurance.

Terms used in life insurance. The insurance company is the *insurer*. The person whose life is insured is the *insured*. The contract between the insurer and the insured is the *policy*. The person to whom the benefits are payable is the *beneficiary*. The amount paid regularly to the company for the protection is the *premium*.

Kinds of policies. Three common types of policies are:

Straight life insurance, under which the insured person must pay the premiums as long as he lives.

Limited payment life insurance, under which the insured pays premiums for a fixed period, such as 20 or 30 years, but is insured for his entire life.

Endowment insurance, under which the insured pays premiums and is insured for a fixed period, such as 20 years, at the end of which he receives cash for the amount of the policy.

Annual Premium for $1,000 Insurance

Age at Issue	Kind of Policy		
	Straight Life	20-Pay. Life	20-Year Endow.
15	$10.31	$18.23	$42.08
20	11.80	20.28	42.13
25	13.64	22.48	42.27
30	16.01	25.40	42.56
35	19.09	28.83	43.14
40	23.31	32.75	44.44
45	28.58	37.59	46.54

Premium rates. The table at the left shows the annual rates charged by one large company for $1,000 of life insurance under several types of policies taken out at various ages.

To find the premium for any other amount, multiply the rate in the table by the number of thousands in the face of the policy. Thus, the premium for a $2,500 policy would be 2.5 times the rate shown in the table.

Exercise 1   Written

The following problems are based on the annual premium rates given in the table on page 228.

1. Find the annual premium on each of the following policies:

Kind of Policy	Age	Face of Policy	
a Straight Life	15	$6,000	$61.86
b 20-Payment Life	25	$5,000	
c 20-Year Endowment	30	$7,500	

2. How much more is the annual premium on a 20-payment life policy for $5,000 at age 20 than on a straight life policy? $42.40

3. How much more is the annual premium on a 20-year endowment policy for $5,000 at age 20 than on a straight life policy?

4. At age 20, how much more is the annual premium on an $8,000, 20-year endowment policy than on a 20-payment life policy?

5. At age 25, how much more is the annual premium on a $3,000, 20-year endowment policy than on a straight life policy?

6. How much more is the annual premium on a straight life policy for $6,000, purchased at age 35, than a similar policy purchased at age 25?

7. At age 25, Roger Chase takes out a 20-payment life policy for $5,000. What total amount will he have paid in premiums by the end of the 20 years? $2,248

8. When he was 35 years old, a man took out a straight life policy for $10,000. He died after making 16 annual payments, and the insurance company then paid the beneficiary the amount of the policy. How much more did the beneficiary receive than the total amount that had been paid to the company in premiums?

9. Leo Fox, age 25, wants to invest not more than $350 a year in life insurance. In even thousands of dollars, what is the largest policy he can buy if he selects (a) straight life insurance, (b) 20-payment life insurance, (c) 20-year endowment insurance?

Dividends. Many insurance companies return part of the premiums to policyholders as dividends. Policies entitled to dividends are called *participating policies*. A dividend notice is sent to the policyholder with the notice of premium due. The policyholder may (1) deduct the dividend from the premium due, (2) leave it with the company to buy additional insurance or to earn interest, or (3) take it in cash.

Cash surrender value. Straight life, limited payment, and endowment policies contain tables of cash surrender values that show the amount of money a policyholder will receive if he cancels his policy. The cash value is also the amount that he can borrow, using the policy as collateral.

I COULD USE THE MONEY, BUT DO I WANT TO CANCEL MY POLICY ?

Group insurance. Employees of a single concern often obtain life insurance under a master policy covering the entire group. This is known as *group life insurance*. The premium is usually less than for a policy of similar amount taken out individually by the members of the group.

Accident, health, and hospitalization insurance can also be obtained under a group plan.

Exercise 2   Written

1. Linda Briggs carries a life insurance policy for $3,000 at an annual rate of $15.64 per $1,000. This year her policy is paying a dividend of $8.28, which she will use to reduce her next premium. What amount should she send to the insurance company when she makes her next premium payment? $38.64

2. Grover carries a policy for $6,000 at the annual rate of $29.18 per $1,000. The dividend this year amounts to $41.04 which he will apply against the next premium. What net amount should he send the company when he makes the next payment?

3. Irwin Powell took out a 20-payment life policy for $7,000 at $35.69 per year per $1,000. If dividends amounting to $902.46 were applied against his premiums during the life of the policy, how much was the net cost of the insurance? $4,094.14

4. At age 32, Will Bain took out a straight life policy for $8,000. At the end of 6 years he turned in the policy for its cash value of $95.24 per $1,000. How much money did he receive?

5. Homer Pell took out a straight life policy for $9,000 at the rate of $17.65 per $1,000 per year. At the end of 10 years he turned in the policy for its cash value of $102 per $1,000. Over the 10 years, dividends amounted to $267.34. What was the net cost of the insurance for the 10 years?

6. On April 7, Colby's life insurance policy has a loan value of $840, and he borrows this amount from the insurance company at 6% interest. Interest is due on premium dates. His annual premium of $102.25 is due on August 5. What is the total amount due on August 5 for the premium and for the interest on the loan for the number of days from April 7 to August 5?

REVIEW ASSIGNMENT **30**

1. a $3.30 is what percent greater than $1.98?

b $26.60 plus 25% of itself equals how much?

c $3.15 is what percent less than $3.60?

d Write the decimal equivalent of $122\frac{3}{8}\%$.

e Find the interest at 7% on $954.66 for 26 days.

f Find the interest at 6% on $2,400 for 157 days.

2. Albert Collins carries a life insurance policy for $8,000 at an annual rate of $21.40 per $1,000. This year his policy is paying a dividend of $52.81, which he will be allowed to deduct from his next premium. What net amount should he send to the insurance company as payment for his next year's premium?

3. Nolan can buy an air conditioner on the installment plan for a total cost of $315, by paying $33\frac{1}{3}\%$ of the cost as a down payment and the balance in equal monthly payments of $14 each. How many months will it take him to pay for the air conditioner?

4. C. E. Brady bought a new car priced at $2,715 and made a down payment of $915. He paid the balance, plus a finance charge of $216, in 24 equal monthly payments. What amount did Brady pay each month?

5. An employee who formerly received $2.75 an hour now receives $2.97. What is the percent increase in his hourly pay?

6. A 7% note for $700, dated March 7, was paid in full on May 15. What was the amount of the payment?

7. To a loan of $550 a finance charge of $68 is added, the total to be repaid in 24 equal monthly payments. Find the annual percentage rate on this loan. (Use the tables on page 205.)

⬤ **8. a** $7.92 is 75% of what amount?

b What amount multiplied by $\frac{3}{4}$ gives $7.80?

⬤ **9.** Butler's checkbook balance on April 30 was $716.11. In making a reconciliation statement, Butler found that a check for $13 was recorded in the checkbook at $31 and that he had no record in his checkbook of a service charge of $1.88 and a deposit of $28.33. Find Butler's correct checkbook balance.

SECTION 31

Investing in Bonds

Persons who have savings in excess of their probable emergency needs may wish to place their surplus funds in investments that pay higher rates of interest than savings banks. Some of the more common types are bonds, stocks, and real estate.

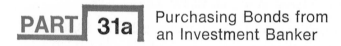

PART 31a   Purchasing Bonds from an Investment Banker

Nature of a bond. A *bond* is a form of long-term promissory note that is issued by a government or a corporation for the purpose of borrowing money.

If a corporation wishes to borrow a large sum of money for a long period of time, the loan may be divided into parts. Each part is represented by a bond. This bond is the corporation's written promise to repay the money on a specified date of maturity, and to pay interest on the loan. The interest is usually paid semiannually. Persons who are willing to lend money to the corporation may buy one or more of the bonds. Those who purchase the bonds are referred to as *bondholders* of the corporation.

> For example, if a corporation such as the United States Steel Corporation wishes to borrow $100,000,000 for ten years, it may issue 100,000 ten-year bonds, each with a face value of $1,000.

Money in large amounts may be borrowed in the same manner by the federal government and by smaller governmental units, such as states, counties, cities, and towns.

Bonds are usually issued in denominations (face value) of $1,000. Occasionally, but not often, they are issued in $500 denominations.

The security for an issue of corporation bonds is often a mortgage on the company's property, such as its land, buildings, or equipment. The mortgage agreement is made between the corporation and a bank or trust company, called the *trustee*. The trustee is appointed by the

Bond

corporation to represent the bondholders as a group in their transactions with the corporation.

Marketing a bond issue. When money is borrowed by issuing bonds, the entire issue is often sold to an *investment banking house*. The banking house sells the bonds to individual investors at a slight advance in price over that which it paid for them.

For example, a corporation may issue 100,000 bonds, each with a face value of $1,000. The banking house may buy them from the corporation at $995 each and perhaps sell them to investors at $1,000 each.

Par value and market value of a bond. Two kinds of value used in referring to a bond are par value and market value.

The *par value* of a bond is its face value, or the amount that appears on the face of the bond. It is the amount that the borrower promises to pay the bondholder at maturity.

The *market value* of a bond is the price at which the bond is currently being sold. The market value may or may not be the same amount as the par value. If the market value is greater than the par value, the bond is said to be selling at a *premium*. If the market value is less than the par value, it is said to be selling at a *discount*. The amount of the premium or discount is the difference between the market value and the par value.

How the market price of a bond is quoted. The market price, or market value, of a bond is quoted as a certain percent of the par value. For example, a price quotation of "97" means 97% of the par value of the bond. The market price of the bond is therefore found by multiplying the par value by the percent.

Thus, if the investment house of Purdy & Company offers Eastern Metal Corporation bonds at 97, the price of one of the corporation's $1,000 bonds is 97% of $1,000, or $970.

$$.97 \times \$1,000 = \$970.$$

Similarly, if the quoted price of a bond is $102\frac{1}{2}$, the price of a $1,000 bond would be $102\frac{1}{2}\%$ of $1,000, or $1,025.

$$1.02\frac{1}{2} \times \$1,000 = \$1,025$$

Likewise, if the quoted price is $102\frac{1}{2}$, the price of a $500 bond would be $102\frac{1}{2}\%$ of $500, or $512.50.

$$1.02\frac{1}{2} \times \$500 = \$512.50$$

To find the amount of an investment in bonds when the market price and the number of bonds purchased are given. To find the amount of an investment in bonds, find the price of one bond and multiply by the number of bonds purchased.

Example

Ronald Burnett purchased seven $1,000 Costal Petroleum Company bonds at 104. What is his investment in bonds?

Solution:

104% = 1.04
1.04 × $1,000 = $1,040, market price of 1 bond
7 × $1,040 = $7,280, total investment

Exercise 1   Oral

State the market price, in dollars and cents, of one $1,000 bond at each of the following quoted prices:

1. 98	3. 103	5. $97\frac{1}{2}$	7. $99\frac{1}{2}$	9. $101\frac{3}{4}$	11. $98\frac{1}{8}$
2. 96	4. 105	6. $107\frac{1}{2}$	8. $96\frac{3}{4}$	10. $97\frac{1}{4}$	12. $104\frac{1}{8}$

Exercise 2   Written

Find the amount invested in each of the following bond purchases:

1. Southeast Petroleum, $1,000 bonds:

a 5 @ 99 $4,950   **b** 3 @ 95   **c** 6 @ 104 $6,240   **d** 4 @ 110

2. Northern Power Corp., $1,000 bonds:

a 7 @ 95   **b** 5 @ 98   **c** 8 @ 107   **d** 12 @ 116

3. Century Industries, $1,000 bonds:

a 3 @ $98\frac{1}{2}$ $2,955 **b** 6 @ $94\frac{1}{2}$ **c** 9 @ $93\frac{1}{2}$ **d** 7 @ $106\frac{1}{2}$

4. Greenfield Stores, Inc., $1,000 bonds:

a 4 @ $87\frac{1}{4}$ **b** 8 @ $98\frac{1}{4}$ **c** 14 @ $105\frac{3}{4}$ **d** 6 @ $118\frac{3}{4}$

REVIEW ASSIGNMENT 31a

1. **a** $2.40 is what percent greater than $1.92?
b $38.40 increased by $37\frac{1}{2}\%$ of itself gives what amount?
c $84 is what percent less than $112?
d Express $115\frac{3}{8}\%$ as a decimal.
e Find the interest at $4\frac{1}{2}\%$ on $537.95 for 29 days.
f $990 \div 22,000 = n$. Find n.
g $95\frac{1}{2}\%$ of $1,000 = p$. Find p.

2. Jasper Hart purchased nine $1,000 Dana Computer bonds at $96\frac{1}{2}$ from an investment banking house. What is the amount of his investment in the bonds?

3. How much did Rice invest in fifteen $1,000 railroad bonds that he purchased from an investment banking house at $104\frac{3}{4}$?

4. Fisher purchased a slide projector priced at $130. He made a down payment of $10. The finance charge was 10% of the unpaid balance. The sum of the unpaid balance and the finance charge was paid by Fisher in 12 equal monthly payments. What was the amount of each monthly payment?

5. The cost of the interest on a single-payment loan of $750 for 8 months is $20. What is the rate of interest?

6. On January 2, Clifford deposited $620 in a bank that pays 6% interest per year, compounded quarterly. Interest was added to his account on April 1, July 1, and October 1. How much did Clifford have on deposit on October 1?

7. Find the due date and the amount due at maturity on a 75-day, 5% note for $1,260, dated June 9.

❱ **8. a** What amount minus 4% of itself gives $26.40?
b Express .25% as a common fraction in lowest terms.

❱ **9.** What should be the sale price of a house and lot in order that the present owner may realize $15,200 on the sale after paying the real estate broker a commission of 5%?

PART | 31b | Purchasing Bonds Through a Broker

Using the services of a broker. After a bond issue has been sold by the investment banking house, a person who wishes to buy some of the bonds must obtain them from a present bondholder who wishes to sell. Likewise, a bondholder who wishes to dispose of his holdings must sell them to some investor who wishes to buy.

Such transactions are seldom carried out directly between the buyer and seller. Usually, they are handled through *bond brokers* or *stockbrokers*.

Each buyer and seller places an order with his local broker to buy or sell a particular bond either at a stated price or at the current market price. Each broker telegraphs the order to his representative on one of the stock exchanges, such as the New York Stock Exchange. It is here that buy and sell orders are received from brokers in all parts of the country and that the actual buying and selling takes place.

The seller is required to surrender his bonds to his broker, who makes the necessary arrangements for the transfer of ownership.

Commission fee. When bonds are bought or sold through a broker, the broker charges a *commission* or *brokerage fee*. The commission on nine or less bonds is $2.50 per bond. When more than nine bonds are involved, the fee may vary with the number and value of the bonds.

To find the amount of an investment in bonds when the market price, commission, and the number of bonds are given. When bonds are purchased through a broker, the amount of the investment is the market price of the bonds plus the commission.

Example

C. O. Gale expects to purchase through a broker four $1,000 Bendix Corp. bonds at 95⅜ plus $2.50 commission per bond. What will be the amount of his investment?

Solution:

$.95\frac{3}{8} \times \$1,000 = \$953.75$, *market price of 1 bond*

Investment:

$4 \times \$953.75$	$= \$3,815.00$,	*market price of 4 bonds*
$4 \times \$2.50$	$= \underline{\hphantom{00}10.00}$,	*commission on 4 bonds*
	$\$3,825.00$,	*total investment* **Ans.**

Exercise **3**   Written

1. Find the amount invested in each of the following bond purchases. The par value of each bond is $1,000, and the commission in each case is $2.50 per bond.

a 6 @ 88 $5,295	**c** 15 @ 91	**e** 8 @ 92½
b 12 @ 94	**d** 16 @ 93	**f** 14 @ 116¾

2. Rosen bought eight $1,000 bonds at 90½; brokerage fee $2.50 per bond. What was the amount of his investment?

3. Gannon purchased nine $1,000 bonds at $875 each. If the cost of the commission was $22.50, what was his total investment?

4. How much money did Barnes invest in twelve $1,000 bonds that he purchased at $1,032.50 each, total brokerage $27?

5. Reo bought four $1,000 bonds at 95¼ and six $1,000 bonds at 87½. What was his total investment in the ten bonds?

When the commission is not stated, assume that it is included in the quoted price.

Daily bond quotation tables. Each day's bond sales on the exchanges are reported the next day on the financial pages of the metropolitan newspapers. Shown at the right are selected quotations from the New York Stock Exchange bond table for a certain day.

Interpreting the bond table. The first item in the table is a report of the sales of American Telephone and Telegraph Company bonds.

Corporation Bonds

— 196- —			Sales in				Net
High	Low	Bonds	$1,000	High	Low	Close	Chg.
84½	75⅝	Am T&T 4⅜s 85	55	77¼	76½	76¾	+¼
89¼	76	Benef Fin 4⅞s 81	12	78	77¾	77¾	−¼
101½	89¼	Cities Svc 6⅛s 97	12	93	92	92	−2⅞
89	78½	Con Edison 5s 87	14	80½	80	80½	+½
106	96½	Sears Roe 6⅜s 93	14	98¼	98	98⅜	.....
105⅞	98¾	Std Brands 6¾s 93	10	100	100	100	+1
99½	88	Std Oil Cal 5¾s 92	36	91	90	91	+1
104½	98	Std Oil NJ 6⅛s 98	87	99½	99¼	99¼	−¼
98⅜	75¾	Unit Air Lin 4¼s 92	101	81½	81	81	.....
85½	72¾	US Steel 4⅝s 96	53	74⅜	74	74	+¼
100	87¾	Wn Union 6⅛s 89	14	91	90½	90½	−½

The figures at the left of the company name show the highest and lowest prices paid for the bonds since the beginning of the year. The high for the year is 84½. The low is 75⅝.

At the right of the name, the "4⅜s" means bonds paying 4⅜% interest. The "85" means that 1985 is the year of maturity. The "55" in the "Sales" column means that 55 bonds were sold that day.

The next three columns show that the high for the day was 77¼, that the low was 76½, and that the price of the closing, or last, sale was 76¾.

The "+¼" in the "Net Chg." (Net Change) column means that the closing price was ¼ higher than the closing price on the preceding day. The closing price on the preceding day must therefore have been 76¾ − ¼, or 76½.

Exercise 4   Written

1. What annual rate of interest is paid on the Cities Service bonds listed in the bond table shown above?

2. In what year are the U.S. Steel bonds due for payment?

3. What was the highest price paid for United Airlines bonds on the day represented by the bond table?

4. What was the highest price paid for Western Union bonds during the year up to the day represented by the table?

5. What was the closing price of Sears Roebuck bonds on the day preceding the day represented by the table?

6. What was the closing price of Consolidated Edison bonds on the day preceding the day represented by the table?

REVIEW ASSIGNMENT **31b**

1. a $5.50 is what percent less than $8.25?

b $16.80 increased by $62\frac{1}{2}\%$ of itself gives what amount?

c Express $102\frac{5}{8}\%$ as a decimal.

d Find the interest at 5% on $1,800 for 143 days.

2. How much did R. D. Cross invest in eight $1,000 Hartford Electric Company bonds at $94\frac{1}{2}$ plus $2.50 commission per bond?

3. How much did John Cowles invest in seven $500 bonds that he purchased at $89\frac{3}{4}$ plus $2.50 commission per bond?

4. An investor purchased twelve $1,000 bonds at $122\frac{5}{8}$. The total commission on the transaction was $30. What was his total investment in the bonds?

5. Phillips works each day from 8:30 a.m. to 4:30 p.m., with an hour out for lunch, for a five-day week (Monday through Friday). What were his total wages last week at $3.25 an hour if he worked full time except for $2\frac{1}{2}$ hours lost on Wednesday?

6. A loan of $500 is repaid in 36 monthly payments of $19.10 each. How much is the finance charge on the loan?

7. Jerry Waldron purchases a camping outfit priced at $335. He makes a down payment of $35. The finance charge is 15% of the unpaid balance. The sum of the unpaid balance and the finance charge is to be paid in monthly installments of $23 each. How many months will it take him to pay for the camping outfit?

8. On an installment loan of $600 there is a finance charge of $84. The total of the loan and finance charge is to be paid in 24 equal monthly installments. What annual percentage rate is charged on this loan? (Use the tables on page 205.)

9. Find the missing amount in each of the following:

a $165\% \times c = \$52.80$

b $78\% \times a = \$35.10$

c $165\% \times \$30 = x$

▶ **10. a** $291.20 is 65% of what amount?

b Express .16% as a common fraction in lowest terms.

▶ **11.** A collector sent his principal $77 after deducting 45% for collecting a bill. What was the amount collected?

▶ **12.** Allard, a salesman, received a salary of $450 a month, a 1% commission on all his sales, and an additional commission of 2% on all monthly sales in excess of $6,000. His sales for January were $18,000, February $15,000, and March $20,800. What was his average monthly income during the three months?

SECTION 32

Investing in Bonds (concluded)

A person's income from bonds is the interest payments he receives from the corporation or governmental unit that issued the bonds. Bond interest is paid at regular intervals, usually semiannually.

PART 32a   Finding Bond Income

Bond interest.   The interest rate of a bond is based on the par value. Since the par value is the principal, the interest formula becomes:

Par Value × Rate × Time = Interest

For example, the interest for one year on a $1,000, 5% bond would be $50.

$1,000 × .05 = $50, interest for 1 year

If the interest is paid semiannually, the amount of each interest payment would be $25.

$1,000 × .05 × ½ = $25, semiannual interest

To find the income from an investment in bonds.   First find the interest on one bond. Then multiply that result by the number of bonds owned. Thus, the annual income from eight $1,000 bonds, bearing 4% interest, would be $320.

.04 × $1,000 = $40, interest on 1 bond

8 × $40 = $320, income from 8 bonds

Exercise 1   Written

1. Find the annual income in each of the following:

a 15 $1,000, 5% bonds $750   e 18 $1,000, 4½% bonds $810
b 20 $1,000, 4% bonds   f 7 $1,000, 6½% bonds
c 15 $1,000, 6% bonds   g 16 $1,000, 5¾% bonds
d 3 $500, 5% bonds   h 9 $500, 4½% bonds

2. What will be the annual income from 15 bonds having a par value of $1,000 each and paying 5½% interest? $825

3. How much is each interest payment on a $1,000, 5% bond if the interest is payable semiannually on June 1 and December 1?

4. What is the annual income on eight $1,000, $6\frac{1}{4}$% bonds?

5. What amount of interest is received on each interest date by a bondholder who owns six $1,000 bonds bearing 5% interest, payable semiannually?

Exercise **2**   Written

For each of the following bond investments, find the bondholder's total investment in the bonds and his total annual income from the investment.

	Bonds Owned	Par Value per Bond	Price Paid	Com. per Bond	Total Investment	Int. Rate	Annual Income
1.	12	$1,000	96	$2.50	$11,550	6%	$720
2.	8	$1,000	$86\frac{1}{2}$	$2.50		5%	
3.	20	$1,000	$102\frac{1}{2}$	$2.25		$6\frac{1}{2}$%	
4.	10	$1,000	$93\frac{1}{4}$	$2.50		$5\frac{1}{2}$%	
5.	5	$ 500	102	$2.50		4%	
6.	6	$ 500	98	$2.50		$4\frac{1}{2}$%	

REVIEW ASSIGNMENT **32** a

1. a What amount is .0425 × $15,000?

b $1,190 ÷ 34,000 is what amount?

c $10.80 is what percent less than $18?

d $56.70 increased by $16\frac{2}{3}$% of itself gives what amount?

e Express $112\frac{7}{8}$% as a decimal.

f Find the interest at 7% on $374.17 for 38 days.

2. Richard White owns fifteen $1,000, $4\frac{1}{2}$% bonds of Armour & Co. What is the amount of his annual income from the fifteen bonds?

3. Walter Carson owns twenty $1,000, 4% Sanders Electric bonds. The interest is payable semiannually.

a How much is the semiannual interest on one bond?

b What total amount of interest income does Carson receive on each interest date?

4. An investor bought three $1,000 bonds at $108\frac{7}{8}$ plus $2.50 commission per bond. What was his total investment?

❷ **5. a** $4.95 is $\frac{3}{8}$ of what amount?

   b Express $\frac{5}{8}\%$ as a decimal.

❷ **6.** Niles is about to sell his house through an agent who charges 5% commission. Niles wishes to realize net proceeds of $28,500 after reducing his asking price $1,000 and paying the commission. What should be his asking price for the property?

PART 32b   Finding the Rate of Income

To find the rate of income on investment. Before making a purchase of bonds, the investor should calculate the rate of income he will receive. Rate of income is the annual income, or interest, expressed as a percent of the investment. It answers the question: The annual income is what percent of the amount invested?

The annual income therefore represents the part. The amount invested represents the base, or whole, with which the part is compared. Hence, the rate of income equals the annual income divided by the investment.

$$\textbf{Rate of Income} \ = \ \frac{\textbf{Annual Income}}{\textbf{Investment}}$$

The term "yield" is often used in referring to the annual income on an investment. For example, it may be said that the "yield" on a certain investment is 4% or that a certain investment "yields" 4%.

Example

What is the rate of income on a $1,000, 5% bond priced at $91\frac{3}{4}$ plus $2.50 commission?

Solution

$.91\frac{3}{4} \times \$1,000\ = \$917.50,\ market\ price$
$\underline{\hphantom{.91\frac{3}{4} \times \$1,000\ = \$917.}2.50,\ commission}$
$\hphantom{.91\frac{3}{4} \times \$1,000\ = \$}\$920.00,\ amount\ invested$

$.05 \times \$1,000\ = \$50,\ annual\ income$

$\dfrac{\$\ 50}{\$920}\ = .0543,\ or\ 5.4\%\ to\ the\ nearest\ tenth\ of\ a\ percent.$ **Ans.**

Exercise 3   Written

Calculate the rate of income to the nearest tenth of a percent.

1. For each bond, find the rate of income on the investment.

	Par Value	Interest Rate	Market Price	Commission
a	$1,000	5%	96½	$2.50 5.2%
b	$1,000	4%	84½	$2.50
c	$1,000	6%	108¼	$2.50
d	$1,000	5½%	86¾	$2.50
e	$1,000	4½%	105¾	$2.50
f	$1,000	6½%	83	$2.50
g	$1,000	5¾%	124	$2.50

2. A $1,000 bond, bearing interest at 5%, was purchased at 69¾, plus $2.50 commission. What is the rate of income on the investment?   7.1%

3. A $1,000, 6½% bond was purchased at 105. What is the rate of income on the investment?

When the commission is not stated, assume that it is included in the quoted price.

4. What is the rate of income on a $1,000, 4½% bond purchased at 85?

5. What is the rate of income on a 5% bond purchased at 90? When the par value is not given, assume that it is $1,000.

6. What is the rate of income on a 6% bond purchased at 112?

⊙ **Exercise 4   Written**

1. a How much annual income does an investor receive from one $1,000, 5% bond?

b How many of the bonds must he purchase in order to have an annual income of $800 from the investment?   16

2. Alcoa Corporation 6% bonds can be purchased at 93½.

a How many bonds must Sidney Larner purchase in order to have an annual income of $1,500 from the investment?

b What will be his total investment in the bonds? $23,375

3. What amount must be invested in Revere Copper 5½% bonds at 112½ in order to yield an annual income of $2,200?

4. Armour & Company $4\frac{1}{2}\%$ bonds can be purchased at $122\frac{3}{4}$. How much money must be invested in the bonds to produce an annual income of $1,350?

5. Drislane can purchase $5\frac{1}{2}\%$ railroad bonds at 85 or $4\frac{1}{2}\%$ gas and electric bonds at 80.

   a Which bond pays the higher rate of income on investment, and what is the rate of income?

   b How much will he have to invest in the bonds that pay the higher rate of income on investment in order to receive an annual income of $1,980?

REVIEW ASSIGNMENT **32** b

   1. a Multiply $13,000 by .82125.

   b Divide 52.5 by 840.

   c What amount is $18\frac{1}{2}\%$ less than $48?

   d $2.25 is what percent smaller than $3.60?

   e Find the interest on $719.50 for 40 days at 6%.

   2. R. E. Ottman owns $8,000, par value, of $5\frac{3}{4}\%$ bonds. What is the amount of his annual income from the investment?

   3. Six $1,000 bonds, bearing interest at $4\frac{3}{4}\%$, are purchased by Ernest Maxwell at 95, including the commission. What is Maxwell's rate of income on his investment?

   4. How much did Marvin Miller invest in four $1,000 bonds that he purchased at $92\frac{1}{8}$ plus commission of $2.50 per bond?

   5. Mr. Duffy deposited $400 in a savings bank on January 2. The bank adds interest quarterly at the rate of 4% a year. How much did Duffy have in his account one year later?

   6. Mr. Drew purchased a television set priced at $350 with a down payment of $50. The finance charge consists of interest for 18 months on the unpaid balance at 6% a year, and a service charge of $6. The total amount owed will be paid in 18 equal monthly payments. What will be the amount of each payment?

   7. John Poole's salary as a postal clerk is $7,150 a year. This is equal to how much a week?

   8. A 7% note for $550, dated October 5, was paid in full on December 12. What was the amount of the payment?

   ▶ **9. a** $8.40 is 25% smaller than what amount?

     b $3.60 is $\frac{5}{6}$ of what amount?

   ▶ **10.** If Paul Patton desires an annual income of $1,200 from the investment, how many $1,000, $3\frac{3}{4}\%$ bonds will he have to buy?

SECTION 33

Investing in Stocks

Instead of raising money by issuing bonds, a corporation may obtain funds by issuing additional shares of its capital stock. A company in need of $1,000,000 for enlarging its factory, for example, might find that it can raise the money by issuing 50,000 shares of stock and selling them at $20 a share.

PART 33a | Finding Broker's Commission and Total Investment

Nature of corporation stock. Investors who buy the shares of a corporation are known as the *shareholders* or *stockholders* of the company. Each shareholder receives a paper, called a *stock certificate*, which states on its face the number of shares he owns. Each certificate is registered with the corporation in the name of the owner.

Stock certificate

When a corporation raises money by issuing stock, it does not promise to repay the amount at some future date as it does when issuing bonds. It does not promise to pay interest. The money obtained from the sale of stock becomes a part of the permanent capital of the corporation. Hence, when an investor purchases a share of stock, he buys a part ownership in the corporation.

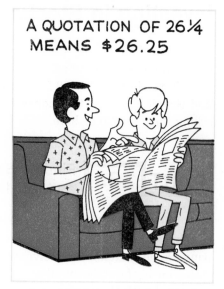

A QUOTATION OF 26¼ MEANS $26.25

As a part owner or shareholder, the investor is entitled to a proportionate share of the profits of the corporation. The profits that the corporation distributes to its shareholders are known as *dividends*. Dividends may be paid quarterly, semiannually, or annually. Among the larger, nationally known corporations it is common practice to pay dividends quarterly.

Marketing a stock issue. An issue of stock is marketed in much the same manner as an issue of bonds. The entire issue is generally sold to an investment banking house. The banking house then sells the shares to individual investors at a somewhat higher price than it paid for them.

Par value and market value of stock. The *par value* of a share of stock is a value that the corporation assigns to the shares before they are issued.

All the shares of a given issue of stock have the same par value. This value may be $1, $10, $25, $50, or $100, or any other value that the corporation may decide to assign to the shares. It is seldom more than $100, however. Many corporations issue stock without assigning any value to the shares. Such stock is referred to as *no-par*, or *no-par-value*, stock.

The *market value* of a share of stock is the price at which the stock is currently being sold. Under the laws of several states, a corporation is not permitted to sell its shares for less than the par value.

After the corporation has disposed of the issue, investors may buy and sell the shares at any price they agree upon. The price that investors may be willing to pay for the shares at any particular time is governed largely by their estimate of the future earning power of the corporation.

How the market price of a stock is quoted. The market price, or market value, of a share of stock is usually quoted as so many dollars per share. For example, a quotation of "$28\frac{3}{4}$" means $28\frac{3}{4}$. The price of one share is therefore $28.75.

Buying and selling stock through brokers. After a stock issue has been sold by the investment banking house, investors who wish to buy some of the shares must obtain them from present shareholders who may wish to sell their holdings. Such purchases and sales are usually made through stockbrokers in the same manner as purchases and sales of bonds, as explained on page 236.

The sellers of the stock are required to surrender their stock certificates to their respective brokers. The brokers make the necessary arrangements for the transfer of ownership of the shares.

Stockbroker's commission. When a person buys or sells stock through a broker, he is charged a commission or brokerage fee for the broker's services. On the New York Stock Exchange, commissions are based on the market value of a 100-share lot, as follows:

Market Value	Commission
Under $100	As mutually agreed
$100 to $400	$2\% + \$3$
$400 to $2,400	$1\% + \$7$
$2,400 to $5,000	$\frac{1}{2}\% + \$19$
$5,000 and above	$\frac{1}{10}\% + \$39$

Thus, if C. D. Hoff buys 100 shares of stock at 34, the market value of the shares is $3,400. The commission is therefore $19 + \frac{1}{2}\%$ of $3,400, which is $19 + $17, or $36.

When two or more 100-share lots are bought or sold, multiply the 100-share rate by the number of lots.

If Mr. Hoff should buy 300 shares of stock at 34, the commission would be 3 × $36, or $108.

If fewer shares than 100 are bought, the commission is $2 less than the amount calculated by using the rates in the table.

Stock transfer taxes. In addition to the commission, the seller is required in some states to pay a stock transfer tax on the shares sold. The buyer is not required to pay a transfer tax.

To find the total cost of a purchase of stock. The total cost, or gross cost, of a purchase of stock is the sum of the market price and the commission.

Market Price + Commission = Total Cost

Example

Ann Kemp bought 50 shares of National Biscuit stock at 54. The commission was based on the table of rates given on page 247, less $2. Find the total cost of the stock.

Solution

Market value, 50 × $54..........		*$2,700.00*
Commission:		
½% of $2,700.00.............	*$13.50*	
Plus....................	*19.00*	*$32.50*
Less...................	*2.00*	*30.50*
Total cost....................		*$2,730.50*
		Ans.

Exercise 1   Written

Find the total cost of each purchase listed below. Use the table of rates shown on page 247. The commission is $2 less than the amount calculated according to that table when the number of shares is less than 100.

	No. of Shares	Name of Stock	Market Price	
1.	200	Bethlehem Steel	35	$7,073
2.	100	American Motors	16	
3.	200	National Airlines	48	
4.	100	Quaker Oats	59	
5.	300	Shell Oil	70	
6.	80	Swift Packing	30	$2,429
7.	3	Wrigley Company	115	
8.	20	Superior Oil	187	

REVIEW ASSIGNMENT 33a

1. a Multiply $14,000 by 1.1675.   **b** Divide 67.5 by 1,800.
c $3.30 is what percent less than $4.95?

2. Find the interest at 6% on $378.53 for 69 days.

3. William Finch purchased 85 shares of Campbell Soup stock at 33. The commission on the purchase was $31.03. What was the total cost of the stock?

4. An investor owns $12,000, par value, of $4\frac{1}{2}\%$ bonds. What is the amount of his annual income from the investment?

5. If eight $500 bonds bearing interest at $6\frac{1}{2}\%$ are purchased at 125, what will be the rate of return on the investment?

6. A loan of $250 is repaid in 18 monthly payments of $15.25 each. What annual percentage rate is charged on this loan? (Use the tables on page 205.)

❯ **7. a** $2.64 is $\frac{3}{8}$ of what amount?
  b $36 is 25% more than what amount?

❯ **8.** Robert Harding wishes to receive an annual income of $2,100 from an investment in some $5\frac{1}{4}\%$ bonds, par value $1,000 each. How many of these bonds must he purchase?

PART 33b   Finding the Income

Dividends. When a corporation decides to distribute profits to the shareholders, it is said to *declare a dividend*. The dividend may be expressed either as a certain percent of the par value of the stock or as a specified amount of money per share.

For example, if a corporation declares a dividend equal to $1\frac{1}{2}\%$ of the par value, and the par value of the shares is $100, the amount of the dividend on each share is $1\frac{1}{2}\%$ of $100, or $1.50. The corporation may therefore announce the declaration of either a dividend of $1\frac{1}{2}\%$ or a dividend of $1.50 per share. In the case of no-par-value stock, the dividend is always expressed as a specified amount per share.

Dividends may be declared quarterly, semiannually, or annually.

Classes of stock. Many corporations issue two classes of stock — common stock and preferred stock.

Common stock is the ordinary stock of a corporation. It does not provide for the payment of any specified rate of dividend.

Preferred stock is stock that bears a specified rate of dividend, such as 5%, or $5 a share. The corporation does not guarantee that the dividend will be paid. It does promise, however, that the dividends will be paid on the preferred stock before any dividends are paid on the common. In other words, the preferred stock ranks ahead of the common stock in the distribution of the profits.

To find the income from an investment in stock. A shareholder's income from a particular stock is represented by the dividends he receives from the corporation. To find the amount of one dividend payment, multiply the dividend on one share by the number of shares.

The yearly income is the total of the dividends received in a year.

Example 1

Floyd Hite owns 20 shares of Bower Corporation stock, par value $100. If the corporation declares a $5\frac{1}{2}\%$ dividend, what is the total dividend Hite should receive?

Solution: $.05\frac{1}{2} \times \$100 = \$5.50$, *dividend on 1 share*
$20 \times \$5.50 = \$110$, *total dividend*

Example 2

What yearly income will John Hobb receive from an investment in 50 shares of Hollis Drug Company common stock if a dividend of $\$.37\frac{1}{2}$ is paid quarterly?

Solution: $50 \times \$.37\frac{1}{2} = \$18.75$, *dividend for 1 quarter*
$4 \times \$18.75 = \$75$, *yearly income*

Exercise 2   Written

Find the total annual dividend received by the shareholder in each of the following:

	Shares Owned	Par Value per Share	Dividend Rate
1.	75	$100	5%, annually $375
2.	85	100	4%, annually
3.	100	50	6%, annually
4.	45	50	7%, annually
5.	60	——	$ .75 per share, quarterly $180
6.	55	——	1.25 per share, quarterly
7.	30	——	.45 per share, quarterly

Daily stock quotation tables. Each day's sales on the stock exchanges are reported the next day on the financial pages of the metropolitan newspapers. Shown at the right are selected quotations from the New York Stock Exchange stock tables for a certain day.

Corporation Stocks

— 196-—				Sales in					Net
High	Low	Stocks	Div.	100s	Open	High	Low	Close	Chg.
65¼	46⅛	Aetna Lif	1.40	340	61¾	62½	61½	61⅝	−¼
58⅜	48	Am T&T	2	40 678	54½	54⅝	54¼	54½	.....
84½	43¼	Cities Svc	2	885	70½	72½	69⅞	71½	+1⅝
81⅜	67⅞	Coca Col	1.20	90	70½	70¾	70¼	70¼	+⅛
41⅜	27¼	Ethyl Cp	.72	94	34	34¼	32⅝	32¾	−1⅜
100⅜	80¼	Gen Elec	2.80	280	92⅞	92⅞	90½	90¾	−1⅞
89⅞	72⅝	Gen Mot	3.40	505	80	80⅜	78½	78⅝	−1⅞
66	48⅜	Nor Pac	2.60	71	63¼	65	63¼	64⅝	+1⅝
133⅝	88	Polaroid	.32	216	118½	119¼	116½	116⅝	−2¼
69⅜	44¼	Sherwn Wm	2	34	54⅜	54⅞	53¾	54⅞	+½
116	97½	Sherwn Wm pf	4.40	13	98½	101½	98½	101½	+2⅝

Interpreting the stock table. The first line in the table gives data on Aetna Life Insurance Co.

The figures at the left of the company name show the highest price, $65¼, and the lowest price, $46⅛, at which the stock has traded since the first of the year.

At the right of the company name, the "1.40" is the annual dividend per share, $1.40.

The "340" in the "Sales in 100s" column means that 340 hundred or 34,000, shares were traded during the day.

The "Open" column shows the price of the stock on the first, or opening, sale of the day, $61¾. The "High" column shows the highest sale price during the day, $62½. The "Low" column shows the lowest price for the day, $61½. The "Close" column shows the price of the last, or closing, sale of the day, $61⅝.

The "−¼" in the "Net Chg." (Net Change) column means that the closing price was ¼ of a point (¼ of $1, or $.25) lower than the close on the preceding day. The closing price on the preceding day must therefore have been 61⅝ + ¼, or 61⅞.

On the last line, the "pf4.40" following the company name means Sherwin Williams preferred stock is paying $4.40 annual dividend.

Exercise 3   Written

1. **a** Which stock in the table sold at the highest price of all during the year?

   b Which sold at the lowest price?

2. Which stock had the highest opening price for the day?

3. **a** For which stock or stocks was the opening price the high for the day?

   b For which was the opening price the low for the day?

4. a For which stock or stocks was the closing price the high for the day?

b For which was the closing price the low for the day?

5. a Which stock or stocks closed above the opening price?

b Which closed below the opening price?

c Which closed at the opening price?

6. What was the preceding day's close of General Motors?

7. What was the preceding day's close of Coca Cola?

REVIEW ASSIGNMENT 33 b

1. a Multiply $12,500 by .0375.

b Divide 1,680 by 16,000.

c $877.40 is what percent of $16,400?

d Find the interest on $598.25 for 46 days at 6%.

2. Arnold Clark purchased 60 shares of American Airlines stock at $35\frac{1}{2}$ and paid $27.65 for commission. What was his total investment in the stock?

3. Petrie owns 85 shares of McAllister Petroleum stock which pays a quarterly dividend of $37\frac{1}{2}$ cents a share. What amount of money should he receive as dividends during a one-year period?

4. How much annual income does Webster receive from 75 shares of Parker Industries preferred stock that pays an annual dividend of 6% on a par value of $50 per share?

5. Louis Colyer owns $14,000, par value, of $4\frac{1}{4}\%$ bonds that he purchased at 108. What is the amount of his annual income from the investment?

6. A $1,000 bond, bearing interest at $4\frac{1}{2}\%$, was purchased for $750. What was the percent of return on the investment?

7. Mrs. Wilcox purchased a refrigerator priced at $360 with a down payment of $60. The finance charge consists of interest for 24 months on the unpaid balance at 6% a year and a service charge of $12. The total amount owed will be paid in 24 equal monthly payments. What will be the amount of each payment?

◗ 8. a $7.50 is $66\frac{2}{3}\%$ of what amount?

b $35 increased by what percent of itself gives $112?

◗ 9. A salesman receives a monthly salary of $395 with a $7\frac{1}{2}\%$ commission on all sales over $6,000 a month. What must be the total of his sales for the current month in order that his total income for the month may be $800?

SECTION 34

Investing in Stocks (concluded)

After purchasing a stock, the investor receives the benefit of the dividend income until he sells it. When he sells the stock, he may receive more or less than he paid for it and so make a profit or suffer a loss on the sale.

PART 34a   Figuring Rate of Income; Proceeds from Sale

To find the rate of income on an investment in stock.   Rate of income on investment, as explained in Section 32, is found by dividing the annual income by the amount invested.

In the case of an investment in stock, the annual income is represented by the annual dividends. The investment is represented by the total cost of the stock. Hence, the rate of income equals the annual dividends divided by the total cost.

$$\text{Rate of Income} = \frac{\text{Annual Dividends}}{\text{Total Cost of Stock}}$$

Exercise 1   Written

1. Find the rate of income on investment for each of the following stocks to the nearest tenth of a percent.

	Total Cost per Share	Par Value per Share	Dividend Rate	Dividend Payable
a	$75	$100	5%	Annually 6.7%
b	80	100	4%	Annually
c	40	50	6%	Annually
d	15	25	5%	Annually
e	30	——	$.40 per share	Quarterly 5.3%
f	50	——	$.65 per share	Quarterly
g	60	——	$.70 per share	Quarterly
h	20	——	$.17½ per share	Quarterly

2. A share of stock costing $50 paid a quarterly dividend of $.56¼. To what rate of income was this equal?

3. Logan owned 36 shares of stock that cost him $2,880, including commission. On each share he received quarterly dividends of $1.20 per share. What annual rate of income did he receive on his investment? 6%

4. Panza purchased 80 shares of stock at $59.50 per share and paid $40 for commission on the entire transaction. The stock pays annual dividends of 6% on a par value of $50. What rate of income does Panza receive on his investment?

To find the proceeds of a sale of stock. When a person sells stock through a stockbroker, he receives the market price less the cost of the commission and taxes. The amount he receives is called the *net proceeds*.

Market Price − (Commission + Taxes) = Net Proceeds

Exercise 2   Written

Find the net proceeds from the sale of the stock in each of the following:

	Name of Stock	Shares Sold	Selling Price	Com- mission	Total Taxes
1.	American Steel	40	55	$27.00	$ 2.05
					$2,170.95
2.	Atlas Electric	100	18	25.00	3.79
3.	Goss Laboratories	60	74	39.20	3.09
4.	Southern Realty	100	9¼	16.25	2.52
5.	Ocean Petroleum	200	44½	82.50	10.18
6.	Crown Electronic	80	35¾	31.30	4.06

REVIEW ASSIGNMENT 34 a

1. a Multiply $18,000 by 1.125.   **b** Divide 3,090 by 15,000.
c $1,404 is what percent of $13,000?
d Find the interest at 6% on $402.60 for 79 days.

2. A share of stock costing $200 paid a quarterly dividend of $2.25. To what annual rate of return was this equal?

3. Coulson purchased a share of 6% stock, with a par value of $50, for a total cost of $75. What rate of income does he receive on his investment?

4. Pendleton owned 80 shares of Reynolds Chemical stock. He ordered his broker to sell the stock at $22\frac{1}{2}$. The broker sold it at that price and charged $23 for commission and $4.04 for taxes and other expenses. What net proceeds did Pendleton receive from the sale of the stock?

5. You can borrow $450 from a consumer finance company and repay the loan in 24 monthly payments of $24.25 each. How much is the finance charge on the loan?

6. Find the date of maturity and the amount due at maturity on a 3-month, 5% note for $950 dated March 5.

◐ **7.** Eva Blair wishes to purchase the number of $1,000, $6\frac{1}{4}\%$ bonds needed to provide an annual income of $500. How many of these bonds will she have to purchase?

PART **34b**   Figuring the Profit or Loss on Sale of Stock

To find the profit or loss on the sale of stock. The profit or loss on a sale of stock is the difference between the total cost of the stock and the net proceeds. If the amount of the net proceeds is greater than the total cost, the result is a profit. If it is less than the total cost, the result is a loss. Thus,

$$\textbf{Net Proceeds} - \textbf{Total Cost} = \textbf{Profit}$$
$$\textbf{Total Cost} - \textbf{Net Proceeds} = \textbf{Loss}$$

Exercise 3   Written

1. Find the profit or loss in each of the following:

	Name of Stock	Shares Traded	Purchase Price	Commission on Purchase	Selling Price	Commission and Taxes on Sale
a	Carib Sugar	40	65	$30.00	78	$34.20
						$455.80
b	Jonas Packing	100	8	15.00	$9\frac{1}{2}$	19.02
c	Acme Drugs	25	25	11.25	22	11.77
d	Allied Oil	20	46	14.20	47	15.42
e	Bell Plastics	80	$25\frac{1}{2}$	25.40	$48\frac{1}{2}$	40.48

2. Vallee bought 40 shares of stock for a total cost of $1,782. He kept the stock for two years, during which time he received quarterly dividends of $.80 per share. He then sold the stock and received net proceeds of $2,170. What was his total gain from owning and selling this stock? **$644**

Add the total dividends received and the profit on the sale of the stock to find the total gain.

3. Murphy purchased 10 shares of stock for a total cost of $742. He kept the stock for three years, during which time he received semiannual dividends of $2.25 per share. He then sold the stock and received net proceeds of $886. What was his total gain from owning and selling this stock?

YOU CAN LOSE YOUR SHIRT IN THE STOCK MARKET

4. Birch bought 20 shares of stock for a total cost of $1,116. After receiving five quarterly dividends of $.90 per share, he sold the stock and received net proceeds of $1,053. What was his net gain from owning and selling the stock?

▶ **5.** Hoyt purchased 200 shares of stock at $25\frac{1}{2}$ plus a brokerage fee of $31.75 for each hundred shares. After receiving a dividend of $.75 per share, he sold the stock at $27\frac{3}{4}$. The expense connected with the sale of the stock consisted of a brokerage fee of $32.88 for each hundred shares and taxes totaling $10.12 on the entire sale transaction. What was Hoyt's total gain from owning and selling the stock?

▶ **Exercise 4**   **Written**

1. A chemical stock paying an annual dividend of $3.60 can be purchased at 80. A steel stock paying $2.25 can be purchased at 45. What rate of income is provided by the stock that yields the higher rate? (Disregard commission.)

2. Which investment offers the better rate of income: a food stock paying $2.75 annually, bought at 50; or an oil stock paying $1.90 annually, bought at 40? (Disregard commission.)

3. Hover Corporation stock pays an annual dividend of $6 a share. How many shares would you have to own in order to receive an annual income of $300 from the stock?

4. Galaxie Cement stock pays a regular annual dividend of $4 a share.

   a How many shares must you purchase in order to receive an annual income of $800 from the investment?

b What will be your total investment in the stock if you purchase it at 65 and pay $45.50 per 100 shares for commission?

5. A certain stock pays regular quarterly dividends of $.87$\frac{1}{2}$ a share. How much must be invested in the stock at 45 to receive annual dividends of $70 if the broker charges $14 for commission?

6. At $75 a share, how much must be invested in a 5% stock, par value $100, in order to receive annual dividends of $900? (Disregard commission.)

The expression "5% stock" means a stock that pays dividends at the annual rate of 5%.

REVIEW ASSIGNMENT 34b

1. a Multiply $17,000 by .04125.   **b** Divide 364 by 13,000.
c $1,023 is what percent of $15,500?
d Find the interest at 6% on $622.12 for 47 days.

2. Pearson sold 20 shares of Gayton Scientific stock at 57$\frac{1}{2}$. The broker's commission was $16.50, and the taxes and other expenses totaled $1.03. What net proceeds did Pearson receive from the sale of the stock?

3. Dayton bought 80 shares of stock at a total cost of $4,200. He kept the stock one year, during which time he received quarterly dividends of $.95 a share. He then sold the stock and received net proceeds of $4,760. What was the amount of Dayton's gain from owning and selling this stock?

4. What is the rate of return on a share of stock which costs $120 and which pays a quarterly dividend of $1.65?

5. A certain $1,000 bond that bears interest at 6% can be purchased for $800. What will be the rate of income on the investment if the bond is purchased at that price?

6. Mr. Murrow purchased a new car priced at $3,300. His old car was taken in trade for $1,500 as the down payment. The unpaid balance, plus a finance charge of $270, was to be paid in 30 equal monthly payments. What was the amount of each payment?

7. A loan of $250 was repaid in 12 monthly payments of $23.75 each. What was the annual percentage rate charged on this loan? (Use the tables on page 205.)

8. a What amount decreased by $\frac{3}{8}$ of itself equals $16?
b Express .03$\frac{1}{3}$ as a common fraction in lowest terms.

9. A collector sent his principal $108.50 after deducting 38% for collecting an account. What was the amount collected?

SECTION 35

Investing in Real Estate

An investor may purchase a house and rent it to a tenant. The rent he charges should be sufficient to cover the various ownership expenses and provide him a reasonable income on his investment.

PART 35a Figuring Rent Income

Gross income and net income from real estate investments. The rent that a property owner receives from a tenant is his *gross income* from the property. His *net income* is the amount remaining after deducting his ownership expenses. The income and expenses are usually figured on an annual basis.

For example, Alfred Kramer bought a one-family house for $8,500 that he rented last year to a tenant for $100 a month. He received for the year a gross income of $12 \times \$100$, or $1,200. His expenses for the year for taxes, insurance, repairs, etc., totaled $520. His net income from the investment was therefore $1,200 − $520, or $680 for the year.

RENT INCOME ISN'T ALL PROFIT!

APARTMENT FOR RENT

Expenses. In calculating his net income, the owner should include all the expenses connected with the ownership of the property. These expenses usually consist of cash payments for such items as taxes, insurance, repairs and upkeep, and interest on the mortgage if there is a mortgage on the property.

Besides the cash payments, the owner should include an allowance for the decrease in the value of the property. Even though a house, for example, is kept in good repair, it gradually wears out and becomes less valuable. Furthermore, with the passage of time, changes in style of architecture or changes in the character of the neighborhood may make the property less desirable and thus decrease its value. This decrease in value, resulting from wear and the passage of time, is called *depreciation*. For residential and business property the annual rate of depreciation may average from 2% to 4% of the value of the building.

To find the annual net income from an investment in real estate. The annual net income is the amount remaining after deducting the annual expenses from the annual rental income.

Annual Rental Income − Annual Expenses = Annual Net Income

Exercise 1   Written

1. Find the house owner's annual net income in each of the following cases.

	Monthly Rent Income	Annual Expenses					
		Taxes	Repairs	Insurance	Interest	Depreciation	Other Expenses
a	$ 95	$170	$122	$24	$237	$200	$15 $372
b	140	250	155	30	215	230	17
c	235	425	215	50	None	375	19
d	190	370	165	35	None	320	16

2. Hurley bought a house and lot for $15,000, paying $6,000 in cash and giving a mortgage for the balance. He rented the house immediately to a tenant for $170 a month, and for the first year his expenses were:

7% interest on the mortgage of $9,000
2% depreciation on the house valued at $12,000
Taxes, repairs, insurance, and other expenses, $685
What was his net income for the year? $485

3. Janda bought a two-family house for $18,000, paying $8,000 in cash and giving a 6% mortgage for the remainder. During the first year of ownership, he received $105 a month for the rent of each apartment. His expenses for the year were:

Interest at 6% on the amount of the mortgage
2% depreciation on the building valued at $15,500
Taxes, repairs, insurance, and other expenses, $835
What was his net income for the year?

To find the rate of income on an investment in real estate. The rate of income is based on the owner's cash investment in the property. It is found by dividing the annual net income by the cash investment.

$$\text{Rate of Income} = \frac{\text{Annual Net Income}}{\text{Cash Investment}}$$

Exercise 2 Written

1. Find to the nearest tenth of a percent the rate of income the owner realizes on his cash investment in each of the following:

	Cash Investment	Monthly Rental Income	Annual Expenses	
			Interest on Mortgage	Other Expenses
a	$ 4,000	$100	$ 5,000 @ 7%	$ 540 7.8%
b	7,000	140	$ 5,000 @ 6%	730
c	15,000	300	$10,000 @ 8%	1,580
d	12,000	225	$ 8,000 @ $5\frac{1}{2}$%	1,240
e	9,000	110	None	650

2. Morris bought a two-family house for $16,000, paying $6,000 cash and giving a 7% mortgage for the remainder. During the first year, he rented each apartment at $100 a month. In addition to interest on the mortgage, other expenses for the year amounted to $1,080. What rate of income, to the nearest tenth of a percent, did he receive on his cash investment? 10.3%

3. For $35,000 Rider can buy a piece of store property which rents for $400 a month. Taxes, insurance, and miscellaneous expenses average $1,045 annually. Depreciation and repairs are estimated at $1,025 a year. If he pays $35,000 cash for the property, what rate of income will he realize on his investment?

4. Healy bought a four-family apartment house for $45,000, paying $20,000 cash and giving a mortgage at 7% for the balance. For the first year, each of the four apartments was rented at $130 a month. Expenses for the year were:

Interest at 7% on the mortgage of $25,000
Depreciation at 2% of the cost of the property
Taxes, insurance, and other expenses, $1,825
Find his rate of income to the nearest tenth of a percent.

REVIEW ASSIGNMENT 35a

1. **a** Find the amount that is 40% more than $35.50.
   b Find the amount that is $37\frac{1}{2}$% less than $18.80.

2. Find the interest on $533.18 for 89 days at 6%.

3. Hill bought a house for $18,400, giving $6,400 cash and a 7% mortgage for the balance. In addition to the interest on the mortgage, his annual expenses were: taxes, $336; insurance, $95; repairs, $215; and depreciation at 2% of the cost of the property. He rented the house for $200 a month. What was Hill's net rate of return on his cash investment, to the nearest tenth of a percent?

4. Heffner bought 60 shares of Lennox Instrument stock at $38\frac{1}{2}$. The broker charged $28.10 for commission. What was Heffner's total investment in the stock?

5. Campbell bought stock for $125 a share, including the broker's commission. The stock paid an annual dividend of 6% on a par value of $100. What rate of income did Campbell receive on his investment?

PART 35b   Figuring the Rent to Charge

To find the rent that must be charged to yield a given rate of income. If the owner desires a stated rate of return on his investment, the annual rental income must be sufficient to cover all annual expenses plus the amount of the net income desired.

Annual Rental Income = Annual Expenses + Annual Net Income

The monthly rent that should be charged is found by dividing the required annual rental income by 12.

Exercise 3   Written

1. In each of the following, find the monthly rent the owner must charge in order to realize the desired annual net income.

	Cost of Property	Desired Annual Net Income	Annual Expenses	
a	$16,000	9% of cost	$ 960	$200
b	25,000	8% of cost	1,720	
c	18,000	9% of cost	1,380	
d	42,500	7% of cost	2,725	
e	62,500	8% of cost	3,820	

2. B. D. Stone pays $24,000 cash for a two-family house. Annual expenses are estimated to average $1,440. He desires an annual income of 8% on his investment. What monthly rental should he charge each tenant? $140

3. A house cost $14,000. Annual expenses are: taxes, $350; insurance, $42; repairs, $234; water, $18; depreciation, 2% of the cost of the house. What monthly rent must the owner charge in order to realize 9% net income on his investment?

❯ **4.** Hilton purchases a four-family apartment house for a total cost of $33,500, giving a 7% mortgage for $20,000 and paying the balance in cash. Annual expenses in addition to interest on the mortgage average $2,410. What monthly rent, to the nearest dollar, must Hilton charge for each of the four apartments in order to obtain 10% net income on his cash investment?

REVIEW ASSIGNMENT **35 b**

1. a $90 is what percent of $36?

b What amount is 28% more than $75?

c $18.80 decreased by $37\frac{1}{2}$% of itself gives what amount?

d Find the interest at 6% on $629.15 for 29 days.

2. Mr. Walton purchased a house for $18,000. For how much a month must the house be rented to yield 9% on the original cost and to provide also for the following annual expenses: depreciation, 2% of purchase price; taxes, $460; insurance, $110; repairs, $270?

3. Loomis bought a house for $17,000, paying $6,000 in cash and giving a 7% mortgage for the balance. During the first year, he rented the house for $210 a month. Taxes were $430, repairs and depreciation 4% of the cost of the property, and insurance $94. What rate of income did he receive on his cash investment?

4. Mapes bought some stock at a total cost of $55 per share. During the first year he owned the stock, Mapes received four quarterly dividends of $.85 each per share. What annual rate of income, to the nearest tenth of a percent, did he receive on his investment?

5. Hawkins ordered his broker to sell 60 shares of Computer Science stock at $76\frac{1}{4}$. The commission on the sale was $39.88, and the taxes and other expenses totaled $3.10. What were the net proceeds of the sale?

❯ **6.** Don Gregory desires an annual income of $3,900 from an investment in some $6\frac{1}{2}$%, $1,000 bonds. How many of these bonds must he purchase?

PART | 35c | Special Problems

▶ **To find the investment, given the annual net income and the rate of income.** When the annual net income and the rate of income are known, the amount of the owner's cash investment in the property can be found by dividing the annual net income by the rate of income.

$$\text{Cash Investment} = \frac{\text{Annual Net Income}}{\text{Rate of Income}}$$

▶ Exercise **4** Written

1. Watts is considering the purchase of an apartment house that yields an average annual net income of $3,920. What is the highest price he can afford to pay for it if he desires 8% net income on his investment? $49,000

2. Bishop figures that a certain piece of property will yield an annual net income of $1,485. How much can he afford to pay for it if he wishes to earn 9% on his investment?

3. The total annual rental of a piece of property is $2,800. The annual expenses are $1,365. What is the highest price you can pay for it and still have a 7% return on your investment?

4. The total monthly rental income from a four-family house is $450. The annual expenses total $2,000. If you want to net 8% on your investment, what is the highest price you can afford to offer for the house?

5. A house rents for $160 a month. Annual expenses average $815. How much can Taft afford to pay for the house if he wants to net $8\frac{1}{2}$% on the investment?

▶ **Capital outlay.** A property owner should distinguish carefully between his capital outlay and his expenses. His capital outlay consists of his original investment plus any subsequent expenditures for additions and improvements that make the property more valuable than it was when he acquired it. Such expenditures should be added to his original investment to give his total investment in the property.

On the other hand, expenditures for repairs and replacements do not increase the value of the property. They merely maintain the property in the same condition as when it was acquired. These expenditures should be treated as expenses and deducted from his gross income from the property.

▶ **Exercise 5   Written**

THE NEW DRIVEWAY INCREASES MY CAPITAL INVESTMENT, BUT THE REPAINTING IS JUST AN EXPENSE

1. Washburn buys a house for $12,000. He spends $3,000 for additions and improvements and then rents the house for $190 a month. Taxes and insurance cost $485 a year, and he allows $560 a year for upkeep and depreciation. What is his rate of income on investment, calculated to the nearest tenth of a percent?   **8.2%**

2. L. W. Hull can purchase a house for $8,000. It will cost an additional $4,000 for reconditioning and modernization. The total annual expense is estimated at $780. What monthly rent would he have to charge, after modernizing the house, in order to realize a net income of 8% on his total investment?

3. O. J. Howe is considering the purchase of a house priced at $7,000. It will cost an additional $1,000 for certain improvements, after which the house can be rented for $95 a month. Annual expenses will average $520. What is the highest amount he can afford to offer for the property in its present condition if he wishes to net 8% on his investment?

REVIEW ASSIGNMENT **35** c

1. a What percent of $45 is $54?

b $56 increased by 45% of itself gives what amount?

c Find the interest on $189.75 for 86 days at 6%.

d Find the interest on $180 for 134 days at 5%.

2. What monthly rent must be charged for a house costing $14,000 to realize a net income of $7\frac{1}{2}\%$ on the original investment if taxes are $350, repairs and depreciation, $550, and insurance, $90?

3. Bickford is buying a washer priced at $280. An allowance of $30 is being given him for his old washer as a down payment. The installment contract provides for 6% interest on the unpaid balance and a service charge of $3.80. On a 12-month contract, what will be the amount of each monthly payment?

4. What is the rate of income on a $500 bond, bearing interest at 5%, if it is purchased for $400?

5. Robertson bought an apartment house for $30,000, paying $10,000 in cash and giving a 7% mortgage for the remainder. He rented it for $450 a month. Besides interest on the mortgage, his expenses for the year were as follows: taxes, $910; fuel oil, $940; electricity, $170; insurance, $180; miscellaneous, $240; depreciation, $600. What rate of income did he receive on his cash investment?

6. A loan of $360 is to be repaid in 18 monthly payments of $21.80 each. What is the annual percentage rate on this loan? (Use the tables on page 205.)

◗ **7.** Express .012 as a common fraction in lowest terms.

◗ **8.** The total annual rental of a piece of business property is $6,790. The annual expenses are $3,350. What is the highest price you can afford to pay for the property if you desire a net return of 8% on your investment?

GENERAL REVIEW

1. a Add: $6\frac{1}{4}$, $4\frac{1}{3}$, $9\frac{1}{5}$.   **d** Divide $36\frac{1}{4}$ by $\frac{1}{2}$.
b Subtract $138\frac{7}{8}$ from $238\frac{1}{3}$.   **e** Multiply .87 by .759.
c Multiply $24\frac{1}{3}$ by $12\frac{1}{2}$.   **f** Find $\frac{1}{4}\%$ of $596.
g Express $\frac{7}{19}$ as a percent to the nearest tenth of a percent.

2. Barber's checkbook balance on May 31 was $483.17. His May bank statement showed a balance of $540.14. There was a service charge of $1.55 which had not been deducted in the checkbook. Checks were outstanding for $10.18, $31.12, and $17.22. Prepare a reconciliation statement.

3. Edith Rand, an office worker, is paid $98.25 for a $37\frac{1}{2}$-hour week. What is her hourly rate of pay?

4. Watkins, an appliance salesman, is paid a monthly salary of $500, plus 10% commission on all sales in excess of $8,000 in a single month. For the months of May, June, and July, his sales were $9,140, $7,830, and $11,370, respectively. What was the amount of Watkins' total earnings for the three months?

5. Hoff is employed on the basis of an 8-hour day with time and one-half for overtime. His regular hourly pay is $2.45. During one week he worked the following hours:

Mon., 8; Tues., 6; Wed., 8; Thurs., 10; Fri., 10

From Hoff's total earnings, 4.8% was deducted for FICA taxes. In addition, $16.60 was deducted for federal withholding tax. What net amount did Hoff receive as take-home pay for the week?

6. A salesman's average sales for 9 weeks were $1,245 a week. After computing that average, he worked 3 weeks and his sales amounted to $1,254, $1,169, and $1,232, respectively. Find his average weekly sales for the 12 weeks, to the nearest dollar.

7. For a 3-month period, a student received $5.25 as interest on his savings account of $420. What annual rate of interest did this savings bank pay him?

8. The Wolfe Steel Company sold $6,000,000 (par value) of bonds to raise funds for enlarging its plant. The bonds pay interest at the rate of $6\frac{3}{4}\%$. What is the total cost of the interest per year on these bonds?

9. Mr. Clary obtained a bank loan on his note for $750. The bank deducted in advance 24 months' interest at 6% on the amount of the note and gave Clary the proceeds. Clary repaid the note in 24 equal monthly payments.

a What was the amount of the finance charge on this loan?

b What was the amount financed?

10. A table that retails for $80 cash may be purchased for $11.20 down and $4.75 a month for 16 months. By what percent does the installment price exceed the cash price?

11. Palmer deposited $840 in a savings bank on April 1. The bank adds interest quarterly at the rate of 4% per year. How much did Palmer have in his account one year later?

12. A 7% note for $550 dated May 10 was paid in full on July 16. What was the amount of the July 16 payment?

13. Henry Marden purchased 30 shares of common stock at a total cost of $2,429, including the broker's commission. He kept the stock 2 years and received regular quarterly dividends of $1.75 per share. He then sold the stock and received $2,669.50 as net proceeds from the sale. What was Marden's total gain from owning and selling this stock?

14. On December 31, James Wheeler's checkbook showed a balance of $742.61, and his bank statement showed a balance of $766.04. There was a service charge of $2.18 reported on the bank statement. A deposit of $135 on December 31 had not been recorded on the bank statement, and checks were outstanding for $121.06 and $49.55. A check for $25 had been recorded on the check stub as $15. Prepare a reconciliation statement.

15. On January 2, R. D. Burns deposited $800 in a savings bank that pays 5% interest per year. On July 1 he made an additional deposit of $400. Interest was added to his account on April 1, July 1, and October 1. How much money did he have in his account on October 1?

UNIT Eight

Home Expense Problems

SECTION 36

Owning a Home

In recent years an increasing percentage of families have become homeowners. Owning a home may or may not be cheaper than renting. Often it costs more; but many families feel that the advantages of home ownership are worth the extra cost.

PART 36a Figuring Ownership Costs

Expense of home ownership. The annual or monthly expense of home ownership includes such items as taxes, insurance, repairs, depreciation, and interest on the mortgage loan. It should also include interest on the owner's cash investment in the property, because he loses the interest he would have received had he invested the money in some other way.

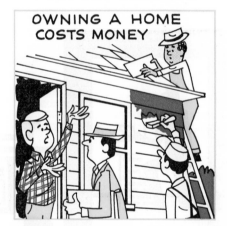

OWNING A HOME COSTS MONEY

Exercise 1 Written

1. Emil Pitt can purchase a one-family house for his own use for $12,000 cash. He estimates the annual expense for taxes, insurance, repairs, and depreciation at $780. In order to make the cash payment, he will have to withdraw the amount from a savings account that pays 5% interest annually. What will it cost him per month to own the house? **$115**

In the total annual expense, include the interest lost on the amount withdrawn from the savings bank.

2. Dan Moss is paying $98 a month for rent of a house which he can purchase for $9,600 cash. He estimates that taxes will amount to $240, repairs $144, insurance $36, and depreciation $192, annually. He can earn 5% on his money in a savings account. How much would he save annually by owning the house instead of renting it?

3. Greer can rent a certain house for $1,860 a year or he can purchase it for $14,500 by paying $6,000 cash and giving a 7% mortgage for the remainder. He estimates taxes will be $420, insurance $35, depreciation $295, and other expenses $320 a year. Allowing 5% interest on his cash investment, what would be the yearly cost of owning the home?

4. a In Problem 3, would it be cheaper for Greer to rent the house or to buy it?

b How much would be saved annually by the cheaper method?

5. H. W. Myer, proprietor of a retail clothing business, can buy for $37,500, cash, the building in which his store is located. The annual expense for taxes, insurance, repairs, depreciation, and other items is estimated at $1,980. He considers his money is worth 6% to him in his business. Which would be cheaper, and how much cheaper per month, to buy the building or to continue renting it at $380 a month?

Building a home. Many people prefer to have a house constructed according to their own plans instead of buying one already built. This requires both the purchase of a building lot and the construction of the house.

The total cost of the lot consists of the purchase price and the cost of the title search, legal fees, and any other expenses of acquiring ownership of the property. It should also include the cost of grading and landscaping.

The total cost of the home includes the total cost of the lot, all construction costs, and the cost of the architect's and builder's services if there are any expenditures for these items.

Arrangements may be made with a building contractor to construct the house either for a contract price or on what is known as the *cost-plus basis*. Under the latter plan, upon completing the work, the builder submits a bill for the total amount he has spent for labor, materials, and other items, plus a percentage of the total for his services.

Exercise 2   Written

1. Boris Hake bought a building lot 65 ft. wide by 175 ft. deep for $2,600. The title search cost $52 and legal fees cost $85. What was the total cost of the lot? $2,737

2. Floyd Parke purchases a lot having a frontage of 75 ft. He pays $45 a front foot for the land and, in addition, pays $208 for legal fees and title search. What is the total cost of the lot to Mr. Parke?

3. Byron Tice contracted with the Rossi Building Company to construct a house according to his plans and specifications on the basis of cost plus 20%. On completion of the work, the building company showed its costs were $28,345.60. What amount did Mr. Tice have to pay the building company? $34,014.72

4. Kenyon estimates the cost of building a house as follows: Lot, $3,000; lumber and other materials, $7,400; electrical, plumbing, and heating installations, $5,600; labor, $9,800; other expenses, $700. He can buy a similar house already built for $25,000. By what percent does the cost of building the house exceed the cost of the house already built?

5. A contractor offered to build Julian Kent a house on a cost-plus-15% basis. The expenditures by the contractor were as follows:

Excavating, $475   Plumbing, $2,645
Masonry, $1,960   Heating, $2,825
Carpentry and lumber, $16,450   Electrical work, $1,840
Painting, $1,800   Other expense, $1,375

What was the total cost of the house to Kent?

6. Ira Doyle, desiring to build his own home, bought a lot costing a total of $3,500. He paid an architect $375 for drawing plans for the house. A building contractor agreed to build the house on the basis of cost plus 20%. The contractor's costs of labor and materials totaled $29,750. Mr. Doyle also paid a landscape gardener $900 for landscaping the grounds.

   a What was the total cost of the house?

   b What was the total cost of the land?

   c What was the total cost of the house and land?

The total cost of the house consists of the cost of the labor and materials, the builder's fee, and the architect's fee. The total cost of the land consists of the cost of the lot and the landscaping.

REVIEW ASSIGNMENT 36 a

   1. a Multiply $16,000 by .25364.

   b Divide 63 by 14,000.

   c $24.75 is what percent greater than $22.50?

2. Norton pays $145 a month rent for a house that he can buy for $13,500. How much would he save in a year by buying the house if the taxes, repairs, depreciation, and insurance will cost $930, and money is worth 5%?

3. A dwelling cost $18,000. Annual expenses are estimated at $1,080. What monthly rent must the owner charge in order to realize 7% net income on the investment?

4. Pillsbury purchased 80 shares of Ford Motor stock at $54\frac{1}{4}$ and paid a commission charge of $38.70. What was his total investment?

5. What is the amount of Joel Dunn's annual income from 80 shares of stock that pay quarterly dividends of $62\frac{1}{2}$¢ a share?

6. Stiles bought stock at a total cost of $75 a share. The stock paid an annual dividend of $4\frac{1}{2}$% on a par value of $100. What rate of income did Stiles receive on his investment?

7. A stock that pays a semiannual dividend of $2.25 can be purchased for a total cost of $95. What is the rate of income on the investment, to the nearest tenth of a percent?

PART 36b Financing the Purchase

Financing the purchase of a home with a mortgage. A person buying a home usually borrows a part of the purchase price from a bank

or some other lender. He does this by signing a note and giving the lender a mortgage on the property. The mortgage serves as security for the repayment of the loan. It gives the lender the right to take possession of the property if the borrower fails to pay the interest and principal in accordance with the agreement.

WE CAN PAY FOR IT IN 30 YEARS!

FOR SALE

Amortized mortgages. Most mortgages provide for the gradual repayment or amortization of the loan over the life of the mortgage. Usually, equal monthly payments are required. Each pays off a small part of the principal plus the interest due on the unpaid balance.

The table on page 272 shows the monthly payments necessary to amortize loans of various amounts over different periods of time at 7% interest.

7%   MONTHLY PAYMENT TO AMORTIZE A LOAN   7%

Term→ Loan ↓	5 Years	10 Years	15 Years	20 Years	25 Years
$ 1,000	19.81	11.62	8.99	7.76	7.07
3,000	59.41	34.84	26.97	23.26	21.21
5,000	99.01	58.06	44.95	38.77	35.34
8,000	158.41	92.89	71.91	62.03	56.55
10,000	198.02	116.11	89.89	77.53	70.68
15,000	297.02	174.17	134.83	116.30	106.02
20,000	396.03	232.22	179.77	155.06	141.36

Using the amortization table. Assume that Craig Grogan is about to purchase a home costing $20,000. He has $5,000, and his local bank will lend him $15,000 on a 20-year, 7% mortgage on the property. For determining the monthly payments necessary to pay off the loan, the bank uses an amortization table similar to the one shown above.

On the "$15,000" line of the table, $116.30 appears in the "20 years" column. This is the monthly payment necessary to pay off the loan in 20 years.

In 20 years there are 20 × 12, or 240 months. The total amount Grogan will pay the bank over the period of 240 months is 240 × $116.30, which is $27,912.

Since the loan is for $15,000, he will be paying $27,912 − $15,000, or $12,912, for interest over the 20-year period. The average monthly interest cost will be $12,912 ÷ 240, or $53.80.

Exercise 3   Written

In each of the following nine problems, find (a) the monthly payment necessary to amortize the loan, (b) the total of all the payments, (c) the total interest cost, and (d) the average monthly interest cost, to the nearest cent.

1. Drake borrows $8,000 on a 15-year, 7% amortized mortgage.   (a) $71.91; (b) $12,943.80; (c) $4,943.80; (d) $27.47

Amt. of Loan	Int. Rate	Term of Loan	Amt. of Loan	Int. Rate	Term of Loan
2. $1,000	7%	5 yr.	**5.** $20,000	7%	15 yr.
3. 5,000	7%	20 yr.	**6.** 15,000	7%	25 yr.
4. 3,000	7%	10 yr.	**7.** 10,000	7%	10 yr.

8. Greeley is financing the purchase of a home with a $5,000 mortgage. He agrees to pay off the loan, with 7% interest, in equal monthly payments over a 10-year period.

9. Osborne purchases a home for $30,000, paying $10,000 in cash and carrying the remainder on a 7% mortgage that is to be amortized with equal monthly payments over 25 years.

REVIEW ASSIGNMENT **36** b

1. a What percent of $75 is $120?

b Find the number of days from April 2 to July 24.

c Find the interest at 6% on $215.35 for 87 days.

2. Corley considers purchasing for $34,500 the building in which his store is located. He estimates the annual expenses as follows: taxes, $1,035; insurance, $175; repairs and depreciation, $1,250. His money is worth 6% to him in his business.

   a Which would be cheaper, to buy the building or to continue to rent the store at $425 a month?

   b How much would he save annually?

3. Tyler purchased a two-family house for $16,000, paying $6,000 in cash and giving a 6% mortgage for the balance. During the first year, he rented each apartment for $85 a month. Total expenses for the year, including interest, amounted to $1,560. What rate of return did Tyler realize on his cash investment?

4. A 60-day note for $675, dated May 25, bears interest at 5%. Find the date of maturity of the note and the total amount due for payment on the date of maturity.

5. An air conditioner that sells for $150 cash can be purchased for $30 down and $10.90 a month for 12 months.

   a What is the finance charge on the installment purchase?

   b What is the amount financed?

   c What is the finance charge per $100 of amount financed?

   d What is the annual percentage rate? (Use the table on page 212.)

6. Hall paid a total of $1,315 for 30 shares of stock. He kept the stock three years during which time he received regular quarterly dividends of $.60 per share. He then sold the stock and received $1,286 after all expenses had been deducted. What was Hall's net gain from owning and selling this stock?

▶ **7. a** $54 is $\frac{4}{9}$ of what amount?

   b Express .08$\frac{3}{4}$ as a common fraction in lowest terms.

▶ **8.** The annual rent from an apartment house is $6,080. The annual total expenses are $2,960. What is the highest price you can afford to pay for the house if you desire 7$\frac{1}{2}$% net income on your investment?

SECTION 37

Taxes on the Home

Assessed valuation of real estate. One of the major expenses of owning real estate is the property tax levied and collected by the community in which the property is located.

The amount of the tax is based upon the *assessed valuation* of the property. This value is determined by local tax assessors. The assessed value is often lower than the market value of the property, sometimes as little as 25% or 30% of the market value.

The tax rate. The amount of tax a property owner must pay depends upon the assessed valuation of his property and the tax rate.

The method of expressing the tax rate varies in different communities. In some, the rate is expressed as a certain number of *dollars* for each $100 or $1,000 unit of assessed valuation; as, for example, $2.85 per $100 or $28.50 per $1,000.

In others, the rate may be expressed as a certain number of *mills* or *cents* for each $1 unit of assessed valuation, such as 28.5 mills per $1 or 2.85 cents per $1.

To find the amount of a property owner's tax when the tax rate is expressed in dollars per $100 or per $1,000 of assessed valuation. Each property owner receives a tax bill once or twice a year from his local tax collector. The bill shows the assessed valuation of his property, the tax rate, and the amount of the tax.

For example, the tax bill Frederick Montgomery received today shows that he owns property assessed at $3,500. It shows also that the rate is $2.462 on each $100, and that the tax due is $86.17. The tax due is figured in this manner:

$3,500 ÷ $100 = 35, number of $100 units in $3,500
35 × $2.462 = $86.17, amount of tax

If the tax were $24.62 per $1,000, Montgomery's tax would be found in the following manner:

$3,500 ÷ $1,000 = 3.5, number of $1,000 units in $3,500
3.5 × $24.62 = $86.17, amount of tax

Exercise 1 Written

1. Find the amount of the tax bill in each of the following:

	Assessed Valuation	Tax Rate	
a	$ 8,000	$3.987 per $100	$318.96
b	13,000	4.226 per $100	
c	9,600	5.325 per $100	
d	$10,500	$55.45 per $1,000	$582.23
e	8,400	35.60 per $1,000	
f	7,200	27.90 per $1,000	

2. The tax rate in Weston for the current year is $5.348 per $100. What should be the amount of R. Y. Milton's tax bill if he owns property assessed at $7,800?

3. What tax must Mark Blaine pay on his home, which is assessed at $9,300, if the tax rate is $27.43 per $1,000?

4. To the nearest cent, find the tax on property assessed at $4,500 if the tax rate is $5.1268 per $100.

5. The tax rate in the village of Linvale is $4.6355 per $100. If real estate worth $6,000 is assessed for 80% of its value, find the amount of the tax bill. $222.50

6. The tax rate in a certain village is $5.3635 per $100 of assessed valuation. Vernon Kress owns two pieces of real estate in this village, valued at $8,400 and $7,200, respectively, and assessed at 75% of their value. Find the total tax that he must pay.

To find the amount of a property owner's tax when the rate is expressed in mills or cents per $1. To find the tax when the rate is expressed in terms of mills or cents per $1, first change the mills or cents to an equivalent number of dollars. Then multiply that result by the number of dollars of assessed valuation.

Since there are 10 mills in one cent and 100 cents in one dollar, there are 1,000 mills in one dollar. Hence, to change mills to dollars, divide the number of mills by 1,000 and prefix a dollar sign to the result. Thus,

$$36.4 \text{ mills} = \$.0364 \ (36.4 \div 1,000)$$

Similarly, since there are 100 cents in one dollar, to change cents to dollars, divide the number of cents by 100.

$$2.87 \text{ cents} = \$.0287 \ (2.87 \div 100)$$

Example

The tax rate in Kenholm is 34.5 mills per dollar of assessed valuation. Find the tax to be paid on property assessed at $4,000.

Solution	Explanation
34.5 mills = $.0345	The number of dollars equivalent to
4,000 × $.0345 = $138	34.5 mills is 34.5 ÷ 1,000, or $.0345. The rate, 34.5 mills per $1, is therefore
Ans. *$138*	equal to $.0345 per $1.

Since the tax is $.0345 on each dollar of assessed valuation, the tax on $4,000 is 4,000 × $.0345, or $138.

Exercise 2   Written

1. Find the amount of tax to be paid in each of the following:

Assessed Valuation	Tax Rate per $1		Assessed Valuation	Tax Rate per $1
a $ 6,800	45 mills $306		**e** $ 8,000	4.15 cents $332
b 7,200	31 mills		**f** 7,500	3.45 cents
c 11,400	28.5 mills		**g** 12,000	3.25 cents
d 8,500	9.31 mills		**h** 6,500	.95 cents

2. The tax rate in Leetown is 53 mills per dollar of assessed valuation. Find the tax to be paid on property assessed at $16,400.

3. What tax must Arnold Rice pay on his home, which is assessed at $9,500, if the tax rate is 44.5 mills per $1?

4. Thomas Gable owns real estate valued at $13,200, which is assessed at $\frac{4}{5}$ of its value. If the tax rate is 39.4 mills per $1, what is the amount of Mr. Gable's tax bill? $416.06

5. The tax rate in School District No. 5 is 34.2 mills per dollar of assessed valuation. What total tax must W. A. Munsey pay if he owns two pieces of property valued at $22,000 and $8,000, respectively, which are assessed at 60% of their value?

REVIEW ASSIGNMENT **37**

1. a Multiply $8,500 by .09846.

b $132 is what part less than $220?

c $240 is what percent of $96?

d Find the interest on $375 for 97 days at 6%.

2. Westfall owns a house and lot assessed at $8,200. The tax rate in his community last year was $53.221 per $1,000 of assessed valuation. What was the amount of Westfall's tax bill for this house and lot last year?

3. You are offered a portable typewriter by dealer *A* for a down payment of $20, with 52 weekly payments of $2.50 each. Dealer *B* offers a similar typewriter for a down payment of $25, with 12 monthly payments of $10 each. How much will you save by accepting the better of the two offers?

4. An investor bought six $1,000 bonds at $88\frac{3}{8}$. How much did he invest in the bonds if the brokerage charge was $2.50 per bond?

5. An investor pays $600 for a $1,000 bond bearing interest at $4\frac{1}{2}$%. What will be the rate of income on his investment?

6. What is the rate of income on a $5\frac{1}{2}$% bond purchased at 110?

When the par value per bond is not given, assume a par value of $1,000 and solve accordingly.

7. Mr. Dell obtained a mortgage loan of $10,000 on his new home and agreed to repay the principal and interest in payments of $90 a month over a period of 15 years. What amount of money will he have paid for interest during the life of the mortgage?

8. Some furniture that sells for $450 cash can be purchased for $50 down and $19.90 a month for 24 months.

a What is the finance charge on the installment purchase?

b What is the amount financed?

c What is the annual percentage rate?   (Use the table on page 212.)

⊗ **9.** Express .13$\frac{1}{3}$ as a common fraction in lowest terms.

⊗ **10.** How many $1,000, 6% bonds must be purchased in order to obtain an annual income of $4,500 from the investment?

SECTION 38

Insuring the Home

The purpose of insuring a home is to protect the homeowner against loss resulting primarily from damage to or destruction of the property by fire.

PART 38a   Figuring the Premium

Fire insurance and extended coverage. Protection against loss by fire can be obtained from a fire insurance company at a nominal cost.

For a small additional premium, *extended coverage* can be obtained. This is additional insurance which includes protection against loss from such causes as windstorm, lightning, hail, rain, water, smoke, falling aircraft, and explosion.

Terms used in insurance. The company from which the insurance is purchased is referred to as the *insurer*. The person who is protected against loss is known as the *insured*. The contract between the insurance company and the insured is called the *policy*. The amount of insurance for which the policy is written is referred to as the *face* of the policy. The sum that is paid to the insurance company for the protection provided by the policy is called the *premium*.

Premium rates. Premium rates are usually based on $100 units of insurance or coverage as it is sometimes called. Thus, the annual rate on Matt Denby's house is quoted by the fire insurance company at $.40 per $100. If Denby insures the house for $12,000, the premium for one year is $48.

$12,000 ÷ $100 = 120, number of $100 units in $12,000

120 × $.40 = $48, amount of premium for one year

The basic rates are annual rates or rates for one year. Rates for the common longer terms are generally as follows:

Term	Term Rate
3 years	2.7 times the annual rate
5 years	4.4 times the annual rate

Thus, if the annual rate is $.40 per $100, the rate for a three-year policy, for example, would be 2.7 times $.40, or $1.08 per $100.

Exercise 1 Written

1. Find the premium for one year in each of the following:

	Face of Policy	Annual Rate			Face of Policy	Annual Rate
a	$ 9,000	$.27	$24.30	d	$17,000	$.42
b	8,000	.24		e	14,500	.54
c	13,000	.31		f	24,800	.66

2. Find the total premium on each of the following policies for the term indicated:

	Face of Policy	Annual Rate	Term of Policy			Face of Policy	Annual Rate	Term of Policy
a	$12,000	$.30	3 years	$97.20	d	$25,000	$.44	3 years
b	7,500	.20	3 years		e	16,000	.35	5 years
c	15,000	.25	5 years		f	40,000	.60	5 years

3. What is the annual fire insurance premium on a house insured for $18,500 at $.29 per $100?

4. A house valued at $14,000 is insured annually for 80% of its value at 32 cents per hundred. What is the amount of the annual premium?

5. Amato insures his house each year for $13,500 at the annual rate of $.20 per $100. A 3-year policy, however, costs 2.7 times as much as a 1-year policy. How much would Amato save by buying a 3-year policy instead of three separate 1-year policies?

$8.10

6. A house was insured for $20,000 for a five-year term. The quoted rate was $.28 per $100 for a one-year policy or 4.4 times that amount for a five-year policy. How much was saved in one five-year period by taking out one five-year policy instead of a one-year policy every year for five years?

7. McCoy insured his house for three years for $12,500. The rate for the entire three-year period was 59.4 cents per $100. What was the average annual cost of this policy?

8. Norton buys a 5-year fire insurance policy for $22,500 at a total rate of $.792 per hundred. What is the average annual cost of the insurance?

Short-term policies and cancellations by the insured. A fire insurance policy for less than a year is called a *short-term policy*. The premium is determined by taking a certain percent of the annual premium. This percent is obtained from a table of standard short-term rates.

For example, the table shows that the premium on a policy for 6 months is 60% of the premium for one year. Thus, if the premium on a 1-year policy is $50, the premium on a 6-month policy is 60% of $50, or $30.

The short-rate percents are used also in finding how much is to be refunded when a policy is canceled by the insured. For example, if the insured cancels a 1-year policy at the end of six months, the company will retain 60% of the premium and refund 40%. If the premium for the year was $50, the amount refunded would be 40% of $50, or $20.

❯ Policies canceled by the insurance company. On a policy canceled by the insurance company, the refund must be calculated on a *pro rata basis*. This means that the amount of the refund must be in proportion to the unexpired time.

For example, suppose the insured pays a premium of $50 on a 1-year policy and the company cancels the policy at the end of 90 days. The unexpired time is 365 − 90, or 275 days. Hence, 275/365, or

55/73, of the premium must be refunded. This amount is 55/73 × $50, or $37.67.

Exercise 2   Written

1. According to the table of short-term rates, the premium on a 90-day policy is 35% of the annual premium. Find the premium on a 90-day policy of $7,500 if the annual rate is $.64 per $100.

$16.80

2. A man insures a building for $30,000 for 9 months. What premium does he pay if the annual rate is $.44 per $100 and the premium for 9 months is 80% of the annual premium?

3. On March 18, Riston took out a 1-year fire insurance policy on his house for $12,500, paying an annual premium of $.40 a $100. Eight months later he sold the house and canceled the policy. How much should be refunded to Riston if 74% of the yearly premium is retained by the insurance company? $13

4. Berger paid $91 for a 3-year policy and canceled it 14 months after it was issued. The insurance company retained 42.4% of the premium and returned the remainder.

a What amount did Berger receive from the company?

b What did the insurance cost him for the 14 months?

❯ 5. Hill paid $40 for the premium on a 1-year fire insurance policy. After it was in force 155 days, the policy was canceled by the insurance company. How much should the company return to Hill?

REVIEW ASSIGNMENT 38a

1. a Divide 817 by 95,000.

b $105 is what part less than $135?

c What amount is 25% less than $35.48?

d Express .75 as a common fraction in lowest terms.

e Find the interest on $987.50 for 11 days at 5%.

2. Lee insures his house valued at $15,500 at 80% of its value. If the rate is $.44 per $100, find the amount of the premium.

3. The annual insurance rate on Nord's house is $.36 per $100. The 3-year rate is 2.7 times as much. If Nord insures the house for $13,000, how much would he save by buying one 3-year policy instead of a 1-year policy each year for 3 years?

4. Bemis insured his house valued at $17,500 for 80% of its value for 3 years. The rate for the entire 3-year policy was $.837 per $100. What was the average yearly cost of this insurance?

5. What monthly rent must be charged for a house costing $14,500 to realize a net income of 8% on the investment if the annual expenses amount to $700?

6. The tax rate for the current year in a certain community is $25.22 per $1,000. If property worth $17,500 is assessed for 40% of its value, what will be the amount of the tax bill?

7. A mortgage loan of $5,000 is to be repaid over a period of 15 years at the rate of $45 a month. What will be the total cost of the interest over the 15-year period?

8. A family pays $155 a month rent for a house it can buy for $15,400. Annual expenses are estimated at $1,000. If money is worth 5%, would it be cheaper to buy the house or to continue renting it? How much cheaper would it be per year?

❯   **9. a** What amount increased by 25% of itself equals $220?
     b What amount decreased by $\frac{2}{5}$ of itself equals $2.25?

❯   **10.** The total rental income from a business building is $8,700. The annual expenses are $4,140. What is the highest price a buyer should pay for the property if he desires a net return of 8% on his investment?

PART 38b   Settlement of Fire Loss

Settlement of loss under an ordinary policy. In the event of fire damage, the insurance company must be immediately notified. The company then sends an adjuster to examine the property and decide upon the amount of the loss. Under an ordinary policy, the company will pay the full amount of the loss up to the face of the policy. The company is not liable, however, for any loss in excess of the amount for which the property is insured.

Exercise 3   Oral

State the amount of fire loss the insurance company will pay under an ordinary policy in each of the following cases:

	Property Insured for	Fire Loss		Property Insured for	Fire Loss
1.	$16,000	$3,200	5.	$6,000	$4,500
2.	9,500	9,000	6.	5,000	5,800
3.	8,000	5,000	7.	8,000	3,000
4.	7,000	9,000	8.	7,500	7,800

Division of fire loss among several companies. Property is sometimes insured with more than one company. In such cases, when fire damage occurs, the amount of the loss is distributed among the companies in proportion to the amount of each policy.

Example

An apartment house is insured in the Concord Insurance Company for $50,000 and in the Patriot Insurance Company for $30,000. How much should each company pay on a fire loss of $32,000?

Solution

$50,000 + $30,000 = $80,000,$ *total insurance*

$\dfrac{\$50,000}{\$80,000} = \dfrac{5}{8},$ *proportion of loss borne by the Concord Insurance Company*

$\dfrac{\$30,000}{\$80,000} = \dfrac{3}{8},$ *proportion of loss borne by the Patriot Insurance Company*

$\dfrac{8}{8},$ *total*

$\dfrac{5}{8} \times \$32,000 = \$20,000,$ *amount paid by the Concord Insurance Company*

$\dfrac{3}{8} \times \$32,000 = \$12,000,$ *amount paid by the Patriot Insurance Company*

$\$32,000,$ *total*

Exercise **4**   Written

1. In the following, find each company's share of the fire loss.

	Fire Loss	Amount of Insurance Carried by		
		American Company	Pioneer Company	Webster Company
a	$2,000	$ 4,500 $1,200	$ 3,000 $800	None None
b	4,800	7,500	None	$ 4,500
c	3,200	10,000	2,500	None
d	5,400	5,000	15,000	10,000
e	4,500	20,000	10,000	15,000
f	1,500	3,000	7,500	4,500

2. An apartment building was insured in the Fidelity Insurance Company for $28,000 and in the Heritage Insurance Company for $20,000. How much should each company pay on a fire loss of $18,000? Fidelity, $10,500; Heritage, $7,500

3. On a building worth $45,000 the following insurance policies were carried: Liberty Insurance Company, $20,000; Mutual Underwriters Company, $15,000; Casualty Insurance Company, $10,000. How much should each company pay in case of a fire loss amounting to $9,450?

4. The Danforth Corporation owns a factory building which it has insured for $4,000 with Company *A*, for $12,000 with Company *B*, and for $16,000 with Company *C*. A fire loss of $13,000 has occurred. What amount should the Danforth Corporation receive from each of these insurance companies?

◉ **Coinsurance.** Most fires result in only small or partial losses. Seldom does a fire cause total destruction of the property. For this reason there is a tendency on the part of property owners to take out only enough insurance to cover the probable partial losses.

To induce property owners to carry adequate coverage, insurance companies offer reduced rates on policies containing what is known as a *coinsurance clause.* Under this clause, the company is liable for the full amount of any loss or damage up to the face of the policy, provided the property is insured for an amount not less than a specified percent of its value. The percent specified may be 60%, 70%, 80%, or 90%, although it is generally 80%. If the clause specifies 80%, for example, it is said to be an *80% coinsurance clause.*

◉ **Settlement of a fire loss under a coinsurance clause.** Under coinsurance, if property is insured for an amount equal to or greater than the specified percentage of its value, the insurance company is liable for the full amount of any loss up to the face of the policy.

For example, if a house valued at $10,000 is insured under an 80% coinsurance clause for $8,000, which is exactly 80% of the value, the insurance company will be liable for the full amount of any loss up to the face of the policy, $8,000. If the house is insured for $9,000, which is greater than the 80% minimum, the company will be liable for the full amount of any loss up to $9,000.

On the other hand, if the face of the policy is less than the minimum amount indicated by the coinsurance clause, the company is liable for only that fraction of the loss which is equal to the ratio of the face of the policy to the minimum amount.

Thus, if the house valued at $10,000 is insured for only $7,000, which is less than the $8,000 minimum, the company will be liable for only $\frac{7}{8}$ of any loss that occurs, since $7,000 is $\frac{7}{8}$ of $8,000. Hence, in the event of a fire causing $4,000 loss, the company will pay only $\frac{7}{8}$ of $4,000, or $3,500. In other words,

$$\text{Amount Paid by the Company} = \frac{\text{Face of Policy}}{80\% \text{ of Value of the Property}} \times \text{Amount of Loss}$$

In no case, however, will the company pay an amount greater than the amount of the loss or the face of the policy.

The coinsurance type of policy is widely used in insuring business property. It is also used to some extent in insuring residential property, although most residences are insured under ordinary policies.

◉ Exercise 5   Written

1. Find the amount for which the insurance company is liable in each of the following:

	Face of Policy	Amount of Loss	Value of Property	Coinsurance Clause	
a	$28,000	$ 6,400	$40,000	80%	$5,600
b	15,000	4,000	25,000	80%	
c	20,000	7,800	30,000	80%	
d	9,000	3,000	12,500	80%	
e	14,000	13,500	20,000	90%	
f	7,200	5,600	9,000	80%	
g	26,000	28,000	30,000	80%	
h	52,000	25,000	50,000	90%	

2. Don Joslin's house is valued at $15,000. He insured it for $8,000 under a policy containing the 80% coinsurance clause. If fire should cause a $7,500 loss to the house, how much would Mr. Joslin receive under his policy? $5,000

3. A house valued at $12,000 is insured for $8,800, the insurance policy containing an 80% coinsurance clause. What amount must the company pay in case of a fire loss of $6,600?

4. Pearce insured his building worth $30,000 for $21,000 under a fire insurance policy containing an 80% coinsurance clause. If a fire loss of $10,000 occurs, what amount of money should Pearce collect from the insurance company?

REVIEW ASSIGNMENT **38b**

1. a $325 is what part greater than $250?

b $54.24 minus 25% of itself leaves what amount?

c Find the number of days from March 25 to June 8.

d Find the interest at 7% on $372.15 for 40 days.

2. Ritz has a fire insurance policy for $6,000 on his house with the American Insurance Company and another for $9,000 with the Globe Insurance Company. A fire in the house caused a loss of $3,200. How much should Ritz collect from each company?

3. The tax rate this year in Avondale is $51.50 per $1,000. If property worth $25,000 is assessed at 60% of its value, find the amount of the tax bill on this property for this year.

4. Paul Nolan purchased 60 shares of the 7% preferred stock of the Norpax Chemical Corporation at $110. The par value of the stock is $100. What annual dividend does Mr. Nolan receive from this stock?

5. Stern bought some stock at a total cost of $41 per share. The stock paid an annual dividend of 5% on a par value of $50. What rate of return did Stern receive on his investment, to the nearest tenth of a percent?

6. Judson bought 80 shares of stock at a total cost of $4,200. He kept the stock one year, during which time he received regular quarterly dividends of $.45 a share. He then sold the stock and received net proceeds of $4,760. What was Judson's total gain from owning and selling this stock?

7. A 6% note for $1,150, dated April 17, was paid in full on the following July 2. What was the amount of the payment?

8. A lounge chair is offered by dealer A for a down payment of $17.50, with 12 monthly payments of $12.75 each. Dealer B offers a similar chair for a down payment of $6.50 with 52 weekly payments of $3.25 each. How much will the buyer save by taking the better of the two offers?

9. The cash price of a rug is $315. Mrs. Henry purchased the rug by making a down payment of $35 and 18 monthly payments of $17.75 each. What annual percentage rate did Mrs. Henry pay for the privilege of purchasing the rug on the installment plan? (Use the table on page 212.)

10. Marsh insured his house for $9,000 under a policy which contains an 80% coinsurance clause. A fire loss of $2,200 occurred. If the house was valued at $15,000, what amount of money would Marsh collect from the insurance company?

SECTION 39

Checking Electric and Gas Bills

The quantity of gas and electricity consumed in the home is measured by meters.

A company representative reads the meters at regular intervals, usually once a month. In some communities the readings are made every two months.

The meter readings supply the information needed for determining the amount of the customer's bill for the period.

PART 39a   The Electric Bill

Reading the electric meter.   Electric current is measured by an electric meter in units called *kilowatt-hours*, abbreviated as K.W.H. or kw-hr. A kilowatt is 1,000 watts of electric current. A kilowatt-hour represents the flow of 1,000 watts for one hour.

Electric meter

The meter above is read by reading the four dials from left to right. The figure taken from each dial is the last one the pointer has passed. The last figures passed are as follows:

Dial	10,000	1,000	100	10
Last figure passed	7	9	3	2

The reading is 7,932, which means 7,932 kilowatt-hours.

Exercise 1   Oral

Give the reading of each of the following electric meters:

Checking the electric bill. The customer's bill for electricity is usually based on monthly meter readings. The bill illustrated below shows the May 20 reading, 5,610, and the June 19 reading, 5,894. The difference, 284, is the number of kilowatt-hours used during the month.

Electric bill

The amount of the bill, $7.51, is based on the schedule of rates shown below and is found as follows:

First 20 kw-hr.	$1.25
Next 50 kw-hr. at 3.5¢	1.75
Next 130 kw-hr. at 2.5¢	3.25
Next 84 kw-hr. at 1.5¢	1.26
Amount of bill	$7.51

ONTARIO GAS & ELECTRIC CO.
Net Monthly Electric Rate

First	20 kw-hr., or less	$1.25
Next	50 kw-hr.	3.5¢ per kw-hr.
Next	130 kw-hr.	2.5¢ per kw-hr.
Over	200 kw-hr.	1.5¢ per kw-hr.

Exercise 2   Written

In working these problems, use the schedule of rates given above.

1. Find the number of kilowatt-hours used by each customer and the amount of each customer's bill:

	User	Meter Readings		Kilowatt-Hours Used	Amount of Bill
		July 31	August 31		
a	Walter Keeler	481	568	87	$3.43
b	Cora Hobson	1,349	1383		
c	Nathan Lennon	1,682	1818		
d	Willis Noonan	769	975		
e	Howard Ramsey	124	485		

2. Edgar Ashton's electric bill for April shows a reading of 6,691 for April 30 and a reading of 6,527 for March 31. Added to the bill is a local sales tax of 3% on the total charge for the electricity. What is the total amount of the bill? $5.51

3. Simon Elkin's electric meter last month read 8,668. The reading this month is 9,206. What is his total monthly bill, including a tax of 5%?

4. Lisa Cody's electric bill shows a reading of 2,560 on June 23 and a reading of 4,003 on July 23. Added to the bill is a local sales tax amounting to 4% of the total charge for the electricity. What is the total amount of her electric bill for the month?

Cost of operating electric appliances. Many electric appliances are marked to show the number of watt-hours of electricity they use in one hour. An electric light bulb, for example, may be marked "60 WATT." This number is called the *rating* of the bulb. It means that the bulb uses 60 watt-hours of electricity in one hour.

If a 60-watt bulb burns for 10 hours, it will use 10 × 60, or 600 watt-hours of electricity. This is equal to .6 kw-hr, since 600 ÷ 1,000 = .6. If the rate is 5¢ per kw-hr., the cost of the electricity is .6 × 5¢, or 3¢.

Appliances using electric motors are rated in terms of horsepower (HP). One horsepower (1 HP) is equal to 746 watts. Hence, a 1 HP motor would use 746 watt-hours of electricity in one hour.

A FEW PENNIES PAY FOR—

40 MINUTES OF TOAST | 10 HOURS OF LIGHT

Exercise 3   Written

1. Find the kilowatt-hours of electricity used by each of the following appliances for the indicated hours of operation.

	Appliance	Rating	Hours in Operation	
a	Light bulb	75 watts	130	9.75
b	Toaster	800 watts	$5\frac{1}{2}$	
c	Heater	1,600 watts	7	
d	Electric Motor	3 HP	4	8.952
e	Power Saw	$\frac{1}{2}$ HP	6	
f	Vacuum Cleaner	$1\frac{1}{2}$ HP	8	

2. Find the cost of operating:

a Four 75-watt light bulbs, six hours each day for November at $.05 per K.W.H.   **$2.70**

b A 660-watt toaster, 15 minutes a day for 30 days at $.06 per K.W.H.

c A 2-watt electric clock, all day every day for one year at $.04 per K.W.H.

d A 250-watt TV-set, four hours a day each day for March at $.04$\frac{1}{2}$ per K.W.H.

e A $\frac{1}{2}$ HP vacuum cleaner, two hours a week for one year at $.05 per K.W.H.

f A $\frac{1}{2}$ HP electric refrigerator, twelve hours a day for 30 days at $.03$\frac{1}{2}$ per K.W.H.

REVIEW ASSIGNMENT **39** a

1. a Express 1$\frac{1}{2}$ as a decimal.

b $200 is what part smaller than $320?

c $196.50 minus 66$\frac{2}{3}$% of itself leaves what amount?

d Find the interest at 4$\frac{1}{2}$% on $873.45 for 22 days.

e Find the interest on $240 for 113 days at 5%.

2. Varden's electric meter read 8,154 kw-hr. on March 1 and 8,712 kw-hr. on April 1. He paid the following rates:

The first 20 kw-hr. at 5¢ per kw-hr.
The next 50 kw-hr. at 3$\frac{1}{2}$¢ per kw-hr.
The remaining kw-hr. at 2¢ per kw-hr.

What was the amount of Varden's electric bill for March?

3. A certain stock that regularly pays a quarterly dividend of $1.15 can be bought for a total cost of $92 per share. What rate of return will a purchaser of this stock earn on his investment?

4. Poole can buy a used car for $1,050 cash, or for $350 down and $62.50 a month for 12 months. He has enough cash for the down payment and can borrow the balance of the cash price for 12 months at 6%. How much would he save by borrowing to pay cash for the car?

5. Dean purchased a house for $20,000, paying $8,000 in cash and giving a 7% mortgage for the balance. During the first year, he rented the house for $225 a month. Besides interest on the mortgage, other expenses for the year totaled $1,204. What was Dean's rate of income on his original cash investment?

6. A building was insured in three companies as follows: Allied Co., $16,000; Lincoln Co., $18,000; United Co., $6,000. Find each company's share of a fire loss amounting to $3,240.

▶ **7. a** Express .11$\frac{2}{3}$ as a common fraction in lowest terms.
　　b Express $\frac{7}{8}$% as a decimal.

▶ **8.** A building valued at $24,000 was insured for $15,000 under an 80% coinsurance-clause policy. A fire caused a loss of $6,400. How much did the insurance company pay?

PART **39b** The Gas Bill

Reading the gas meter. For cooking and heating purposes many homes use natural or artificial gas. Gas is measured in cubic feet by a meter as shown below.

Gas meter

The meter shown above measures in units of 100 cubic feet. The dials are read from left to right, exactly the same as the dials on an electric meter (page 287). The reading is 484. This means 484 hundred cubic feet which, expressed completely in figures, would be written 48,400 cubic feet.

Many gas companies omit the two end zeros, recording and reporting the readings in units of 100 cubic feet.

Checking the gas bill. The following bill of Miss Barbara Wagner is based on the meter illustrated above.

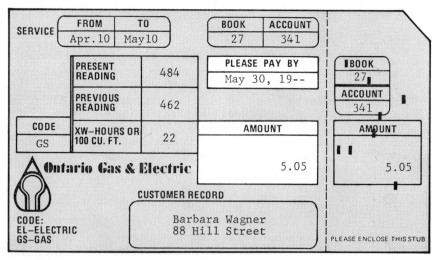

Gas bill

The present meter reading is 484. The reading the preceding month was 462. Hence, 22 hundred cubic feet of gas have been consumed during the month.

The rates of the Ontario Gas and Electric Company are:

ONTARIO GAS & ELECTRIC CO. Net Monthly Gas Rate	
First 300 cu. ft. or less a month..	$1.20
Next 1,700 cu. ft. a month........	21¢ per 100 cu. ft.
Next 5,000 cu. ft. a month........	14¢ per 100 cu. ft.
All over 7,000 cu. ft. a month........	10¢ per 100 cu. ft.

The calculation of Barbara Wagner's bill is as follows:

First 300 cu. ft........................... $1.20
Next 1,700 cu. ft. at 21¢ per 100 cu. ft....... $3.57
Next 200 cu. ft. at 14¢ per 100 cu. ft........ $ .28
Amount of bill.......................... $5.05

Exercise 4   Written

In working these problems, use the schedule of rates given above.

1. Given below are the meter readings shown on the bills of several customers of the Ontario Gas & Electric Co. Find the cubic feet of gas consumed by each user and the amount of each user's bill.

	User	Meter Readings		Cu. Ft. of Gas Used	Amount of Bill
		Present	Prior		
a	Jerome Eckert	409	383	2,600	$5.61
b	Elmer Herber	637	625		
c	Martha Amsler	885	860		
d	Lowell Norwood	290	233		
e	Stella Riley	140	58		

2. On Vivian Redmond's February gas bill the present reading is 366, the previous reading, 321. Find the amount of her gas bill, including a sales tax of 5%. $8.68

3. Eli Nolan's gas meter read 43,700 cubic feet on Oct. 10 and 48,600 cubic feet a month later. There is a local sales tax of 2% on all gas bills. What was Nolan's total bill for the month?

❯ **4.** Wesley Coleman, a customer of the Ontario Gas & Electric Co., desires to keep a record of the amount of gas his family uses each month. He finds, however, that he has lost his receipted gas bill for April. He looks in his checkbook and finds that the check written for the April gas bill was $6.73. How many cubic feet of gas did his family use during April?

REVIEW ASSIGNMENT **39** b

1. a Express $2\frac{1}{4}$ as a decimal.

b $200 is what part smaller than $320?

c What amount is $83\frac{1}{3}\%$ larger than $16.20?

d $28.50 is what percent of $19?

e Find the interest on $282.27 for 100 days at 6%.

2. The June reading of a gas meter was 42,400 cu. ft. while the May reading was 37,600 cu. ft. At $1.85 per thousand cu. ft., find the amount of the gas bill.

3. Blair's electric meter on August 2 read 9,758 K.W.H. A month later it read 10,032 K.W.H. At an average of $3\frac{1}{2}¢$ per K.W.H., find the amount of Blair's electric bill.

4. Davison insures his house for 80% of its value under a 3-year policy. The house is valued at $18,000, and the rate for the entire 3-year period is $.945 per $100. What will be the average annual cost of this insurance?

5. A house and lot worth $18,000 is assessed at 45% of its value. If the tax rate is $62.122 per $1,000 of assessed value, what is the amount of the tax on this property?

6. Sears is paying $110 a month for a house that he can buy for $10,500. The annual expenses are estimated at $735. If money is worth 5%, which would be cheaper, to buy the house or to continue renting it? How much would be saved annually?

7. At the Essex Savings Bank, interest on savings is paid at the rate of 5% a year, compounded quarterly. If Dayter's savings account has a balance of $1,600 on July 1, how much money would be available to him on July 1, 12 months later?

❯ **8. a** $2.28 is $\frac{3}{4}$ of what amount?

b Express $.04\frac{4}{5}$ as a common fraction in lowest terms.

c $216 is what percent greater than $96?

❯ **9.** An apartment building rents for $7,200 a year. Annual expenses are estimated at $3,450. What is the highest price an investor should pay for this property if he must have $7\frac{1}{2}\%$ net income on his investment?

Checking Water Bills

The water meter. The charge for water is by the gallon or by the cubic foot. The quantity consumed is measured by a water meter. The face of a typical water meter is shown at the left.

The figures are read directly from the register below the center of the face. The reading is 13,876 cubic feet.

The needle measures parts of one cubic foot on the dial around the circumference of the face. This dial is used only for testing purposes.

If the previous reading was 9,026 cubic feet, the amount consumed during the period would be 13,876 − 9,026, or 4,850 cubic feet.

Water meter

Present reading	13,876 cubic feet
Previous reading	9,026 cubic feet
Amount consumed	4,850 cubic feet

Meter rates. Water rates vary in different communities. A typical schedule of quarterly rates is shown below.

SUBURBAN WATER COMPANY
Quarterly Meter Rates for Water

First 1,200 cu. ft. or less........$6.50, minimum charge
Next 3,600 cu. ft..............40¢ per 100 cu. ft.
Next 15,000 cu. ft.............30¢ per 100 cu. ft.
Over 19,800 cu. ft.............18¢ per 100 cu. ft.

The water bill. After reading a customer's meter, the water company prepares and sends his water bill. The bill illustrated on page 296 is based on the meter shown above. It shows the present reading, 13,876 cubic feet; the previous reading, 9,026 cubic feet; and the quantity consumed, 4,850 cubic feet.

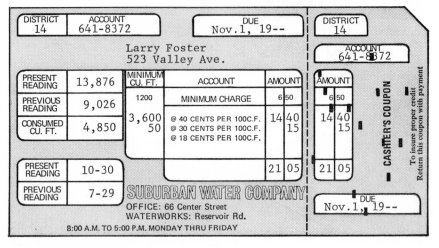

Quarterly water bill

Checking the water bill. The charges on the foregoing bill are based on the schedule of rates shown on page 295. The detailed charges and total bill are:

First 1,200 cu. ft., minimum charge	$ 6.50
Next 3,600 cu. ft. @ 40¢	14.40
Next 50 cu. ft. @ 30¢	.15
Total bill	$21.05

Exercise 1   Written

In working these problems, use the schedule of rates given on page 295.

1. Find the amount of the bill for each of the following quantities of water:

a 2,800 cu. ft. $12.90   **b** 1,100 cu. ft.   **c** 2,400 cu. ft.

2. Figure the cost of the water in each of the following:

a Previous reading,   6,940; present reading,   9,290. $11.10

b Previous reading, 43,260; present reading, 48,380.

c Previous reading, 28,370; present reading, 29,740.

3. Today, B. K. Radley's water meter reads 25,118 cubic feet. Three months ago it read 24,742 cubic feet. Find the amount of the water bill for the period.

4. A water meter read 35,469 cubic feet on April 30 and 55,609 cubic feet on July 31. What should be the amount of the water bill for this quarterly period?

REVIEW ASSIGNMENT **40**

1. a Multiply $14,200 by .0415.

b $105 is what percent less than $120?

c Express $1\frac{3}{4}$ as a decimal.

d Find the interest on $515.90 for 33 days at 5%.

2. Williamson's water meter read 92,364 cu. ft. on June 15 and 96,010 cu. ft. on September 15. Using the schedule of rates on page 295, find the amount of his water bill for the period.

3. The tax rate in Falmouth is 27.5 mills per dollar of assessed valuation. Find the tax on property assessed at $6,450.

4. A building valued at $22,500 was insured for 80% of its value at 35¢ per $100. What was the amount of the premium?

5. Taft insured his house for $6,000 with Company *A* and for $9,000 with Company *B*. A fire loss of $3,200 occurred. How much should Taft collect from each of these insurance companies?

6. James Bryce buys a house as an investment for $10,000. Annual ownership expenses are estimated at $520. What rent per month must he charge to obtain 8% net income on his investment?

7. A United States Savings Bond bought today for $18.75 will mature in 7 years and be worth $25. How many of these bonds must we buy today in order that their maturity value shall be $375?

8. Otis bought some stock at a total cost of $1,460. The market price of the stock was $32 a share, and the cost of the broker's commission was $20. How many shares did Otis buy?

9. Wilkes can buy an outboard motor for $280 cash or on the installment plan by making 30 monthly payments of $11.50 each. What annual percentage rate will he pay for the use of the merchant's money if he buys the motor on the installment plan? (Use the table on page 212.)

◉ **10. a** $48 is $\frac{1}{6}$ less than what amount?

b Express $.22\frac{1}{2}$ as a common fraction in lowest terms.

◉ **11.** A certain stock pays a dividend of 5% annually. The par value of the stock is $100 per share. How many shares of this stock must an investor purchase in order to obtain an annual income of $1,200?

◉ **12.** A building valued at $20,000 was insured for $14,000 under a policy with an 80% coinsurance clause. A fire caused a loss of $6,200. How much did the insurance company pay?

SECTION 41

Checking Telephone Bills

Limited and unlimited telephone service. Two kinds of local telephone service, limited and unlimited, are often available for residential subscribers.

Under the *unlimited-service plan*, the subscriber pays a flat monthly rate, regardless of the number of local calls he makes.

Under the *limited-service plan*, he pays a lower monthly rate which entitles him to a limited number of calls, such as 60 or 75 a month. If he exceeds this number, there is an extra charge for each additional call.

Taxes on telephone service. There is a federal tax of 10% on all telephone service. There may also be state and local taxes running from 2% to 5%, depending upon the locality.

The telephone bill. Telephone bills are prepared monthly by the telephone company. The bill shown below was received by Harvey Lockwood.

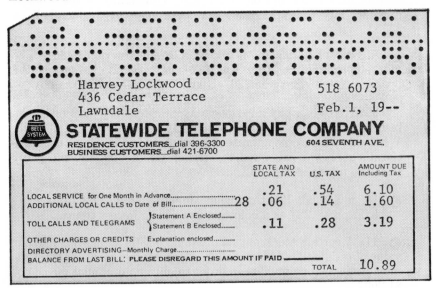

Harvey Lockwood
436 Cedar Terrace
Lawndale

518 6073

Feb. 1, 19--

STATEWIDE TELEPHONE COMPANY

RESIDENCE CUSTOMERS   dial 396-3300   604 SEVENTH AVE.
BUSINESS CUSTOMERS   dial 421-6700

	STATE AND LOCAL TAX	U.S. TAX	AMOUNT DUE Including Tax
LOCAL SERVICE for One Month in Advance....................	.21	.54	6.10
ADDITIONAL LOCAL CALLS to Date of Bill...............28	.06	.14	1.60
TOLL CALLS AND TELEGRAMS {Statement A Enclosed....... {Statement B Enclosed.......	.11	.28	3.19
OTHER CHARGES OR CREDITS Explanation enclosed..........			
DIRECTORY ADVERTISING—Monthly Charge............................			
BALANCE FROM LAST BILL: PLEASE DISREGARD THIS AMOUNT IF PAID ━━━			
		TOTAL	10.89

Telephone bill

Each item on a telephone bill consists of the company's charge for the service, the federal tax of 10%, and the state and local taxes if there are any. Each tax is figured separately and added to the company's charge to give the total of the item.

In the bill in the illustration, the local service charge is $5.35; and additional calls are $.05 each, both subject to the 10% federal tax and a 4% local tax. The charge for toll or long distance consists of the company charge of $2.80 plus the federal and local taxes.

The taxes and total amount of each item on the bill were computed in the following manner:

Local Service		Additional Calls		Toll Calls	
Monthly charge	$5.35	28 Calls @ 5¢	$1.40	Toll charges	$2.80
10% Fed. tax	.54	10% Fed. tax	.14	10% Fed. tax	.28
4% Local tax	.21	4% Local tax	.06	4% Local tax	.11
Total	$6.10		$1.60		$3.19

Exercise 1   Written

1. In each of the following, find the total monthly cost of the unlimited local service at the given rate.

	Kind of Line	Monthly Rate	Federal Tax	Local Tax	State Tax	
a	Individual	$5.45	10%	None	2%	$6.11
b	Two-party line	5.20	10%	None	None	
c	Four-party line	4.40	10%	3%	None	
d	Individual	5.80	10%	None	5%	
e	Two-party line	4.60	10%	2%	3%	

2. In a certain community, residential telephone rates for limited local service are as follows:

Individual line, $5.35 a month for 75 calls or less
Two-party line, $4.15 a month for 60 calls or less
Additional calls, $.05 each

In each of the following find the total cost of the local service at the monthly rate, the total cost of the additional local calls, and the total telephone bill for the month.

	Kind of Line	Total Local Calls Made	Federal Tax	State Tax	
a	Individual line	128	10%	5%	$9.21
b	Two-party line	187	10%	None	
c	Two-party line	94	10%	4%	
d	Individual line	340	10%	3%	

3. For local residential telephone service, Joan Gordon pays $4.75 a month for 75 calls or less and $.05 for each additional call, plus taxes. In July she made a total of 211 calls. Her bill for July was $12.95, which included the federal tax of 10% and a state tax of 2%. Was $12.95 the correct amount?

4. You are paying $5.25 a month for 75 local calls or less and $.05 for each additional call, plus the 10% federal tax. If you average 125 calls a month, how much would you save each month by paying $6.25, plus the 10% tax, for unlimited service?

5. Knapp's toll slip for February shows four toll calls charged at $.65, $1.35, $.70, and $.85, exclusive of taxes. Find the total charge for the toll calls, including the 10% federal tax.

REVIEW ASSIGNMENT **41**

1. a Divide 37,650 by 125,000.

b $270 is what part smaller than $315?

c Express $3\frac{1}{8}$ as a decimal.

d Find the interest at 6% on $198.05 for 106 days.

2. On Hallet's telephone bill for April, the company's charge for local service was $6.85 and for toll calls, $5.45. Both items were subject to a federal tax of 10% and a local tax of 3%. What was the total amount of the bill, including the taxes?

3. On July 8, Neal's water meter read 19,134 cu. ft. The reading on April 8 was 13,676 cu. ft. Using the schedule of rates on page 295, find the amount of Neal's water bill for the period.

4. Sloan bought some stock at a total cost of $55 per share. During the first year he owned the stock, he received four quarterly dividends of $.65, $.75, $.75, and $.95, respectively, on each share. What rate of return did he receive on his investment, to the nearest tenth of a percent?

5. Girvin owns property assessed at $11,200. The tax rate last year was 47 mills per dollar of assessed value. What was the amount of Girvin's tax bill on this property last year?

6. Bell's house is insured for $15,500 at an annual rate of $.38 per $100. If a three-year policy costs 2.7 times as much as a one-year policy, how much would Bell save by buying a three-year policy instead of three separate one-year policies?

7. $7.20 is $37\frac{1}{2}$% less than what amount?

8. An oil stock with a par value of $100 pays an annual dividend of $4\frac{1}{2}$%. How many shares of this stock must an investor purchase in order to obtain an annual income of $675?

Practicing Thrift in Buying

Ways of saving on purchases. Worthwhile savings can often be made by buying an article in large quantities instead of small quantities. Money can also be saved by buying at anniversary and clearance sales, and at special sales when stores sell goods at advertised discounts from regular prices.

I WONDER IF I REALLY SAVED ANYTHING BY BUYING THE BIG ONE?

Exercise 1   Written

1. Canned pears are priced at 37¢ a can, 2 cans for 70¢. How much is saved by buying 2 cans at one time instead of 2 cans separately?

2. A 1-lb. can of shortening costs 33¢; a 3-lb. can, 87¢. How much is saved by buying one 3-lb. can instead of three 1-lb. cans?

3. How much is saved if 12 cans of beets are bought at $1.89 a dozen instead of $.17 each?

4. How much is saved by buying 6 cans of tomato juice at 2 cans for 43¢ instead of buying 6 cans separately at 23¢ each?

5. During a "One Cent Sale" a drug store offers two articles of the same kind for the regular price of one plus 1 cent. How much is saved by buying during the sale 2 tubes of tooth paste regularly priced at 55¢ and 2 bottles of shampoo at 75¢?

Exercise 2   Written

1. At an end-of-season sale, Mrs. Austin purchased a winter coat that was reduced from $89.50 to $59.75 and a suit that was reduced from $59.95 to $47.50. What total amount did she save?

2. Stockings regularly priced at $1.39 a pair are sold during an anniversary sale at 3 pairs for $3.49. How much is saved on the purchase of 6 pairs?

3. During a preseason sale in August, Lola Benton purchased a winter coat at 10% off the regular price of $149.

a How much did she save by purchasing the coat in August?

b How much did she pay for the coat?

4. A hardware store offers all local city employees a courtesy discount of 8%. Roy Kent, a local school teacher, buys a power mower priced at $69.95. How much does he pay for it?

5. At the Morgan Furniture Store, Roland Young purchased a lawn chair priced at $59.50 and two porch chairs priced at $14.75 each. The store allowed a 5% discount for immediate cash payment. How much did Mr. Young save by paying cash?

Comparing prices. Many articles are put up in packages containing different quantities at different prices. In order to make comparisons and select the lower priced item, the given prices must be converted to prices per ounce, pound, quart, or some other appropriate unit of measure. In some cases, it may be easier to compare the quantities that can be obtained for the same amount of money, such as 1¢, 10¢, 25¢, or some other convenient amount.

Exercise **3**   Written

1. A 3-lb. can of ham is priced at $3.79. A 5-lb. can of the same ham is priced at $5.89. What is the price of each per pound, to the nearest cent? Which can is the cheaper per pound?

2. A 4-oz. jar of instant coffee is priced at $.79. A 6-oz. jar of a different brand is priced at $1.29. What is the price of each per ounce? (Retain the fraction of a cent in the unit price.) Which is the cheaper?

3. Sweet corn of the same size and quality is priced at 4 ears for 29¢ in one store and 6 ears for 39¢ in another. Find the cost per dozen ears in each case. Which is the better buy?

4. A package of 70 sheets of notebook paper is priced at 25¢. A package of 22 sheets of the same paper is priced at 10¢. At the rate of 22 sheets for 10¢, how many sheets would you get for 25¢? Which is the more economical package?

5. Determine which quantity is the cheaper in each of the following:

a A 7-oz. can of one brand of tooth powder for 95¢ or a 4-oz. can of another brand for 51¢.

b Lemons priced at 10 for 43¢ or 6 for 31¢.

c A 2-lb. box of borax for 37¢ or a 5-lb. box for 79¢.

d A bottle containing 6 fluid ounces of hair tonic for 99¢ or one containing 4 fluid ounces for 62¢.

e A 4½-oz. tube of tooth paste for 49¢ or a 5-oz. tube for 59¢.

REVIEW ASSIGNMENT 42

1. a $84 is what part greater than $48?

b What amount is ⅓% of $345?

c Express 1⅜ as a decimal.

d Find the interest on $792.35 for 23 days at 6%.

2. A savings bond bought today for $37.50 will mature in 7 years and be worth $50. How many of these bonds must we buy today in order that their maturity value shall be $1,750?

3. Graff can buy a refrigerator for $370 cash, or for $40 down and $30 a month for 12 months. Graff has enough cash for the down payment. He can borrow the balance for 12 months at 6%. How much would he save by borrowing in order to buy the refrigerator at the cash price?

4. An 80-day note for $348, bearing 5% interest, is dated March 10. Find the date of maturity of the note and the total amount due at maturity.

5. Bessom bought 20 shares of stock at a total cost of $1,580. He kept the stock for three years, during which time he received regular quarterly dividends of $.65 per share. He then sold the stock and received net proceeds of $1,660. What was his total gain from owning and selling this stock?

6. Clancy insured his house for $12,000 with Company *A* and for $8,000 with Company *B*. A fire loss of $2,300 occurred. How much should Clancy collect from each of these insurance companies?

◗ 7. A house valued at $16,500 is insured for $11,000 under a policy containing an 80% coinsurance clause. What amount must the company pay in case of a fire loss of $1,500?

GENERAL REVIEW

1. a Multiply 245.1 by 10.4.

b Divide 249.24 by 6.7.

c Add: 6¼, 4⅓, 16½, 8⅝.

d Multiply 24⅓ by 9⅛.

e Divide 17⅗ by 2¾.

f Express 16/25 as a percent.

2. A piece of real estate is assessed at $9,800. Find the tax to be paid if the rate is 63 mills per dollar.

3. According to her June bank statement, Grace Newport's bank balance on June 30 was $364.27. Her checkbook balance on that date was $319.02. There was a service charge of $1.14 and checks were outstanding for $21.65, $3.98, $12.47, and $8.29. Prepare a reconciliation statement.

4. The merchandise inventory of Porter & White was $35,200 on July 1 and $37,400 on September 30. Sales for the quarter were $42,540, and the purchases were $30,560. What was the firm's gross profit for the quarter?

5. For the first week of April, Dorr had gross earnings of $128.73. He claims three exemptions. Using the tables on pages 106 and 108, find the income tax and FICA tax that were deducted from Dorr's gross earnings for that week.

6. Proctor can purchase a power lawn mower for $250 cash or on the installment plan by paying 10% more. He chooses the installment plan and makes a down payment of $100. The balance is to be paid in equal monthly payments of $8.75 each. How many months will it take him to pay for the mower?

7. Brady is paying $137.50 per month rent for a house that he can buy for $13,500 cash. If he buys the house, his total annual ownership expenses are estimated to be $1,465. How much money may he expect to save each year by buying the house?

8. As an investment, Byrne purchased a house for $14,000 cash and rented it for $145 a month. During a recent year, his expenses on the house were: taxes, $275; repairs, $165; depreciation, 2%; insurance, $64; other expenses, $88. For that year, what was Byrne's rate of income on his investment?

▶ **9.** Express .250 as a common fraction in lowest terms.

▶ **10.** A salesman is paid a regular monthly salary of $525, plus a commission on all sales in excess of $6,500 in any single month. Last month his total sales were $10,300 and his total earnings were $981. What rate of commission did he receive?

▶ **11.** The annual ownership expenses of a four-family house average $1,440. The house rents for a total of $260 a month. What is the highest price an investor can afford to pay for this house if he desires a net return of 7% on his investment?

▶ **12.** On June 30, Hyde's checkbook showed a balance of $891.62. His bank statement for June showed a balance of $884.31 for that date. Checks were outstanding for $23.19 and $44.50. A slip enclosed with the canceled checks showed that his account had been charged $75 for a U.S. Savings Bond bought for him by the bank. Prepare a reconciliation statement.

UNIT Nine

Transportation Problems

SECTION 43

Automobile Ownership

Before purchasing an automobile, a person would do well to make an estimate of the annual operating expense to see whether he can afford it. This expense should include all money payments for license fees, insurance, garage rent, gasoline, oil, tires, repairs, and general upkeep. It should also include interest on the investment and an allowance for depreciation of the car.

PART 43a   Figuring Automobile Depreciation

Automobile depreciation. Depreciation refers to the loss of value of an article through use and the passage of time. An automobile, for example, decreases in value as it grows older. The total depreciation is the difference between the original cost of the car and the amount received for it when it is sold or traded in.

Thus, if a person buys a car for $3,000 and four years later trades it in for $1,000, the total depreciation is $2,000.

$3,000 original cost
1,000 trade-in value
—————
$2,000 depreciation

Figuring the annual automobile depreciation. The cost of operating an automobile is usually figured on an annual basis. When this is done, the annual depreciation has to be estimated, because the actual depreciation will not be known until the car is traded in or sold.

The approximate annual depreciation can be determined in the following manner:

1. Estimate the number of years of service life of the car.
2. Estimate the trade-in or resale value of the car at the end of its service life.
3. Subtract the trade-in or resale value from the original cost to find the estimated total depreciation.
4. Divide the total depreciation by the number of years of service life.

Example

An automobile costing $3,400 is estimated to have a trade-in or resale value of $800 at the end of five years.
Find the average annual depreciation.

Solution:

  $3,400 original cost
  *   800 trade-in value*

  $2,600 total depreciation

  $2,600 ÷ 5 = $520, average annual depreciation.   **Ans.**

This method of estimating the annual depreciation is called the *straight-line method*. It spreads the total depreciation expense evenly over the service life of the car.

Exercise 1   Written

1. Find the annual depreciation in each of the following:

	Original Cost	Trade-in Value		Annual Depreciation
		At End of	Amount	
a	$2,600	4 years	$ 700	$ 475
b	3,200	5 years	700	
c	3,800	3 years	1,250	
d	3,500	6 years	350	

2. A car costing $3,000 today is estimated to have a trade-in value of $1,050 three years later. What is the annual depreciation?

3. Howell bought a car for $3,300. After using it for six years, he bought a new car costing $3,750 by trading in the old one and paying $3,000 in cash. What was the amount of the average annual depreciation of the old car?

Rate of depreciation. Under the straight-line method of spreading depreciation, the average annual depreciation is often expressed as a percent of the original cost. The average annual depreciation therefore represents the part; and the original cost represents the base, or whole, with which the part is compared.

$$\text{Rate of Depreciation} = \frac{\textbf{Average Annual Depreciation}}{\textbf{Original Cost}}$$

Thus, if the average annual depreciation of an automobile is $600 and the original cost is $3,000, the rate of depreciation is 20%.

$$\text{Rate of Depreciation} = \frac{\$600}{\$3,000} = .2 = 20\%$$

Exercise 2 Written

1. Find the rate of depreciation in each of the following:

	Original Cost	Trade-in Value		Rate of Depreciation
		At End of	Amount	
a	$3,200	5 years	$ 800	15%
b	3,000	3 years	1,020	
c	3,500	6 years	560	
d	4,000	4 years	1,120	

2. Pauley purchases an automobile for $2,800. He estimates it will be serviceable for five years and will then have a trade-in value of $420. What is the estimated rate of depreciation?

REVIEW ASSIGNMENT 43 a

1. **a** Multiply $13,500 by .0635.
b What percent less than $168 is $140?
c Find the interest at 6% on $613.49 for 41 days.

2. Miller purchased a car for $2,290. Six years later he was allowed $370 for it toward the purchase of a new car. What was the average yearly amount of depreciation?

3. A car that cost $2,500 was traded in for $300 after eight years of use. What was the average annual rate of depreciation of the car?

4. The tax rate in a certain city is $52.071 per $1,000. What is the tax on a piece of property assessed at $3,500?

5. A 6% note for $1,600, dated May 14, was paid in full on the following August 10. What was the amount of the payment?

6. Brown's electric bill showed meter readings of 6,232 kw-hr. on February 5 and 6,416 on March 5. Added to the bill was a sales tax of 6%. Using the schedule of rates on page 289, find the amount of Brown's bill for the month ending March 5.

7. The cash price of a color TV set is $360. The set can be purchased on the installment plan by making 30 monthly payments of $14.80 each. What annual percentage rate is paid by the installment purchaser? (Use the table on page 212.)

⟩ 8. $36 is $\frac{1}{3}$ smaller than what amount?

⟩ 9. A stock with a par value of $100 pays an annual dividend of 5%. George Folsom wishes to purchase the number of shares needed to give him an annual income of $600.

a How many shares of the stock must he purchase?

b What will be his investment in the stock if he purchases it at $85\frac{1}{2}$? (Disregard the brokerage fee.)

PART **43b** Figuring Annual Operating Cost

Total annual cost of automobile operation. The total annual operating cost is the sum of all the annual expenses, including depreciation and interest on the original cost.

Example

On a car that cost $3,200, Keegan's annual payments for taxes, gasoline, oil, repairs, and other maintenance expenses total $625.
Allowing 5% on the original cost for interest and 15% for depreciation, find the total annual operating cost.

Solution:

Taxes, gasoline, oil, etc.	$ 625
Interest, 5% of $3,200	160
Depreciation, 15% of $3,200	480
Total annual operating cost	$1,265 **Ans.**

Exercise 3   Written

1. Find the total annual operating cost:

	Original Cost	Interest Allowance	Depre-ciation	Other Expenses	Total Oper-ating Cost
a	$2,800	5%	15%	$510	$1,070
b	3,500	4%	18%	750	
c	3,650	4%	16%	670	
d	3,200	5%	20%	610	

2. Hake bought a car for $2,750. Car expenses for the first year were: gasoline and oil, $335; repairs and miscellaneous expenses, $47; insurance, $95; license plates, $17; interest on investment at 4%; depreciation at 20%. Find the year's total operating cost.
$1,154

3. Kowalski's car expense record for last year shows the following summary of cash payments: gasoline and oil, $320; insurance, $197; license plates, $18; repairs, $75; other expenses, $40. What was the average weekly cash expense for operating the car?

4. Before buying an automobile costing $3,250, Bob Sherman estimates his first year's car expenses as follows: license plates, $19.50; insurance, $215; gasoline and oil, $375; interest at 5% on the cost of the car; repairs, $35; depreciation, 35% of the cost of the car. Find the total estimated cost of operating the car the first year.

Exercise 4   Written

1. What will be the cost of license plates for an automobile weighing 3,500 pounds if the rate is 50 cents for each 100 pounds?

2. A car used 14 gallons of gasoline on a trip of 215 miles. How many miles, to the nearest tenth of a mile, did it average per gallon?

3. On a trip of 540 miles, R. K. Besko used 32 gallons of gasoline, costing 35.8 cents per gallon.

a How many miles did he average per gallon, to the nearest tenth of a mile?

b What was the total cost of the gasoline used on the trip?

c What was the cost of the gasoline per mile traveled, computed to the nearest tenth of a cent?

4. Henry Evans drove his automobile 9,120 miles last year. His expenses in connection with the car were as follows:

570 gallons of gasoline at 36¢ per gallon	$205.20
Oil and lubrication	27.50
Insurance	195.00
Estimated depreciation	550.00
Repairs and parts	60.00
License plates	18.00
Miscellaneous expenses	38.70

a What was the average cost per mile of operating the car last year?

b How many miles per gallon of gasoline did he obtain?

5. On five successive days a deliveryman listed his mileage as follows: 88, 156, 105, 77, 92. If his truck averaged 14 miles per gallon of gasoline, how many gallons should he have used during these five days?

6. Last year, Floyd Mansion drove his car 9,195 miles. He averaged 15 miles to the gallon and paid $.36 per gallon (tax included) for gasoline. How much did he spend for gasoline, including tax, last year?

Exercise 5   Written

1. Fry started on a motor trip at 9:30 a.m. and reached his destination at 2:15 p.m. On the way he stopped one hour for lunch and to buy gasoline. What was his actual driving time?

3 hr., 45 min.

2. Find the actual driving time:

	Start on Trip at	Reach Destination at	Time Out for Lunch	Driving Time
a	8:30 a.m.	4:15 p.m.	1 hr.	
b	8:45 a.m.	3:30 p.m.	1 hr. 15 min.	
c	9:45 a.m.	5:15 p.m.	45 min.	
d	7:15 a.m.	5:45 p.m.	1 hr. 15 min.	

3. Bauer's driving time on a trip of 301 miles was 7 hours. What was his average speed in miles per hour?

4. Gleason drove 57 miles in one hour and thirty minutes. What was his average speed in miles per hour?

5. Find the speed in miles per hour:

Miles Driven	Driving Time		Miles Driven	Driving Time		Miles Driven	Driving Time
a	186	6 hr.	d	195	$3\frac{3}{4}$ hr.	g	36	*45 min. 48
b	180	$4\frac{1}{2}$ hr.	e	21	$\frac{3}{4}$ hr.	h	15	25 min.
c	72	$2\frac{1}{4}$ hr.	f	36	$\frac{2}{3}$ hr.	i	30	40 min.

*Change the minutes to a fraction of an hour before dividing.

6. Washburn drives 18 miles in 24 minutes. At that rate, how far will he drive in one hour?

7. How far will a truck travel in 3 hours and 45 minutes if its average speed is 36 miles an hour?

REVIEW ASSIGNMENT **43 b**

1. a Divide 43,688 by 215,000.
b $210 is what part smaller than $245?
c Find the interest on $401.27 for 31 days at 6%.
d Find the interest on $360 for 145 days at 4%.

2. Rudd drove from his home to Fresno, a distance of 144 miles, in $4\frac{1}{2}$ hours. What was his average speed in miles per hour?

3. On an automobile trip, Dolf drove from 8:45 a.m. until 4:35 p.m., with one hour and fifteen minutes out for lunch and for buying gasoline. What was his actual driving time?

4. An automobile that cost $2,724 four years ago can be traded in today for $900. What is the average annual depreciation?

5. Hartnett purchased a new car for $3,150. At the end of three years he sold it for $1,260. What was the average annual rate of depreciation of the car?

6. Ronald Ordway bought a car for $3,800. His car expenses for last year were: gasoline and oil, $326; repairs, $49; insurance, $179; license plates, $22; interest on original investment at 5%; depreciation, 18%. Find the total operating cost for last year.

▷ **7. a** $5.60 is $37\frac{1}{2}$% less than what amount?
b Find the interest at $5\frac{1}{2}$% on $613.44 for 55 days.

▷ **8.** A salesman is paid $550 a month and a commission of 8% on sales in excess of $8,000 in any month. What must be the total of his sales for one month in order that his total earnings for the month may be $850?

SECTION 44

Insuring the Automobile

Kinds of automobile insurance. The most common types of automobile insurance are the following:

Bodily Injury, which covers the owner's liability for injury to other persons. Minimum basic limits of coverage are $5,000 for injury to one person and a total of $10,000 when two or more persons are injured in one accident. Minimum coverage of $10,000 and $20,000 is often recommended or required.

Property Damage, which covers damage to other people's property. The minimum limit is generally $5,000.

Comprehensive Damage, which covers damage to one's own car resulting from fire, theft, vandalism, missiles, falling objects, windstorm, hail, lightning, and flood.

Collision Insurance, which covers damage to one's own car resulting from collision or upset. A popular coverage is the "$50-deductible." Under this coverage the insured bears $50 of the loss and the insurance company the remainder. If one's car is damaged to the extent of $160, for example, the company will pay $110 of the loss.

Automobile insurance premiums. Premiums for automobile insurance vary from one locality to another. As a rule they are much higher in large cities and thickly populated areas than in small cities and rural districts.

Premiums for bodily injury and property damage are higher on cars used for business purposes than on cars used for pleasure only or for driving to and from work. In many districts, premiums are higher for drivers under twenty-five years of age than for drivers over twenty-five.

Sample annual premiums for cars in a medium-rate district are shown in the tables on page 314.

Table 1 shows bodily injury and property damage premiums for three classes of use. The premiums are for limits of $10/20,000 for bodily injury, and $5,000 for property damage.

Table 2 shows the percents to apply to the premiums in Table 1 if higher limits of coverage are desired. For example, if bodily injury coverage of $20/40,000 is desired, the premium is 110% of the premium given in Table 1.

TABLE 1.   SAMPLE ANNUAL PREMIUMS FOR BODILY INJURY AND PROPERTY DAMAGE

Type of Insurance	Limits	Used for		
		Pleasure Only	Driving to Work	Business
Bodily Injury	$10/20,000	$72.00	$83.00	$104.00
Property Damage	$5,000	$29.00	$33.00	$41.00

TABLE 2.   RATES FOR HIGHER LIMITS

Bodily Injury		Property Damage	
Maximum Limits	Percent of $10/20,000 Premium	Maximum Limits	Percent of $5,000 Premium
$20/40,000	110%	$10,000	105%
$25/50,000	113%	$25,000	108%
$50/100,000	121%	$50,000	113%

Exercise 1   Written

In solving these problems, use Table 1 and Table 2 for finding the cost of the bodily injury and property damage coverage.

1. Find the total annual premium for the bodily injury and property damage on each of the following cars:

	Used for	Coverage		
		Bodily Injury	Property Damage	
a	Pleasure only	$10/20,000	$5,000	$101
b	Driving to work	$10/20,000	$5,000	
c	Pleasure only	$20/40,000	$5,000	$108.20
d	Driving to work	$10/20,000	$10,000	
e	Business	$25/50,000	$25,000	

2. On a car which he uses for business purposes, Leo Hite purchases $20/40,000 bodily injury and $5,000 property damage coverage for one year. What is the total cost of the premium?
$155.40

3. Cody purchases the following coverage on a car which he uses for pleasure only: $50/100,000 bodily injury; $25,000 property damage. What is the total annual premium?

4. Freda Beach has a car which she uses for driving to work. From the Kemp Agency she purchases $25/50,000 bodily injury and $5,000 property damage coverage for one year.

In addition she purchases comprehensive damage insurance costing $8 and $50-deductible collision insurance costing $58.

What is the total cost of these coverages?

5. On April 1, Keefe insures his car with the American Insurance Co. for one year, paying $117.52 for bodily injury coverage, $41 for property damage, and $9 for comprehensive damage.

Eight months later he sells the car and cancels the policy. The short term rate for an eight-month period is 74% of the annual premium. How much should the company refund to Keefe?

6. On May 1, Ridgeway purchased automobile insurance which included $50-deductible collision coverage. Four months later his car was damaged in a collision, and the repair bill amounted to $746.25. How much did he receive from the insurance company in settlement of the bill?

REVIEW ASSIGNMENT 44

1. a Add 47.58, 299.3, 3.975, and 95.66.

b Divide $14\frac{1}{6}$ by $1\frac{2}{3}$.

c Find the interest at $7\frac{1}{2}\%$ on $410.75 for 25 days.

2. Fulton purchased a car six years ago for $2,880. Today, he is trading it in for $450 toward the price of a new car. What was the average annual depreciation of the old car?

3. Gilbert started on a trip at 10:45 a.m., spent forty-five minutes for lunch on the way, and reached his destination at 3:00 p.m. What was his actual driving time?

4. At the start of a trip, Walsh's speedometer read 3,982 miles. At destination it read 4,162. Walsh's driving time was $3\frac{3}{4}$ hours. What was his average speed in miles per hour?

5. McCarthy drives 36 miles in 45 minutes. At that rate, how far will he drive in one hour?

6. Sullivan owned 80 shares of stock. This stock paid a quarterly dividend of $.27$\frac{1}{2}$ per share. What amount of money did he receive as dividends during a period of one year?

7. Castle insured his office building for $30,000 with the Reliable Insurance Company and for $18,000 with the Star Insurance Company. If a fire loss of $2,400 occurs, what amount should be paid by the Star Company?

SECTION 45

Using Public Travel Agencies

Travel by railroad, bus, and airplane. For the individual who does not want to use an automobile, the public travel agencies available are the railroad, motor bus, and airplane.

The railroad is a relatively speedy and inexpensive means of transportation. Travel by bus is often slower but usually cheaper than by rail. Air travel is usually fastest and most expensive.

For each kind of service, the cost to the traveler depends on the distance traveled. The longer the distance, the greater the cost.

A federal tax of 5% is levied on airline tickets for travel within the United States.

Exercise 1   Written

In solving the problems in this exercise, use the timetable given below at the right.

1. How many miles is it from —
a Harmon to Syracuse?   251
b Albany to Rochester?
c Utica to Buffalo?

2. How long does it take to travel from —
a New York to Syracuse?   5 hr.
b Albany to Buffalo?
c Rochester to Buffalo?
d Utica to Syracuse?

Miles		71 Daily
		AM
0	Lv New York (Grand Central Terminal)	
33	Lv Harmon............	8:30 9:22
142	Ar Albany—Rensselaer	11:10
	Lv Albany—Rensselaer	11:15
237	Lv Utica..............	12:40
284	Ar Syracuse...........	1:30
	Lv Syracuse...........	1:35
370	Lv Rochester.........	2:50
437	Ar Buffalo	4:00

3. At what average speed in miles per hour, to the nearest mile, does Train No. 71 travel from —
a New York to Albany?   53   **c** Syracuse to Buffalo?
b Albany to Syracuse?   **d** New York to Buffalo?

4. If Train No. 71 is running 45 minutes late, at what time should it arrive at the following points:
a Albany   **b** Syracuse   **c** Buffalo

5. If train No. 71 is running 45 minutes late, at what time should it leave the following points:

a Albany   **b** Utica   **c** Rochester

6. If the rate of fare is $4\frac{3}{4}$ cents a mile, what would be the fare from New York to Utica?

Exercise 2   Written

1. The railroad fare in coaches to Miami is $54.26. The same trip may be made by bus for $45.20. How much will be saved in transportation cost if a family of three adults makes a one-way trip to Miami by bus?

2. The first-class Pullman fare from St. Louis to San Francisco is $82.55. A lower berth costs $23.15 additional. Find the cost of two tickets to San Francisco with lower berth accommodations.

3. The railroad fare from Richmond to Jacksonville is $23.74. The distance is 610 miles. What is the fare per mile, figured to the nearest tenth of a cent?

4. The price of a round-trip railroad ticket between Newport and Toledo is $17.20. The distance between Newport and Toledo is 214 miles. Find the average cost, to the nearest tenth of a cent, of transportation per mile for the round trip.   4.0¢

5. LaRue is traveling from Buffalo to Denver and return. The one-way fare is $56.38. The round-trip fare is $99.17. What percent would LaRue save, to the nearest whole percent, by purchasing a round-trip ticket instead of two one-way tickets?

6. A jet flight of 728 miles takes 1 hour and 45 minutes. The one-way fare for the trip is $45.86.

  a What is the average speed of the plane in miles per hour?

  b What is the cost per mile, to the nearest tenth of a cent?

7. A train leaves Chicago at 3:00 p.m. daily and arrives at its destination at 11:25 p.m. the same day. The cost of a coach ticket on this train is $17.35. A bus leaves Chicago at 3:45 p.m. daily and arrives at the same destination at 1:45 a.m. the following day. The bus ticket costs $15.00.

  a How much time is saved by taking the train?

  b By what percent, to the nearest whole percent, is the cost by bus less than the cost by train?

8. A bus travels 15 miles in 18 minutes. At that rate, how far will the bus travel in one hour?

REVIEW ASSIGNMENT 45

1. a $98 is what part greater than $56?

b What amount is $\frac{1}{3}\%$ of $435?

c Find the interest on $275.85 for 43 days at 6%.

2. A round-trip railroad ticket between Milford and Charleston costs $41.92. The distance between Milford and Charleston is 508 miles. What is the average cost, to the nearest tenth of a cent, of transportation per mile for the round trip?

3. Brickman drove 96 miles in 2 hours and 40 minutes. What was his average speed in miles per hour?

4. At 48 miles an hour, how far will a car travel in 2 hours and 15 minutes?

5. At 40 miles an hour, how many hours will it take to drive 170 miles? Express your answer as a mixed number.

6. As an investment, Mr. Ferber purchased for cash a house costing $17,000. Total annual ownership expenses average $1,030. What monthly rent must he charge for the house in order to obtain a net return of 7% on his original investment?

7. A car which cost $3,200 when new had a trade-in value of $650 after five years of use. What was the average annual rate of depreciation, to the nearest whole percent?

8. For a 3-month period, Mr. Elliott used 5,722 cubic feet of water. Based on the rates below, what will be Mr. Elliott's water bill for this period?

First 1,200 cu. ft.   60¢ per 100 cu. ft.

Next 3,600 cu. ft.   44¢ per 100 cu. ft.

Next 15,000 cu. ft.   32¢ per 100 cu. ft.

9. a Express $\frac{5}{8}\%$ as a decimal.

b $1.05 is $\frac{2}{5}$ larger than what amount?

10. A certain steel stock pays a regular quarterly dividend of $37\frac{1}{2}$¢ per share. Paul York wishes to purchase the number of shares that will provide him an annual income of $450.

a How many shares of the stock must he purchase?

b What will be his investment in the stock if he purchases it at $35\frac{1}{2}$? (Disregard the broker's commission.)

11. Patterson insured his building worth $30,000 for $21,000 under a fire insurance policy containing an 80% coinsurance clause. If a fire loss of $4,000 occurred, what amount of money would Patterson collect from the insurance company?

SECTION 46

Shipping Goods

Transportation of goods. Common methods of shipping articles and goods are parcel post, express, and freight. Small packages going short distances are usually sent by parcel post. Larger packages going longer distances may be sent by parcel post or express. Heavy, bulky goods are ordinarily sent by freight.

HOW SHALL I SEND THIS?

The shipping charges depend in part upon the weight of the shipment. Under all three methods of shipping, a fraction of a pound is counted as a full pound.

Parcel post. Parcel-post rates vary with the weight and the zone in which the delivery point is located. The table below shows the rates to all zones for packages up to 10 pounds in weight.

Weight 1 pound and not exceeding	Local	Zones						
		1 and 2	3	4	5	6	7	8
		Up to 150 miles	150 to 300 miles	300 to 600 miles	600 to 1,000 miles	1,000 to 1,400 miles	1,400 to 1,800 miles	Over 1,800 miles
2 pounds	$0.50	$0.60	$0.60	$0.65	$0.70	$0.80	$0.85	$0.90
3 pounds	.50	.65	.70	.75	.85	.95	1.05	1.15
4 pounds	.55	.70	.75	.85	.95	1.10	1.20	1.35
5 pounds	.55	.75	.80	.90	1.05	1.25	1.40	1.60
6 pounds	.55	.80	.90	1.00	1.15	1.40	1.55	1.75
7 pounds	.60	.90	.95	1.10	1.30	1.50	1.75	1.95
8 pounds	.60	.95	1.00	1.15	1.40	1.65	1.90	2.15
9 pounds	.65	1.00	1.05	1.25	1.50	1.80	2.05	2.35
10 pounds	.65	1.05	1.15	1.35	1.65	1.90	2.25	2.55

A parcel-post package may be insured. The shipper pays an insurance fee based upon the value placed on the package. The fee schedule is shown in the table at the right.

For an additional fee of 10 cents, the shipper may obtain a return receipt from the person to whom an insured parcel-post package is sent if the package is insured for more than $15.

Schedule of Insurance Fees	
Coverage	Fee
Up to $15	20¢
15.01 to 50	30¢
50.01 to 100	40¢
100.01 to 150	50¢
150.01 to 200	60¢

Exercise 1   Oral

1. Using the table of parcel-post rates on page 319, state the cost of sending each of the following packages by parcel post.

	Weight	Destination		Weight	Destination
a	6 lb.	Zone 3	e	$3\frac{1}{2}$ lb.	Zone 8
b	5 lb.	Zone 7	f	$7\frac{3}{4}$ lb.	Zone 4
c	10 lb.	Zone 5	g	8 lb. 14 oz.	Zone 2
d	4 lb.	Zone 8	h	6 lb. 2 oz.	Zone 1

   i A 3-pound parcel to a city 180 miles away

   j A $4\frac{3}{4}$-pound parcel to a city 1,375 miles away

2. Using the schedule of insurance fees shown above, state the cost of insuring a parcel-post package valued at:

a	$15	c	$50	e	$18	g	$125
b	$100	d	$8	f	$65	h	$162

Express. Express rates are published in schedules of rates for shipments of various weights from 1 pound to 100 pounds. If a shipment weighs over 100 pounds, the 100-pound rate is applied to the weight.

For example, at the rate of $32.15 per 100 pounds, the charge for a 160-pound shipment from Los Angeles to New York would be $51.44.

$$160 \div 100 = 1.60$$
$$1.60 \times \$32.15 = \$51.44$$

The express company insures a package up to $50 in value without extra charge. A person may insure any value above $50 by paying an extra charge for each additional $100. A fraction of $100 is counted as a full $100.

Air express. Packages requiring very prompt delivery can be sent by air express. The rates are considerably higher than for railway express.

Freight. Freight rates are usually rates per 100 pounds. The minimum charge is the rate for 100 pounds. For a shipment weighing more than 100 pounds, the charge is based on the actual weight and is figured in the same manner as an express charge.

Exercise 2   Written

1. Pierre Cody sends a 9-pound parcel-post package from New Orleans, Louisiana, to Atlanta, Georgia, which is 495 miles away. He insures the package for $150 and asks for a return receipt. What is the cost of making the shipment? $1.85

2. Justin Hoit, living in Portland, Maine, sends to his son Jack a 7-pound parcel-post package. His son lives in Jacksonville, Florida. The distance from Portland to Jacksonville is 1,323 miles. If Mr. Hoit insures the shipment for $50, what is the cost of sending the package?

3. A parcel post package going from New York to Philadelphia is limited in weight to 40 pounds. In size, it must not exceed 72 inches in length and girth combined.

The *girth* is the distance around the package at its thickest part. Thus, if a carton is 30 in. long, 10 in. wide, and 4 in. thick, the girth is 10 + 4 + 10 + 4, or 28 in. The combined length and girth is 30 + 28, or 58 in.

Which of the following packages may be sent by parcel post from New York to Philadelphia and which may not?

	Length	Width	Thickness	Weight	
a	19 in.	10 in.	6 in.	25 lb.	Yes
b	36 in.	12 in.	8 in.	18 lb.	
c	22 in.	8 in.	4 in.	43 lb.	
d	42 in.	6 in.	3 in.	39 lb.	
e	26 in.	12 in.	11 in.	30 lb.	

4. A postal clerk had to weigh 4 packages to be sent to the fifth zone and to determine the postage on them. Each package weighed 3 lb. 12 oz. and was to be insured for $50. Find the total amount required to mail and insure the packages.

5. Enos Gibbons, a farmer, ships by express 139 pounds of dressed turkeys to Washington, D.C. The scheduled rate is $2.66 a hundred pounds. What is the total express charge?

6. The air express rate on a 132-pound shipment to Austin, Texas, is $15.80 a hundred pounds. Find the total shipping cost.

7. C. O. Neal sends a 115-pound express shipment of clothing, valued at $675, from San Diego to Baltimore, Md., and insures it for full value. The express company insures the shipment up to $50 in value without charge, but charges an insurance fee of 25¢ for each additional $100 of value, or fraction thereof. What is the total insurance charge on the shipment?

8. The freight rate between Trenton, N.J., and Hartford, Connecticut, on a certain class of goods is $2.95 per 100 pounds. What would be the total freight charge on a shipment consisting of 3 crates weighing 180 pounds each and 2 cartons weighing 145 pounds each?

REVIEW ASSIGNMENT 46

1. a $396 is what part greater than $297?
b Divide $4,093.10 by $305,000.
c Find the due date of a 75-day note dated April 19.
d Find the number of days from May 18 to September 5.
e Find the interest on $428.70 for 33 days at 6%.
f Find the interest at 6% on $362.50 for 34 days.

2. A clerk in the post office had to weigh 5 packages to be sent to the fourth zone and determine the postage on them. Each package weighed 2 lb. 4 oz. and was to be insured for $10. Using the schedules of rates and fees on pages 319 and 320, find the total amount required to mail and insure the 5 packages.

3. The freight rate between Denver and Topeka on a certain class of goods is $4.95 per 100 pounds. What would be the total freight charges on a shipment of goods, of the foregoing class, consisting of 4 cases weighing 185 pounds each and 3 cartons weighing 65 pounds each?

4. A round-trip railroad ticket between Laporte and Melrose costs $33.65. The distance between Laporte and Melrose is 351.5 miles. Find the average cost, to the nearest tenth of a cent, of transportation per mile for the round trip.

5. Bradford drives 28 miles in 35 minutes. At that rate, how far will he drive in one hour?

6. At 48 miles an hour, how many hours will it take to drive 108 miles? Express your answer as a mixed number.

7. What would be the answer to Problem 6 in terms of hours and minutes?

8. What is the rate of return on a share of stock that costs $32 and pays regular quarterly dividends of $.28 a share?

> **9.** A certain stock pays a regular quarterly dividend of 75¢ per share. The stock is quoted at $52\frac{1}{4}$. How much money must Jerry Ford invest in this stock at that price in order to obtain an annual income of $2,400? (Disregard the broker's commission.)

GENERAL REVIEW

1. a Multiply 154.3 by 25.6. **d** Subtract $8\frac{2}{3}$ from $25\frac{1}{6}$.

   b Divide 484.42 by 5.3. **e** Multiply $24\frac{1}{5}$ by $5\frac{1}{3}$.

   c Add $15\frac{3}{4}$, $8\frac{1}{5}$ and $22\frac{1}{2}$. **f** Divide $16\frac{1}{2}$ by $\frac{3}{4}$.

2. A salesman receives a commission of $4\frac{1}{4}\%$ on all sales. His total sales last month were $10,000. What was the amount of his commission last month?

3. Mitchell started on an automobile trip at 8:45 a.m. and arrived at his destination at 4:15 p.m. He spent one hour and fifteen minutes for eating lunch and buying gasoline. How much time did he spend in actual travel?

4. Wilbur Harrison has a car for which he paid $3,150. His car expenses for last year were: gasoline and oil, $364; insurance, $155; interest at 4% on the cost of the car; depreciation, 18% of the cost of the car; repairs and other expenses, $73. Find the total cost of operating the car last year.

5. Mr. Bacon purchased a new car for $2,985. During the first year, he drove the car 8,121 miles. The total car expense for the first year was $1,010. Find the operating cost per mile to the nearest tenth of a cent.

6. The rate for first-class mail is 6¢ per ounce or fraction thereof. Find the total cost of sending the following by first-class mail:

     28 typewritten reports, each weighing $3\frac{1}{4}$ oz.

     32 letters, each weighing $1\frac{1}{4}$ oz.

     8 letters, each weighing $\frac{3}{4}$ oz.

7. Elise Morgan is paid $105.60 for a 40-hour week, plus time and a half for overtime. Last week she worked 46 hours. What were her total earnings for the week?

8. For one week Ritter has gross earnings of $125.14. He claims four exemptions. Using the tables on pages 106 and 108, find the income tax and FICA tax that the employer should withhold from Ritter's gross earnings.

9. Two partners, Ryan and Mapes, share net profits in the ratio of 7 to 8, respectively. Find the amount of each partner's share of a net profit of $16,950.

10. For a 3-month period, a student received $2.25 interest on his savings account of $180. What annual rate of interest did this savings bank pay him?

11. In the Freemont High School the enrollment in business mathematics increased from 160 students last year to 200 this year. With the same percent of growth over this year, what enrollment in business mathematics can be expected next year?

12. On August 4, Mr. Fisk borrowed $632.75 on a 90-day note at 7%. He repaid the note when it came due for payment.

a What was the total amount of money Mr. Fisk repaid?

b On what date did Mr. Fisk repay the loan?

13. A sofa priced at $180, cash, can be purchased for $18 down and 12 monthly payments of $14.70 each. By what percent does the installment price exceed the cash price?

14. Dow can buy a washer for $225 cash or on the installment plan by paying $20.50 a month for 12 months. He can borrow $225 at the bank for 12 months at 6% interest. How much will Dow save by borrowing and paying cash for the washer?

15. What rate of income does Robert Stoner receive on a 5% bond which he purchased at $62\frac{1}{2}$?

16. Mr. Franklin insured his household furniture, valued at $5,250, against fire loss for 80% of the value, at 86¢ per $100. Find the amount of the premium.

17. Bogart insured his house for $7,500 with the Regal Insurance Company and for $12,500 with the Reliance Insurance Company. If a fire loss of $3,000 occurs, what amount of money would Bogart receive from the Regal Insurance Company?

▶ **18.** A collection agent sent his principal $146.20 after deducting 32% for collecting a bill. What was the amount of the bill the agent collected?

▶ **19.** A stock that pays a regular quarterly dividend of $.62$\frac{1}{2}$ is quoted at $73\frac{1}{2}$. How much money must William Avery invest in this stock in order to receive an annual income of $500? (Disregard the broker's commission.)

▶ **20.** Alan Clay's checkbook balance on April 1 was $694.52. Upon preparing a reconciliation statement, Clay found that the following items had not been recorded in the checkbook: a cancelled check for $19.38; a deposit of $25.33; a service charge of $1.55. Also, a check for $32.40 had been recorded in the checkbook as $23.40. Find the correct checkbook balance.

UNIT Ten

Tax Problems

SECTION 47

Property Tax Rates

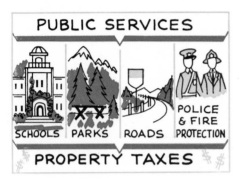

PUBLIC SERVICES

SCHOOLS   PARKS   ROADS   POLICE & FIRE PROTECTION

PROPERTY TAXES

The money needed to pay the expenses of cities, townships, and school districts is obtained chiefly by means of the *property tax*.

Property taxes also provide much if not most of the money needed by county governments and a part of the funds required by some states.

PART 47a Figuring the Decimal Tax Rate

Finding the amount to be raised by property tax. Each local tax district makes an estimate of its expenditures for the coming year. This estimate is called a *budget*.

An estimate is also made of the income that will be received from license fees, permits, fines, and other special sources. The difference between the total budget and the total miscellaneous receipts is the amount that must be raised by the property tax.

In the town of Newfane, for example, the total budget is $180,000; and the estimated miscellaneous receipts are $30,000. The amount to be raised by property tax is therefore $150,000.

Total budget	$180,000
Estimated miscellaneous receipts	30,000
Amount to be raised by property tax	$150,000

The assessment roll. In order that the total tax may be fairly divided among the property owners, the tax assessors place a valuation on each piece of property in the district. They then prepare an assessment roll showing the assessed valuation of each piece of property and the total for the entire district.

Finding the tax rate. The tax rate is a decimal fraction which answers the question: The total tax to be collected from the property owners is what part of the total assessed valuation? It is found by dividing the tax by the assessed valuation.

$$\text{Tax Rate} = \frac{\text{Total Tax}}{\text{Total Assessed Valuation}}$$

In Newfane, the total property tax is $150,000, and the total assessed valuation is $3,000,000. The tax rate is therefore .05.

$$\text{Tax Rate} = \frac{\$150,000}{\$3,000,000} = .05$$

Thus the total tax is .05 of the total assessed valuation.

Each property owner will therefore pay a tax equal to .05 of the assessed valuation of his property. If Glenn Heath, for example, owns property assessed at $7,000, the tax he must pay is .05 of $7,000, or $350.

$$.05 \times \$7,000 = \$350$$

Exercise 1   Written

1. Find the decimal that expresses the tax rate in each of the following. When the division is not exact, carry the decimal correct to five places.

	Assessed Valuation	Total Tax			Assessed Valuation	Total Tax
a	$2,000,000	$ 96,000	.048	f	$3,850,000	$ 82,775
b	$5,000,000	$260,000		g	$1,425,000	$ 48,750
c	$4,500,000	$153,000		h	$4,400,000	$181,500
d	$2,800,000	$ 25,200		i	$5,320,000	$278,000
e	$4,250,000	$ 97,750		j	$4,130,000	$128,600

2. Find the amount to be raised by property tax and the tax rate.

	Assessed Valuation	Total Budget	Miscellaneous Receipts	Raised by Property Tax	Tax Rate
a	$12,500,000	$491,200	$63,700	$427,500	.0342
b	$10,250,000	$548,600	$52,500		
c	$ 9,375,000	$495,000	$15,000		

3. The money to be raised by taxes in Rockville is $131,150. The assessed valuation of the property is $5,375,000. Find the tax rate.   .0244

4. In a community with a total assessed valuation of $3,525,000, a real estate tax of $152,280 is to be raised. What tax rate will be necessary to collect this amount of money?

5. In Eastport, $790,280 is to be raised by means of the real estate tax. The assessed valuation of the real estate in Eastport is $23,000,000. What tax rate will be necessary?

6. The budget for next year for the town of Woodmont requires $454,000 to meet all expenses. Fines, licenses, and other revenue will provide $76,000. The taxable property in the town has a total assessed valuation of $8,400,000. What tax rate must be levied on property in Woodmont next year?

REVIEW ASSIGNMENT **47** a

1. a Divide 9,880 by 760,000.

b Find the number of days from June 2 to August 28.

c Find the interest at 5% on $542.75 for 22 days.

2. In the town of Weston the budget for the coming year is $796,650. Miscellaneous income is estimated at $162,950. The balance is to be raised by a property tax on a total assessment roll of $9,000,000. Find the tax rate, correct to five decimal places.

3. The tax rate in Bayview is $57.213 per $1,000 of assessed valuation. Find the tax to be paid on property assessed at $6,700.

4. Carlin drives 21 miles in 45 minutes. At that rate of speed, how far would he travel in an hour?

5. An automobile costing $3,500 has a trade-in value of $700 at the end of five years. What is the annual rate of depreciation?

6. Bernard is offered a television set on the installment plan for a total cost of $360. He is to pay 30% of this cost as a down payment and the balance in 12 equal monthly payments. What will be the amount of each monthly payment?

7. A store property worth $28,000 rents for $3,600 a year. Annual expenses are as follows: repairs, $350; taxes, $798; insurance, $120; other expenses, $415. The annual net income is what percent of the value of the property, figured to the nearest tenth of a percent?

8. a $4.80 is $62\frac{1}{2}$% of what amount?

b $6.58 is what percent greater than $2.80?

9. For one quarterly period, Mr. Milano's water bill was $9.50. The water company charges $6.00 for the first 9,000 gallons and 50¢ for each additional thousand gallons thereafter. How many gallons of water did Mr. Milano use that quarter?

PART 47b | Changing the Base of the Tax Rate

Changing a decimal rate to a rate per $1, $100, or $1,000. The tax rate obtained by dividing the total tax by the total assessed valuation is a decimal and is referred to as the *decimal rate*.

It is common practice, however, to change the decimal rate to a rate in terms of dollars per $100 or per $1,000. It is sometimes changed to a rate in terms of cents or mills per dollar. The method of converting the decimal rate is illustrated by the following examples. The decimal rate is .05342.

Decimal Rate	Base	Rate in Terms of Base
.05342 × $100		= $5.342 per $100
.05342 × $1,000		= $53.42 per $1,000
.05342 × 100 cents		= 5.342¢ per $1 (100 cents)
.05342 × 1,000 mills		= 53.42 mills per $1 (1,000 mills)

Exercise 2   Written

1. Copy the following table and complete it by filling in the blanks for the equivalent rates.

	Decimal Rate	Rate in Dollars per $100	Rate in Dollars per $1,000	Rate in Cents per $1	Rate in Mills per $1
a	.05173	$5.173	$51.73	5.173¢	51.73
b	.05052				
c	.04825				
d	.05022				
e	.00934				

2. In a community with a total assessed valuation of $3,650,000, a real estate tax of $186,880 is to be raised. What tax rate per $1,000 will be necessary to collect this amount of money?

$51.20

3. Ennis paid $138.04 taxes on his house assessed at $4,700. What was the tax rate per $1,000?

4. The assessed valuation of the taxable property in the village of Benton is $11,000,000. The total amount necessary to meet the expenses of the village government for the coming year is $584,625. Of this amount, it is estimated that $75,300 will be received from special licenses, fees, and other miscellaneous sources. What tax rate per $1,000 will need to be levied to raise the necessary funds? Carry the decimal correct to five places.

5. The taxable property of a certain school district is assessed at $7,500,000. The total budget necessary to maintain the schools for the coming year is $894,900. Part of this expense will be met by money received from the state and from other sources, the total of which is estimated at $436,400. Find the tax rate per $1,000, correct to the nearest cent.

REVIEW ASSIGNMENT **47** b

1. a Express a tax rate of .00963 as a rate per $1,000.
b $225 is what part smaller than $270?
c What amount is $\frac{2}{3}\%$ of $465?
d Find the interest on $625.40 for 44 days at 6%.

2. The taxable property in a city is assessed at $32,000,000. The total amount necessary to meet the general expenses of the city for the coming year is $2,308,282. The estimated amount of receipts from various miscellaneous sources is $384,212. Find the tax rate per $1,000. (Carry the decimal correct to five places.)

3. Gilligan started on a trip in his automobile at 8:30 a.m. and arrived at his destination at 3:45 p.m. He spent one hour and thirty minutes eating lunch and buying gasoline. What was his actual driving time for this trip?

4. On a house that cost $8,500, the average annual expenses are: taxes, $223; repairs and depreciation, $340; insurance, $36. What monthly rent must be charged for this house in order to realize a net income of 7% on the original investment?

5. A round trip railroad ticket between Philadelphia and Pittsburgh costs $36.50. The distance between Philadelphia and Pittsburgh is 354 miles. What is the average cost per mile, to the nearest tenth of a cent, for the round trip?

▶ **6. a** $2.10 is $\frac{2}{7}$ of what amount?
b Sixteen is what percent of $5\frac{1}{3}$?

▶ **7.** A certain stock, quoted at 96, pays a dividend of $6\frac{3}{4}\%$ annually. The par value of this stock is $100. How much money must be invested in this stock in order to obtain a yearly income of $2,700? (Disregard the broker's commission.)

SECTION 48

Sales and Excise Taxes

Sales tax. Many cities and states levy a retail sales tax. The tax is usually collected from the purchaser by the merchant, who passes it on to the proper tax official.

Finding the sales tax. Shown at the right is the tax schedule used in a community where a 5% sales tax is levied.

When the sale exceeds one dollar, the appropriate amount in the schedule is added to the product of the whole number of dollars times 5 cents.

Amount of Sale	Sales Tax
$.01–$ .10	0
.11– .25	1¢
.26– .45	2¢
.46– .65	3¢
.66– .85	4¢
.86– 1.10	5¢
More than $1.10 (whole dollars)	5¢ on each dollar

Thus, the tax on a pair of shoes costing $7.49, for example, would be 38 cents.

Tax on $7.00 (7 × tax on $1, or 7 × 5¢) . . . .   35¢
Tax on   .49 (per schedule — $.46 to $.65) . . . .   3¢
Tax on $7.49 . . . .   38¢

Exercise 1 Oral

Using the schedule shown above, state the amount of the sales tax on each of the following sales.

Amount of Sale	Sales Tax		Amount of Sale	Sales Tax		Amount of Sale	Sales Tax
1. $ .36		4.	$ .82		7.	$1.67	
2. $1.36		5.	$2.82		8.	$3.15	
3. $2.36		6.	$ .67		9.	$5.50	

Excise taxes. The federal government levies an excise tax on amounts paid for telephone and telegraph service, admission tickets, and fares for air travel.

Exercise 2   Written

1. For each of the following, find the amount of the sales tax and the total cost to the customer. Base the tax on the retail price, and figure it to the nearest cent. Where the sales tax is 5%, you may use the tax table shown on page 331.

	Article	Retail Price	Sales Tax Rate	Sales Tax	Total Cost
a	Wallet	$ 5.95	3%	$.18	$6.13
b	Watch	24.95	5%		
c	Traveling case	34.45	6%		
d	Clock	18.35	4%		

2. For the period ending January 27, Mull used 6,400 cubic feet of gas at the average price of 23 cents per 100. There was added to the bill a local sales tax of 5%. What was the total of Mull's gas bill for the period?

3. The price of a certain airline travel ticket is $88.40 for an adult. Children under 12 are charged half fare. All tickets are subject to a 5% federal tax. Find the total cost, including taxes, of tickets for two adults and one child under 12.

4. The price of a theater ticket is $2 before taxes are added. A federal tax of 10% on admissions applies to the amount in excess of $1 paid for each admission. There is also a local sales tax of 5% on the full price of each admission. What will be the cost of 5 theater tickets?

⬤ Exercise 3   Written

1. In each of the following, the given cost includes the sales tax at the indicated rate, based on the retail price of the article. For each item you are to find the retail price and the amount of the tax.

	Article	Total Cost	Sales Tax Rate	Retail Price	Sales Tax
a	Desk	$36.05	3%	$35.00	$1.05
b	Shoes	13.00	4%		
c	Suit	50.99	3%		
d	Ring	26.25	5%		
e	Purse	14.04	4%		

2. An electric toaster sold for $24.99, which included a sales tax of 2% on the merchant's retail price. What was the retail price of the toaster before the tax was added? $24.50

3. Marie Hallenbeck paid $35.91 for an airplane travel ticket. This price included a 5% federal tax on the airline's price of the ticket. What was the airline's price of this ticket before the tax was added?

4. During the last three months of last year, a store's sales totaled $25,750. This total included a 3% city sales tax that was charged to and collected from each customer on each sale. What total amount of sales tax did the store collect from the customers during the three months?

REVIEW ASSIGNMENT **48**

1. a Find $\frac{1}{6}$% of $4,950.

b $175 is what part greater than $105?

c Find the interest at 6% on $291.27 for 45 days.

d Find the interest on $540 for 137 days at 5%.

e Express a tax rate of 42 mills on $1 as a rate on $1,000.

2. A watch marked to sell at $48.95 is subject to a 6% sales tax on the marked price. What price must the customer pay for this watch?

3. In one county the total expense budget for last year was $1,104,170. Miscellaneous income was $186,300. The balance was raised by a property tax on a total assessment roll of $43,600,000.

   a Find the tax rate per $1,000, to the nearest cent.

   b What was Gilson's tax if his property was assessed at $9,800?

4. Milstein paid $2,800 for a car. After using it for four years, he purchased a new one costing $2,900 by trading in his old car and paying $2,300 in cash. What was the amount of the average annual depreciation of the old car?

5. A 6% note for $1,450, dated March 16, was paid in full on the following May 31. What was the amount of the payment?

▶ **6. a** $345 is $\frac{2}{5}$ smaller than what amount?

   b $3.90 is $\frac{2}{3}$ greater than what amount?

▶ **7.** Bob Ellis paid $28.09 for an archery set. This amount included a 6% sales tax on the merchant's selling price. What was the selling price of this set before the tax was added?

SECTION 49

Social Security Taxes and Benefits

Employees, their employers, and self-employed persons are taxed under the Federal Insurance Contributions Act to provide funds for the payment of retirement and other benefits to retired and disabled workers and their dependents.

This tax is known as the *FICA* or *Social Security Tax*. The provisions regarding the social security tax are subject to change by an act of Congress.

RETIREMENT, SURVIVORS, DISABILITY & HOSPITAL INSURANCE

CONTRIBUTIONS PAID DURING WORKING YEARS BY EMPLOYERS EMPLOYEES SELF-EMPLOYED PEOPLE

| Retirement | Survivors | Disability | Hospital |

PART 49a Figuring the Tax

Tax on employee and employer. The employer is required to deduct and remit to the federal government a certain percent of the employee's earnings every pay day. Thus, if the tax rate is 4.8% and the earnings are $125, the deduction will be 4.8% of $125, or $6.

$$.048 \times \$125 = \$6$$

A person who earns more than $7,800 in one calendar year is taxed on the first $7,800 only.

The employer is taxed at the same rate on the taxable wages he has paid. During the month of April, for example, the owner of the Rogers Pet Shop paid taxable wages amounting to $500. The tax he must pay is 4.8% of $500, which is $24.

$$.048 \times \$500 = \$24$$

Tax on self-employed person. The self-employment tax is imposed on the first $7,800 of annual net earnings from self-employment. The rate is higher than the rate paid by wage earners.

Exercise 1   Written

1. Find to the nearest cent the FICA tax at 4.8% that should be deducted from each of the weekly wages shown below.

a Lisa Carter....$ 96.00 $4.61   **d** Allan Herber...$150.00

b James Drexel...   72.00   **e** Mae Marino....   78.64

c Hans Flagler... 104.00   **f** Irene Sands....   81.40

2. During the month of May the Aluminco Corp. paid taxable wages totaling $6,370. What was the amount of the FICA tax levied on the company if the rate was 4.8%? $305.76

3. Bob Roe, whose income is derived from self-employment, had a self-employment net income of $7,280 last year. Find the amount of his self-employment tax at 6.9%.

4. Julius Moak is a self-employed person. His net income from self-employment last year was $8,436.20. At 6.9%, what was the amount of his self-employment tax for the year?

5. Moss Rigg receives an annual salary of $9,600, payable monthly. How much must be deducted from his salary for social security taxes at 4.8% for the following months?

a First month   **b** Ninth month   **c** Tenth month

REVIEW ASSIGNMENT 49a

1. a What amount is $\frac{5}{6}$% of $5,250?

b $161 is what percent less than $175?

c Find the interest at 4% on $842.70 for 11 days.

d Express a tax rate of 31 mills on $1 as a rate on $1,000.

2. Using the tax schedule on page 331, find the sales tax on a purchase consisting of a dress, $29.45; a coat, $38.50; and a hat, $7.98.

3. The cash price of a stereo radio is $225. The installment price is $30 down and 10 monthly payments of $21 each. How much money would be saved by purchasing the radio for cash?

4. An automobile dealer accepts Morton's old car and $2,500 in cash in exchange for a new car priced at $3,350. Morton purchased his old car 4 years ago for $2,950. What was the amount of the average annual depreciation on Morton's old car?

5. A speed of twenty-one miles in thirty-six minutes is equivalent to how many miles an hour?

6. a What amount is 125% greater than $25?

b $7.50 is $33\frac{1}{3}$% less than what amount?

PART **49b** Social Security Benefits

Finding the primary amount. A worker who has met the employment requirements of the law may retire at age 65 or older and receive monthly retirement payments for the rest of his life. The amount he is entitled to each month is called his *primary amount.*

In most cases, the primary amount depends upon the worker's average monthly earnings since 1950 on which he has paid social security taxes. This average, which is rounded to the next lower multiple of $1 if it is not an even multiple of $1, is called his *average monthly earnings.*

PARTIAL TABLE OF
PRIMARY BENEFITS

Average monthly earnings		
At least	But not more than	Primary amount
$621	$623	$210
624	627	211
628	630	212
631	634	213
635	637	214
638	641	215
642	644	216
645	648	217
649	650	218

The corresponding primary amount is determined from a table contained in the Social Security Act.

As shown in the table, for average monthly earnings of $621, $622, or $623, the primary amount is $210; for $624, $625, $626, or $627, it is $211; and so on.

A worker may retire when he reaches age 62 if he wishes. If he does, his payments will be 80% of the primary amount shown in the table. For each month he waits after 62, his payments are proportionately more.

A worker who becomes disabled before age 65 is eligible for monthly payments as if he had reached retirement age.

Exercise 2   Written

1. The following workers are retiring at age 65. Using the table, find each worker's primary amount.

Worker	Average Monthly Earnings		Worker	Average Monthly Earnings
a Gail Hall	$624	$211	d Linn Mays	$647
b Ellis Kane	641		e Susan Rudd	632
c Irene Lynn	636		f Rick Rossi	650

2. Dexter Mann is disabled at age 39. His average monthly earnings are $622. What is his primary amount?

3. Clay Bly is 62 today. His average monthly earnings are $629. How much will he receive each month if he retires today on payments equal to 80% of his primary amount? $169.60

4. Edith Page decides to retire today at age 63 on $86\frac{2}{3}\%$ of her primary amount. Her average monthly earnings are $643. How much retirement pay will she receive each month?

Dependents' and survivors' benefits. A retired or disabled worker's wife and his dependent children under age 18 (or up to age 22 if attending school full time) are each entitled to monthly payments of one half of the worker's primary amount.

If there are no children, the wife of a retired or disabled worker is not eligible for her entire full benefit until she is 65. She may, however, start receiving payments at age 62. If she does, her monthly benefit will be 75% of what it would be if she were 65. For each month she waits after 62, her monthly benefits are proportionately more.

If an insured worker dies, his widow and dependent children under 18 (or up to age 22 if in school full time) are entitled to *survivors' benefits*. The widow and each child receive three fourths of the worker's primary amount. If there are no children, the widow receives no benefits until age 62, when she begins receiving $82\frac{1}{2}\%$ of the primary amount. Or, if she chooses, she may start benefits at age 60, but at a reduced rate. Disabled widows may qualify for benefits as early as age 50.

The total family benefit may not exceed $434.40, or 80% of the worker's average earnings, whichever is smaller. If the computed total family benefit exceeds the allowable maximum, the benefits of the wife and children or survivors are reduced proportionately to bring the total down to the allowable maximum.

If the amount of a benefit is not an exact multiple of 10 cents, it is raised to the next higher multiple of 10 cents. For example, a benefit that figures out at $44.25 is raised to $44.30.

Exercise 3   Written

1. Edward Kimball is retiring at age 70. His average monthly earnings are $640. His wife is 65. What total monthly payment will he and his wife receive? $322.50

2. When Hans Erway retired at age 65, his average monthly earnings were $626. His wife was 61. When she became 62, she elected to begin receiving a wife's benefit at 75% of what it would be if she were 65. What total monthly benefit have Mr. Erway and his wife been receiving since she became 62? $290.20

3. An insured worker dies and is survived by a widow aged 59. His average monthly earnings are $635. How much will the widow be entitled to receive each month after she reaches age 62?

4. An insured worker dies and is survived by a widow and two dependent children under 18. His average monthly earnings are $623. What total monthly amount will the widow and children receive?

REVIEW ASSIGNMENT **49** b

1. a $405 is what part smaller than $540?
b Find $\frac{1}{3}\%$ of $7,350.
c Find the interest on $359.40 for 71 days at 6%.
d Express 13 mills as a decimal part of $1.

2. In a town with a total assessed valuation of $8,250,000 a real estate tax of $433,125 is to be raised. What tax rate per $1,000 will be necessary to collect this amount?

3. The cash price of an air conditioner is $345. The installment price is $35 down and 12 monthly payments of $28.50 each. In order to pay cash for the air conditioner, Bissell borrows the money from a bank for 12 months at a total interest cost of $24.15. How much money does he save by borrowing and purchasing the air conditioner at the cash price?

4. Loeb insured his office building for $25,000 with the Peerless Insurance Co. and for $35,000 with the Royal Insurance Co. If a fire loss of $4,500 occurs, what amount of money should Loeb receive from each of these companies?

5. A typewriter which cost $270 when new was worth $65 five years later. Find the average annual rate of depreciation, correct to the nearest tenth of a percent.

6. Kilmer drives his car 18 miles in 27 minutes. What is his speed in miles per hour?

▶ **7. a** $13.20 is $37\frac{1}{2}\%$ more than what amount?
   b $1.60 is $\frac{5}{4}$ of what amount?

▶ **8.** A house valued at $12,500 was insured for $9,500 under a policy containing an 80% coinsurance clause. A fire caused a loss of $1,150. How much of the loss was borne by the insurance company?

▶ **9.** A certain bracelet costs the customer $10.14, including a sales tax of 4%. What is the price of this bracelet before the tax is added?

SECTION 50

Income Taxes

The federal government and many of the states impose a tax on the incomes of their citizens. The estimated tax on income from salary or wages is withheld by the employer when the wages are paid.

PART 50a   Federal Income Taxes

Federal income tax return. The withholding tax applies only to the salary or wages of the taxpayer. It does not apply to his income from other sources, such as rent, interest, dividends, and profits on investments. Hence, at the end of the year, the taxpayer is required to file a tax return with the Internal Revenue Service. In the return, the taxpayer provides all the data needed for figuring his actual tax liability so that any additional amount due may be collected or any overpayment refunded.

UNCLE SAM GETS PART OF THIS

The calculation of the tax is based on the taxable income remaining after subtracting certain deductions from the gross income.

Gross income. *Gross income*, in general, includes income from wages, salaries, commissions, bonuses, tips, competitive prizes and awards, dividends, interest, rents, gain on sales of property, and profit from a business or profession.

Net income. *Net income* is gross income minus certain allowable deductions. These deductions consist chiefly of contributions to charitable or religious organizations; interest paid on personal debts; property, sales, and state or local income taxes; losses on sales of stocks, bonds, and rental property; expenses in operating a business or carrying on a profession; and certain miscellaneous expenses connected with one's employment.

Exercise 1   Written

In each of the following find the net income for the year.

1. B. R. Ganey had for the year a gross income of $6,400 and claimed the following deductions: contributions to church and Community Chest, $165; interest on mortgage, $258; real estate taxes, $372. $5,605

2. Last year, W. H. Lear had the following income: salary, $7,600; interest on bank deposits, $85; bond interest, $68.
He claimed the following deductions: contributions, $240; real estate taxes, $380; interest on mortgage, $420; membership dues in professional associations, $35.

3. Drew Nord's income last year consisted of the following: salary, $7,400; commissions, $845; bonus, $125; interest, $93.
He claimed deductions as follows: interest on mortgage, $435; taxes, $342; contributions, $325; miscellaneous deductions, $47.

Taxable income. From his net income, a taxpayer is allowed to deduct one exemption of $600 for himself, one for his wife if he is married, and one for each dependent. The remainder is his *taxable income*.

Thus, if a taxpayer is married and has one dependent child, he may deduct $600 for himself, $600 for his wife, and $600 for the child, making a total of $1,800. If his net income is $5,000, his taxable income is $5,000 − $1,800, or $3,200.

The amount of the exemption is changed from time to time by act of Congress.

Exercise 2   Oral

For each taxpayer listed below, state how many exemptions he may deduct and the amount of his taxable income.

Taxpayer	Exemption Status	Net Income
1. Eve Beale	Single	$5,700
2. Harold Gordon	Married	$8,450
3. Cliff LeRoy	Married, 2 dependent children	$9,680
4. Dora Keefe	Single, dependent mother and sister	$6,850
5. Ivan Graff	Married, dependent father, and 3 dependent children	$7,800
6. Ethan Reedy	Widower, dependent father and mother, and 2 dependent children	$9,850

Tax rate schedules. The amount of one's income tax depends on the amount of his taxable income and his qualification as a taxpayer. A portion of the tax rate schedule for each class is shown on page 342.

Schedule I applies to single persons who do not qualify for the rates in Schedules II and III and to married persons filing separate returns.

Schedule II applies to married couples who file joint returns. The rates are lower than those in Schedule I.

A *joint return* is a single return that includes the income, deductions, and exemptions of both husband and wife. Even though one spouse had no income, a husband and wife can make a joint return so as to take advantage of the lower rates.

Schedule III applies to unmarried persons who qualify as heads of households. In general, an unmarried person who maintains a home which he shares with a dependent or with an unmarried child, grandchild, or stepchild, even though such child is not a dependent, may qualify as a head of household.

The rates in Schedule III are lower than the rates in Schedule I but higher than those in Schedule II.

Using the tax rate schedules. The use of the tax rate schedules is shown in the solution of the example given below.

Example

Henry York has a taxable income of $9,000. He is single and does not qualify as a head of household. Find the amount of his income tax.

Solution:		Explanation
Tax on first $8,000	*$1,630*	Mr. York determines his tax from Schedule I. The third line of the schedule shows that the tax is $1,630 plus 28% of the excess over $8,000.
28% of $1,000	*280*	
Total income tax	*$1,910*	
Ans. *$1,910*		

The excess of $9,000 over $8,000 is $1,000. His tax is therefore $1,630, plus 28% of $1,000, or $1,910.

Schedule I. SINGLE TAXPAYERS not qualifying for rates in Schedules II and III, and MARRIED PERSONS FILING SEPARATE RETURNS

If the taxable income is: *The tax is:*

Over— But not over—		of excess over—
$4,000 — $6,000	$690, plus 22%	— $4,000
$6,000 — $8,000	$1,130, plus 25%	— $6,000
$8,000 — $10,000	$1,630, plus 28%	— $8,000
$10,000 — $12,000	$2,190, plus 32%	— $10,000

Schedule II. MARRIED TAXPAYERS FILING JOINT RETURNS and CERTAIN WIDOWS AND WIDOWERS

If the taxable income is: *The tax is:*

Over— But not over—		of excess over—
$4,000 — $8,000	$620, plus 19%	— $4,000
$8,000 — $12,000	$1,380, plus 22%	— $8,000
$12,000 — $16,000	$2,260, plus 25%	— $12,000
$16,000 — $20,000	$3,260, plus 28%	— $16,000

Schedule III. UNMARRIED (or legally separated) TAXPAYERS WHO QUALIFY as HEADS OF HOUSEHOLD

If the taxable income is: *The tax is:*

Over— But not over—		of excess over—
$4,000 — $6,000	$660, plus 20%	— $4,000
$6,000 — $8,000	$1,060, plus 22%	— $6,000
$8,000 — $10,000	$1,500, plus 25%	— $8,000
$10,000 — $12,000	$2,000, plus 27%	— $10,000

Exercise 3   Written

1. Using Schedule I, find the tax on each of the following taxable incomes reported by single persons not heads of households.

a $5,000 $910 **b** $7,000   **c** $6,500   **d** $8,200   **e** $9,400

2. Using Schedule II, find the tax on each of the following taxable incomes reported by married couples filing joint returns.

a $5,000   **b** $6,300   **c** $7,200   **d** $8,400   **e** $16,300

3. Using Schedule III, find the tax on each of the following taxable incomes of persons qualifying as heads of households.

a $7,000   **b** $6,200   **c** $5,600   **d** $7,700   **e** $6,800

4. Luke Nash, a single man not qualifying as head of household, reported a taxable income of $4,800 for the year. He also reported total withholding taxes of $887 deducted from his wages by his employer.

a What was his actual tax liability? $866

b What was his overpayment or balance of tax due? $21

5. Mr. and Mrs. Lanza, in a joint tax return, reported a taxable income of $12,400 for the year.

a Find their actual tax liability.

b What amount should they remit with their tax return to the District Director of Internal Revenue if income taxes totaling $2,230 were withheld from their wages during the year?

6. Iver Bates submitted the following facts in his income tax return: salary, $8,240; interest received, $50. He claimed deductions as follows: taxes, $445; interest on mortgage, $325; contributions, $220. He is unmarried but qualifies as head of household and claims two exemptions. A total of $1,298 for income taxes was withheld from his wages during the year.

a Find his actual tax liability.

b Find the amount of his overpayment or balance of tax due.

REVIEW ASSIGNMENT **50 a**

1. a $8.75 is what part greater than $7?

b What percent of $22.50 is $67.50?

c What amount is $\frac{2}{3}\%$ of $2,340?

d Express 28 mills as a decimal part of $1.

e Find the interest on $735.50 for 22 days at $4\frac{1}{2}\%$.

2. For one year, Fred Snow, a single man, had a taxable income of $6,892 after all deductions for exemptions had been made. Using Schedule I on page 342, find the amount of his federal income tax for that year.

3. The tax rate in Linden is $61.20 per $1,000 of assessed valuation. What tax must Mr. Napoli pay if his property, valued at $13,500, is assessed for 60% of its value?

4. An automobile dealer accepts Orner's old car and $2,500 in cash in exchange for a new car priced at $2,950. Orner purchased his old car five years ago for $2,600. What was the amount of the average annual depreciation of Orner's old car?

5. Duffy started on an automobile trip at 9:45 a.m. and reached his destination at 3:10 p.m. He spent one hour and fifteen minutes for lunch and fifteen minutes for obtaining gasoline. What was his actual driving time for this trip?

6. A train travels 9 miles in 10 minutes. What is its speed in miles per hour?

7. a $7.50 is what percent greater than $3?

b Express $\frac{2}{3}\%$ as a decimal.

PART 50b State Income Taxes

State tax rates. An income tax is also levied by about three fourths of the states. The state income tax laws are patterned after the federal law. The rates are different from the federal rates and vary among the different states.

The following is a partial list of rates used by one state. These rates are applied to the taxable income.

2% of the first $1,000   5% of the next $2,000
3% of the next $2,000   6% of the next $2,000
4% of the next $2,000   7% of the next $2,000

Exercise 4   Written

1. Using the list of state income tax rates given above, find the tax on each of the following taxable incomes.
a $2,280 $58.40 **b** $3,500   **c** $6,200   **d** $2,700   **e** $7,400

2. When Warner prepared his state income tax return for last year, he figured that the amount of his taxable income, after all deductions had been made, was $2,645 for the year. This amount was subject to the tax rates listed above. What was the total of Warner's state income tax for the year?

3. Mendel's state income tax return for last year showed a taxable income of $5,238 after all deductions had been made. This income was subject to the tax rates listed above. Find Mendel's total state income tax for the year.

REVIEW ASSIGNMENT 50 b

1. In making out their federal income tax return for one year, Mr. and Mrs. Kantor, who filed a joint return, reported a taxable income of $9,164. By using Schedule II on page 342, find the amount of their federal income tax for that year, rounded to the nearest dollar.

2. Last year, Mr. Mayo had a taxable income of $4,734. This income was subject to a state income tax of 2% on the first $1,000, 3% on the next $2,000, and 4% on the next $2,000 or any part thereof. What was the amount of Mr. Mayo's state income tax for last year, rounded to the nearest dollar?

3. On a cross-country automobile trip, Mr. Posner traveled 6,156 miles and used 342 gallons of gasoline. How many miles per gallon of gasoline did Mr. Posner obtain on the trip?

4. After six years of use, a typewriter which cost $230, when new, had a trade-in value of $35. Find, to the nearest whole percent, the average annual rate of depreciation of this typewriter.

5. How many hours and minutes will it take to drive 130 miles at an average speed of 40 miles an hour?

6. The amount of money to be raised by taxes in the village of Greenville is $751,161. The assessed valuation of the property in the village is $12,214,000. What will be the village tax rate per $1,000 of assessed valuation?

❯ **7.** The price of a basketball is $13.02, which includes a sales tax of 5%. What is the price of this basketball before the sales tax is added?

GENERAL REVIEW

1. a Multiply 310.7 by 38.6.   **d** Subtract $6\frac{1}{3}$ from $17\frac{1}{4}$.

b Divide 109.18 by 5.3.   **e** Multiply $18\frac{1}{2}$ by $6\frac{1}{3}$.

c Add: $7\frac{5}{6}$, $10\frac{1}{3}$, $5\frac{4}{9}$, $13\frac{1}{2}$.   **f** Divide $52\frac{1}{2}$ by $2\frac{1}{3}$.

g Express 76% as a common fraction in simplest form.

h Express $16\frac{3}{5}$ as it should appear according to good business usage.

2. The merchandise inventory of the Roger Morse Company was $32,450 on October 1 and $27,965 on December 31. Sales for the quarter were $51,275, and the purchases were $29,360. What was the company's gross profit for the quarter?

3. Roy Graham, a factory hand who works on a piece-rate basis, completes 65 pieces on Monday, 68 on Tuesday, 75 on Wednesday, and 73 on Thursday. If he is paid 40¢ for each piece, how many pieces must he complete on Friday in order that his earnings for the five days may average $28 a day?

4. Kerr, Melick, and Sachs had gross wages of $124.37, $128.52, and $125.88, respectively, during the week ending March 10. By using the Social Security Employee Tax Table on page 108, determine the total amount of the FICA tax withheld from the gross wages of these three employees.

5. Grossman, a salesman, is paid $4\frac{1}{2}$% commission on all sales up to and including $6,500, and $6\frac{1}{2}$% on all sales in excess of $6,500 in any one month. Last month his sales were $9,800.

a What amount of commission did he earn at the $4\frac{1}{2}$% rate?

b What amount of commission did he earn at the $6\frac{1}{2}$% rate?

6. On May 15, Clausen borrowed $540, giving his 90-day, 7% interest-bearing note as security. Find the date of maturity of Clausen's note and the total amount Clausen will have to repay when the note matures.

7. Vaughn can borrow $200 from a consumer finance company and repay it in 18 monthly installments of $13.75 each.

   a What is the finance charge on this loan?

   b What is the amount financed?

   c What is the finance charge per $100 of amount financed?

8. Mrs. Beach purchased some furniture priced at $410, with a down payment of $60. The finance charge consists of interest for 12 months at 6% on the unpaid balance, and a service charge of $7. The total amount will be paid in 12 equal monthly payments. What will be the amount of each payment?

9. A building is insured with three companies: American Insurance Co., $15,000; National Insurance Co., $30,000; Zenith Insurance Co., $35,000. If a fire occurs, for what percent of the total loss will the National Insurance Co. be liable?

10. Anderson bought 80 shares of Bethlehem Steel stock at 35⅜. The brokerage on the purchase was $31.15. What was the total cost of this stock to Anderson?

11. Williams has a balance of $600 in his savings account on January 2. The bank pays interest at the rate of 5% a year, compounded quarterly. How much money will Williams have in the account on October 1, nine months later?

⊙ **12.** On May 1, Brink's checkbook balance was $635. His bank statement on that date showed a balance of $650.40. Checks for $42.90 and $27 were outstanding. The statement showed that the bank had deducted a service charge for $2 for the month. Brink discovered that a deposit of $52.50 had been recorded twice in the checkbook by mistake. Prepare a reconciliation statement.

⊙ **13.** For one quarterly period, Mr. Goodman's water bill was $9.38. The water company charges $6.50 for the first 1,200 cubic feet or less, and 40¢ per hundred for the next 3,600 cubic feet. How many cubic feet of water did Mr. Goodman use during that period?

⊙ **14.** Jack Norcross purchased a camera at a total cost of $30.68, which included a sales tax of 4%.

   a What was the price of the camera before the sales tax was added?

   b What was the amount of the sales tax?

UNIT Eleven

Problems of a Small Business

SECTION | 51

The Balance Sheet

Assets. To establish and operate a business, a person must have property of various kinds. A retail grocer, for example, must have a stock of groceries and other merchandise for sale to his customers. He must also have wrapping supplies and store equipment for serving his customers properly and efficiently. Besides these, he must have a supply of cash for making change and paying expenses. This property is called the *assets* of the business.

WHAT ARE THE ASSETS OF THIS SHOE STORE?

Liabilities. A businessman often obtains some of the assets by purchasing them on credit and promising to pay for them at some future date. The persons to whom the debts are owed are called the *creditors* of the business. They have claims against the assets until the debts are paid. These claims of the creditors are called the *liabilities* of the business.

Proprietorship. If the assets are owned free of debt, the proprietor may claim their entire value for himself. If there are liabilities, the proprietor can claim only the value that remains after deducting the liabilities from the assets. His claim against the assets is called his *proprietorship* or capital.*

For example, T. R. Lake, owner of a fabric and sewing supply store, owes the Luster Woolen Co. $1,800 and the Foster Mills $1,200 for merchandise purchased from them on credit. The total liabilities are $3,000. If Lake is using assets worth $38,000, the amount of his proprietorship is $38,000 − $3,000, or $35,000.

---

*Other terms that are used to mean the same as proprietorship, or capital, are *investment, net investment,* and *net worth.*

Assets $38,000 — Liabilities $3,000 = Proprietorship, $35,000

The balance sheet. At regular intervals, but at least as often as once a year, the proprietor takes an inventory of the assets and the liabilities. With this information he prepares a statement called a *balance sheet*. This statement shows the assets, liabilities, and proprietorship of the business.

The following is the balance sheet of T. R. Lake on April 30, 19—:

T. R. LAKE

Balance Sheet, April 30, 19--

Assets		*Liabilities*	
Cash	3,000	Luster Woolen Co.	1,800
Merchandise Inventory	25,000	Foster Mills	1,200
Equipment	9,600	Total Liabilities	3,000
Supplies	400		
		Proprietorship	
		T. R. Lake, Capital	35,000
Total Assets	38,000	Total Liab. and Prop.	38,000

Balance sheet

In the balance sheet, the assets are listed on the left, and the liabilities and proprietorship on the right. This arrangement is based on the fact that the total of all claims against the assets is equal to the total value of the assets. Thus,

Assets, $38,000 = Liabilities $3,000 + Proprietorship $35,000

Exercise 1   Written

1. Willard West, owner of a hardware store, has the following assets: cash, $300; merchandise, $7,400; store equipment, $800; store supplies, $50.

He owes the Lesco Manufacturing Co. $200 and the Shay Tool Co. $500 for merchandise purchased from them on account. What is the amount of his proprietorship? $7,850

2. Allan Faber, owner of an appliance business, has the following assets: cash, $2,200; merchandise, $5,000; store supplies, $150; store equipment, $600; delivery equipment (truck), $2,600; and land and building, $9,400. He owes the First National Bank $800 and the Bennett Manufacturing Company $1,000.

Find the amount of his proprietorship.

3. C. V. Graf, fuel dealer, owns the following assets: cash, $700; merchandise, $3,600; office supplies, $25; office equipment, $350; delivery equipment, $3,400; and land and buildings, $8,500.

He owes the Central Oil Company $650 and the Propa-Gas Company $700.

What is the amount of his proprietorship?

4. On December 31 of last year, Jeff Kerwin, a farm implement dealer, had the assets and liabilities listed below. Prepare for Mr. Kerwin a balance sheet as of December 31.

Cash.................$ 436	Debts owed creditors as follows:	
Merchandise Inventory 8,157	H. H. Glavin..........$137	
Furniture and Fixtures. 375	K. G. Loomis.......... 246	
Delivery Equipment... 1,545		

REVIEW ASSIGNMENT **51**

1. a Multiply 280 by $1\frac{5}{8}$.

b Find the number of days from March 19 to July 14.

c Find the interest at 6% on $461.52 for 82 days.

d Express a tax rate of $18\frac{1}{2}$ mills on $1 as a rate on $1,000.

2. Ray Holmes, owner of Ray's News & Card Shoppe, has the following assets and liabilities on March 1 of the current year: cash, $642; merchandise inventory, $5,422; supplies, $37; land and building, $21,500; furniture and fixtures, $1,870; debt owed to Valley Sales Co., $319; debt owed to Shafer & Brown, $462. Find the amount of Mr. Holmes' proprietorship.

3. The tax rate in Riverford is $7.652 per $100. What is the tax on a piece of property assessed at $11,800?

4. Two business partners, Lennox and Shaw, divide their net income in a ratio of 3 to 2, respectively. Find the amount of each partner's share of a net income of $12,600.

5. Doyle borrowed $1,500 for one month. The interest on the loan amounted to $8.75. What rate of interest did he pay?

6. What is the amount of Henry Klett's annual income from 125 shares of National Paper Company stock if the stock pays a regular quarterly dividend of $87\frac{1}{2}$¢ a share?

SECTION 52

The Income Statement

Sales, returns and allowances, net sales. In any retail business, goods are sold at a higher price than the cost in order to make a profit. The total amount received for goods sold over a period of time is called the *sales* for the period.

Refunds are given to customers for returned goods or for allowances because of defective merchandise. These refunds decrease the income from sales and therefore are deducted from the sales. The amount remaining is called the *net sales*.

Sales − Returns and Allowances = Net Sales

For example, T. R. Lake has sales for April amounting to $10,150, and returns and allowances amounting to $150. His net sales for the month are $10,000. These figures are obtained from the bookkeeping records.

Sales	$10,150
Returns and Allowances	150
Net Sales	$10,000

Gross profit. *Gross profit* is the amount remaining after deducting the cost of goods sold from the net sales. This amount is also called the *margin*.

Net Sales − Cost of Goods Sold = Gross Profit

The goods that T. R. Lake sold during April for $10,000 cost him $6,200. His gross profit for the month is $3,800.

Net Sales	$10,000
Cost of Goods Sold	6,200
Gross Profit	$3,800

Finding the cost of goods sold. Usually a record of the cost of an article is not made at the time the article is sold. Instead, inventories of the merchandise on hand are taken at the beginning and end of the period. The cost of the goods sold is then found by adding the beginning inventory and the cost of the goods purchased, and subtracting from that sum the ending inventory.

$$\text{Beginning Inventory} + \text{Purchases} - \text{Ending Inventory} = \text{Cost of Goods Sold}$$

For example, on April 1, T. R. Lake's merchandise inventory was $23,900. During April he purchased additional goods costing $7,300. On April 30 his merchandise inventory was $25,000. The cost of goods sold during April was $6,200.

Merchandise Inventory, April 1	$23,900
Purchases	7,300
Merchandise Available for Sale	$31,200
Merchandise Inventory, April 30	25,000
Cost of Goods Sold	$ 6,200

The proprietor or his bookkeeper keeps a daily record of the cost of all merchandise purchased. The total of the daily records for the period is the amount of the *purchases*.

Exercise 1   Written

1. Find the net sales and gross profit.

	Sales	Returns and Allowances	Net Sales	Cost of Goods Sold	Gross Profit
a	$13,725	$1,550	$12,175	$ 8,225	$3,950
b	28,619	2,728		17,686	
c	34,673	1,877		19,678	
d	22,144	1,589		14,758	

2. The records of Phelps & Kane, furniture dealers, show the following for the first half of the year: stock of merchandise on hand January 1, $42,350; cost of additional merchandise purchased during the period, $37,225; stock of merchandise on hand June 30, $38,725. What was the cost of the goods sold?

3. The records of the Moderne Hat Shoppe show the following for the quarter ending June 30: merchandise inventory April 1, $4,300; purchases for the quarter, $6,550; net sales for the quarter, $11,375; merchandise inventory June 30, $4,600. Find the cost of goods sold and the gross profit for the period.

Net income. In any mercantile business such expenses as rent, salaries, advertising, and other items of expense connected with the operation of the business are necessary. These expenses are called the *operating expenses, overhead,* or *cost of doing business.* They decrease the profits of the business and must therefore be subtracted from the gross profit. The amount remaining is known as the *net income* or *net profit.*

Gross Profit − Operating Expenses = Net Income (Net Profit)

T. R. Lake's gross profit for April is $3,800, and his operating expenses are $3,100. His net income for the period is $700.

Gross Profit on Sales	$3,800
Operating Expenses	3,100
Net Income	$ 700

Net loss. If the operating expenses are greater than the gross profit, the gross profit is subtracted from the operating expenses. The result is a *net loss.*

Operating Expenses − Gross Profit = Net Loss

Exercise 2   Written

1. Find the gross profit and the net income.

	Net Sales	Cost of Goods Sold	Gross Profit	Operating Expenses	Net Income
a	$ 8,975	$ 6,255	$2,720	$1,962	$758
b	17,433	10,659		5,978	
c	26,705	17,359		7,633	
d	13,820	10,365		2,788	

2. Ray Hershey, a clothier, had net sales of $9,000 for the month of February. Operating expenses for the month totaled $2,300 and the cost of goods sold amounted to $5,800. Find his gross profit and his net profit or net loss for the month.

3. The records of H. A. Isen showed the following for the year ending December 31: merchandise inventory January 1, $18,000; purchases, $46,000; net sales, $80,000; merchandise inventory December 31, $16,000; operating expenses, $24,000. Find the cost of goods sold, the gross profit, and the net income.

4. For the last six months of a recent year, the financial records of a small business showed the following information: merchandise inventory, July 1, $25,750; merchandise inventory, December 31, $20,400; purchases, $60,000; gross sales, $98,500; sales returns and allowances, $2,600; operating expenses, $31,200. Find the net sales, cost of goods sold, gross profit, and net profit or net loss.

Income statement. At regular intervals, such as once a month or year, the owner of a business prepares a statement showing the amount of his sales, cost of golds sold, operating expenses, and net income for the period. This statement is usually called an *income statement*. Occasionally it is referred to as a *profit and loss statement*.

The following is T. R. Lake's income statement for April, 19—.

T. R. LAKE
Income Statement
For the Month Ended April 30, 19--

Income:		
Net Sales — Fabrics...................	$5,900	
Net Sales — Sewing Accessories.........	4,100	
Total Income.......................................		$10,000
Cost of Goods Sold:		
Fabrics............................	$3,700	
Sewing Accessories....................	2,500	6,200
Gross Profit on Sales..............................		$ 3,800
Operating Expenses:		
Salaries and Wages....................	$1,600	
Rent..............................	700	
Advertising..........................	200	
Taxes..............................	90	
Utilities............................	100	
Depreciation of Equipment..............	80	
Supplies............................	60	
Miscellaneous Expense.................	270	
Total Operating Expenses.........................		3,100
Net Income......................................		$ 700

Income statement

Percentage analysis of the income statement. Most businessmen make a percentage analysis of the income statement. This analysis shows what percent each major item is of the net sales.

The percentage analysis of T. R. Lake's income statement for April, in condensed form, is shown below.

Net Sales	$10,000	100%
Cost of Goods Sold	6,200	62%
Gross Profit on Sales	$ 3,800	38%
Operating Expenses	3,100	31%
Net Income	$ 700	7%

In figuring the percentages, the net sales are always used as the base, or whole, with which the other items are compared. Therefore the net sales are always 100%.

Exercise 3   Oral

State the percentage analysis of each of the condensed income statements given below.

	1.	2.	3.
Net Sales	$3,000	$5,000	$4,000
Cost of Goods Sold	2,100	3,000	2,600
Gross Profit	$ 900	$2,000	$1,400
Operating Expenses	600	1,250	1,200
Net Income	$ 300	$ 750	$ 200

Exercise 4   Written

1. A. Z. Baker's business had net sales of $30,000. The cost of goods sold was $16,500, and the gross profit was $13,500.

a The cost of goods sold was what percent of net sales?

b The gross profit was what percent of net sales?

2. For the last six months of a year, a firm made a gross profit of $24,000 on net sales of $60,000. Operating expenses for the period were $19,200. The net income was $4,800.

a The operating expenses were what percent of net sales?

b The net income was what percent of net sales?

3. Part of the records of the Penlee Company for a recent year showed the following information: net sales, $200,000; cost of goods sold, $128,000; operating expenses, $52,000.

a Find the gross profit and net income.

b Make a percentage analysis for cost of goods sold, gross profit, operating expenses, and net income.

REVIEW ASSIGNMENT **52**

1. a Multiply 380 by $1\frac{1}{3}$.

b What amount is 42% greater than $27?

c Find the interest on $842.60 at 6% for 75 days.

d Express 12.5 mills as a decimal part of $1.

2. Mr. Harper operates a retail sporting goods store. His sales for the year were $85,750. The cost of the goods he sold was $57,485. His operating expenses amounted to $17,975. His net profit was what percent of the sales for the year?

3. Stuart Manley, a salesman, is paid a salary of $95 a week and a commission of 5% of his net sales. Last week his gross sales were $1,950, and customer returns amounted to $85. How much did Mr. Manley earn last week?

4. Everett Warner expects this month's sales will run 20% less than last month's. If his sales last month were $11,650, what are his estimated sales for this month?

5. Wells purchased a television set on the installment plan, making a down payment of $40 and 12 monthly payments of $20 each. The cash price of the set was $250. What was the amount of the finance charge on this purchase?

6. Byers purchased Eastern Electric stock at a total cost of $75 per share. He received an annual dividend of 3% on a par value of $100. What is his rate of income on the investment?

7. The Maywood School District sold $4,245,000 (par value) of $4\frac{3}{4}$% bonds to provide funds for new school construction. What is the total cost of the interest per year on these bonds?

8. At 40 miles per hour, how many minutes will it take to drive 18 miles?

9. The assessed valuation of taxable property in a certain school district is $9,420,000. The gross cost of operating the schools amounts to $702,955. The school district's income from state money and other sources is $304,960. Find the tax rate per $1,000.

10. .03 times what amount equals $17.85?

11. Clara purchased a three-piece suit for $34.45. This cost included a sales tax of 6%.

a What was the price of this suit before the tax was added?

b What was the amount of the tax?

Figuring Payrolls

Payroll register. On page 112 you saw how timecards are used for keeping a record of the hours worked and the earnings of each employee. From the information on the timecards, the payroll clerk prepares the weekly payroll register.

NAME	No. of EXEMP-TIONS	TOTAL HOURS REGULAR	TOTAL HOURS OVER-TIME	HOUR RATE	TOTAL EARN-INGS	FICA	FED. INC. TAX	GROUP INS.	HOSP.	TOTAL	NET PAY
R. Alden	2	40	4	$2.60	$119.60	$5.74	$14.10	$ .90	$2.20	$22.94	$96.66
D. Bayer	1	40	2	3.00	129.00	6.19	18.60	.90	1.20	26.89	102.11
K. Dodge	3	39	1	3.10	125.55	6.03	13.50	.90	2.20	22.63	102.92
TOTALS					$374.15	$17.96	$46.20	$2.70	$5.60	$72.46	$301.69

PAYROLL REGISTER   WEEK ENDED July 24, 19--

Payroll register

The payroll register shows the total earnings, the deductions, and the net pay for each employee, and the totals for all the employees. Some registers also include columns for showing the number of hours worked each day by each employee.

Exercise 1   Written

1. Use the withholding table on page 106 and find the amount of income tax that should be withheld from the indicated weekly wages of the employees listed below. The number of exemptions each employee claims is shown in parentheses after his name.

a W. F. Barba (3) $108.50
b R. S. Colby (1) $114.90
c E. L. Fell (3) $130.00
d A. D. Hale (1) $134.90

e H. B. Kipp (2) $135.25
f R. E. Main (4) $137.50
g A. G. Paro (2) $140.00
h C. R. Segal (5) $143.28

2. Use the social security tax table on page 108 and find the amount of social security tax that should be withheld from the indicated weekly wages of the employees listed below.

a O. E. Duncan $119.15
b H. L. Ellis $124.10
c E. J. Graff $124.90
d A. C. Judge $125.82

e H. J. Lewis $128.16
f M. B. Oates $129.30
g S. J. Remo $125.75
h C. M. Unger $125.01

3. Copy and complete the following payroll register. Time and a half is paid for overtime. Use the withholding table on page 106 and the social security tax table on page 108 to determine the amounts of the income and FICA taxes.

Traver Bros., for the week ended March 25, 19--.

Name	No. of Exemptions	Total Hours Reg.	Total Hours O.T.	Hour Rate	Total Earnings	FICA	Inc. Tax	Ins.	Total	Net Pay
L. R. Clay	6	40	0	$2.95				$3.00		
A. T. Houk	0	40	3	2.80				1.00		
H. A. Wall	5	39	1	3.20				2.60		
Totals										

4. Under the social security laws, the employer is required to pay an FICA tax on the total employees' taxable wages at the same rate as that paid by the employees.

a At 4.8%, what amount must Traver Bros. (Problem 3) pay for the week ended March 25?

b For the quarter ended June 30, the Hawn Company paid wages totaling $26,235 that were taxable for social security. The tax rate was 4.8%. What was the amount of the company's FICA tax for this quarter?

Exercise 2 Written

1. Copy the portion of the payroll register given below and supply the missing amounts. Time and a half is paid for overtime, which is time worked in excess of 8 hours on any day.

Name	Time Record M	T	W	T	F	Total Hours Reg.	Total Hours O.T.	Hour Rate	Earnings Reg.	O.T.	Total
C. H. Barth	8	9	9	8	8			$3.12			
F. A. DeVoe	7	0	9	8	8			3.30			
R. J. Glass	8	9	9	8	9			3.10			
Totals											

2. Copy and complete the following payroll register. Time and a half is paid for overtime. Use the withholding table on page 106 and the social security table on page 108 to determine the amounts of the federal income and FICA taxes.

Tenney & Sons, for the week ended May 12, 19– –.

Name	No. of Exemptions	Total Hours Reg.	O.T.	Hour Rate	Total Earnings	Deductions FICA	Fed. Inc. Tax	State Inc. Tax	Total	Net Pay
E. D. Fisk	4	40	4	$2.80				$2.00		
J. E. Mull	1	40	0	3.10				3.20		
L. L. Volk	3	38	1	3.00				2.10		
Totals										

Change sheet and change memorandum. Unless the employees are paid by check, the payroll clerk must obtain from the bank sufficient money in the proper denominations to pay each employee in currency.

CHANGE SHEET *July 24, 19--*	NET WAGES		$20	$10	$5	$1	50¢	25¢	10¢	5¢	1¢
K. Alden	96	66	4	1	1	1	1		1	1	1
D. Bayer	102	11	5			2			1		1
K. Dodge	102	92	5			2	1	1	1	1	2
TOTALS	301	69	14	1	1	5	2	1	3	2	4

Change sheet

CHANGE MEMORANDUM		
DENOMINATION	NO.	AMOUNT
$20.00	14	280 00
10.00	1	10 00
5.00	1	5 00
1.00	5	5 00
.50	2	1 00
.25	1	25
.10	3	30
.05	2	10
.01	4	04
TOTAL		301 69

Change memorandum

He therefore prepares a change sheet, shown above, to determine the number of bills and coins needed to pay each employee in the largest denominations possible.

The totals of the change sheet are then listed on a change memorandum, shown at the left. The payroll clerk takes to the bank the change memorandum and a check for the total, and receives the currency in the desired denominations.

Exercise 3   Written

1. For each of the following, prepare a change sheet and a change memorandum like those shown on page 359.

a Maxco, Inc., for the week ended Oct. 16, 19—:

| W. Kamp $117.82 | H. Maul $120.64 |
| E. Lind   94.40 | C. Wise   112.48 |

b Wood Company, for the week ended Nov. 23, 19—:

| N. Luft $128.32 | L. Rath $141.95 |
| H. Metz   112.65 | Y. Tate   122.08 |

2. The following information is shown in the column totals of a payroll register for the week ended May 16:

Total earnings of employees......	$820.00
Federal income tax..............	72.60
State income tax................	8.70
FICA tax.....................	29.49
Insurance....................	18.30

What amount of cash should be withdrawn from the bank to meet this payroll?

REVIEW ASSIGNMENT 53

1. a Multiply 30 by $1\frac{3}{8}$.   **b** Divide 18 by $1\frac{2}{3}$.

c Find the interest at 6% on $472.50 for 81 days.

d Express a tax rate of $21 per $1,000 in mills on $1.

2. Fisk owns 40 shares of Scott National stock that cost him $1,600, including brokerage charges. On each share, he receives regular quarterly dividends of $.75 each. What annual rate of return does Fisk receive on his investment?

3. The tax rate in Holt is $6.1213 per $100 of assessed valuation. Find the tax to be paid on property assessed at $6,700.

4. Motler insures his $22,000 house at 90% of its value. At a rate of 37¢ per $100, find the amount of the premium.

5. A car costing $2,500 was traded in for $475 at the end of $4\frac{1}{2}$ years. What was the average annual rate of depreciation?

▶ **6.** .04 times what amount = $25.22?

▶ **7.** The price of a golf cart, including a 4% sales tax, is $20.75.

a What is the price of this golf cart, to the nearest cent, before the sales tax is added?

b What is the amount of the sales tax on this golf cart?

SECTION 54

Preparing and Using Charts

Many businessmen prepare charts to picture the results of their business operations. The charts show relationships and trends more clearly than do figures in a table.

PART 54a   Bar and Line Charts

Vertical bar charts. The vertical bar chart below shows the daily sales of Jackson Men's Shop for one week. There is one bar for each day, Monday through Saturday, as indicated at the bottom. The length of each bar is proportional to the sales for that particular day. The scale on which the bars are laid off, or measured, is shown at the left.

Each vertical division on the chart paper represents $100, as shown by the scale at the left. The length of each bar was made accurate to the nearest $50. For example, actual sales for Monday were $942.81. Before this was plotted, it was rounded to the nearest $50, giving $950. The top of the bar for Monday was therefore placed midway between the divisions representing $900 and $1,000.

JACKSON MEN'S SHOP

DAILY SALES
WEEK ENDING JUNE 9, 19--

Vertical bar chart

Horizontal bar charts.   The horizontal bar chart below shows the sales by departments of the Jackson Men's Shop for the quarterly period ending June 30.   It is similar to a vertical bar chart except that the bars are extended horizontally.

JACKSON MEN'S SHOP

SALES BY DEPARTMENTS
QUARTER ENDING JUNE 30, 19--

CLOTHING

ACCESSORIES

SHOES

HATS

0   10   20   30   40
THOUSANDS OF DOLLARS

Horizontal bar chart

Before being plotted, the figures represented by each bar were rounded to the nearest $1,000.   For example actual sales of $37,462.50 would be shown as $37,000.

Line charts.   The line chart below shows the sales of the Jackson Men's Shop by months from January through December.

JACKSON MEN'S SHOP

MONTHLY SALES
YEAR ENDING DECEMBER 31, 19-

THOUSANDS OF DOLLARS

40

30

20

10

0

J   F   M   A   M   J   J   A   S   O   N   D

Line chart

The time scale, which extends from left to right, is shown at the bottom of the chart.   The value scale, which extends from bottom to top, is shown at the left.

Before being plotted, the monthly sales figures were rounded to the nearest $1,000.   The line was charted by first plotting dots showing each month's sales.   The dots were then connected by a line drawn with a ruler.

Lines could be included to show the operating expenses and net profit by using a solid line for the sales, a dotted line for the operating expenses, and a dash-and-dot line for the net profit, or lines of different colors could be used.

Exercise 1   Oral

1. The vertical bar chart on page 361 shows the daily sales to the nearest multiple of $50. Thus, the sales on Monday, for example, were approximately $950. Using the information shown on the chart, answer the following questions:

a On which day were the sales the largest?

b On which day were the sales the smallest?

c On which days did the sales exceed $1,200?

d On which two days were sales nearest the same amount?

2. The line chart on page 362 shows the monthly sales to the nearest $1,000. Thus, the sales for January were approximately $23,000; for February, $17,000; and so on. Using the information on the chart, answer the following questions:

a What were the approximate sales for each of the months from March to December, inclusive?

b In which month were the sales the highest?

c In which month were the sales the lowest?

d In which months did the sales exceed $26,000?

e In which months did the sales fall below $20,000?

3. The chart below shows Simon Arnold's weekly sales for the first five weeks of the current year. Using the information shown on the chart, answer the following questions.

a What were Arnold's approximate sales during the fourth week?

b In which week did he make the smallest total sales?

c In which two weekly periods were his sales nearest the same amount?

d What was the percent increase in sales from the second week to the third?

e What was the percent decrease in sales from the third week to the fourth?

f What were the approximate total sales for the five weeks?

4. The chart below shows the marks Janet Marino received in ten tests in science. Using the information shown on the chart, answer the following questions:

MARKS RECEIVED BY JANET MARINO IN TEN SCIENCE TESTS

Test Marks in Percents

Test No. 1 2 3 4 5 6 7 8 9 10

a What was Janet's mark on test 6?

b What was the number of the test on which she made the lowest mark?

c What was the difference between the marks obtained on tests 6 and 7?

d What was the difference between the marks obtained on tests 5 and 7?

Exercise 2   Written

Use chart paper with 10 divisions to the inch.

1. Prepare a vertical bar chart showing the facts:

Angelo's News Shop
Daily Sales, March 16 to 23, 19--

| Sun. $90 | Tues. $60 | Thurs. $110 | Sat. $140 |
| Mon. 70 | Wed.   80 | Fri.   70 | |

Use the title given above and let each vertical division represent $10 of sales. Label each multiple of $50 in the vertical scale at the left. Place the bars two spaces apart.

2. Listed below are the monthly sales of the Nolan Store for six months. Prepare a vertical bar chart showing this information.

Nolan Store
Sales for January–June, 19--

| January $7,000 | March $ 9,000 | May $11,000 |
| February 5,000 | April   14,000 | June   8,000 |

Let each vertical division represent $1,000 of sales and label each multiple of $5,000 in the vertical scale.

3. Prepare a horizontal bar chart showing the following facts:

Acme Appliance Service
August Sales, 19--

TV and Radios	$3,700	Freezers	$1,400
Washers	2,600	Ranges	1,100
Refrigerators	2,200	Other Appliances	900

Let each horizontal division represent $100 of sales, and mark the scale at the bottom of the chart to show each multiple of $1,000.

4. For the annual school concert, the six ticket sellers in the sophomore class sold the number of tickets indicated below. Show this information on a horizontal bar chart.

Annual School Concert
Tickets Sold by Sophomores

| Diana | 46 | Leslie | 35 | Phil | 28 |
| Elsa | 42 | May | 31 | Russ | 23 |

Let each horizontal division represent two tickets, and mark the scale at the bottom of the chart to show each multiple of 10.

5. Show the following information on a line chart:

Daily Snack Stand Sales
June 2–9, 19––

| Sun. $340 | Tues. $240 | Thurs. $290 | Sat. $420 |
| Mon. 260 | Wed. 310 | Fri. 330 | |

Let each vertical division represent $10 of sales. Use every fifth vertical line to represent the days.

6. The table below shows Jean Rand's typewriting speed in net words per minute on ten consecutive timed tests. Using the title and the data, prepare a line chart showing these facts.

Jean Rand's Typewriting Speed
Net Words Per Minute

Test 1, 28 words	Test 4, 32 words	Test 8, 34 words
Test 2, 32 words	Test 5, 32 words	Test 9, 35 words
Test 3, 33 words	Test 6, 33 words	Test 10, 38 words
	Test 7, 30 words	

Let each vertical division represent 1 word. Use every other vertical line to represent the numbered tests.

⊳ **7.** Construct a horizontal bar chart showing the sales made last year in six departments of the Lakeport Department Store.

Clothing........$56,364.81	Shoes..........$30,691.70
Furniture....... 47,718.22	Rugs........... 21,408.44
Dry Goods...... 42,225.15	Notions........ 10,039.56

Let each division on the horizontal scale represent $2,000, and plot each bar to the nearest $1,000.

⊳ **8.** The monthly sales of the Manville Department Store for the first six months of the last two years are shown in the tables at the top of page 366. Prepare a line chart showing the sales for each six-month period. Use a red line for the sales of this

Month	Last Year	This Year
Jan.	$55,280	$62,745
Feb.	48,730	50,945
Mar.	57,820	60,220

Month	Last Year	This Year
April	$57,180	$56,740
May	56,375	51,935
June	50,820	54,265

year; a black line for the sales of last year. If no red pencil is available, use a solid pencil line for the sales of this year and a dotted line for last year.

Let each vertical division represent $2,000 and plot each month's sales to the nearest $1,000. Use every fifth vertical line to represent the months.

REVIEW ASSIGNMENT **54a**

1. **a** $24 is what part greater than $14.40?

b $225.50 is what percent less than $275?

c Find the interest at 6% on $801.15 for 32 days.

2. For one year, Elmer Gantry, a single man, had a taxable income of $9,324, after all deductions for exemptions had been made. By using Schedule I on page 342, determine the amount of his federal income tax for that year, to the nearest dollar.

3. The money to be raised by local taxes in a certain village is $618,815. The assessed valuation of the property is $14,650,000. Find the tax rate per $1,000 of assessed valuation, correct to the nearest cent.

4. Prepare a change sheet and a change memorandum, like those shown on page 359, for the following payroll of Selig and Kirk:

B. E. Ewing $108.34   S. J. Meyers $87.57
A. J. Heinz   113.37   E. F. Sherry   94.92

5. Copy the portion of the payroll register shown below and supply the missing amounts. Eight hours constitute a regular day, and time and a half is paid for time worked in excess of 8 hours.

Name	Time Record					Total Hours		Hour Rate	Earnings		
	M	T	W	T	F	Reg.	O.T.		Reg.	O.T.	Total
B. T. Dunn	8	8	8½	7	8			$2.80			
S. R. Knox	7	9	8	8	9			3.05			
F. L. Pier	8	6½	8	8	8½			2.94			
						Totals					

PART 54b Rectangle and Circle Charts

Rectangle charts. A rectangle chart is used to show the relationships of parts to the whole and to each other. The entire rectangle, which may be constructed either vertically or horizontally, represents the whole. Sections of the chart represent the parts.

The rectangle chart at the right shows the total sales of The Ronan Corporation for last year. Sections of the rectangle show the amount of sales represented by cost of goods sold, operating expenses, and net profit.

A rectangle chart may also be used when the parts are expressed in terms of percents instead of dollar amounts. The entire rectangle represents 100%; and the scale at the left is marked off in convenient divisions of 100%, such as 1%, 2%, 5%, or 10%.

Circle charts. A circle chart is often used to show the percent relationships between the parts and the whole. The complete circle, 360°, represents the whole, 100%. The circle chart below shows in percents the same information that is presented in dollar values in the rectangle above.

Rectangle chart

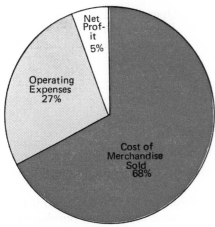

Circle chart

In constructing the circle, it was first necessary to change the dollar amounts to percents and then to convert each percent into degrees. For example, the cost of merchandise sold was found to be 68% of the sales ($225,200 ÷ $330,500). The equivalent in degrees was found to be 245° (68% of 360°). The degrees in the remaining sections of the circle were found in the same manner. A circle was then drawn with a compass and the angles laid off with a protractor.

Exercise 3   Written

1. Prepare a rectangle chart, constructed vertically, to show the information in the table at the right, taken from the records of the Automotive Parts Corporation. The figures show the make-up of the store's sales dollar.

Cost of Merchandise Sold	$ .60
Operating Expenses	.23
Net Income	.17
Sales	$1.00

Make the rectangle an inch and a half wide. Let each vertical division represent $.02.

2. Prepare a rectangle chart to show the information given at the right, taken from the records of Lewis Mott. Let each vertical division equal 2%.

Cost of Merchandise Sold	62%
Operating Expenses	28%
Net Income	10%
Sales	100%

3. The sales for last year in the four departments of the Mountain Tourist Center were as follows:

Novelties............50%   Cards 25%
Stationery...........20%   Candy............... 5%

a On a circle chart, how many degrees should be used to represent the sales of each department?

b Construct a circle chart showing the percent for each department.

4. The Arlen family budgets its monthly income of $400 as shown below. Construct a circle chart showing each expenditure and its percent.

Food...............$100   Operating............$90
Housing............. 80   Development.......... 60
Clothing............ 30   Savings.............. 40

REVIEW ASSIGNMENT 54 b

1. a Divide 25 by $1\frac{3}{8}$.

b What part less than $255 is $170?

c Find the interest at 5% on $694.30 for 21 days.

d Express tax rate of 13.2 mills on $1 as a rate on $1,000.

2. John Cain bought an automobile for $2,500 and used it for $5\frac{1}{2}$ years. He then was allowed $575 for it toward the purchase of a new car. What was the average yearly amount of depreciation?

3. Dolvin bought 45 shares of Midland Power preferred stock. This stock paid an annual dividend of $4\frac{1}{2}\%$ on a par value of $50 per share. What was his annual income from the 45 shares?

4. A building is insured with three companies: Peerless Insurance Co., $20,000; Royal Insurance Co., $28,000; Farmers Insurance Co., $32,000. If a fire loss occurs, for what percent of the total loss will the Royal Insurance Co. be liable?

5. Finch purchased a house for $12,000, paying $5,000 in cash and giving a $6\frac{1}{2}\%$ mortgage for the balance. During the first year, he rented the house for $135 a month. Besides interest on the mortgage, other expenses for the year totaled $700. What was Finch's rate of return on his original cash investment?

6. Seven weeks ago, Mr. Kline bought 50 shares of stock at $13\frac{1}{4}$ per share. The brokerage charges were $11.63. Today, he sold the 50 shares at $10\frac{1}{8}$ per share, and $11.32 was deducted for brokerage charges and taxes. What was the amount of Mr. Kline's loss in this transaction?

7. A house valued at $13,500 was insured for $9,000. The policy contained an 80% coinsurance clause. The owner paid a premium of $.702 per $100 for a 3-year policy.

   a What was the average annual cost of the policy?

   b A fire caused a loss of $7,200. How much did the insurance company pay?

GENERAL REVIEW

1. a Multiply 164.2 by 6.4.   **d** Subtract $8\frac{2}{3}$ from $25\frac{1}{6}$.
b Divide 582.12 by 6.3.   **e** Multiply $54\frac{1}{5}$ by $5\frac{1}{3}$.
c Add $15\frac{3}{4}$, $8\frac{1}{5}$, $22\frac{1}{2}$, $3\frac{7}{8}$.   **f** Divide $22\frac{1}{2}$ by $\frac{3}{4}$.
   g Express $\frac{3}{7}$ as a decimal to the nearest hundredth.

2. Mrs. Dysart works part time in a state where a tax for disability insurance is deducted at the rate of $\frac{1}{2}$ of 1% of weekly earnings with a maximum deduction of 30 cents in one week. Her earnings in two successive weeks were $58 and $69. What amount was deducted in each week for disability insurance?

3. At 45 miles an hour, how many hours and minutes will it take to drive 195 miles?

4. Irwin Hatch, an auctioneer, sold goods amounting to $7,862.50 for the Bradford Mercantile Agency and charged 15% commission. How much commission did he receive?

5. Boyer borrowed $850 on his 6% interest-bearing promissory note dated March 10. He paid the note and interest on the following June 4. What total amount did he pay on June 4?

6. Griffin receives $2.24 an hour for a 40-hour week with time and a half for overtime. During one week he worked 10 hours a day, Monday through Friday. His employer deducted 4.8% for social security, $10 for savings bonds, and $12.50 for withholding tax. How much money did Griffin receive?

7. Earl Bain borrows $250 from the personal loan department of his bank and repays it in nine monthly payments of $28.82 each. How much is the finance charge on this loan?

8. Mr. Chase owns 10 shares of stock that cost him $800, including the broker's commission. On each share, he receives quarterly dividends of 90 cents each. What annual rate of return does Mr. Chase receive on his investment?

9. The Temple Power & Light Corp. sold $8,450,000 (par value) of bonds to provide funds for an addition to its generating plant. The bonds pay interest at the rate of $7\frac{1}{4}\%$. What is the total cost of the interest per year on these bonds?

10. Myron Cohen purchased some stock at $32 per share. The total cost was $2,751, including the broker's commission of $31. How many shares of this stock did Mr. Cohen purchase?

11. Judith Grant bought an automobile for $2,430. She paid $810 cash. The balance was handled through a finance company to which she was to make equal monthly payments for 36 months. The company's finance charge for the transaction amounted to $340.20. What amount did Miss Grant pay the finance company each month?

❯ **12.** Change .325 to a fraction in lowest terms.

❯ **13.** Jerry Radley's bank statement as of November 30 showed a bank balance of $1,342.16. His checkbook balance was $1,405.66. Checks outstanding were No. 81 for $26.40 and No. 87 for $17.20. A deposit of $75, made by mail on November 30, had not been received by the bank in time to be added to the statement. A check for $32.10 had not been entered in the checkbook. Prepare a reconciliation statement.

❯ **14.** A salesman is paid $500 a month and a commission of $\frac{5}{8}\%$ on all sales in excess of $25,000 in any single month. What must be the amount of his sales each month in order that his total monthly earnings may be $800?

❯ **15.** What should be the owner's asking price for a house and lot in order that he may realize $26,600 on the sale after reducing the price $1,000 and paying the real estate agent a 5% commission?

UNIT Twelve

The Retailer's Buying Problems

SECTION | 55 |

Purchasing Merchandise

When a retailer needs merchandise, he orders it from a wholesaler or a manufacturer. He may telephone or telegraph the order; he may place the order by mail, using an order letter or an order form; or he may order goods directly through a salesman.

PART | 55a | Invoices and Records

Purchases invoice. Upon filling the order, the seller mails the retailer an *invoice*, which shows the quantity, description, and price of each article shipped.

Shown below is the invoice that Carlton Roper received for a shipment of goods he ordered from the Maxwell Paper Company.

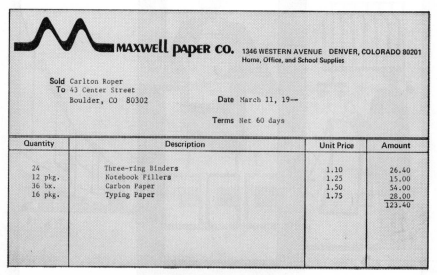

MAXWELL PAPER CO. 1346 WESTERN AVENUE   DENVER, COLORADO 80201
Home, Office, and School Supplies

Sold Carlton Roper
To   43 Center Street
     Boulder, CO 80302   Date March 11, 19--

                                 Terms Net 60 days

Quantity	Description	Unit Price	Amount
24	Three-ring Binders	1.10	26.40
12 pkg.	Notebook Fillers	1.25	15.00
36 bx.	Carbon Paper	1.50	54.00
16 pkg.	Typing Paper	1.75	28.00
			123.40

Invoice

Checking the purchases invoice.   When the goods arrived, Mr. Roper checked the quantity of each item with the invoice to see that the correct quantities had been received. He then checked the extensions and total of the invoice to see that the multiplication and addition had been done accurately.

Terms of sale.   Wholesalers and manufacturers generally sell *on account* and allow the customer a *credit period* of 30 to 90 days in which to pay.

The conditions under which payment of an invoice is to be made are called the *terms of sale*. In the illustration on page 372, the terms of sale are indicated in the expression "Terms Net 60 days" in the lower right-hand corner of the heading of the invoice.

Terms of "Net 60 days," or "n/60," as often written, mean that credit is granted for a period of 60 days. The full amount is due for payment within 60 days after the date of the invoice.

Finding the due date of an invoice.   The due date is found by counting ahead, from the date of the invoice, the number of days shown in the terms.

60 *days*
20 *days left in March*
40
30 *days in April*
10 *days in May*

For example, the invoice in the illustration on page 372 is dated March 11, and the terms are n/60. The invoice is due for payment 60 days after March 11, or on May 10, as shown at the left.

Exercise 1   Written

1. The following invoice has been received and you are asked to verify the extensions and the total:

12 dozen bars Soap	@	$1.50	$ 18.00
15 dozen cans Tomatoes	@	2.75	41.35
6 dozen cans Peaches	@	3.95	23.70
5 dozen bots. Catsup	@	2.25	11.25
25 dozen cans Tuna Fish	@	3.85	96.25
			$190.55

Copy the invoice on a separate sheet of paper. Then as you check the correctness of each figure, place a check mark (√) at its immediate right. This mark indicates work completed and guards against repetition and confusion.* If a figure is incorrect, indicate at the right the correct amount.

*Check marks are regularly used by office clerks and bookkeepers to indicate that figures have been verified for accuracy.

2. The Home Decorator's Supply Company purchased the following items from the Vincent Paint Company; invoice dated May 24; terms net 60 days:

48 qt.	Color Varnish	@	$1.10
56 qt.	Enamel	@	1.50
24 gal.	Thinner	@	1.75
36 gal.	Barn Paint	@	2.75
48 qt.	Paint Remover	@	.75
180 qt.	Wall Paint	@	1.05
120 qt.	Clear Sealer	@	.90

You are to (a) make the extensions, (b) find the total amount of the invoice, and (c) find the due date of the invoice.

Purchases, returns and allowances, net purchases. The total cost of all the goods purchased in the course of a week, month, or year is called the *purchases* for that period.

Some of the goods may be returned to the seller, or the seller may grant an allowance because of defective merchandise or other reasons. These returns and allowances decrease the cost of the purchases and should be deducted from the purchases. The amount remaining is the *net purchases.*

Purchases − Returns and Allowances = Net Purchases

Carlton Roper's purchases for March were $4,260.94, and his returns and allowances were $63.80. His net purchases were therefore $4,197.14.

Purchases	$4,260.94
Returns and allowances	63.80
Net purchases	$4,197.14

Purchases records. The proprietor or his bookkeeper keeps a daily record of the purchases and the returns and allowances. Separate records are often kept for each department or for each kind of merchandise purchased.

Exercise 2   Written

1. During the first six months of last year, the purchases of the Pearlman Company were $32,610. Returns and allowances amounted to $1,370. Find, to the nearest tenth of a percent, what percent the returns and allowances were of the purchases.

2. Last month the Patton Drug Company made the purchases and purchases returns shown in the table below.

Items	Pur- chases	Returns	Net Pur- chases
Drugs	$3,465	$256	
Cosmetics	5,678	307	
Fountain Supplies	1,221	35	
Stationery	2,107	79	
Novelties	787	46	
Totals			

a Copy the table and show: the net purchases of each item, the total purchases, the total returns, and the total net purchases.

b Prove the total net purchases by subtracting the total returns from the total purchases.

3. The table below at the right shows the purchases for the three departments of Coburn's Clothing Store for the first three months of the current year.

a. Copy the table and show: the total purchases for each month, the total purchases of each department for the three months, and the total purchases for the three months.

Month	Cloth- ing	Hats	Shoes	Total Pur- chases
Jan.	$1,324	$568	$623	
Feb.	1,613	608	581	
Mar.	1,847	561	612	
Totals				

b Prove the total of the "Total Purchases" column by adding the totals of the three columns at the left.

REVIEW ASSIGNMENT 55 a

1. a What percent of $37.50 is $90?

b Divide 24 by $1\frac{3}{4}$.

c $25.20 is what percent more than $22.50?

d Find the due date of an 80-day note dated August 9.

2. An invoice containing the following items has been received and you are asked to check the extensions and total. Point out any errors you find and give the correct amount of the invoice.

25 cases canned beets	@	$4.65	$116.25
32 cases canned peas	@	5.15	164.80
5 cases canned beans	@	6.05	30.25
24 cases canned tomatoes	@	6.25	152.00
			$464.30

3. Using the title and information given below, prepare a bar chart showing the facts:

Average Daily Temperatures

March 10–March 16, 19—

| Sunday 25° | Tuesday 38° | Thursday 43° | Saturday 26° |
| Monday 31° | Wednesday 41° | Friday 33° | |

4. What is the rate of return on a $4\frac{1}{2}\%$ bond purchased at 75?

5. A mortgage loan of $8,000 is to be repaid over a period of 20 years at the rate of $62 a month. What will be the total cost of the interest over the 20-year period?

6. Find the missing amount in each of the following:

a $.03 \times p = \$16.50$ **b** $4\% \times s = \$19$

PART 55b Aliquot Parts (continued)

Combinations of aliquot parts. The unit price of an item on an invoice is sometimes a combination of an aliquot part and the base.

For example, on the invoice on page 372, the unit price of the first item is $1.10. $1.10 is equal to $1 + $.10. Since $.10 is $\frac{1}{10}$ of $1, $1.10 is equal to $1 + $\frac{1}{10}$ of $1.

In the same way, $1.25 is equal to $1 + $\frac{1}{4}$ of $1. Also, $2.50 is equal to $2 + $\frac{1}{2}$ of $1. In each case, the unit price is equal to the base, or a multiple of it, plus a fractional part of the base.

Some of the commonly used combinations of aliquot parts are:

$$\$1.10 = \$1 + \tfrac{1}{10} \text{ of } \$1 \qquad \$1.50 = \$1 + \tfrac{1}{2} \text{ of } \$1$$
$$\$1.12\tfrac{1}{2} = \$1 + \tfrac{1}{8} \text{ of } \$1 \qquad \$2.50 = \$2 + \tfrac{1}{2} \text{ of } \$1$$
$$\$1.25 = \$1 + \tfrac{1}{4} \text{ of } \$1$$

Multiplication by combinations of aliquot parts. Multiplication by aliquot parts may be applied to multiplication by combinations of aliquot parts.

Example

Find the cost of 24 three-ring binders at $1.10.

Solution: $\$1.10 = \$1 + \tfrac{1}{10} \text{ of } \$1$
$24 \times \$1 = \$24$
$\tfrac{1}{10} \times \$24 = \$2.40$
$\$24 + \$2.40 = \$26.40$ **Ans.**

Exercise 3   Oral

For each problem recite the solution and give the product.

	1.	2.	3.
a	17 @ $1.10	28 @ $1.50	14 @ $2.50
b	16 @ $1.12½	22 @ $1.10	56 @ $1.12½
c	32 @ $1.25	16 @ $2.50	36 @ $1.25
d	18 @ $1.50	22 @ $1.50	43 @ $1.10
e	12 @ $2.50	44 @ $1.25	88 @ $1.12½
f	24 @ $1.12½	35 @ $1.10	48 @ $1.25

REVIEW ASSIGNMENT 55 b

1. a Find the product of $65 \times 1\frac{2}{3}$.

b Find the interest on $565 for 28 days at 6%.

c Express a tax rate of 15.3 mills on $1 as a rate on $1,000.

2. Check the following extensions on an invoice. Point out any errors and give the correct total.

250 scratch pads	@	$10.80 per C	$27.00
7 dozen rulers	@	15.50 per gross	9.40
3 gross pens	@	5.40 per gross	16.20
9 dozen notebooks	@	21.00 per gross	15.75
15 cans ink	@	15.00 per dozen	17.75
			$66.10

3. A car costing $3,000 is estimated to depreciate in value at the annual rate of 15% of the original cost. What is the amount of the average monthly depreciation on this car?

4. Gale's taxable income for one year was $5,180. The federal income tax was $690 on the first $4,000, plus 22% of the excess over $4,000. During the year, the employer deducted $920.40 from Gale's wages for federal withholding taxes. How much did Gale still owe on his income tax for that year?

5. On May 10, Mr. Wagner purchased 60 shares of stock at $18\frac{1}{8}$ per share. The brokerage charges were $15.88. On July 8, he sold the 60 shares at $16\frac{3}{4}$ per share, and $17.33 was deducted for brokerage and taxes. What was the amount of Mr. Wagner's loss in this transaction?

6. Find the missing amount in each of the following:

a $.97 \times n = \$320.10$ **b** $96\% \times y = \$240$

7. a $360 is 4% less than what amount?

b $.01\frac{1}{2}$ times what amount equals $14.37?

SECTION 56

Figuring Trade Discounts

Many wholesalers and manufacturers sell to the retailer at a price called the *list price* or *catalog price* and allow him a discount on this price. A discount of this kind is called a *trade discount*. The price to the retailer is the list price less the trade discount. It is called the *invoice price, net price,* or *invoice cost.*

PART 56a Single Discounts

To find the trade discount and the invoice price. A trade discount is usually expressed as a percent. This percent is always based on the list price. The list price is therefore multiplied by the rate of discount to find the amount of the discount.

Rate of Discount × List Price = Trade Discount

The invoice price is found in the following manner:

List Price − Trade Discount = Invoice Price

Example

The list price of a color TV set in the catalog of the Jaybarth Company is $360. The discount allowed to a retailer is 25%. How much does a retailer pay for the set?

Solution:

List price $360
Trade discount   90 (25% of $360)
                   ─────
Invoice price $270 **Ans.**

Check

100% of list price = List price
Subtract 25% of list price = Trade discount
          ─────────
75% of list price = Invoice price
75% of $360 = $270, invoice price

Reasons for allowing trade discounts. Trade discounts are used by manufacturers and wholesalers who sell by catalog and whose prices must be changed often because of changes in production costs. The retailer is supplied with a catalog and a *discount sheet*. The latter shows the discounts that are allowed on the prices in the catalog. When price changes are necessary, a revised discount sheet is issued. This saves the expense of printing and distributing new catalogs.

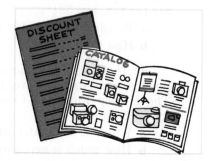

In some cases the catalog price is the advertised retail price. The retailer is allowed a discount on this price so that he may make a satisfactory gross profit. If he sells the article at the catalog price, his gross profit is the amount of the trade discount.

Trade discounts are also used to induce the retailer to buy in larger quantities. For example, a discount of 10% may be allowed on a purchase of 100 articles; 12% on a purchase of 200; 15% on a purchase of 300; and so on. These are known as *quantity discounts*.

Exercise 1   Written

In each of the following problems, find the invoice price by the method given in the solution of the illustrative example on page 378. Then check it by the method used in checking the answer to the illustrative example.

1. Find the amount of the trade discount and the invoice price in each of the following:

	Article	List Price	Trade Discount	Trade Discount	Invoice Price
a	Tennis racket	$12.50	40%	$5	$7.50
b	Adding machine	$150	30%		
c	Wrist watch	$60	45%		
d	Auto battery	$18	15%		
e	Washing machine	$240	35%		
f	Food blender	$30	25%		
g	Electric mixer	$37.50	$33\frac{1}{3}$%		

2. How much would the Hansen Hardware Store have to pay for 15 dozen hammers if the quoted price of the hammers is $48 a dozen, less 32%? **$489.60**

3. Otto Reid, a furniture dealer, obtains quotations on rugs from two wholesale firms. The Luxor Sales Agency offers a certain rug for $85, less 40%. The firm of DeVoe and Son offers the same rug for $78, less $33\frac{1}{3}$%.

a Which firm offers the lower price?

b How much lower?

4. The Roth Manufacturing Company offers to sell a dining-room set to Austin Lowe, furniture dealer, for $250, less 30%. The Holden Furniture Company offers a set of similar quality for $225, less 20%.

a Which is the better offer?

b How much is saved by taking advantage of it?

REVIEW ASSIGNMENT 56 a

1. a Find to the nearest cent $133\frac{1}{3}$% of $35.

b Find the interest at 6% on $175 for 88 days.

c Find the interest on $1,800 for 137 days at 4%.

d Express a tax rate of $13.50 on $1,000 as mills on $1.

2. A dealer purchased a floor polisher listed at $27.50, less 30%. How much did he pay for this floor polisher?

3. Using the title and information given below, prepare a bar chart showing the facts.

Jan's Ski Area
Daily Attendance
January 2–January 8, 19—

Sun.	490	Thurs.	320
Mon.	210	Fri.	380
Tues.	260	Sat.	450
Wed.	240		

4. The assessed valuation of property in Winsted is $12,440,000. The total budget for the year is $809,800. Total deductions from the budget for miscellaneous income are $32,300. Find the tax rate per $100.

5. How many minutes will it take Mr. Donaldson to drive 21 miles at the rate of 35 miles an hour?

6. Find the missing amount in each of the following:

a .02 × w = $10.50   **b** 5% × z = $4.30

7. a What amount increased by $\frac{2}{3}$ of itself equals $9.30?

b $55.80 is 55% more than what amount?

PART **56b** Rate of Trade Discount

To find the rate of trade discount. The rate of trade discount is always based on the list price. Hence, the rate is found by dividing the amount of the discount by the list price.

$$\text{Rate of Trade Discount} = \frac{\text{Trade Discount}}{\text{List Price}}$$

Exercise **2**   Written

1. Find the amount and rate of trade discount in each of the following:

	Article	List Price	Invoice Price	Trade Discount Amount	Trade Discount Rate
a	Men's hats	$ 12	$ 7.20	$4.80	40%
b	Tire chains	9	5.85		
c	End table	60	33.00		
d	Lamp	26	19.50		
e	Desk	135	90.00		

2. A catalog lists an electric motor at $90. The same motor is billed to the retail dealer at $72. What rate of trade discount is allowed? 20%

3. An electric range listed at $280 is sold to the retailer at $182. What is the rate of trade discount?

◆ 4. The Econway Market ordered $100 worth of packaged cheese from the Star Farm Products Company and was given an additional $20 worth free.

    a What was the total value of the goods received by the Econway Market?

    b The value of the free goods is what percent of the value of the entire shipment?

◆ 5. The Boulevard Market ordered from the United Wholesale Company 24 cases of salad dressings at $7.50 a case and was given 3 additional cases free.

    a At $7.50 a case, what was the value of the entire shipment?

    b What rate of trade discount is represented by the three cases of free goods?

⬤ **6.** On an order for 5 dozen boxes of face powder at $1.05 a box, a druggist received an extra dozen free. What rate of trade discount does this represent?

⬤ **7.** A grocer is given an extra case of detergent on an order for nine cases. This is equal to what rate of discount?

REVIEW ASSIGNMENT **56** b

1. a Divide 40 by $3\frac{1}{2}$.

b Find to the nearest cent $166\frac{2}{3}\%$ of $70.

c Find the interest at 6% on $325 for 39 days.

d Express a tax rate of $9.75 on $1,000 in mills on $1.

2. A stamp album listed at $17.50 is billed to the retailer at $10.50. What is the rate of trade discount?

3. A camp stove, listed in the manufacturer's catalog at $28.95, is sold to a retailer at $33\frac{1}{3}\%$ off list. What is the invoice price to the retailer?

4. A delivery truck that cost $4,200 is estimated to depreciate in value at the annual rate of 15% of the original cost. Find the value of the truck at the end of the fourth year.

5. On a bar chart a one-inch line represents $500. How long a bar must be drawn to represent $1,250?

⬤ **6. a** $12 is $\frac{8}{5}$ of what amount?

b .98 times what amount equals $622.30?

c $16.80 is $\frac{3}{8}$ less than what amount?

PART 56c Series of Discounts

Trade discount series. A trade discount may consist of two or more discounts, called a *series of discounts* or a *discount series.*

For example, the Sterling Plumbing Company, a manufacturer of plumbing equipment, lists an electric water heater in its catalog at $150 and allows discounts of 25%, $12\frac{1}{2}\%$ and 10%.

In finding the invoice cost, the first discount is based on the list price; the second, on the remainder after deducting the first discount; the third, on the remainder after deducting the second discount; and so on.

Example

The quoted price of a water heater is $150, less 25%, 12½%, and 10%. Find (a) the invoice price and (b) the amount of the trade discount.

Solution:

(a) $150.00   *list price*
     37.50   *1st discount (25%, or ¼, of $150)*
$112.50   *1st remainder*
    14.063   *2d discount (12½%, or ⅛, of $112.50)*
$ 98.437   *2d remainder*
     9.844   *3d discount (10%, or 1/10, of $98.437)*
$ 88.593* *3d remainder, or invoice price, $88.59* **Ans.**

Check:

(b) $150.00   *list price* $37.50   1st discount
    88.59   *invoice price*   14.063   2d discount
$ 61.41   *discount*   9.844   3d discount
                             $61.407   total discount

$61.41   **Ans.**

*To insure accuracy in the cents column, intermediate results should be carried correct to 3 decimal places. The final result is rounded to the nearest cent.

The order in which the discounts are taken does not affect the final result.

Exercise **3**   Written

In each of the following problems, check the calculation of the invoice price by taking the discounts in a different order from the one you first used.

1. Find the invoice price and the amount of the trade discount in each of the following:

List Price	Trade Discounts	(Invoice Price)		List Price	Trade Discounts	(Invoice Price)
a $45.00	20%, 10%	$32.40		f $250	20%, 10%, 10%	$162.00
b $32.00	25%, 20%			g $125	25%, 20%, 10%	
c $57.00	33⅓%, 20%			h $200	50%, 40%, 10%	
d $18.00	25%, 10%			i $120	25%, 20%, 5%	
e $65.00	10%, 10%			j $105	30%, 15%, 10%	

2. The Cleanair Sales Co. purchases an air conditioner, list price $240, less 25% and 15%. What is the invoice price? $153

3. What is the invoice price of 4 watches, purchased by Milstein Jewelers, which are listed at $87.50 each, with the following discounts: 30%, 20%, and 10%?

4. Greene's Garden Tool Co. sells a lawn and garden tractor listed for $500, with discounts of 20%, 12½%, and 5%. Find the invoice price.

5. What would the Price Hardware Company pay for 32 dozen wood chisels listed at $32.50 a dozen, with discounts of 20%, 15%, and 5%?

6. Drury and Company offers to deliver an order for goods at $1,200 list price, less 25%, 20%, and 10%. Goss Bros. offers similar goods at the same list price less 30%, 20%, and 5%. How much would be saved by taking advantage of the better offer?

To find the single discount equal to a discount series. When the same series applies to different price quotations, time can be saved in finding the invoice costs by using the single discount that is equal to the series.

The single discount can be found in two steps, as follows:

(1) Find the invoice price in percent by applying the discounts to the list price expressed as 100%.

(2) Subtract the invoice price in percent from 100%, the list price. The result is the single rate equivalent to the series.

Example

Find the single discount equal to the series 20%, 10%, and 5%.

Solution

	Step 1		Step 2	
100%	list price		100%	list price
20%	1st discount (20%, or		68.4%	invoice price
	⅕, of 100%)		31.6%	single discount
80%	1st remainder			
8%	2d discount (10%, or			31.6% **Ans.**
	1⁄10, of 80%)			
72%	2d remainder			**Check:**
3.6%	3d discount (5%, or		20%	1st discount
	1⁄20, of 72%)		8%	2d discount
68.4%	3d remainder, or in-		3.6%	3d discount
	voice price		31.6%	total single discount

Exercise **4**   Written

In each of the following find the single discount that is equivalent to the series.

1. 25%, 20%   40%   4. 25%, 20%, 20%   52%   7. 20%, 16⅔%, 10%

2. 20%, 12½%   5. 30%, 20%, 12½%   8. 33⅓%, 20%, 10%

3. 16⅔%, 10%*   6. 20%, 20%, 12½%   9. 20%, 10%, 5%

*When finding a single discount equivalent to a series and the series includes a percent in the form of a mixed number, such as 16⅔%, this percent should be applied last to facilitate the calculations. This instruction should be followed in problems 7 and 8 also.

REVIEW ASSIGNMENT **56** c

1. a Divide 16½ by 1⅜.

b What part greater than $3 is $4.80?

c Find to the nearest cent 133⅓% of $23.

d $1.25 is what part smaller than $2?

2. What single rate of discount is equivalent to the series 30% and 15%?

3. The Ashford Furniture Company offers to deliver a china cabinet to Price & Thurston at $400 list price, less 30% and 15%. The Newdale Furniture Company offers to deliver the same kind of cabinet at $480 list price, less 30%, 15%, and 10%.

a Which is the better offer?

b How much would be saved by taking advantage of it?

4. An article listed at $30 is sold for $24. What is the rate of discount?

5. A typewriter that cost $325 depreciates 12% in value each year. Find the value of the typewriter at the end of the sixth year.

6. At an average speed of 45 miles an hour, how many minutes will it take Mr. Fullerton to drive 39 miles?

7. On a bar chart a one-inch line represents $50. How long a bar must be drawn to represent $275?

8. Find the missing amount in each of the following:

a .98 × b = $401.80   **b** 95% × c = $304

▶ **9.** A residence valued at $25,000 is insured for $18,000 under a policy carrying an 80% coinsurance clause. A fire caused a loss of $6,500.

a What amount was the insurance company required to pay?

b What percent of the fire loss was borne by the owner?

SECTION 57

Figuring Cash Discounts

Most wholesalers and manufacturers allow the retailer to deduct a small percent of the invoice price for the early payment of an invoice. Such a deduction is called a *cash discount*.

PART 57a Finding the Cash Price

Terms of sale with cash discount included. The cash discount allowed on an invoice is indicated in the terms. Examples of two typical terms and their meanings are the following:

2/10, n/30. These terms mean that 2% may be deducted if payment is made within 10 days from the date of the invoice; otherwise the full invoice price is due for payment within 30 days.

2/10, 1/30, n/60. These terms mean that 2% may be deducted if the invoice is paid within 10 days or 1% if paid within 30 days; otherwise the full amount is due within 60 days.

In the expression, "2/10, n/30," the 2 indicates the rate of cash discount, 2%. The 10 indicates the number of days in the *discount period*, 10 days. Both the discount and the credit period are measured from the date of the invoice.

Thus, if the terms are 2/10, n/30 on an invoice dated May 1, the last date on which the discount may be taken is May 1 + 10 days, or May 11. If not paid on May 11, the full invoice price is due on May 1 + 30 days, or May 31.

Exercise 1 Oral

1. State the last date on which the cash discount may be taken in each of the following:

Date of Invoice	Terms		Date of Invoice	Terms
a Aug. 16	2/10, n/30		**d** April 25	2/10, n/60
b Aug. 31	3/10, n/30		**e** Oct. 28	3/15, n/60
c Sept. 20	3/15, n/60		**f** Jan. 20	2/30, n/60

2. State what rate of cash discount, if any, may be deducted in each of the following:

	Date of Invoice	Terms	Date Paid
a	Mar. 26	1/10, n/30	April 5
b	May 22	3/15, n/60	June 4
c	July 25	3/10, n/90	Aug. 5
d	Sept. 18	2/30, n/60	Oct. 17
e	Oct. 10	2/10, 1/30, n/60	Oct. 28
f	Feb. 28	3/10, 2/30, n/60	Mar. 9
g	Jan. 15	3/5, 2/20, n/60	Feb. 10
h	Nov. 1	3/10, 1/30, n/60	Dec. 1

To find the cash discount and the cash price. When an invoice is paid within the discount period, the amount paid is the invoice price less the cash discount. This amount is called the *cash price*.

The percent representing the rate of cash discount is always based on the *invoice price*. Hence, the invoice price is multiplied by the rate to find the amount of the discount.

Rate of Cash Discount × Invoice Price = Cash Discount

Since the cash discount is a deduction from the invoice price, it is subtracted from the invoice price to find the cash price.

Invoice Price − Cash Discount = Cash Price

Exercise 2   Written

Find the amount needed to pay the following invoices on the dates indicated.

	Date of Invoice	Amount of Invoice	Terms	Date Paid
1.	July 27	$450	2/10, n/30	Aug. 6 $441
2.	Nov. 24	675	3/10, n/30	Dec. 3
3.	June 13	780	2/10, 1/30, n/60	July 12 $772.20
4.	Aug. 21	844	5/10, 2/30, n/60	Sept. 17
5.	April 6	520	2/10, 1/30, n/30	May 26

Trade and cash discounts. When both a trade discount and a cash discount are allowed on an invoice, the trade discount is subtracted first to give the invoice price. The cash discount is then calculated on the invoice price.

Exercise 3   Written

Find the cash price of each of the following invoices. Each was paid within the discount period.

	List Price	Trade Discount	Terms	
1.	$800	25%, 10%	2/30, n/60	$529.20
2.	550	20%, 15%	1/10, n/30	
3.	700	30%, 10%	2/10, n/30	
4.	650	20%, 20%	3/10, n/60	
5.	250	20%, 10%, 5%	5/10, n/60	

REVIEW ASSIGNMENT 57 a

1. a Multiply $28\frac{1}{2}$ by $22\frac{3}{4}$.

b Find, to the nearest cent, $137\frac{1}{2}\%$ of $3.

c Express a tax rate of 42 mills on $1 as a rate on $1,000.

2. An invoice of goods bought on May 28 has terms of 5/10, 2/30, n/60. What is the last possible date on which payment may be made to obtain the largest cash discount?

3. An invoice of goods amounting to $675 was dated July 28. If the terms were 3/10, 2/30, n/60, what amount would be required to pay for the goods on August 22?

4. M. C. Lodge purchased goods amounting to $1,100, less 20% and 10%; terms 1/10, n/30. The invoice was dated May 8, and was paid on May 18. What was the amount of the cash payment?

5. A catalog lists a certain rug at $85. The same rug is billed to merchants at $59.50. What rate of discount is allowed?

6. One factory offers a motor for $195, less 25% and 20%. Another factory offers a motor of equal value for $190, less $33\frac{1}{3}\%$ and 10%. Which is the better offer and how much better?

7. What single discount equals the series 25% and 10%?

◗ **8.** Dick purchased a guitar for $41.58. This cost included a 5% sales tax on the merchant's selling price. What was the amount of the sales tax on Dick's purchase?

PART 57b   Borrowing the Cash Price

Borrowing to take advantage of a cash discount. Frequently, the retailer does not have the cash needed for paying an invoice within the discount period. If he doesn't, it will usually pay him to borrow the money and take the discount. The amount he saves is the discount less the cost of the interest on the loan.

Cash Discount − Cost of Interest = Amount Saved

Example

On June 5, Webb and Sons bought merchandise invoiced at $1,500 with terms of 2/10, n/30. In order to pay the bill on June 15 and take advantage of the 2% discount, the firm borrowed the money at its bank for 20 days at 6%. How much was saved by borrowing to take advantage of the discount?

Solution:

Invoice price	*$1,500.00*
Cash discount	*30.00 (2% of $1,500)*
Cash price	*$1,470.00, the amount borrowed*

Interest on $1,470.00 for 20 days at 6% = $4.90

$30.00	*cash discount*
4.90	*cost of interest*
$25.10	*amount saved by borrowing to take advantage of the discount.* **Ans.**

Exercise 4 Written

1. By borrowing $875 for 60 days at 6% interest, H. K. Sutton was able to pay cash and obtain a cash discount of $27 on an invoice. What amount did he save by borrowing the money and taking the discount? $18.25

2. Jay Herrick can obtain $19.50 cash discount on an invoice by borrowing $650 at 6% interest for 90 days. What amount will he save by borrowing?

3. On March 18, W. M. Duncan purchased merchandise invoiced at $900 with terms of 3/10, n/30. In order to pay for the goods on March 28 and take advantage of the discount, Duncan borrowed the money at his bank for 20 days at 6%. How much did he save by borrowing to take advantage of the cash discount? $24.09

4. In order to take advantage of the cash discount on a bill of goods, dated June 5, amounting to $750, with terms of 2/10, n/90, G. L. Haven borrowed enough money to pay the bill on June 15, giving his 80-day note at 6%. How much did he save?

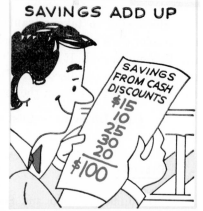

SAVINGS ADD UP

SAVINGS FROM CASH DISCOUNTS
$15
10
25
30
20
$100

5. The Ardmont Furniture Company purchased a quantity of furniture amounting to $3,000 on terms of 2/10, n/60. In order to take advantage of the cash discount, the company borrowed the money for 50 days at 6% and paid the bill. How much did the company gain by borrowing the money?

6. A dealer buys goods on terms of 2% discount for immediate payment, net 30 days. On an invoice amounting to $960, how much would be saved by borrowing the money at 6% for 30 days in order to take advantage of the cash discount?

REVIEW ASSIGNMENT **57** b

1. a Multiply $24\frac{2}{3}$ by $18\frac{3}{4}$.   **b** Divide 30 by $2\frac{1}{4}$.
   c What percent of $4.50 is $6?

2. On August 28, Bellinger purchased an invoice of merchandise amounting to $1,700 with terms of 3/10, n/60.

   a What was the amount of the check he wrote to pay the invoice on September 7?

   b In order to make the payment, Bellinger borrowed that amount for 50 days at 6%. How much did he save by borrowing to take advantage of the discount?

3. What will be the amount of the check sent in payment of an invoice amounting to $1,350; terms 5/10, 2/30, n/60; dated September 26; and paid October 5?

4. On May 8, E. L. Flanders, a retailer, purchased a bill of goods listed as $1,540, less 10% and 5%; terms 2/10, n/60. He paid the bill on May 18. What was the amount of the check he drew to make the payment?

5. Butler Brothers offer to fill an order for goods at $2,220, less 15% and 10%. Rose & Filkins ask $2,250, less 25%. Which is the better offer and how much better?

6. What single discount equals the series 20% and 5%?

PART 57c   Cash Discount Rate

To find the rate of cash discount. The rate of cash discount is always based on the invoice price. Therefore the rate is found by dividing the amount of the discount by the invoice price.

$$\text{Rate of Cash Discount} = \frac{\text{Cash Discount}}{\text{Invoice Price}}$$

Exercise 5   Written

1. Find the missing items in each of the following:

	Invoice Price	Cash Price	Cash Discount	Rate of Discount
a	$350	$343	$7	2%
b	375	360		
c	420	399		
d	600	582		
e		735	15	
f		266	14	
g		776	24	

2. An invoice of jewelry amounting to $500 is settled within the discount period by a cash payment of $490.

a What is the amount of the cash discount? $10

b The cash discount is what percent of the invoice price? 2%

3. A check for $436.50 is drawn within the discount period in payment of an invoice amounting to $450. What rate of cash discount is allowed?

4. By paying cash, $114, a retailer saves $6 on an invoice of sporting goods. What is the rate of cash discount?

5. A retailer saved $5 by accepting the cash discount terms and paying an invoice within the discount period. The amount he paid was $195. What rate of cash discount was allowed?

Exercise 6   Written

1. The cash discount on an invoice is $13.50. The rate of discount is 3%. What is the invoice price? $450

2. By taking the 2% cash discount on a bill of goods a merchant saved $8.46. What was the invoice price of the goods?

3. A retailer saved $34.67 by taking a 5% cash discount on an invoice. What was the invoice price of the merchandise?

4. By taking a 4% cash discount on an invoice, a retailer saved $15.80. What was the invoice price of the merchandise?

5. The cash discount offered on an invoice is 3%. What per-cent of the invoice price is the cash price?

6. $873 represents the cash price of a bill of goods after de-ducting a cash discount of 3%. What is the invoice price? $900

7. The cash price of an invoice is $313.60 after deducting a 2% cash discount. What is the invoice price?

8. A merchant paid $636.50 in settlement of an invoice less a cash discount of 5%. What was the amount of the invoice before the discount was deducted?

REVIEW ASSIGNMENT **57** c

1. Harris is billed $485 for a purchase of goods. If he pays within 10 days, he needs to pay only $470.45 to settle the bill in full. What percent of cash discount will he earn if he pays within 10 days?

2. On March 12, Tompkins purchased merchandise amounting to $2,450, terms 2/10, n/30. How much would he save by borrow-ing the necessary amount on March 22 for 20 days at 6% so as to take advantage of the discount?

3. The average annual depreciation of an office calculator is $101.70. The calculator cost $847.50 when new. What is the value of this calculator after four years of use?

4. Prepare a bar chart to show the facts given below.

Gary's Roadside Stand
Daily Sales, July 6–July 12, 19—

Sun. $360	Tues. $170	Thurs. $210	Sat. $320
Mon. 220	Wed. 260	Fri. 250	

5. On a bar chart, a one-inch line represents $200. How long must a bar be drawn to represent $750?

6. Find the missing amount in each of the following:
a $.96 \times a = \$336$ **b** $97\% \times b = \$388$

▶ **7. a** $16.25 is 130% of what amount?
b .97 times what amount equals $814.80?

▶ **8.** By taking a cash discount of 2% on an invoice, a merchant saved $13.29. What was the invoice price of the merchandise?

Buying Expense

Nature of buying expense. Buying expense is a merchant's expense of purchasing merchandise and getting it delivered to his place of business. In a small business it consists chiefly of parcel post, express, freight, and trucking charges.

Buying expense increases the cost of goods purchased. It is therefore added to the invoice price, or to the cash price if a cash discount is taken. If there are no other expenses connected with the purchase, the sum is the total cost of the merchandise.

Invoice Price (or Cash Price) + Buying Expense = Total Cost

Transportation charges on purchases. A price quotation from a wholesaler or a manufacturer usually specifies the *f.o.b.* or free delivery point. This is the point beyond which the buyer must pay the transportation charges. The initials f.o.b. stand for "free on board."

For example, the Sterling Plumbing Company, Cleveland, quotes to Hope Bros., Buffalo, a price of $95, *f.o.b. Buffalo*, for an electric water heater. This mean that the Sterling Company will pay the transportation charges from Cleveland to the Buffalo transportation terminal. If the quoted price were $95, *f.o.b. Cleveland*, Hope Bros. would have to pay the transportation charges.

Exercise 1   Written

1. S. I. Berman, office furniture dealer in Dixon, purchased 15 files from Wald & Company, Chicago, at $95, less 25% and 20%, f.o.b. Chicago. Transportation charges were $51.60.

a What was Berman's total cost of the 15 files? $906.60

b What was the average total cost per file?

2. The Keenan Men's Shop, at Benton, ordered 2 dozen men's shirts from the Longwear Shirt Company, Troy, N.Y., quoted at $47.50 a dozen, less 20% and 10%, f.o.b. Troy. The company prepaid the parcel-post charges on the shipment, $2.05, and added that amount on the invoice.

a What was the total cost of the order?

b What was the average total cost of each shirt?

3. Kern, a retailer, can purchase a certain article from four different manufacturers. He constructs the following schedule of the comparative cost of each manufacturer's product:

Manu-facturer	List Price of Article	Trade Discounts	Invoice Price of Article	Transpor-t⁻tion	Total Cost of Article
A	$80	10%, 10%		$4.33	
B	90	15%, 10%, 10%		4.50	
C	80	15%, 5%		4.25	
D	70	5%		4.75	

a Find the invoice price and the total cost of the article of each manufacturer.

b If the quality of the article and the service are approximately the same for all manufacturers, from which manufacturer should the article be purchased?

REVIEW ASSIGNMENT 58

1. a Multiply 27 by $2\frac{3}{4}$.   **b** Divide $37\frac{1}{2}$ by $1\frac{7}{8}$.
c What amount is 110% greater than $8.50?
d Find the number of days from May 8 to October 3.
e Express $8\frac{1}{2}$ mills as a decimal part of $1.

2. Seim purchased a clock listed at $62.50 with discounts of 25%, 20%, and 10%. How much did Seim pay for this clock?

3. A firm in Salem offers you an invoice of merchandise for $480, less 20%, 10%, and 10%, f.o.b. your city. A company in Melrose offers similar merchandise at $500, less 25% and 20%, f.o.b. Melrose. The freight charges from Melrose to your city are $18.75. How much is saved by taking advantage of the better offer?

4. Prepare a bar chart to show the facts given below.

Lubin's Clothing Store
Average Daily Sales — May, 19—

Berry	$380	Jarvis	$460	Platt	$610
Ernst	580	Loder	360	Soule	550

5. What single rate of discount is equivalent to the series 20% and 15%?

6. $3\% \times r = \$12.60$. Find the missing amount.

GENERAL REVIEW

1. **a** Multiply 45.72 by 2.08.   **d** Subtract $8\frac{2}{3}$ from $75\frac{3}{5}$.

   b Divide 67.14 by 1.8.   **e** Multiply $48\frac{1}{4}$ by $8\frac{1}{3}$.

   c Add: $6\frac{5}{14}$, $15\frac{2}{7}$, $8\frac{1}{2}$, $4\frac{3}{4}$.   **f** Divide $12\frac{2}{3}$ by $3\frac{1}{6}$.

   g Express $\frac{5}{9}$ as a decimal to the nearest hundredth.

   h Express $\frac{6}{7}$ as a percent to the nearest tenth of a percent.

2. Ralph Malone's checkbook balance on July 1 was $716.33. His bank statement showed a balance of $800.58 on that date. There was a service charge of $1.15 which had not been deducted in his checkbook. Outstanding checks were: No. 79, $24.18; No. 82, $61.22. Prepare a reconciliation statement.

3. A piece of property is assessed at $13,500. Find the tax to be paid if the rate is 59 mills per dollar.

4. Mrs. Wells can buy a washer for $230 cash or on the deferred payment plan by paying $25 down and 15 monthly payments of $16 each. What is the amount of the finance charge under the deferred payment plan?

5. Collen can purchase a used car for $875 cash, or for a down payment of $295 and $52 a month for 12 months. He has enough cash for the down payment and can borrow the balance from a bank for 12 months at 6%. How much can he save by borrowing to pay cash for the car?

6. Sexton bought some stock at a total cost of $1,490, including the broker's commission of $20. The market price of the stock was $42. How many shares of this stock did Sexton buy?

7. Mr. Morgan purchased 40 shares of stock at $27\frac{1}{2}$. Brokerage for the entire transaction amounted to $16. The stock pays regular quarterly dividends of $32\frac{1}{2}$¢ per share. What annual rate of income, to the nearest tenth of a percent, does Mr. Morgan receive on his investment?

8. Find the date of maturity and amount due at maturity on a 4-month, 5% note for $960, dated September 20.

9. Brate's store building is insured for $42,000 at an annual rate of $.75 per $100. A 3-year policy costs 2.7 times as much as a 1-year policy. How much would Brate save by buying a 3-year policy instead of three 1-year policies?

10. Gowdy insured an apartment building for $10,000 with Company A, for $15,000 with Company B, and for $25,000 with Company C. A fire loss of $7,000 occurred. What amount should Gowdy collect from each of these insurance companies?

11. A machine costing $1,725 was estimated to depreciate in value at the annual rate of 8% of the original cost. What was the amount of the average monthly depreciation of this machine?

12. Bishop bought an automobile for $3,100. During the first year, the car expenses were: insurance, $185; license plates, $19; gasoline and oil, $288; repairs, $44; interest at 6% on the cost of the car; depreciation at 25% of the cost of the car. Find the total car expense for the year.

13. The total assessed valuation of taxable property in a certain village is $6,140,000. The amount to be raised by real estate taxes this year is $439,010. What tax rate per $100 is needed to collect this amount?

14. Burrick's state income tax return for last year showed a taxable income of $2,562. This amount was subject to a tax of 2% on the first $1,000 and 3% on the next $2,000 or fraction thereof. What was the total amount of Burrick's state income tax for last year?

15. A school entertainment was given on two successive evenings. For the two evenings a total of 380 tickets was sold at 75¢ each and 1,360 at 50¢ each. Expenses totaled $297. Find the net profit on the two entertainments.

16. The Social Security Act requires the employer to pay an FICA tax on the total taxable wages at the rate paid by the employees. During the quarter ended June 30, the Walton Company paid wages totaling $14,685 that were taxable at 4.8%. What was the Walton Company's FICA tax for that quarter?

17. On a certain bar chart, a bar one inch long represents $500. What amount is represented by a bar $5\frac{1}{2}$ inches long?

● **18.** Express .525 as a fraction in lowest terms.

● **19.** On November 30, Robert Oakley's checkbook balance was $849.12. His bank statement showed a balance of $1,191.86. Checks were outstanding for $79.84, $59.73, and $27.60. A deposit of $175.57 had been omitted from the check book by error. Prepare a reconciliation statement.

● **20.** A salesman receives a salary of $500 a month and a commission of 4% on all sales. What must be the amount of his sales each month in order that his total monthly income may be $850?

● **21.** During the first quarter of the year, a store's sales totaled $35,880, including a 4% retail sales tax that was charged and collected on each sale. What total amount of sales tax did the store collect during this quarter?

UNIT Thirteen

The Retailer's Selling Problems

SECTION 59

Sales Records

Cash register. A cash register provides a record of cash received and cash paid out. The one shown at the left records each transaction on a paper tape. The total of each kind of transaction is printed on the tape at the end of the day.

Courtesy of The National Cash Register Company

Cash register

Proving the cash. At the end of the day, a count is made of the money in the register money drawer. This amount should be the same as the difference between the register total of cash received and the total "paid outs." If it is not, the cash is either *over* or *short*.

Example

At the end of the day, May 16, H. H. Gray's cash register showed total cash received, $146.80, and total cash paid out, $3.20. The cash in the money drawer was $143.15. Prepare a cash proof showing the cash over or short, if any.

Cash Proof, May 16, 19—

Register total of cash received	*$146.80*
Register total of cash paid out	*3.20*
Remainder to be accounted for	*$143.60*
Cash on hand in money drawer	*$143.15*
Cash short	*$ .45*

In the foregoing example, the cash is *short* 45¢ because the cash in the money drawer, $143.15, is 45¢ less than the amount to be accounted for, $143.60.   If the cash on hand had been 45¢ more than $143.60, the cash would have been *over* 45¢.

The cash in the money drawer may include a change fund that was placed there at the beginning of the day. If it does, the amount of the fund should be included in figuring the cash to be accounted for, as shown in the cash proof given below.

Cash Proof, July 28, 19—

Change fund	$ 25.00	
Register total of cash received	344.70	$369.70
Register total of cash paid out		6.15
Remainder to be accounted for		$363.55
Cash on hand in money drawer		$363.75
Cash over		$ .20

Exercise 1   Written

1. At the beginning of the day, April 9, G. K. Harmon placed $25 in change in the money drawer of his cash register. The cash register readings at the end of the day showed total cash received, $275.23, and total cash paid out, $9.64. The cash on hand in the money drawer at the end of the day was $290.84. Prepare a statement of the proof of the cash, showing the cash over or short.

25¢ over

2. On the morning of September 4, C. H. Payne placed $20 in change in the money drawer of his cash register. At the end of the day, the cash register record showed that $198.42 had been taken in, that $6.34 had been paid out in cash refunds, and that Mr. Payne had taken out $15 for his personal use. The amount of cash on hand in the money drawer at the end of the day was $197.58. How much was the cash short or over?

3. Stein had $50 in change in his cash register at the beginning of the day, March 1. At the end of the day there was $338.58 in the cash register. The register totals showed that he had taken in $307.43 and paid out $18.75 during the day. How much was the cash over or short?

4. Enid King, cashier at the Campus Lunch, started the day with $75 in change. When she went off duty, she sorted her counter checks and found that she had the following:

32 for 25¢	36 for 45¢	93 for 65¢	74 for 85¢
24 for 30¢	43 for 50¢	104 for 70¢	72 for 90¢
26 for 35¢	38 for 55¢	132 for 75¢	62 for 95¢
30 for 40¢	74 for 60¢	110 for 80¢	

Enid had $720.30 in the cash drawer. She had made no payments. How much was her cash short or over?

Records of sales. Cash sales and cash refunds for goods returned are recorded on the cash register tape. Charge sales and goods returned by charge customers are recorded on sales slips and credit slips.

The daily totals of the cash sales, charge sales, and returns and allowances are recorded in a sales summary book. In many stores, these records are kept so as to show the totals for each department and for each salesclerk.

Exercise 2   Written

1. The table below shows the sales and sales returns for the four departments of Joseph's Clothing Store for February 5 of the current year.

DAILY SUMMARY — CASH SALES
February 5, 19—

Department	Sales	Sales Returns	Net Sales
Clothing	$3,734	$38	
Hats	632	7	
Shoes	806	15	
Furnishings	925	16	
Totals			

a Copy the table and show: the net sales for each department, the total sales, the total sales returns, and the total net sales.

b Prove the total net sales by subtracting the total sales returns from the total sales.

2. The table below at the right shows the cash sales and charge sales for the six departments of Ben's Auto Supply and Repair for January 16 of the current year.

a Copy the table and show: the total sales for each department, the total cash sales, the total charge sales, and the total sales for the day.

b Prove the total of the "Total Sales" column by adding the totals of the "Cash Sales" and "Charge Sales" columns at the left.

DAILY SALES SUMMARY
January 16, 19—

Department	Cash Sales	Charge Sales	Total Sales
Tires	$95.60	$84.30	
Batteries	76.54	65.46	
Parts	66.68	54.23	
Accessories	24.25	15.20	
Labor	56.80	34.75	
Other	28.20	6.45	
Totals			

3. Last year the sales of the Fairlane Corporation were $92,400. Sales for this year are expected to increase by 14% over last year. What are the expected sales of the Fairlane Corporation for this year?

4. Kay's Bookstore sold the following books during one year:

Jan. 794	April 354	July 531	Oct. 2,040
Feb. 968	May 270	Aug. 1,620	Nov. 1,326
Mar. 482	June 235	Sept. 5,163	Dec. 3,461

a Find the total number of books sold during the year.

b Find the average number of books sold per month.

c During which months did the sales exceed the average?

5. For the month of October last year, the sales of Draper's Gift Shop were $3,000. For October of the current year the sales were $3,750.

a What was the amount of the increase or decrease in sales?

b What was the percent of increase or decrease?

6. Find, to the nearest tenth of a percent, the increase or decrease in sales for each of the two departments indicated below:

Department	Last Year	This Year	Percent Increase	Percent Decrease
Paint	$36,800	$39,200		
Wallpaper	19,200	18,600		

REVIEW ASSIGNMENT **59**

1. a Add: $9\frac{2}{3}$, $12\frac{3}{4}$, $15\frac{5}{6}$.   **b** Divide $23\frac{1}{3}$ by $1\frac{5}{9}$.

c $40.15 is what percent smaller than $55?

d Find the interest at 6% on $1,150 for 17 days.

2. On the morning of May 2, J. R. Rudd placed $30 in change in the money drawer of his cash register. The readings at the end of the day showed total cash received, $481.32, and total cash paid out, $24.88. The cash on hand in the money drawer at the end of the day was $486.59. How much was the cash short or over?

3. A canoe listed at $220 is billed to the retailer at $192.50. What is the rate of trade discount?

4. An invoice for $350 can be fully settled by paying $339.50 within 10 days from the date of the invoice. What percent of cash discount is allowed?

5. On July 8, Larkin purchased merchandise amounting to $800, less 10%, 10%, and 5%. The terms were 2/10, n/30; and he paid the invoice on July 18. What was the amount of the check that he drew to make the payment?

6. What single discount is equivalent to the series 20%, 25%, and 10%?

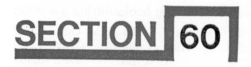

SECTION 60

Figuring Retail Discounts

The price at which a retailer offers to sell an article is usually written on the article itself or on a price tag or a ticket attached to the article.

PART 60a The Rate of Discount

Marked price, discount, and selling price. The price at which an article is offered for sale is called the *marked price* or *retail price*. To keep goods moving, the prices of some articles have to be reduced. The amount of the reduction is called the *discount* or *markdown*. The price which the customer pays is the *selling price* or *sales price*. The discount or markdown is equal to the marked price less the selling price.

Marked Price − Selling Price = Discount

The selling price equals the marked price less the discount.

Marked Price − Discount = Selling Price

In cases where no discount or markdown is offered, the selling price is the same as the marked price.

To find the rate of discount. Expressed as a rate, the discount is always based on the marked price. Therefore the discount is divided by the marked price to find the rate of discount.

$$\text{Rate of Discount} = \frac{\text{Discount}}{\text{Marked Price}}$$

Exercise 1 Written

1. Find the amount and the rate of discount in the following:

	Article	Marked Price	Sold For	Discount Allowed Amount	Discount Allowed Percent
a	Swimsuit	$13.00	$ 9.75	$3.25	25%
b	Radio	75.00	63.75		
c	Chinaware	47.50	38.00		

2. In the window of a dress shop, a dress is marked "$38.95 — was $47.50." At what rate was the price reduced? 18%

3. At the Leisure Mart, the price of a chair that regularly sells for $55 is reduced to $33.50. What is the rate of markdown on this chair to the nearest tenth of a percent?

4. A sportcoat that had been marked $33 was sold during a special sale for $28.89. What percent discount, to the nearest tenth of a percent, was allowed?

5. Aubrey Bader purchased a suit of clothes at the Towne Clothing Store for $72.75. The clerk added, without charge, a belt worth $2.25. To what rate of discount was this equivalent?

Exercise 2   Written

1. Men's shirts regularly priced at $4.25 each are sold during a special sale at 2 for $7.65. What percent does a customer save by buying two shirts at the sale price? 10%

2. Ties that regularly sell at $2.50 each are offered at the special price of 3 for $5. What rate of discount is offered?

3. The subscription price of the *Tourist* magazine is $8 for one year. A 2-year subscription is offered for $14 and a 3-year subscription for $20.

    a What rate of discount is offered on the purchase of a 2-year subscription?

    b Of a 3-year subscription?

4. The Bestbuy Store has combs which it sells regularly at 25¢ each. During its annual "One Cent Sale" the store offers to sell 2 combs for the price of one plus 1¢. This is equivalent to what rate of discount?

REVIEW ASSIGNMENT 60a

    1. a Multiply $34\frac{3}{8}$ by 26.   **b** Multiply $63\frac{3}{8}$ by $24\frac{2}{3}$.

    c Find the due date of a 60-day note dated October 21.

    d What amount is $162\frac{1}{2}\%$ of $2.80?

    e Find the interest on $950 for 77 days at 6%.

2. At an end-of-season sale, suits marked $75 were reduced to $57. What was the percent of markdown on these suits?

3. On June 8 a retailer purchased an invoice of goods amounting to $900, terms 2/10, n/60. In order to take advantage of the discount, he borrowed the needed amount on June 18 for 50 days at 6% and paid the invoice. How much did he save by borrowing to take advantage of the discount?

4. A firm in Portland offers you an invoice of merchandise for $860, less 30% and 20%, f.o.b. your city. Another company in Medford offers similar merchandise at the same list price less 25%, 20%, and 10%, f.o.b. Medford. The freight charges from Medford to your city are $25.70. How much is saved by taking advantage of the better offer?

5. Find the single discount that is equivalent to the series 20%, $16\frac{2}{3}$%, and 10%.

◐ **6.** A merchant saved $36 by taking a cash discount of $1\frac{1}{2}$%. What was the invoice price of the merchandise he purchased?

PART 60b Finding the Selling Price

To find the discount and the selling price when the marked price and rate of discount are known. The rate of discount or markdown is always based on the marked price. The marked price is therefore multiplied by the rate to find the amount of the discount.

Rate of Discount × Marked Price = Discount

The discount is then subtracted from the marked price to find the selling price.

Marked Price − Discount = Selling Price

Exercise 3   Written

1. Find the discount and the selling price in the following:

	Article	Marked Price	Discount Allowed	Amount of Discount	Selling Price
a	Table	$70.00	$12\frac{1}{2}$%	$8.75	$61.25
b	Golf cart	15.50	30%		
c	Binoculars	69.50	20%		
d	Shaver	21.90	$16\frac{2}{3}$%		
e	Paintbrush	1.89	25%		

2. How much does the customer pay for a travel clock marked $9.75 if a retail discount of 16% is allowed? $8.19

3. Wool sweaters formerly priced at $16.50 were marked down 22%. What was the markdown price?

4. During a special sale, the price of a dinette set is marked down 20% from $69.50. What is the special sale price?

5. The price of a desk lamp is reduced 40% from the original price of $5.95. How much will the desk lamp cost the purchaser at the reduced price?

❿ **To find the marked price when the selling price and rate of discount are known.** Sometimes the selling price and rate of discount are known, and the marked price is to be found.

Example

A jeweler sold a silver bowl to a customer for $27 after deducting a discount of 10% from the marked price.
What was the marked price of the bowl?

The percent given in the problem is based on the marked price, which is unknown. The problem tells us, however, that if 10% of the marked price is subtracted from the marked price, the remainder is $27.

Marked Price − 10% of Marked Price = $27

Since the percent is based on the marked price, the marked price is the base, or whole, and is therefore 100% of itself.

Solution: $100\% \times$ *marked price* = *Marked price*
$\underline{-10\% \times}$ *marked price* = *Discount*
$90\% \times$ *marked price* = $\overline{Selling\ price}$ = *$27*
Marked price = *$27 ÷ 90%*
= *$27 ÷ .9 = $30* **Ans.**

Check: Marked Price − Discount = Selling Price
$30 − 10% of $30 = $30 − $3 = $27

---

❿ **Exercise 4 Written**

1. During a sale, a store sold shovels at 30% off the marked price. The selling price was what percent of the marked price?

2. The Roger Bruce Luggage Shop sells a flight bag to a customer for $63, which is 16% less than the marked price.

a The selling price is what percent of the marked price?

b How much is the marked price? $75

3. An electric freezer is sold for $238, which is 15% under the marked price.

a What percent of the marked price is the selling price?

b How much is the marked price?

4. After allowing a retail discount of $12\frac{1}{2}\%$, a shoe dealer sold a pair of shoes for $14.77. What was the marked price?

5. At what price should the Numart Discount House mark a hi-fi set in order that the selling price may be $71.25 after allowing an advertised discount of 25% on the marked price?

REVIEW ASSIGNMENT 60b

1. a Divide $16\frac{1}{2}$ by $2\frac{3}{4}$.

b $4.86 is what percent more than $3.60?

c Find the interest on $1,450 for 13 days at $7\frac{1}{2}\%$.

d Find the interest on $1,200 for 154 days at 5%.

e Express $12\frac{1}{2}$ mills as a decimal part of $1.

2. In the window of a clothing store a suit is marked "$59.50 — Formerly $85." At what rate was the price reduced?

3. A retailer purchased goods on September 30 for $1,343.20; terms, 3/10, 2/30, n/90. The bill was paid on October 29. How much more would have been saved if the invoice had been paid on October 10?

4. A rotisserie broiler listed at $35 is sold for $29.75. What rate of discount is allowed?

5. The Gracie Company offers to fill an order for goods at $925, less 20% and 10%; terms, n/60. For the same goods, Granger Bros. ask $950, less 30%; terms 2/10, n/30.

a Assuming that the customer will pay cash for this merchandise, which is the better offer?

b How much better?

6. a What number divided by $8\frac{2}{3}$ gives $15\frac{3}{4}$?

b What amount increased by $\frac{3}{8}$ of itself equals $26.40?

7. A store saved $21.63 by taking the $2\frac{1}{2}\%$ cash discount offered on an invoice of merchandise. What was the amount of the invoice before the discount was deducted?

8. A retailer wishes to receive $31.50 for a pair of binoculars after allowing the customer a discount of 10% on the marked price. What should be his marked price for the binoculars?

Figuring Profits on Sales

A store owner frequently wants to know how much gross profit or net profit he is making on a single article or unit of the article that he has sold. He also may want to know the rate of profit he has realized and compare it with the rate shown by the percentage analysis of the income statement.

PART 61a   Gross and Net Profit

To find the gross profit. The gross profit is found by subtracting the cost from the selling price.

Selling Price − Cost = Gross Profit

The term "cost" means the total cost; that is, the invoice price, or cash price, plus the buying expenses.

Example

The VanAllen and Stewart Store bought 150 men's summer suits for $4,165 and paid $95 for transportation charges on the purchase. During the regular season the store sold 120 of the suits at $45 each. At the end of the season, the remaining suits were closed out at $35 each.

What was the amount of the store's gross profit on the entire lot?

Solution

First, find the selling price of the entire lot.		Second, find the total cost of the purchase.	
120 suits @ $45	$5,400	Invoice price	$4,165
30 suits @ $35	1,050	Transportation charges	95
Selling price	$6,450	Total cost	$4,260

Third, find the gross profit.

Selling price	$6,450
Cost	4,260
Gross profit	$2,190 **Ans.**

If the cost is more than the selling price, the selling price is sub-tracted from the cost. The result represents a loss.

Cost − Selling Price = Gross Loss

Exercise 1   Written

1. The Wash and Wear Shop bought a job lot of 250 cotton dresses for $1,285 and paid $40 for transportation charges on the purchase. The store sold 120 of the dresses at $9.95, 80 at $7.75, and the remainder at $5.50. What was the store's gross profit on the entire lot? $764

2. Miriam's Hat Center purchased 40 dozen hats at $54 a dozen and paid $30 for express charges on the shipment. The store sold 380 of them at $6.95 and the remainder at $4.95. What was the store's gross profit on the entire lot?

3. A produce dealer purchased 180 bags of potatoes at $3.16 a bag and paid $25.60 for transportation charges. If he sold the entire lot at $4.15 a bag, what gross profit did he realize?

4. C. M. Bost, hardware dealer, purchased a dozen pliers for $40, less 35%, paid $1.74 for express charges, and then sold them at $2.75 each. What was his gross profit on the pliers?

To find the net profit. The net profit is found by deducting the operating expenses from the gross profit.

Gross Profit − Operating Expenses = Net Profit

If the operating expenses are greater than the gross profit, the gross profit is subtracted from the operating expenses. The result repre-sents a net loss.

Operating Expenses − Gross Profit = Net Loss

Operating expenses — such as salaries, rent, heat, light, and similar items — apply to all the goods sold during the period. The amount that applies to a single article is not known. It can be esti-mated, however.

For example, if the recent income statements show that the operating expenses average 25% of the sales, it is assumed that the operating expenses are 25% of the amount of an individual sale. Hence, if an article is sold for $80, the operating expenses connected with the sale are estimated at 25% of $80, or $20.

Example

S. A. Klein, retail furniture dealer, pays $105 for a desk and sells it for $175. What is his estimated net profit on the desk if his operating expenses average 32% of the net sales?

Solution: *Selling price*	*$175*	
— Cost	*105*	
Gross profit	*$ 70*	
— Operating expenses	*56*	*(32% of $175)*
Net profit	*$ 14*	**Ans.**

The net profit may also be found by subtracting the sum of the cost and the operating expenses from the selling price.

Selling Price — (Cost + Operating Expenses) = Net Profit

In this manner, the solution would be:

Selling price		*$175*
Deduct:		
Cost	*$105*	
Operating expenses,		
32% of $175	*56*	*161*
Net profit		*$ 14*

Exercise 2 Written

1. The Plaza Auto Supply Store buys tires at $11.20 and sells them at $18.50. The store figures its operating expenses at 24% of net sales. What net profit is realized on each tire? $2.86

2. Rockwell Brothers, retail paint dealers, bought a quantity of paint for $495 and sold it for $825. They estimate their overhead at 28% of net sales. What was their net profit?

3. A store bought 30 gold bracelets for $450, less 10% and 10%. It sold 15 of the bracelets at $25 each, 10 at $20.50, and 5 at $18. What amount of net profit did the store realize if its cost of doing business is 35% of net sales?

4. Streeter buys toasters at $16 each, less 20% and 10%, plus transportation of $.68 on each toaster. If he sells them at $19 and his operating expenses are 25% of net sales, what is his net profit on each toaster?

5. The Sweet Shop bought 300 boxes of candy at $1.20 a box. The shop sold 290 boxes at $2 a box. Ten boxes were damaged and thrown away. The shop's operating expenses average 26% of net sales. What net profit was realized on the entire transaction?

REVIEW ASSIGNMENT 61 a

1. a Find the due date of a 120-day note dated April 7.

b Find the interest at 6% on $875 for 73 days.

c Express a tax rate of $8.25 on $1,000 as a rate in mills on $1.

2. An invoice for $385 can be settled in full by paying $365.75 within 10 days from the date of the invoice. What rate of cash discount is being allowed?

3. A motor boat listed at $510 is billed at $382.50. What rate of discount is allowed?

4. On June 29, Briscoe bought 10 electric irons at $15.45 each, less 20% and 10%; terms, 2/10, n/30. What was the amount of the check he drew on July 9 to pay for these irons?

5. The Marlon Men's Shop bought 30 dozen straw hats for $1,497, delivered. They sold 180 hats at $7.50 each, 120 at $5.50 each, and the remainder at $3.75 each.

a What was the gross profit on the entire lot?

b What was the average gross profit per hat?

6. a What number divided by $4\frac{1}{2}$ gives $8\frac{2}{9}$?

b $7.20 is $\frac{15}{16}$ of what amount?

c $21\frac{7}{8}$ is what part greater than $12\frac{1}{2}$?

7. A hardware dealer wishes to mark a power mower so that he may receive $114.75 for it after allowing the customer a discount of 15%. What should be the marked price?

PART 61b | Rate of Markup

To find the rate of markup, or rate of gross profit, and the rate of net profit, based on the selling price of an article. The price a merchant pays for an article, including any buying expense, is the merchant's *cost* of the article. The price at which he sells it, or expects to sell it, is the *selling price* or *retail price*.

The amount by which the selling price exceeds the cost is known as the *markup, gross profit,* or *markon.* When expressed as a percent, the rate of markup or gross profit is usually based on the selling price.

$$\text{Selling Price} - \text{Cost} = \text{Markup (Gross Profit)}$$

$$\text{Rate of Markup (Gross Profit)} = \frac{\text{Markup (Gross Profit)}}{\text{Selling Price}}$$

The rate of net profit is found by dividing the net profit by the selling price.

$$\text{Rate of Net Profit} = \frac{\textbf{Net Profit}}{\textbf{Selling Price}}$$

Exercise 3   Written

1. The Leather Shop pays $23.40 for a briefcase and marks it to sell for $39. The markup is what percent of the selling price?
40%

2. A clothier buys men's belts at $30 a dozen and sells them at $3.75 each. What is his percent of gross profit based on the selling price?

3. Haley's Clothing Store finds from past experience that an average gross profit of $37\frac{1}{2}\%$ of net sales must be realized to cover expenses and provide a satisfactory net profit.

    a If topcoats that can be sold at $75 each are offered to the store at $48.75 by the manufacturer, what percent of gross profit would the store realize on the selling price of each coat?

    b Is this percent greater or less than the rate desired by the store?

    c How many percent greater or less?

4. A retailer buys pencils at $2.70 a gross and sells them at 2 for 5¢. What percent of the selling price does the retailer gain?

5. Marc Milstein buys humidifiers at $46.80 each and marks them to sell at $80. If he allows a discount of 10%, what is his rate of profit on the selling price?

6. The Fruit Mart bought 20 boxes of grapefruit (40 to a box) at $5.70 a box. They had to throw out 40 grapefruit that had spoiled. They sold the remainder at 4 for 75¢. What was their percent of profit on the selling price?

Exercise 4   Written

1. Benny's Auto Supply Store buys batteries at $11.55 each and sells them at $17.50. The cost of doing business is 26% of net sales. The net profit on each battery is what percent of the selling price? 8%

2. The Fuller Decorating Shop buys tablecloths at $10.40 each and marks them to sell at $16. The store's overhead is estimated at 25% of net sales. What rate of net profit does the store realize on each tablecloth that it sells at the marked price?

3. World of Fabrics buys spreads at $98.28 a dozen and sells them at $13 each. What rate of net profit is earned on the selling price if the operating expenses are 29% of net sales?

4. A quantity of goods that cost $1,482 is sold for $1,950. The overhead expense chargeable to the transaction amounts to $292.50. What is the percent of net profit on the selling price?

REVIEW ASSIGNMENT **61b**

1. a Subtract $32\frac{3}{4}$ from $61\frac{1}{8}$.
b Multiply $38\frac{5}{8}$ by $24\frac{1}{2}$.
c Find the number of days from March 15 to July 1.
d Find the interest on $1,375 for 14 days at 6%.

2. An invoice dated October 29 has terms of 3/10, 1/30, n/60. What is the final date on which this invoice may be paid in order to get the largest cash discount?

3. A grocer pays 69¢ for a pound package of butter and sells it for 92¢. What is his rate of profit on the selling price?

4. A furniture dealer marked a chair to sell at $62.50. During a special sale, it was sold for $50. What was the rate of discount on the marked price?

5. An office equipment dealer purchases an office desk for $250, less 20%, 10%, and 5%, and sells it for $300, less 15%. What amount of gross profit does he realize?

6. Patten can buy some display cases for his store from the Quality Show Case Company, an out-of-town firm, for $3,200 less 25% and 20%. In addition, he will have to pay $105 for freight, trucking, and installation charges. The Wayne Display Company, a local concern, will sell him similar display cases for $3,300, less $33\frac{1}{3}$% and 10%, with no additional charge for delivery and installation. How much would Patten save by accepting the better of the two offers?

7. What single percent of discount is equal to a series of discounts of 25%, 20%, and 10%?

8. Find the missing amount in each of the following:
a $60\% \times \$27 = N$ **b** $60\% \times p = \$27$ **c** $160\% \times c = \$24$

9. a What number divided by $12\frac{3}{8}$ gives $3\frac{1}{3}$?
b $.98\frac{1}{2}$ times what amount equals $738.75?
c $4.20 is $\frac{5}{12}$ smaller than what amount?

10. A merchant saved $9.72 by taking a cash discount of 3%. What was the amount of the invoice?

SECTION 62

Pricing Goods—Sales Price Basis

In pricing goods, the rate of markup may be based on either the selling price or the cost price. In a retail business it is usually based on the selling or retail price.

PART 62a Price-lined Merchandise

To find the cost price of an article when the selling price and rate of markup on selling price are known. A retailer often stocks each kind of article in three or four price lines.

A men's clothing store, for example, may specialize in suits that sell at $60, $65, $70, and $75; shoes at $8.97, $10.97, $12.97, and $14.97; shirts at $2.95, $3.75, and $4.50; and so on.

When the store owner must buy more articles in a particular line, the selling price is already known. His problem is to find the highest price he can afford to pay for the article.

Example

The owner of The Casual Fashions Shop has to buy dresses for the line that sells at $12.99. He knows that his markup must be 40% of the selling price in order to cover expenses and a satisfactory net profit. What is the highest price he can afford to pay?

The highest price he can pay represents his cost, which is found by subtracting the markup from the selling price.

$$\text{Selling Price} - \text{Markup} = \text{Cost}$$

Since the markup is 40% of the selling price, the amount of the markup is 40% of $12.99.

Solution: *Selling price* $12.990
              Markup   5.196 *(40% of $12.99)*
                     $\overline{\$7.794}$ *or $7.79*

The highest price he can afford to pay is $7.79.   **Ans.**

The answer in the example, which is $7.79, can be checked in this manner:

Check: 100% of selling price = Selling price
         −40% of selling price = Markup
         ‾‾‾‾‾‾‾‾‾‾‾‾‾‾‾‾‾‾‾‾‾‾‾‾‾‾‾‾‾‾‾‾‾‾‾‾‾
          60% of selling price = Cost
                 60% of $12.99 = $7.79, Cost

Exercise 1   Written

1. The owner of Town and Country Styles has to buy coats for the line that sells for $50. What is the most he can pay for this line if the markup must be 37% of the selling price? $31.50

2. What is the most that the store owner should pay per dozen for neckties which retail at $2.50 each, if he must realize 34% markup on the retail price?

3. The Shoe Bazaar has a 36% markup on casual shoes that sell for $5.75 a pair. What is the cost per pair to the store?

4. What is the highest price a store can pay for ladies' handbags that retail for $8.75 each, if the store must have a markup of 44% of the selling price?

Marking goods. When goods are placed in stock, they are usually marked to show the selling price. Some stores also mark the cost price. The selling price is marked in everyday numerals; but, to keep the cost secret, the cost price is marked in *code*. The code often consists of a word or group of words containing ten different letters which are used in place of digits. For example:

H E   W A S   Y O U N G
1 2   3 4 5   6 7 8 9 0

Using this code, a cost price of $37.50 would be written WOSG or WO.SG. When the decimal point is not shown, it is understood to be in the same position as the decimal point in the selling price.

When a digit is repeated one or more times in succession, an extra letter, called a "repeater," is sometimes used.

For example, using "Z" as a repeater, a price of $29.90 would be written ENZG. Without the repeater symbol it would be written ENNG.

Exercise **2**   Written

In Problems 1 to 3 write each price in code, using the indicated code words. Omit the decimal point in the coded price.

	Code Words	Re-peater	Price				
			a	b	c	d	e
1.	HE WAS YOUNG	(None)	$1.50	$6.75	$15.50	$28.37	$ 4.00
2.	BALTIMORES	X	.93	7.70	18.00	35.55	44.25
3.	STRONG MILE	Y	1.13	3.95	.55	60.60	13.35

4. Write in numeral form each price given in code below. The code words are GOLD PRINCE. The repeater is A.

a DLP   **c** ORN   **e** GALE   **g** LOAP

b IDE   **d** GRAP   **f** CEA   **h** NIP

REVIEW ASSIGNMENT **62** a

1. a Subtract $56\frac{4}{5}$ from $221\frac{3}{4}$.

b Divide $7\frac{1}{8}$ by $9\frac{1}{2}$.

c Find the interest at 6% on $565 for 83 days.

2. On the price tag of each article, Bob's Bike Shop marks the cost price in code. The code word BLACKSTONE is used as the key for numbers 1 through 0. The tag on a certain bicycle bears the code mark AKOE. If the bicycle is sold for $59.75, what is the amount of the gross profit on the sale?

3. A store owner has to buy car coats for the line that retails at $13.95. What is the highest he can afford to pay for this line if his markup must be 36% of the selling price?

4. A clothier buys neckties at $28 a dozen and sells them at $3.50 each. What percent of markup does he realize on the selling price?

5. A delivery truck that cost $4,500 is estimated to have trade-in value of $500 five years later. What will be the estimated value of the truck at the end of the third year?

6. On March 10, a retailer purchased goods invoiced at $1,340, terms 3/10, n/90. In order to take advantage of the cash discount, he borrowed the necessary amount for 80 days at 6% and paid the invoice on March 20. How much did he save?

▷ 7. Golf jackets that cost $9 had been selling for $15 at the
rate of 10 a day. When the price was reduced to $13.50, the sales
increased to 18 a day. What was the percent of increase in the
daily profit?

PART 62b Determining the Selling Price

▷ **To find the price at which an article should be sold to yield a
given rate of markup, based on the selling price.** Sometimes a store
owner purchases an article which is not in one of his price lines and
which must be priced individually. In this case the cost price is known,
and his problem is to find the selling price that will give the desired rate
of markup.

Example

Tony's Auto Center buys an order of car radios at $39 each. The
owner knows that his markup must be 40% of the selling price in order
to cover expenses and provide a satisfactory net profit.
What is the lowest price at which the radios can be sold and still
realize the desired rate of markup?

The percent given in the problem is based on the selling price,
which is unknown. The problem indicates, however, that if 40% of
the selling price is subtracted from the selling price, the difference is
$39.

Selling Price − 40% of Selling Price = $39

Since the percent is based on the selling price, the selling price is
the base, or whole, and is therefore 100% of itself.

Solution: $100\% \times selling\ price = Selling\ price$
$40\% \times selling\ price = Markup$
$\overline{60\% \times selling\ price = Cost = \$39}$
$Selling\ price = \$39 \div 60\%$
$= \$39 \div .6 = \$65$

The lowest price at which he can sell the radio is $65. **Ans.**

Check: Selling Price − Markup = Cost
$65 − 40% of $65 = $65 − $26 = $39

▷ Exercise **3**   Written

1. Find the retailer's selling price in each of the following.
The rate of markup is based on the selling price.

	Cost	Markup	Selling Price			Cost	Markup	Selling Price
a	$15.51	45%	$28.20		d	$ 2.05	$37\frac{1}{2}\%$	
b	33.90	40%			e	54.60	40%	
c	10.53	35%			f	7.56	$33\frac{1}{3}\%$	

2. For how much must a retailer sell baseballs that cost him $.87 if he desires a markup of 42% on the selling price? $1.50

3. Stafford purchased ladies' scarves from a wholesaler for $2.37 each. He wishes to make a gross profit of 40% on the selling price. At what price must he sell each scarf in order to make this gross profit?

4. Day's Department Store bought place mats at $14.28 per dozen. At what price must each mat be sold to gain 32% on the retail price?

5. The Shoe Giant bought 1,500 pairs of shoes of the same style and quality for $9,000. At what price per pair should the store sell the shoes to gain $37\frac{1}{2}$% of the selling price?

6. Max the Clothier bought sport shirts at $40 per dozen, less 25% and 10%. At what price must each shirt be sold to make a gross profit of 40% on the retail price?

▸ **To find the price at which an article should be sold to cover the operating expenses, expressed as a percent, and yield a given rate of net profit.** When the rate of operating expenses and rate of net profit are given and both are based on the selling price, the selling price is found in two steps:

1. Add the percents representing the operating expenses and net profit. The sum represents the rate of gross profit.

2. Find the selling price by the method explained on page 416.

▸ **Exercise 4**   Written

1. Find the retailer's selling price in each of the following. The operating expenses and net profit are based on the selling price.

	Retailer's Cost	Operating Expenses	Desired Net Profit	Retailer's Selling Price
a	$41.73	27%	8%	$64.20
b	5.34	25%	15%	
c	25.90	34%	10%	
d	20.15	24%	14%	

2. A cabinet sink is billed to the U-Build-It-Store at $119. If the store's operating expenses amount to 20% of the sales, at what price must the sink be sold to make a net profit of 12% on the selling price? $175

3. Marx Hardware buys power saws at $29.70 each. If they compute their cost of doing business at 27% of sales, for how much must they sell each saw in order to make a profit of 7% of the selling price?

4. An electric dishwasher is billed to a dealer at $141. He allows his salesman a commission of 5% on sales and figures his overhead expenses at 25% of sales. At what price should he sell the dishwasher to gain a net profit of 10% on the selling price?

5. A store operator estimates his selling expenses to be 16%, other overhead expenses 10%, and net profit 6%, all based on the selling price. At what price must he sell goods that cost him $289 in order to cover expenses and make the desired net profit?

▶ REVIEW ASSIGNMENT **62 b**

1. a Find $3\frac{2}{3}\%$ of $225.
b $39.15 is 145% of what amount?

2. A dealer pays $9.75 for a table cloth. At what price should he sell it to make a profit of 35% on the selling price?

3. A store bought an ice cream freezer for $20, less 25% and 10%. The transportation charges amounted to $.75. The store desires a markup of 40% on the retail price. What should be the store's retail price for this freezer?

4. An end table costs a retailer $28.50. His expenses average 30% of his sales. At what price should he sell the table to realize a net profit of 10% on the selling price?

5. Blanchard bought a topcoat for $34.45, including a sales tax of 6%. What was the price of the topcoat before the tax was added?

6. By paying an invoice within the discount period to take advantage of a cash discount of 5%, a merchant settled the invoice with a cash payment of $741. What was the amount of the invoice?

7. At what price should a retailer mark an article so that he may receive $3.74 for it after allowing the customer a discount of 12%?

8. Craft's bank statement showed a balance of $1,342.66 on August 31. His checkbook balance on that date was $1,214.15. The outstanding checks were: No. 72, $15.88; No. 77, $38.45; No. 81, $25.18. Craft discovered that he had not entered in his checkbook a deposit of $49 made on August 21. Prepare a reconciliation statement.

SECTION 63

Pricing Goods—Cost Price Basis

As stated on page 413, merchants as a rule use the selling price as the base for the rate of markup or rate of gross profit. There are some, however, who use the cost price as the base.

PART 63a | Finding the Markup Rate and the Selling Price

To find the rate of markup, or rate of gross profit, based on the cost of one article or a quantity of the article. When the cost price is used as the base, the rate of markup or gross profit is found by dividing the markup or gross profit by the cost.

$$\text{Rate of Markup (Gross Profit)} = \frac{\text{Markup (Gross Profit)}}{\text{Cost}}$$

In the foregoing formula, the term "cost" refers to the total cost; that is, the invoice price, or cash price, plus the buying expenses.

Exercise 1   Written

1. In each of the following find the retailer's markup, rate of markup on cost, and rate of markup on selling price.

	Retailer's Cost	Retailer's Selling Price	Markup	Rate of Markup On Cost	Rate of Markup On Selling Price
a	$ 7.50	$ 9.00	$1.50	20%	$16\frac{2}{3}\%$
b	5.00	7.50			
c	12.00	15.00			
d	15.75	21.00			
e	6.75	11.25			
f	2.80	4.00			

2. The Superior Carpet Sales Co. bought carpeting for $1,350 and sold it for $2,250.

    a The markup was what percent of the cost?

    b The markup was what percent of the selling price?

3. The House of Birch bought a cabinet for $120, less 25%, and sold it for $144.

a What was the rate of markup based on the cost? 60%

b What was the rate of markup based on the selling price?
$$37\tfrac{1}{2}\%$$

4. The catalog price of a camera is $60. The Camera Shop buys one at the catalog price, less $33\tfrac{1}{3}\%$ and 10%, and sells it at the catalog price. The gain is what percent of the cost?

5. A tape recorder listed at $120 is bought by a dealer at the list price less 20% and 10%. If he sells the recorder at the same list price less 10%, what percent of the cost does he gain?

To find the price at which an article should be sold to yield a given rate of markup based on the cost. When the rate of markup is based on the cost, the selling price is calculated in two steps:

1. Find the amount of the markup. Since the rate of markup is based on the cost, the amount of the markup is found by multiplying the cost by the rate.

Rate of Markup × Cost = Markup

2. Find the selling price by adding the markup to the cost.

Cost + Markup = Selling Price

Example

A dealer buys an end table for $30. He knows that his markup must be 60% of the cost in order to cover expenses and provide a satisfactory net profit. What is the lowest price at which he can sell the table and still realize the desired rate of markup?

Solution:

(1) *60% of $30 = .6 × $30 = $18, markup*
(2) *Cost $30*
    Markup   18
    Selling price $48

The lowest price at which he can sell the table is $48.   **Ans.**

Check:

    100% of cost = Cost
    +60% of cost = Markup
    160% of cost = Selling price
    160% of $30 = $48, selling price

Exercise 2   Written

1. A dealer paid $46.50 for an office chair and $2.75 for the express charge. What is the lowest price at which he may sell the chair if he desires a 52% mark-up, based on the cost? $74.86

2. An equipment dealer marks his goods 56% above cost. At what price should he mark a water pump that cost him $58.15, plus a shipping charge of $4.35?

WHAT PRICE SHALL I MARK THE TOMATOES SO I CAN MAKE 33⅓% PROFIT?

3. Daw's Hardware buys electric drills at $22, less 25% and 10%, plus a shipping charge of $.75 on each drill. At what price should the drills be marked to gain $37\frac{1}{2}$% on the cost?

4. An outboard motor is billed to a dealer at $240, less $33\frac{1}{3}$% and 5%, plus a delivery charge of $6.75. What should be his selling price of the motor if he desires a markup of 40% on the cost?

5. Joe Sardo, fruit dealer, buys 30 crates of raspberries (12 baskets to the crate) at $6.09, delivered. He estimates that 12 baskets will spoil and will have to be thrown away. At what price per basket must he sell the remainder in order to make a profit of $33\frac{1}{3}$% on the cost of the 30 crates?

REVIEW ASSIGNMENT 63a

1. a Find the due date of a 75-day note dated May 13.

b What amount is $112\frac{1}{2}$% greater than $3.28?

c Find the number of days from June 27 to November 9.

d Find the interest at 6% on $625 for 74 days.

2. A golf cart that cost $15 sold for $23.25. The profit was what percent of the cost?

3. A dealer marks goods 56% above the gross cost. At what price, to the nearest cent, should he mark a pair of water skis costing $23.55, on which he had to pay express charges of $1.16?

4. On July 28, Filmore purchased 8 office desks at $119.50 each, less 15% and 10%; terms 2/10, n/30. For what amount should Filmore write a check in payment of these office desks on August 7?

5. An invoice for $635 was settled in full by a payment of $615.95 within 10 days from the date of the invoice. What percent of cash discount was allowed?

6. Keppler can buy some office furniture from a local dealer for $960, less 25% and 10%. An out-of-town company will sell him the same type of furniture for $910, less 30%. If he buys from the out-of-town firm, he must also pay transportation charges of $26.25. How much will Keppler save by taking the better of the two offers?

❯ **7.** Cross, a home furnishings dealer, needs a gross profit of 36% on the selling price in order to cover expenses and have a satisfactory net profit. At what price must he sell a blanket costing $7.84 in order to obtain the desired markup?

❯ **8.** An electric refrigerator is billed to a dealer at $324, less 25%. The dealer's overhead expenses amount to 20% of the sales. At what price must he sell the refrigerator in order to make a net profit of 8% on the selling price?

PART 63b | Special Problems

To find what rate of markup, based on cost, is equal to a given rate based on selling price. The rate of markup on cost which is equal to a given rate on selling price is found in this manner:

1. Express the markup and the cost as percents of the selling price.

2. Divide the markup percent by the cost percent.

Example

What rate of markup, based on the cost, is equal to a markup of 20% on the selling price?

Solution:

$$(1) \quad 100\% \text{ of selling price} = \text{Selling price}$$
$$\underline{- \ 20\% \text{ of selling price} = \text{Markup}}$$
$$80\% \text{ of selling price} = \text{Cost}$$

$$(2) \quad \text{Rate of markup on cost} = \frac{\text{Markup}}{\text{Cost}} = \frac{20\%}{80\%} = \frac{1}{4} = 25\% \quad \textbf{Ans.}$$

Exercise 3   Written

1. In each of the following, find what rate of markup, based on the cost, is equal to the stated rate of markup on the selling price. Express the result to the nearest tenth of a percent.

	Markup on S.P.	Markup on Cost		Markup on S.P.	Markup on Cost
a	30%	42.9%	e	27%	
b	35%		f	39%	
c	45%		g	53%	
d	55%		h	36%	

2. In order to make a gross profit of 40% of the selling price, an article should be marked up what percent of the cost? $66\frac{2}{3}\%$

3. What percent of the cost should an article be marked up so as to yield 25% markup on the selling price?

4. What rate of markup on cost is equal to a markup of $37\frac{1}{2}\%$ on selling price?

❯ **To find the cost price of an article when the selling price and the rate of markup on cost are known.** To find the cost price, first express the selling price as a percent of the cost. Then divide the selling price by that percent.

Example

The owner of the LaMode Dress Shop has to buy skirts for the line that sells for $9.97. He knows that his markup must be 65% of the cost in order to cover expenses and yield a satisfactory net profit. What is the highest price he can afford to pay for the skirts?

Solution: $100\% \times cost = Cost$
$\underline{+65\% \times cost = Markup}$
$165\% \times cost = Selling\ price = \$9.97$
$Cost = \$9.97 \div 165\%$
$= \$9.97 \div 1.65 = \$6.042 = \$6.04$

The highest price he can afford to pay is $6.04.   **Ans.**

Check: $6.04 + 65\% of $6.04 = $6.04 + $3.93 = $9.97

> ### Exercise **4**   Written

1. In each of the following find the highest price the retailer can afford to pay and still realize the indicated rate of markup on the cost.

	Retailer's Selling Price	Desired Markup	Highest Cost Price			Retailer's Selling Price	Desired Markup	Highest Cost Price
a	$18.75	56%	$12.02		d	$26.60	52%	
b	7.95	50%			e	75.95	55%	
c	12.96	60%			f	11.89	64%	

2. The owner of May's Slimline Shop has to buy suits for the line that sells for $47.79. What is the highest price he can pay for this line if his markup must be 62% of the cost? $29.50

3. A specialty store sells a line of earrings at $2.97 a pair. At what price does the store buy them if its markup on this line is 65% of the cost?

4. What does an article cost the merchant if he sells it for $89.25 and gains 70% on the cost?

5. What is the most that the Midtown Men's Shop should pay per dozen for wallets that retail for $5.89 each if the store must realize 55% markup on the cost?

REVIEW ASSIGNMENT **63 b**

1. A clothier buys sweaters at $50 a dozen and sells them at $7 each. Find the clothier's rate of gain on the cost.

2. A dealer marks goods at $62\frac{1}{2}$% above the gross cost. Find his marked price of an article costing $36 on which he had to pay $2 for transportation charges.

3. A gain of 22% on the selling price is equal to what percent gain on the cost, computed to the nearest tenth of a percent?

4. An article that cost $123.50 was sold for $98.80. What was the percent of loss, based on the cost?

5. During a special sale, a chair that had been marked $75 was sold for $62.50. What percent discount was allowed?

6. What single rate of discount is equal to the series 20%, $12\frac{1}{2}$%, and 5%?

7. A store uses the code word CUMBERLAND, with X as a repeater, in marking the cost price in code on its goods.

a Write the code mark for an article costing $14.49.

b What is the cost price of an article that bears the code mark UDEX?

❯ **8.** What is the highest price per pair a shoe dealer should pay for shoes that retail at $13.95 if he desires to make a profit of 55% on the cost?

GENERAL REVIEW

1. a Add $3\frac{5}{16}$, $6\frac{1}{8}$, $15\frac{3}{4}$, and $4\frac{1}{2}$.   **c** Divide $11\frac{2}{3}$ by $1\frac{3}{4}$.

b Subtract $8\frac{2}{3}$ from $15\frac{5}{12}$.   **d** Multiply $44\frac{1}{2}$ by $6\frac{1}{4}$.

e Express $\frac{8}{11}$ as a decimal to the nearest hundredth.

2. Prepare a line chart showing the following facts:

Average Daily Temperatures

March 1–March 7, 19—

| March 1 29° | March 3 15° | March 5 32° | March 7 34° |
| March 2 24° | March 4 35° | March 6 38° | |

3. Trotta is paid $2.72 an hour for a 40-hour week with time and one-half for overtime. During the week of April 2, he worked 45 hours. He claims three exemptions. By using the tables on pages 106 and 108, find the income tax and FICA tax that were deducted from Trotta's gross earnings for that week.

4. Wallace purchased a new car priced at $2,700. His old car was taken in trade for $900 as the down payment. The finance charge was 16% of the unpaid balance. The sum of the unpaid balance and the finance charge was paid in 24 equal monthly payments. What was the amount of each payment?

5. Platt purchased 200 shares of stock at a total cost of $7,065. After receiving a dividend of $1.50 per share, he sold the stock and received $6,715.86 after all expenses had been deducted. What was Platt's gain or loss from owning and selling this stock?

6. Provo bought a two-family house for $12,500, paying $4,500 in cash and giving a 6% mortgage for the balance. During the first year, he rented each apartment for $67.50 a month. In addition to the interest on the mortgage, other expenses for the year amounted to $717. What annual percent of net return did Provo earn on his cash investment?

7. A cash register costing $450 was estimated to have a service life of 10 years, at the end of which time it would have a trade-in value of $50. What would be the estimated value of this cash register after it had been used four years?

8. What is the tax rate per $1,000 if the tax is $568.35 on a piece of property assessed at $13,500?

9. The budget of Westbrook shows that the total amount to be raised by real estate taxes is $1,776,420. The total assessed valuation for Westbrook is $21,300,000. What will be the tax rate per $100 of assessed valuation?

10. On March 1, Mr. Rasker's gas meter read 39,800 cubic feet. On April 1, the meter reading was 47,400 cubic feet. The rate was $1.65 per 1,000 cubic feet. What was the amount of Mr. Rasker's gas bill for the month of March, including a 4% sales tax?

11. Dalrymple purchased a car for $2,850 and during the first year drove it 12,500 miles. His car expenses for the year were as follows: depreciation at 20% of the cost of the car; interest at 6% on the cost of the car; gasoline, oil, insurance, repairs, and other expenses, $571. Find the operating cost per mile, to the nearest tenth of a cent.

❯ **12.** The balance in Ralph Kilmer's checkbook on July 31 was $1,142.31. His July bank statement showed a balance of $1,147.86 on that date. Checks outstanding were: No. 134, $27.82; No. 141, $19.55; No. 144; $33.18. Kilmer found that he had entered a deposit of $35 in his checkbook a second time by mistake and that a deposit of $40 had not been received by the bank in time to be recorded on the bank statement. Prepare a reconciliation statement.

❯ **13.** A salesman receives a commission of 8%. What was the total of his sales on a day when his commission was $31?

❯ **14.** On April 1, King deposited $500 in the Union Savings Bank. He made an additional deposit of $350 on July 1. The bank pays 5% interest per year, compounded quarterly. Interest was added to King's account on July 1 and October 1.

   a What total amount did King have on deposit on October 1?
   b What total amount of interest did King's savings deposits earn for him during the two interest periods?

❯ **15.** The price of a camera is $28.86, which includes a sales tax of 4% on the regular retail price. What is the amount of the sales tax on this camera?

UNIT Fourteen

Problems of the Wholesaler

SECTION 64

Sales Invoice

Many of the purchases of a retailer are made from a wholesaler. The problems of the wholesaler are, for the most part, similar to those of the retailer. A few, however, are peculiar to the wholesaler or occur more often in a wholesale business. One of these problems involves the use of the sales invoice.

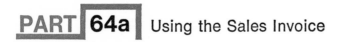

PART 64a   Using the Sales Invoice

Checking the invoice. Upon filling an order, the wholesaler mails the retailer an invoice, which is an itemized statement of the goods shipped. The illustration below shows the invoice that the wholesaler, Ferguson-Slade Company, sent to R. C. Hanson, a retailer.

			205 Linton Avenue Utica, New York 13503		
			FINEST FISHING EQUIPMENT		
	Jf FERGUSON-SLADE CO.				
SOLD TO	R.C. Hanson 64 East Johnson, St. Scranton, PA 18503		DATE March 5, 19--		
TERMS 2/10, n/30			SHIPPED VIA Parcel Post Prepaid		
75	Lures	1.28		96	00		
175	Leaders	.12		21	00		
25	Lines	1.65		41	25	158	25
	Less 20% and 10%					44	31
						113	94
	Parcel Post Prepaid and Charged					2	45
						116	39

Sales invoice

The invoice is made out on a typewriter, billing machine, or some form of automated equipment. At the same time, one or more additional copies are made by means of carbon paper. The original copy is sent to the customer. The carbon copies are used by the wholesaler for bookkeeping and other purposes. Before it is sent to the customer, the invoice is checked to see that all the amounts are correct.

Exercise 1 Written

1. Check the extensions, the trade discount, and the total amount of the invoice illustrated on page 428.

2. Find the amount of the check drawn in payment of the same invoice if the invoice is paid on March 15.

Cash discount is figured on the invoice price, or net price, after deducting the trade discounts. If freight, express, or other charges appear on the invoice, the cash discount is figured on the net amount before these charges are added.

Customer's account. The wholesaler keeps an account with each customer to show how much the customer owes. A common form of a customer's account, sometimes called a *self-balancing account*, is illustrated below. This account shows a record of the Ferguson-Slade Company's transactions with the customer, R. C. Hansen.

NAME	R. C. Hansen				
ADDRESS	64 East Johnson St., Scranton, Pa. 18503				
DATE	EXPLANATION	CHARGES	CREDITS	BALANCE	
19- - Mar. 1	Balance			250	00
5	2/10, n/30	116 39		366	39
8	Return		10 00	356	39
9			250 00	106	39
15			106 39	—	

Customer's account

Explanation of the R. C. Hansen account. On March 1, a new account page was started for R. C. Hansen. He owed $250 on that date, so $250 was entered in the "Balance" column of the account.

On March 5, the amount of the sales invoice of that date, $116.39, was entered in the "Charges" column; and the terms, 2/10, n/30, were entered in the "Explanation" column. The new balance was found by adding $116.39 to the preceding balance. The sum, $366.39, was entered in the "Balance" column.

On March 8, Mr. Hansen returned $10 of the merchandise on the invoice of March 5. The amount, $10, was entered in the "Credits" column; and "Return" was written in the "Explanation" column. The new balance, $356.39, was found by subtracting $10 from the preceding balance, $366.39.

On March 9, Mr. Hansen paid the balance owed on March 1, $250, less a cash discount of 2%. Upon making this payment, Mr. Hansen no longer owed the $250; so $250 was entered in the "Credits" column. The new balance, $106.39, was entered in the "Balance" column.

On March 15, Mr. Hansen paid the invoice of March 5, less a cash discount of 2%. The amount due on the invoice was $116.39 less the return of $10, or $106.39. Upon making this payment, Mr. Hansen no longer owed the $106.39; so $106.39 was entered in the "Credits" column. Since there was then no balance in the account, a short line was drawn in the "Balance" column.

Exercise **2**   Written

1. H. B. Keller, 608 Grand Street, is a customer of the Porter Wholesale Co. Rule up an account form like the one on page 429. In this account, make a record of the company's transactions with Mr. Keller as indicated by the following facts:

June 1. The balance of Mr. Keller's account was $357.80.

12. Sold goods to Mr. Keller, $185.40; terms, 30 days.

15. Mr. Keller returned $30 of the goods on the sale of May 12.

20. Mr. Keller paid the balance due on June 1, $357.80.

26. Sold goods to Mr. Keller, $275; terms, 30 days.

July 10. Mr. Keller paid the invoice of June 12 amounting to $185.40 less the $30 return of June 15.

2. In an account form like the one on page 429, record the following facts concerning the Mariano Supply Company's account with N. M. Cahill, a customer whose address is 466 Caplan Avenue.

July 1. The balance in Mr. Cahill's account was $233.75.

3. Mr. Cahill paid the July 1 balance, $233.75.

12. Sold goods to Mr. Cahill, $346.25; terms, 2/10, n/30.

20. Sold goods to Mr. Cahill, $184.75; terms, 2/10, n/30.

22. Mr. Cahill paid the invoice of July 12, $346.25.

25. Mr. Cahill returned $18.75 of the goods on the invoice of July 20.

REVIEW ASSIGNMENT **64** a

1. **a** Find the number of days from April 2 to September 15.
b Find the interest at 4% on $775 for 82 days.

2. A newspaper advertisement reads as follows: "Slacks that were $10.50, reduced to $7.95." What percent do you save, to the nearest whole percent, by buying at the sale price?

3. The tax rate in Loring is $5.2631 per $100 of assessed valuation. Find the tax on property assessed at $8,700.

4. A catalog lists an article at $30. The selling price is $26.25. What rate of trade discount is offered?

5. A markup of 40% on the selling price is equal to what rate of markup on the cost?

PART 64b   Aliquot Parts (concluded)

Aliquot parts of 100. In Section 6 you learned the method of multiplying by an aliquot part of $1. The same method can be used in multiplying by an aliquot part of 100.

For example, the first item listed in the invoice on page 428 is 75 Lures @ $1.28. The quantity 75 is $\frac{3}{4}$ of 100. In this case, 100 is the base; and $\frac{3}{4}$ is the fractional equivalent of 75 in relationship to the base.

Hence, to find the cost, we can multiply $1.28 by the fraction, $\frac{3}{4}$, and by the base, 100.

Example

Find the cost of 75 lures at $1.28.

Method 1	Method 2
$75 \times \$1.28 = ?$	$75 \times \$1.28 = ?$
Since $75 = \frac{3}{4}$ *of 100*	*Since* $75 = \frac{3}{4}$ *of 100*
the problem becomes	*the problem becomes*
$\frac{3}{4} \times 100 \times \$1.28 = ?$	$\frac{3}{4} \times 100 \times \$1.28 = ?$
$\frac{3}{4} \times \$1.28 = \$.96$	$100 \times \$1.28 = \$128$
$100 \times \$.96 = \$96$ **Ans.**	$\frac{3}{4} \times \$128 = \$96$ **Ans.**

The solutions show two methods of doing the multiplication:

Method 1. Multiply first by the fractional equivalent ($\frac{3}{4}$) and then by the base (100).

Method 2. Multiply first by the base (100) and then by the fractional equivalent ($\frac{3}{4}$).

When the multiplication is to be done mentally, the numbers can often be held in mind more easily by Method 1.

Table of aliquot parts of 100. The common aliquot parts of 100 are shown below.

$50 = \frac{1}{2}$	$12\frac{1}{2} = \frac{1}{8}$	$87\frac{1}{2} = \frac{7}{8}$	$16\frac{2}{3} = \frac{1}{6}$
$25 = \frac{1}{4}$	$37\frac{1}{2} = \frac{3}{8}$	$33\frac{1}{3} = \frac{1}{3}$	$83\frac{1}{3} = \frac{5}{6}$
$75 = \frac{3}{4}$	$62\frac{1}{2} = \frac{5}{8}$	$66\frac{2}{3} = \frac{2}{3}$	

Exercise 3　Oral

For each of the following, recite the solution and give the product. For example, the recited solution of the problem, 25 @ \$.48, would be one of the following:

25 equals $\frac{1}{4}$ of 100	25 equals $\frac{1}{4}$ of 100
$\frac{1}{4}$ times \$.48 equals \$.12	100 times \$.48 equals \$48
100 times \$.12 equals \$12	$\frac{1}{4}$ times \$48 equals \$12

	1.	2.	3.	4.
a	25 @ \$.36	$12\frac{1}{2}$ @ \$.64	$87\frac{1}{2}$ @ \$.80	$16\frac{2}{3}$ @ \$1.80
b	50 @ .64	$37\frac{1}{2}$ @ .40	$33\frac{1}{3}$ @ .66	$83\frac{1}{3}$ @ .18
c	75 @ .16	$12\frac{1}{2}$ @ .32	$66\frac{2}{3}$ @ .24	$66\frac{2}{3}$ @ .45
d	25 @ .96	$62\frac{1}{2}$ @ .72	$87\frac{1}{2}$ @ .64	$83\frac{1}{3}$ @ .54
e	75 @ .32	$37\frac{1}{2}$ @ .56	$33\frac{1}{3}$ @ .39	$16\frac{2}{3}$ @ 1.26

Exercise 4　Oral

For each of the following, recite the solution and give the product.

	1.	2.	3.	4.
a	25 @ \$2.80	$16\frac{2}{3}$ @ 72¢	$12\frac{1}{2}$ @ 96¢	$12\frac{1}{2}$ @ 72¢
b	$62\frac{1}{2}$ @ 88¢	50 @ \$2.46	25 @ \$1.28	$33\frac{1}{3}$ @ 69¢
c	$87\frac{1}{2}$ @ 32¢	$83\frac{1}{3}$ @ 42¢	$66\frac{2}{3}$ @ \$.24	$87\frac{1}{2}$ @ \$.40
d	$33\frac{1}{3}$ @ \$.45	$37\frac{1}{2}$ @ \$.64	$62\frac{1}{2}$ @ 56¢	75 @ 48¢
e	75 @ \$.44	$66\frac{2}{3}$ @ 60¢	50 @ \$1.88	$37\frac{1}{2}$ @ 32¢

Combinations of aliquot parts of 100. The quantity on an invoice is sometimes a combination of an aliquot part and the base.

For example, in the invoice on page 428, the quantity of the second item is 175. 175 is equal to 100 + 75. Since 75 is $\frac{3}{4}$ of 100, 175 is equal to 100 + $\frac{3}{4}$ of 100. The quantity is therefore equal to the base plus a fractional part of the base.

Some of the common combinations of aliquot parts of 100 are the following:

$$125 = 100 + \tfrac{1}{4} \text{ of } 100 \qquad 175 = 100 + \tfrac{3}{4} \text{ of } 100$$
$$150 = 100 + \tfrac{1}{2} \text{ of } 100 \qquad 250 = 200 + \tfrac{1}{2} \text{ of } 100$$

The method of multiplication by aliquot parts may be applied to multiplication by combinations of aliquot parts. Thus, the calculation of the cost of 175 leaders at \$.12 would be:

THAT'S ALL - NO MORE ALIQUOT PARTS!!

$$175 = 100 + \tfrac{3}{4} \text{ of } 100$$
$$100 \times \$.12 = \$12$$
$$\tfrac{3}{4} \times \$12 = \$9$$
$$\$12 + \$9 = \$21 \textbf{ Ans.}$$

Exercise 5   Oral

For each problem, recite the solution and give the product.

	1.	2.	3.	4.
a	125 @ \$.24	150 @ \$.42	250 @ 12¢	125 @ \$4.40
b	150 @ .22	125 @ .32	150 @ \$2.50	250 @ \$1.20
c	175 @ .16	250 @ .16	125 @ 28¢	150 @ \$6.10
d	250 @ .14	175 @ .44	150 @ \$4.50	125 @ \$1.60

REVIEW ASSIGNMENT 64 b

1. a What is the due date of a 90-day note dated May 29?

b Find the number of days from March 15 to July 20.

c Find the interest at 4% on \$740 for 85 days.

2. A dealer purchased 15 tennis rackets at \$17.50, less $33\tfrac{1}{3}\%$ and 10%. He sold them at the same list price less 10%. What was his markup on each tennis racket?

3. A store bought chocolate bars for \$1.92 a box (24 bars) and sold them for 10¢ a bar. What was the percent of markup based on the selling price?

4. A fruit dealer purchased a crate of melons, 3 dozen melons to the crate, for \$9.45. He sold the melons at 35¢ apiece. What was his rate of markup based on the cost?

5. A markup of 60% on the selling price is equal to what rate of markup on the cost?

SECTION 65

Promissory Notes and Bank Discount

The seller sometimes requires the buyer either to pay cash or to sign a promissory note for the amount of the purchase. If he accepts a note, he may keep it and collect the amount due at maturity, or he may sell it to his bank at any time before the maturity date.

PART 65a   Customer's Note

Marcus Building Company's note. Shown below is the 90-day, 6% note for $850 that the Marcus Building Company signed and gave to Gordon Fallon, wholesale dealer, for the purchase of construction equipment and supplies. The terms of the sale were: *90-day, 6% note.* The note serves as a written acknowledgment of the debt and fixes a definite time for its payment.

$ 850.00	WESTPORT, CONN. ___ August 1, ___ 19--
Ninety days	AFTER DATE ___ we ___ PROMISE TO PAY TO
THE ORDER OF ___ Gordon Fallon	
Eight Hundred Fifty — DOLLARS	
PAYABLE AT ___ Westport National Bank	
VALUE RECEIVED WITH INTEREST AT ___ 6 ___%	*Marcus Building Co.*
No. ___ 87 ___ DUE October 30, 19--	*L. D. Marcus, Pres.*

Interest-bearing note

Collection and payment of notes. A businessman usually collects payment of a note through his bank. The note shown above, for example, was collected by Gordon Fallon through the Trader's Commercial Bank in the following manner:

1. A few days before the due date, October 30, Fallon took the note to the Trader's Commercial Bank and indorsed it to the bank "for collection and credit."

2. The Trader's Commercial Bank immediately forwarded the note to the Westport National Bank, where the Marcus Building Company was a depositor and where the note was payable.

3. On October 30, the Westport National Bank charged the amount of the note and interest, $862.75, to the Marcus Building Company's checking account and remitted the amount to the Trader's Commercial Bank.

4. The Trader's Commercial Bank then credited the amount of the remittance to Fallon's checking account.

Exercise 1 Written

1. On February 10, Alger placed a customer's 60-day, 7% note for $780 with his bank for collection and credit. The bank collected the full amount due and credited it to Alger's checking account. How much was credited to the account? $789.10

2. Barone had a bank balance of $3,097.40 on May 6. On the next transaction, the bank paid Barone's 45-day, 6% note for $925 and charged the payment to his account. What was the balance of the account after this charge was made?

3. Flint's bank balance was $1,936.47. On the next transaction, the bank paid his 70-day, 4% note for $575 and charged it to Flint's account. What was the new balance of the account?

PART 65b Discounting a Note

Discounting a customer's interest-bearing note. If a merchant has a customer's note and is in need of money before the date of maturity, he may sell the note to his bank and receive cash for it.

If he does this, he is said to *discount* the note. The date on which he discounts it is the *date of discount.*

The bank will hold the note until the due date and then collect the maturity value from the maker. The time that the bank holds the note is the *term of discount.* It is the number of days from the date of discount to the date of maturity.

The bank gives the merchant the maturity value of the note less interest on the maturity value for the term of discount. This interest represents the bank's profit on the transaction and is called *bank discount.* The rate at which it is figured is the *discount rate.*

The amount the merchant receives for the note, which is the maturity value less the bank discount, is called the *proceeds.*

The steps in calculating the proceeds are as follows:

1. Find the date of maturity.

The date of the note plus the time specified in the note.

2. Find the value at maturity.

The face of the note plus interest on the face at the rate and for the time specified in the note.

3. Find the term of discount.

The number of days from the date of discount to the date of maturity.

4. Find the bank discount.

The interest at the discount rate on the value at maturity for the term of discount.

5. Find the proceeds.

The value at maturity less the bank discount.

Example

Krom Suppliers receive from C. R. Hanks the note illustrated below. On April 20, they discount the note at 6% at the Mechanics Exchange Bank. What are the proceeds received by Krom Suppliers on April 20?

$400 00   REVERE, IOWA *April 5* 19 - -

____*Sixty days*_____ AFTER DATE __*l*__ PROMISE TO PAY TO

THE ORDER OF __*Krom Suppliers*_____

Four hundred 00/00~~~~~~~~~~~~~~~~~~~ DOLLARS

PAYABLE AT *Revere National Bank*_____

WITH INTEREST AT _6_ %

No. _248_ Due _*June 4, 19 - -*_   *C. R. Hanks*

Solution

(1) *Date of maturity; 60 da. after April 5*   = *June 4*

(2) *Value at maturity*   = *$404.00*

Face of note	$400.00	
Int. on $400 for 60 da. @ 6%	4.00	
Value at maturity	$404.00	

(3) *Term of discount; April 20 to June 4*   = *45 da.*

(4) *Bank discount; int. on $404 for 45 da. @ 6%* = *$3.03*

(5) *Proceeds*   = *$400.97* **Ans.**

Value at maturity	$404.00
Bank discount	3.03
Proceeds	$400.97

Exercise 2   Written

1. Find the proceeds of each of the following notes.

	Face	Interest Rate	Date of Note	Time of Note	Discount Date	Discount Rate	
a	$ 840	6%	May 2	60 da.	May 22	6%	$842.74
b	1,860	6%	Jan. 20	30 da.	Jan. 30	6%	
c	480	6%	July 26	45 da.	Aug. 10	6%	
d	985	6%	Oct. 12	3 mo.	Oct. 24	6%	$986.45
e	1,450	6%	Mar. 28	2 mo.	Apr. 8	6%	
f	530	6%	Sept. 4	4 mo.	Oct. 6	6%	
g	720	4%	May 25	90 da.	June 4	6%	·$717.50
h	1,170	4%	June 25	60 da.	July 10	6%	
i	1,350	5%	Sept. 18	2 mo.	Oct. 9	6%	
j	875	5%	July 22	3 mo.	Aug. 13	6%	

2. On June 20, Conway discounted at his bank a 90-day promissory note for $1,200 which he had received from a customer. The note was dated June 2 and bore interest at the rate of 4% per year. The bank discount rate was 6%. How much did Conway receive as the proceeds of the note? $1,197.46

3. Gerard is the owner of a 3-month, 5% note, made in his favor for $1,800, and dated November 26. He discounts the note at 6% on January 17. How much does he receive for it?

REVIEW ASSIGNMENT 65 b

1. a Add: $2\frac{3}{5}$, $5\frac{1}{3}$, $4\frac{1}{2}$.   c Divide $6\frac{1}{9}$ by $3\frac{2}{3}$.
   b Subtract $12\frac{1}{4}$ from $22\frac{1}{5}$.   d What is $\frac{1}{2}$ of $\frac{1}{4}$?
   e Find the value of $\frac{1}{2} \times 16 \times 18$.
   f Find the interest at $4\frac{1}{2}\%$ on $730 for 95 days.

2. A two-month note dated May 14 is discounted at the bank on June 13. For how many days does the bank charge discount?

3. Find the proceeds of a 60-day note for $840 dated March 29, with interest at 5%, and discounted on April 8 at 6%.

4. Pencils that cost $11 a gross are sold at 10¢ each. Find the gain in percent on the cost, to the nearest whole percent.

5. A gift shop wishes to mark a clock so as to gain 45% on the selling price. What percent above cost, to the nearest tenth of a percent, should the store mark the clock?

6. A lamp that cost $15 has been selling for $25.50. If the same type of lamp costs $17.50 today, at what price should it be sold to make the same rate of profit on its cost?

▶ **7.** The Sentinel Hardware Store bought some lawn sprinklers at $9 each, less 20% and 10%, plus a transportation charge of 17¢. At what price each must the store sell these sprinklers in order to gain 30% on the selling price?

PART 65c Discounting a Note (continued)

Discounting a customer's non-interest-bearing note. The proceeds of a customer's non-interest-bearing note are figured in the same way as the proceeds of an interest-bearing note. In the case of a non-interest-bearing note, however, the value at maturity is the same as the face. Hence, in figuring the proceeds, it is not necessary to calculate the value at maturity.

Example

O'Day Brothers receive from Bruce K. Hallman the note illustrated below. On July 10 they discount the note at 6% at the Second National Bank. What are the proceeds received by O'Day Brothers on July 10?

$750.00   MARSTON, KANSAS June 20,   19—

Sixty days _____ AFTER DATE ____2____ PROMISE TO PAY TO

THE ORDER OF O'Day Brothers

Seven hundred fifty 00/100 _____ DOLLARS

PAYABLE AT Community State Bank

NO. 76   Bruce K. Hallman

Solutions

(1) Date of maturity; 60 days after June 20	= August 19
(2) Value at maturity; same as the face amount	= $750
(3) Term of discount; July 10 to August 19	= 40 days
(4) Bank discount; int. on $750 for 40 da. @ 6%	= $5
(5) Proceeds; $750 − $5	= $745 **Ans.**

Exercise **3**   Written

1. Find the proceeds of each of the following non-interest-bearing notes.

	Face	Date of Note	Time of Note	Discount Date	Discount Rate	
a	$975	Mar. 29	45 da.	Apr. 3	7%	$967.42
b	680	June 23	80 da.	June 27	7%	
c	550	Aug. 12	90 da.	Aug. 12	6%	
d	745	Mar. 1	4 mo.	Apr. 14	5%	
e	930	Sept. 5	3 mo.	Sept. 30	6%	
f	840	July 6	2 mo.	July 6	6%	

2. Levi Brent discounts Silas Webb's 90-day, non-interest-bearing note for $720 on November 12 at 6%. The date of the note is October 21. Find the proceeds of the note. $711.84

3. On June 3, Teal's bank balance was $546.23. On that date he discounted at the bank, at 5%, a customer's 60-day, non-interest-bearing note for $1,400, dated May 22. What was Teal's bank balance after the proceeds were credited to his account?

4. On April 15, Brody's bank account was overdrawn by $226.50. On that date he discounted at his bank a customer's 60-day, non-interest-bearing note for $840 dated April 10. The discount rate was 7%. What was his bank balance after the proceeds were added to his account?

REVIEW ASSIGNMENT **65**c

1. a Divide 75.6 by 180.   **c** What is $\frac{1}{2}$ of $\frac{1}{5}$?
   b Find 118% of 96.   **d** Multiply 28 by $2\frac{2}{7}$.
 e Find the value of $\frac{1}{2} \times 18 \times 12$.
 f Find the interest at $4\frac{1}{2}$% on $355 for 101 days.

2. A 60-day note dated May 18 is discounted on June 14. Find the length of time for which discount is charged.

3. Find the proceeds of a 6-month note for $1,500 dated February 20, with interest at 4%, and discounted July 18 at 6%.

4. Find the proceeds of a 90-day non-interest-bearing note for $1,800, dated April 14, and discounted May 18 at 6%.

5. Find the single discount that is equal to a series of discounts of 20%, 10%, and 5%.

6. Shoes that cost $9 per pair have been selling at $13.95. The same shoes now cost $10. At what price per pair should they now be sold to make the same rate of profit on the cost?

◖ **7.** Williamson wishes to receive $237.50 for an article after allowing the customer a discount of 5%. What should be the marked price of the article?

PART 65d   Discounting a Note (concluded)

Discounting one's own non-interest-bearing note. If a merchant is in need of additional cash but has no customers' notes to discount, he may discount his own non-interest-bearing note and receive the proceeds. In such cases, the date of discount is usually the same as the date of the note. The proceeds are figured in the same way as the proceeds of a customer's non-interest-bearing note.

Example

On September 16, Adam Burbank, a florist, presents to the Flagstaff Union Bank the note illustrated below. The bank discounts the note at 6%. Find the proceeds.

```
$ 500.00                      FLAGSTAFF, ARIZONA____September 16,____19__

  Ninety days                          ___AFTER DATE ____I____  PROMISE TO PAY

TO THE ORDER OF____Flagstaff Union Bank_____

  Five Hundred _____DOLLARS

PAYABLE AT_____

WITH INTEREST AT THE RATE OF____----__% PER ANNUM

NO.___342____  DUE December 15, 19--    Adam Burbank
```

Solution

(1) Date of maturity; 90 days after September 16   = Dec. 15
(2) Value at maturity; same as face amount   = $500
(3) Term of discount; Sept. 16 to Dec. 15   = 90 da.
(4) Bank discount; int. on $500 for 90 da. @ 6%   = $7.50
(5) Proceeds; $500 − $7.50   = $492.50   **Ans.**

Exercise 4   Written

1. Find the proceeds of each of the following non-interest-bearing notes discounted on the same day as the date of the note.

	Face	Date of Note	Time	Discount Rate	
a	$1,950	August 7	80 da.	6%	$1,924
b	1,380	April 22	120 da.	6%	
c	1,575	Sept. 15	4 mo.	6%	
d	1,150	Jan. 20	3 mo.	6%	

2. On March 8, the First Trust Company discounted H. B. Caplan's note for $900, dated March 8, payable in three months, without interest. The discount rate was 5%. What were the proceeds credited to Caplan's account? $888.50

3. On October 14, D. V. Weis received notice from his bank that his account was overdrawn $75.25. On that date he discounted at 7% his 75-day, non-interest-bearing note for $650. What was his bank balance after the proceeds were credited to his account?

REVIEW ASSIGNMENT 65 d

1. **a** What is $\frac{1}{3}$ of $\frac{1}{4}$?   **b** Multiply 35 by $\frac{22}{7}$.
c Find the value of $2 \times 3.14 \times 1\frac{1}{2}$.
d Add: 10.73, 902.1, 5.784, .296.
e What amount is 110% greater than $50?

2. On August 21, Wilkins discounted at his bank a customer's four-month note dated June 29. For how many days did the bank charge the bank discount?

3. On June 11, Hall discounted at his bank a 45-day note for $2,800 which he had received from a customer. The note was dated May 24 and bore interest at 5%. The bank charged 6% discount. What proceeds did Hall receive from discounting this note?

4. John Burk discounts Leo Fry's 3-month non-interest-bearing note for $1,345 on December 18 at 6%. The date of the note is October 15. Find the proceeds of this note.

5. On May 6, Clifton Shaw discounts at the State Bank his own 80-day non-interest-bearing note for $875 and receives credit for the proceeds. The discount rate is 6%.
    a What amount is credited to his account?
    b How much must he pay the bank on the due date of the note?

❯ **6.** By taking the 5% discount offered on a bill of goods, a merchant saved $13.67. What was the amount of the bill before the discount was deducted?

❯ **7.** Parisi, a stationer, buys photo albums at $48 a dozen less 25% and 10%. He estimates his cost of doing business at 34% of sales. At what price must he sell each album in order to make a net profit of 6% on the selling price?

GENERAL REVIEW

1. a Subtract 276.28 from 304.7.   **d** Subtract $6\frac{7}{8}$ from $15\frac{3}{4}$.

b Multiply 47.1 by 3.8.   **e** Multiply $5\frac{4}{9}$ by $1\frac{5}{7}$.

c Divide 162.97 by 37.9.   **f** Divide $13\frac{3}{4}$ by $1\frac{2}{3}$.

g Add: 74.08, 531.7, 2.008, 52.76.

h Add: $6\frac{7}{12}$, $7\frac{3}{4}$, $2\frac{1}{8}$, $11\frac{5}{6}$.

2. A builder purchased $37\frac{1}{2}$ acres of land for a building development. He divided the property into plots of $2\frac{1}{2}$ acres each. How many $2\frac{1}{2}$-acre plots did he have?

3. On a loan of $880 for 90 days the interest charge is $16.50. What rate of interest is charged on this loan?

4. A $1,000 bond earns interest at the annual rate of $5\frac{1}{2}$%, payable quarterly. What is the amount of interest earned on eight of these bonds each quarter?

5. Rhodes can purchase some stock at a total cost of $65 per share, including the broker's commission. The stock pays an annual dividend of 7% on the par value of $50 per share. What rate of income, to the nearest tenth of a percent, will Rhodes receive on his investment if he purchases this stock?

6. On a house that cost $16,000, the total annual ownership expenses average $990. What monthly rent must be charged for this house in order that the owner may receive a net income of $7\frac{1}{2}$% on his investment?

7. Phelps obtained a $4,000 mortgage loan on his house and agreed to repay the principal and interest in payments of $31 per month over a period of 20 years. What amount of money will he have paid for interest during the life of this mortgage?

8. Mr. Adams bought a car for $2,700. After using it for four years, he bought a new car for $3,300 by trading in the old car and paying $2,800 in cash. What was the amount of the average annual depreciation of the old car?

9. An article that cost $103.50 had to be sold for $82.80. What was the percent of loss, based on the cost?

10. Lyle can buy an air conditioner for his store from the Sachs Corporation for $1,700 less 10%, plus an installation charge of $45. He can buy a similar air conditioner from Drake Refrigeration Company for $1,900 less 15%, with no charge for installation. How much will Lyle save by taking the better of the two offers?

11. By borrowing $864 for 50 days at 7% interest, Mr. Barnet obtained the money needed to pay an invoice in cash and take advantage of a cash discount of $36. What net amount did he save by borrowing the money and taking the cash discount?

12. Finkle buys croquet sets for $4.50 each and sells each set for $7.20.

a What is his percent of markup on the cost?

b What is his percent of markup on the selling price?

13. Dell Trailer Sales purchased a tent trailer for $580 less 25%. Transportation charges on the purchase amounted to $40. At what price should the trailer be sold in order to make a gross profit of 28% on the total cost price?

14. Bedell insured his apartment building with three companies: Rome Insurance Company, $27,000; Ithaca Insurance Company, $21,000; Cranston Insurance Company, $12,000. A fire loss of $11,600 occurred. What amount should Bedell collect from each of these insurance companies?

◐ **15.** A car salesman, who receives 6% commission, earned $165 on the sale of a car. What was the selling price of the car?

◐ **16.** On January 2, Loren deposited $900 in the Fulton Savings Bank. He made an additional deposit of $750 on April 1. The bank pays 5% interest per year, compounded quarterly. Interest was added to Loren's account on April 1, July 1, and October 1. What total amount of interest did Loren's savings deposits earn for him during the three quarterly periods?

◐ **17.** How much money must be invested in securities that yield an annual return of 6% on the investment in order to receive an income of $1,500 per year?

◐ **18.** Wynant buys fishing rods from a wholesaler for $5.95 each. How much must he charge for each rod he sells in order to make a gross profit of 30% on the selling price?

SECTION 66

Bankruptcy of a Customer

Insolvency and bankruptcy. Occasionally a debtor firm finds itself unable to pay its debts as they fall due. In this condition the concern is said to be *insolvent*. The creditors or the business itself may request a court to declare the concern *bankrupt*. This the court may do by ordering the concern's property to be administered for the benefit of the creditors. A *trustee*, or *receiver*, then converts the property into cash and distributes it to the creditors.

Settlement in bankruptcy. The cash received by the trustee from the sale of the property is applied first to pay the cost of the bankruptcy proceedings and certain claims that have priority. The remainder is then divided among the creditors in proportion to their claims.

The percent to be paid each creditor is determined by dividing the total cash available by the total of the claims. Thus, if the total cash available is 30% of the total of the claims, each individual creditor will receive 30% of the amount that is owed to him.

Example

Andy Geer, owner of a repair shop, went into bankruptcy owing debts totaling $10,000. His assets were sold for $4,800 cash, and the cost of the bankruptcy proceedings was $550.

 a What percent of the creditors' claims can the trustee pay?
 b How many cents on the dollar will the creditors receive on their claims?
 c How much will the A-Z Wholesale Parts Company receive in settlement of its claim of $600?

Solution

(*a*) *Cash assets* $4,800 $\dfrac{\$\ 4,250}{\$10,000} = .425$

  Bankruptcy expenses   550
  Available for creditors $4,250 $= 42.5\%$ **Ans.**

(*b*) *.425* × *100¢* = *42.5¢* **Ans.**

(*c*) *.425* × *$600* = *$255.* **Ans.**

Exercise 1 Written

1. Shown below are the total debts and cash available for the creditors in four cases of bankruptcy. For each case, find what percent of the creditors' claims the trustee can pay.

HERE IS YOUR SHARE

TRUSTEE

	Total Debts	Cash Available
a	$18,500	$ 6,475 35%
b	12,175	4,870
c	23,400	15,210
d	36,800	12,512

2. Shown below are the total debts and the cash available for the creditors in four cases of bankruptcy. For each case, find the number of cents on the dollar that can be paid to the creditors on their claims.

	Total Debts	Cash Available			Total Debts	Cash Available
a	$19,550	$10,557 54¢	c		$ 9,860	$5,423
b	12,800	4,224	d		22,750	5,915

3. Grant, a bankrupt, owes debts totaling $8,365. The cash available for his creditors is $3,680.60. How many cents on the dollar will the creditors receive?

4. The trustee for the bankrupt firm of Burke & Clark is paying off the firm's debts at the rate of 45 cents on the dollar. How much should W. Snow receive on his claim of $2,304.20?

$1,036.89

5. The creditors of Perry, a bankrupt, are being paid their claims at the rate of 35.2 cents on the dollar. How much will Towne receive on a claim of $927.50?

6. The debts of Unger, a bankrupt, are being paid at the rate of 56.4 cents on the dollar. How much will be received by Rocco to whom Unger owes a debt of $2,645?

Exercise 2   Written

1. Rapp, a bankrupt, owed debts totaling $14,325. The cash available for his creditors was $8,595. How much would be paid to a creditor with a claim of $625? $375

2. Benton, a bankrupt, has liabilities of $16,500. The cash to be distributed among his creditors is $7,425. How much will be paid to a creditor whose claim is $3,300?

3. Caine went into bankruptcy owing a total of $24,680. The cash distributed to his creditors was $5,429.60. What amount was paid to a creditor to whom Caine owed $724?

4. Grover, a bankrupt, owed the following creditors:

C. K. Atwater & Co.............	$ 7,732
Dexter Corporation............	16,597
M. Gilbert & Sons	2,850
LaPorte and Ogden............	5,271

The cash distributed to these creditors was $8,761.50. How much was paid to M. Gilbert & Sons?

REVIEW ASSIGNMENT 66

1. a Multiply $\frac{22}{7}$ by 42.   **b** Divide $\frac{3}{4}$ by $\frac{1}{2}$.
c Find the value of $2 \times 3.14 \times 2\frac{1}{2}$.
d Find the interest on $175 for 103 days at 5%.

2. Benson went into bankruptcy owing a total of $13,420. The cash distributed to his creditors was $3,489.20. How many cents on the dollar did his creditors receive on their claims?

3. Powell, a bankrupt, owes debts totaling $11,750. The net cash available for his creditors is $5,052.50. What amount will be paid to a creditor with a claim of $1,080?

4. To the nearest tenth of a percent, what should be the percent markup on the cost of a dart game in order to realize a markup of 38% on the selling price?

5. A model airplane kit that cost $7.50 sold for $12. Today the same kit costs $8.75. At what price should it now be sold in order to make the same rate of profit on the cost?

6. On October 27, Weiss discounted a customer's 3-month, 6% note for $1,700, dated August 29. The bank discount rate was 5%. Find the net proceeds of the note.

▶ 7. An article costs a dealer $17.25. At what price must he sell it in order to make a markup of 25% on the selling price?

SECTION 67

The Commission Merchant

Commission merchants operate in the wholesale markets of large cities where they sell commodities for producers or buy commodities for manufacturers, processors, and wholesalers. The products commonly sold or purchased on these markets are fruits, vegetables, poultry, butter, cheese, and eggs. For his services in selling or purchasing, the commission merchant charges a commission.

PART 67a   Account Sales

Selling through a commission merchant. Farmers and other producers who are located some distance away from wholesale marketing centers often sell their products through commission merchants at these central markets.

When this is done, the seller, who is called the *principal*, ships his goods to the commission merchant on *consignment*. The commission merchant sells the goods for the best prices he can get, deducts his commission and any expenses he paid in making the sale, and pays the balance to the principal. In this way the producer does not have the burden of finding a market for his products.

To find the net proceeds of a sale of goods by a commission merchant. When a commission merchant sells goods for a principal, the total amount he receives for the goods is the *gross proceeds*. The amount he remits to the principal is called the *net proceeds*.

The net proceeds are found by subtracting the sum of the commission merchant's expenses and commission from the gross proceeds.

Gross Proceeds − Expenses and Commission = Net Proceeds

The merchant's rate of commission on a sale of goods is usually expressed as a percent of the gross proceeds, although sometimes it is a specified amount for each unit of goods sold.

Example

The Amelio Bros. Produce Company received from Vernon Bentley a consignment of 25 crates of lettuce and 30 crates of cauliflower. The company sold 25 crates of lettuce @ $1.80, 20 crates of cauliflower @ $3.20, and 10 crates of cauliflower @ $3.25. The company paid $7.10 for trucking expenses and charges 10% commission. What are the net proceeds the company should remit to Mr. Bentley?	**Solution**
	
	 Gross proceeds:
	 25 crates @ $1.80 $ 45.00
	 20 crates @ 3.20 64.00
	 10 crates @ 3.25 32.50
	 ————
	                 $141.50
	
	 Charges:
	  Trucking $ 7.10
	  Commission,
	  10% of $141.50 14.15 21.25
	 ———— ————
	 Net proceeds $120.25

After selling the goods, the commission merchant sends the principal a check for the net proceeds and a report called an *account sales*. The account sales shows the gross proceeds, the expenses, the commission, and the net proceeds.

The account sales that the Amelio Bros. Produce Company sent to Vernon Bentley is shown below.

Wholesale Dealers In Farm Products

Amelio Brothers
PRODUCE CO.

1246 FRONT AVENUE, NEWARK, N.J. 07102 _____ July 16,   19-- _____

Sales for the Account of __Vernon Bentley__

_____ Westlake, NJ 08359 _____

July	14		25 crates Lettuce		1	80		45	00
			20 crates Cauliflower		3	20		64	00
	15		10 crates Cauliflower		3	25		32	50
								141	50
			EXPRESS						
			FREIGHT						
			DRAYAGE						
			COMMISSION		14	15			
			RET'D EMPTIES						
			TRUCK		7	10		21	25
			Net Proceeds					120	25

Account sales

POULTRY FARM

NET PROCEEDS REMITTED TO THE FARMER

RETAILERS

Exercise 1   Written

1. Find the commission, the total charges, and the net proceeds in each of the following:

	Gross Proceeds	Commission		Other Charges	Total Charges	Net Proceeds
		Rate	Amount			
a	$ 742.60	8%	$59.41	$36.74	$96.15	$646.45
b	654.30	10%		18.23		
c	1,456.20	7%		58.25		
d	896.34	8%		23.08		

2. Bruso sends to a commission merchant a shipment of 100 dressed turkeys weighing a total of 1,850 lbs. The merchant sells the turkeys for 34 cents per pound; he deducts 10% commission and $18.72 for expenses. What proceeds should Bruso receive?
$547.38

3. A peach grower shipped to a commission merchant 3 carloads of peaches of 1,400 boxes each, to be sold on commission. The agent paid freight at 40 cents per box and total storage of $565. He then sold the peaches at $6.75 per box, charging 8% commission. Find the net proceeds.

4. A poultry farmer sent 12 cases of eggs (30 dozen to the case) to a commission merchant. The commission merchant sold the eggs at 46 cents a dozen. His charges were: trucking, $10.65; commission, 10%; other expenses, $3.75. How much should the commission merchant remit to the poultry farmer?

5. Groff bought 850 bags of potatoes at $2.40 and shipped them to a Detroit commission merchant. The commission merchant paid the freight, $382.65, and sold the potatoes for $2,847.50. He deducted the freight charges and 8% commission, and remitted the net proceeds to Groff. What was Groff's profit?

REVIEW ASSIGNMENT 67 a

1. **a** $\frac{5}{8} \times \frac{3}{4} = ?$.   **c** Multiply $2\frac{1}{2}$ by $3\frac{1}{2}$.
   b $\frac{5}{8} \div \frac{1}{2} = ?$.   **d** Divide 6 by $\frac{3}{4}$.
   e Find the value of $2 \times 3.14 \times 3\frac{1}{2}$.
   f Find the interest on $925 for 105 days at $4\frac{1}{2}\%$.

2. An apple grower shipped 350 boxes of apples to a commission merchant. The commission merchant sold the apples at $5.40 a box. He charged 8% for his commission and $56.85 for freight and storage expenses. What amount of money did the grower receive as net proceeds from this sale?

3. A fruit dealer purchased 10 crates of cantaloupes (36 to a crate) at $7.65. He paid $1.80 for delivery charges on the entire lot. At what price each should he sell the cantaloupes in order to make a gross profit of $33\frac{1}{3}\%$ of the total cost?

4. Find the proceeds of a 90-day non-interest-bearing note for $2,800, dated August 10, and discounted on October 11 at 6%.

5. Berger went into bankruptcy owing the following debts:

Earl Frasier................. $1,142.50
Knox Brothers.............. 2,416.84
Levitt & Grant............. 3,017.20
Horton, Incorporated........ 2,623.46

The cash distributed to these creditors was $3,864. What amount was paid to Earl Frasier?

▶ 6. **a** $9 is 28% less than what amount?
   b Express $.07\frac{1}{2}$ as a common fraction in lowest terms.

PART 67b Account Purchase

To find the gross cost of a purchase by a commission merchant. Some commission merchants act as buyers for firms that do not have the time or means for keeping informed about the sources of supply of goods they wish to purchase.

Upon receiving an order to buy, the commission merchant purchases the goods and ships them to the principal. The amount he pays for the goods is the *prime cost* to the principal. The *gross cost* to the principal is the prime cost plus the merchant's expenses and commission. If the commission is a percent, it is based on the prime cost.

Prime Cost + Expenses and Commission = Gross Cost

Example

R. Levitt, Inc. ordered H. O. Boice & Co. to purchase 2,000 lb. butter at 68¢ per lb., and 1,000 lb. cheese at 55¢ per lb. The company made the purchase, paid $33.60 for trucking charges, and charged 8% commission. Find the gross cost to R. Levitt, Inc.

Solution

Prime cost:
2,000 lb. @ 68¢   *$1,360.00*
1,000 lb. @ 55¢   *550.00*
                    —————————
                      $1,910.00

Charges:
  Trucking $33.60
  Commission,
    8% of
    $1,910 152.80   *186.40*
                       —————————
Gross cost   *$2,096.40*

The commission merchant sends the principal an *account purchase.* The account purchase shows the prime cost of each item, the charges paid by the commission merchant, the merchant's commission, and the total amount charged to the principal. The account purchase that H. O. Boice & Co. sent to R. Levitt, Inc. is shown below.

H.O. Boice & Co.
commission merchants   NEW YORK CITY

Purchased for Account of

R. Levitt Inc.
New Haven, CT 06510   November 10, 19--

19-- Nov. 10	2,000 lb. Butter @ 68¢ 1,000 lb. Cheese @ 55¢	1,360 00 550 00	1,910 00
	CHARGES		
	Trucking Commission 8%	33 60 152 80	186 40
	Total charged to your account		2,096 40

Account purchase

Exercise 2   Written

1. Find the commission, the total charges, and the gross cost in each of the following:

	Prime Cost	Commission		Other Charges	Total Charges	Gross Cost
		Rate	Amount			
a	$1,843.60	8%	$147.49	$52.34	$199.83	$2,043.43
b	731.50	10%		38.76		
c	1,354.75	7%		84.20		
d	823.64	9%		35.08		
e	1,574.56	10%		42.63		

2. L. M. Hopper, a milling firm, purchased through a commission merchant 3,000 bushels of corn at $1.65 a bushel. The merchant charged 7% commission, and the freight charges totaled $423.50. What was the gross cost of the corn? $5,720

3. Darwin bought 3,500 pounds of cocoa through a commission merchant at 46 cents per pound. The merchant charged 8% commission. Trucking and other expenses amounted to $56.70. What average total cost per pound did Darwin pay for the cocoa?

4. A commission merchant bought 425 bushels of apples for Herman at $2.60 per bushel and charged 10% commission. Freight, storage, and other expenses amounted to $79.60. Find Herman's average cost per bushel, to the nearest cent.

REVIEW ASSIGNMENT 67 b

1. a $\frac{3}{4} \times \frac{7}{8} = ?$.

   b $\frac{5}{6} \div \frac{1}{2} = ?$.

   c Divide 8 by $\frac{2}{3}$.

   d Multiply $4\frac{1}{2}$ by $2\frac{1}{2}$.

   e Find the interest at 3% on $675 for 130 days.

2. Barlow bought potatoes through a commission merchant. The merchant bought 200 bushels at $3.50, 240 bushels at $3.25, and 300 bushels at $3.10, and charged 8% commission on the purchase. Freight and other charges amounted to $87.65. What total amount did Barlow pay for the potatoes?

3. A farmer sent 650 boxes of apples to a commission merchant. The agent sold 300 boxes at $3.85 and the remainder at $3.70. He deducted 7% commission and $112.45 for freight and other expenses. Find the amount remitted to the farmer.

4. A fruit dealer buys 20 crates of blueberries (16 baskets to the crate) at $5.58 delivered. He estimates that 10 baskets will spoil and will have to be thrown away. At what price per basket must he sell the remainder in order to make a profit of $33\frac{1}{3}\%$ on the cost of the 20 crates?

5. Pullman gave you a 90-day, 6% note for $938, dated July 10. You discounted the note on August 6 at the bank at 6%. How much did you receive for the note?

➤ **6. a** Find $4\frac{1}{6}\%$ of $450.

b $12.60 is $\frac{7}{20}$ of what amount?

➤ **7.** A bankrupt firm paid its creditors 36% of what was due them. Freeman, one of the creditors, received $225. What was the original amount of Freeman's claim?

GENERAL REVIEW

1. a Add: $4\frac{1}{4}$, $2\frac{1}{3}$, $19\frac{1}{2}$, $8\frac{5}{8}$.

b Subtract $16\frac{1}{3}$ from $113\frac{1}{6}$.

c Multiply $56\frac{1}{3}$ by $9\frac{1}{4}$.

d Divide $12\frac{1}{4}$ by $5\frac{3}{4}$.

e Multiply 115.72 by 3.9.

f Divide 1,530.08 by 7.3.

g Express $\frac{11}{17}$ as a percent to the nearest tenth of a percent.

h Express $\frac{2}{7}$ as a decimal to the nearest hundredth.

2. A mini-bike can be bought for $139.95 cash or on the installment plan by paying $35 down and $10 a month for 12 months. What is the amount of the finance charge under the installment plan?

3. A catalog lists a camera at $37.50. What rate of discount should be allowed to make this camera cost the purchaser $30?

4. An invoice for $745 was fully settled by a payment of $722.65 within 10 days from the date of the invoice. What percent of cash discount was allowed?

5. Three months ago, Gould bought 60 shares of stock at $28\frac{1}{8}$ per share. The broker's commission was $21.88. Today, he sold the stock at $26\frac{3}{4}$ per share. The charge for the broker's commission and other expenses was $24.09. What was the amount of Gould's loss on this transaction?

6. The total net sales of a hobby shop for one year were $84,250. The cost of the goods sold was $52,235. The operating expenses amounted to $26,960. The net profit was what percent of the sales for the year?

7. At the Grand Furniture Store, the selling price marked on the price tag of a cushion sofa is $174.95. The store's cost of the sofa is 60% of the selling price. Write the cost of the sofa in code, using the code word CHARLESTON.

8. A watch that cost $12.50 sold for $20. The cost price recently advanced to $13.75. For how much must the watch now be sold in order to make the same rate of profit on the cost?

9. On July 14, Barnard bought goods invoiced at $1,650 with terms of 2/10, n/30. In order to pay the invoice on July 24 and deduct the discount, he borrowed the necessary amount for 20 days at 7%. What net amount did he save?

10. A fruit dealer bought 10 boxes of grapefruit (48 to a box) at $3.05 a box. He threw out 2 dozen that had spoiled and sold the remainder at 10¢ each. To the nearest whole percent, what rate of profit on selling price did he make on the entire transaction?

11. Brate offers to sell merchandise at $1,260, less 15% and 10%. Wells offers to sell similar merchandise for $965; terms 2/10, n/30. Assuming that the customer will pay cash for the goods, which is the better offer, and how much better?

12. A note for 90 days dated April 9 is discounted on May 15. Find the length of time for which discount is charged.

13. What is the bank discount on a $770, non-interest-bearing note that is discounted at 7% 40 days before it is due?

14. The debts of Rossi, a bankrupt, are being paid at the rate of 42.3¢ on the dollar. How much should Levine, a creditor, receive in settlement for a claim of $630?

▶ **15.** On May 1, Nelson's bank statement showed a balance of $342.17. His checkbook balance on that date was $267.08. A service charge of $2.15, a deposit of $25.50, and a canceled check for $15 had not been recorded in the checkbook. Checks were outstanding for $8.08, $36.22, and $22.44. Prepare a reconciliation statement.

▶ **16.** At a special sale, a table sold for $60 after a discount of 20% had been deducted. What was the former selling price?

▶ **17.** An article costs a retailer $20. At what price must he sell it to make a gross profit of 36% on the selling price?

▶ **18.** Wolfe bought 48 suits at $40 each and marked them to sell at a profit of 65% on the cost. At the end of the season he had 8 suits left. To what lowest price may he reduce each suit and still make a gross profit of 55% on the cost of the entire lot?

UNIT Fifteen

Problems of the Manufacturer

SECTION 68

Figuring Cost of Manufacturing

A manufacturer makes the articles he sells. In order to quote a selling price that will give a satisfactory profit, he must keep a record of his manufacturing costs.

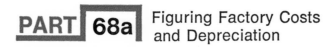

PART 68a Figuring Factory Costs and Depreciation

Elements of factory costs. The manufacturing costs are divided into three classes, as follows:

1. *Raw materials* consists of the costs of materials that are used in manufacturing and which become a part of the finished product.

2. *Direct labor* consists of the cost of the wages of all machine operators and other workmen who work directly upon the articles as they pass through the factory.

3. *Factory expense* or *factory overhead* consists of the cost of the salaries or wages of the factory superintendent, foremen, inspectors, and other factory employees who do not work directly on the manufactured product. Other expenses under this heading include those for rent of building, depreciation of machinery and equipment, heat, light, power, insurance, and factory supplies.

The sum of the costs of the raw materials, direct labor, and factory expense is the total *factory cost*.

Thus, if the costs in manufacturing 1,000 wooden salad bowl sets are $705 for raw materials, $1,832 for direct labor, and $443 for factory expense, the total factory cost is $2,980

Raw materials	$ 705
Direct labor	1,832
Factory expense	443
Total factory cost	$2,980

Exercise 1 Written

1. The records of the Wingate Manufacturing Company show the following manufacturing costs for the goods manufactured during the first quarter of the year: raw materials, $68,772; direct labor, $90,091; factory expense, $40,821. What was the total factory cost of the goods produced during the quarter?

2. For July the manufacturing costs of the Cardell-Ross Company were: raw materials, $22,371; direct labor, $31,643; factory expense, $6,357. What was the total factory cost?

3. The factory cost records of the Pedwear Corporation show the following costs for the quarter ending last December 31:

Raw materials cost $69,841.20.

Direct labor totaled $91,636.50.

Factory overhead consisted of: salaries and wages, $9,000; rent and royalties, $4,125; depreciation and repairs, $5,188; power, heat, and light, $1,427.10; factory supplies, $3,295.35; miscellaneous factory expense, $1,023.45.

a What was the total factory overhead for the quarter?

b What was the total factory cost?

4. In producing 75 dozen sweaters, the Sportingwear Mills incurred the following manufacturing expenses: material, $1,374.45; labor, $1,757.25; factory expense, $988.75. What was the average factory cost of each sweater, figured to the nearest cent?

Depreciation. One of the important items of factory expense is the depreciation of the machinery and equipment. The annual rate of depreciation is found by dividing the estimated average annual depreciation by the original cost.

Example

The estimated life of a machine costing $1,000 is four years. It can be sold as scrap for $100. What percent of the original cost should be included each year in the record of factory expense?

Solution

$1,000 *original cost*	$900 ÷ 4 = $225, *average*
− 100 *scrap value*	*annual depreciation*
$ 900 *total depreciation*	$225 ÷ $1,000 = 22½%. **Ans.**

Exercise 2 Written

1. Find the yearly depreciation and the yearly rate of depreciation for each of the following:

Property	Original Cost	Scrap or Resale Value	Esti- mated Life	Yearly Deprecia- tion	Rate of Deprecia- tion
a Power Drill	$1,800	$180	12 yrs.	$135	7.5%
b Lathe	500	30	10 yrs.		
c Motor	3,000	270	14 yrs.		
d Tools	1,200	48	8 yrs.		
e Conveyor	5,000	325	11 yrs.		
f Planing Machine	7,000	630	7 yrs.		

2. A cutting machine costing $1,800 decreases in value each year at the rate of 8% on the original cost. Find the estimated value of the machine at the end of the sixth year. $936

3. The annual depreciation of the metal-stamping machinery in the factory of the Alumalite Corporation is estimated at 9% of the original cost. What is the amount of the *monthly* depreciation of metal-stamping machinery that cost $4,800?

4. The Star Tool and Die Company purchases a grinding machine for $5,275. It estimates the service life will be 12 years and sets the annual depreciation rate at 7% of the original cost. How much does the company expect the machine will be worth at the end of the 12 years?

REVIEW ASSIGNMENT 68a

1. a $\frac{2}{3} \times \frac{4}{5} = ?$.   **c** Multiply $4\frac{1}{2}$ by $3\frac{1}{2}$.
  b Divide 6 by $\frac{2}{3}$.   **d** Divide $\frac{3}{8}$ by 4.
  e Change 60% to a common fraction in lowest terms.
  f Find the interest on $585 for 140 days at 5%.

2. In manufacturing 500 magazine racks, the costs were as follows: materials, $551.35; labor, $1,011.40; factory overhead, $112.25. Find the average factory cost of each rack.

3. A machine costing $3,225 is estimated to depreciate at the rate of 8% a year. Find the estimated value of the machine at the end of six years of use.

4. A commission merchant bought 550 bushels of apples for Titus at $3.45 per bushel, and charged 8% commission. Freight, storage, and other expenses amounted to $56.91. What was the average cost per bushel to Titus, to the nearest cent?

5. On August 20, George Ingalls discounts at 6% Fred Ewer's four-month non-interest-bearing note for $1,370, dated July 17. Find the proceeds of this note.

◆ **6. a** What number divided by $6\frac{1}{4}$ gives $4\frac{1}{2}$?
   b $21.60 is 35% more than what amount?

◆ **7.** Lamont, a bankrupt, paid his creditors 52% of the amount owed to them. Garfield, one of the creditors, received $220. What was the original amount of Garfield's claim?

PART 68b Distributing the Overhead

Apportionment of factory expenses. In order for the manufacturer to know the manufacturing costs by each department, it is necessary to apportion the factory expense, or overhead, among the various departments. The method of apportionment varies with the nature of the expense. The cost of rent, for example, is usually distributed in proportion to the floor space occupied by the departments.

Example

The factory of the Nemo Metal Products Company pays rent amounting to $8,000. Find the amount that should be apportioned to each of its 3 departments. Department A occupies 1,000 sq. ft. floor space; Department B, 2,500 sq. ft.; and Department C, 1,500 sq. ft.

Solution

$1,000 + 2,500 + 1,500 = 5,000$ sq. ft., total floor space

$Department\ A\ \dfrac{1,000}{5,000}$ or $\frac{1}{5}$ of $8,000 = $1,600

$Department\ B\ \dfrac{2,500}{5,000}$ or $\frac{1}{2}$ of $8,000 = $4,000

$Department\ C\ \dfrac{1,500}{5,000}$ or $\frac{3}{10}$ of $8,000 = \dfrac{$2,400}{$8,000}$

Taxes and insurance charges on the machinery and equipment are distributed on the basis of the value of these items in the various departments. The cost of the power for operating the machinery is apportioned on the basis of the horsepower of the various machine motors and the number of hours they are in operation. Other items of expense are apportioned in various ways, depending upon the preference of the particular factory.

Exercise 3   Written

1. The four factory departments of the Colonial Products Company occupy floor space as follows:

Wood Shop, 2,000 sq. ft. $1,600   Assembly Room, 2,200 sq. ft.
Metal Shop, 1,800 sq. ft.   Finishing Room, 1,500 sq. ft.

The annual rental cost of the factory building is $6,000 and is distributed on the basis of the floor space each department occupies. What amount should be charged annually to each department?

2. The DeMarco Corporation pays its plant manager $16,600 a year. This expense is distributed to the plant departments on the basis of the number of employees in each department. The number of employees is as follows:

Department W, 72   Department Y, 8
Department X, 24   Department Z, 56

What amount should be charged to each department?

3. Operation of the Ferrometal Products Company requires electric power costing $1,800, which is distributed on the basis of the number of horsepower-hours in each department. This number is found by multiplying the horsepower of each factory motor by the number of hours the motor is in operation. The horsepower-hours of each department are as follows:

Department A, 2,800   Department C, 7,000
Department B, 4,200

Find the amount to be charged to each department.

4. The yearly insurance on the machinery and equipment of the Bergman Manufacturing Company amounts to $880 and is

distributed in proportion to the valuation of the machinery and equipment in each department. This valuation is as follows:

Department K, $16,500   Department M, $13,200
Department L,   6,600

How much insurance should be charged to each department?

REVIEW ASSIGNMENT **68 b**

1. a Multiply 24 by $31\frac{1}{2}$.   **c** Subtract $1\frac{5}{16}$ from $3\frac{1}{8}$.
   b Divide $\frac{3}{4}$ by 5.   **d** Divide $5\frac{1}{2}$ by $3\frac{1}{7}$.
   e Change 80% to a common fraction in lowest terms.
   f Change $\frac{7}{20}$ to a percent.
   g Find the due date of a 75-day note dated July 12.
   h Find the interest at 4% on $370 for 150 days.

2. The four departments of a certain factory occupy floor space as follows:

Department A, 6,300 sq. ft.   Department C, 3,500 sq. ft.
Department B, 7,000 sq. ft.   Department D, 4,200 sq. ft.

The annual rental cost of the factory building, $18,900, is distributed on the basis of the floor space occupied. What amount should be charged to each department?

3. A piece of equipment cost $4,250. After 10 years of use it is expected to have a scrap value of $300. What will be the estimated value of this equipment after 7 years of use?

4. A commission merchant bought some produce for Babson for $973 and charged 8% commission on this purchase. Transportation, storage, and other expenses amounted to $31.65. Find the total cost of this produce to Babson.

5. On May 10, Hoyle discounted a customer's 3-month non-interest-bearing note for $1,920, dated March 12. The bank discount rate was 6%. Find the net proceeds Hoyle obtained on this note.

◗ **6. a** Express $.03\frac{1}{8}$ as a common fraction in lowest terms.
   b $37.50 is $\frac{2}{5}$ smaller than what amount?

◗ **7.** Washburn, owner of a men's clothing store, bought 50 suits at $45 each and marked them up 60% on the cost. At the end of the season he had 10 of the suits left. What is the lowest price to which he may reduce each of these 10 suits and still make a gross profit of 54% on the cost of the entire lot?

Pricing Manufactured Articles

A manufacturer must set the selling price of his product at a figure that will cover the manufacturing costs and all other expenses, and yield a reasonable net profit.

Manufacturer's gross profit. A manufacturer finds his gross profit on an article by subtracting the cost from the selling price.

Selling Price — Cost = Gross Profit

The term "cost" means the factory cost of the article.

Selling and administrative expenses, net profit. Besides the factory cost, a manufacturer has expenses for salesmen's salaries and commissions, advertising, office salaries, and other expenses connected with the general operation of the business.

These expenses, which are called the *selling and administrative expenses*, are subtracted from the gross profit to find the net profit.

Gross Profit — Selling and Administrative Expenses = Net Profit

The selling and administrative expenses are usually expressed as a percent of the net sales or selling price.

Exercise 1   Written

1. A handbag that the manufacturer sells for $3.80 has the following manufacturing costs: material, $1.04; labor, $1.29; factory overhead, $.41. What is the manufacturer's gross profit? $1.06

2. A manufacturer sells candlesticks at $5.50 a pair. His manufacturing costs per pair are: material, $1.48; labor, $1.34; overhead, $.83. He estimates the selling and administrative expenses at 24% of the selling price. Find the net profit per pair. 53¢

3. The cost of making a hardwood bookcase is as follows: material, $8.77; labor, $11.75; factory overhead, $6.08. The selling and administrative expense amounts to 20% of the selling price, $38. What is the rate of net profit, based on the selling price?

4. In filling an order for 4,000 pairs of shoes at $12 a pair, the manufacturing costs of the Mulvey and Richards Company were distributed as follows: material, $13,397.50; labor, $18,080.90; factory overhead, $4,610.40. The company estimates the selling and administrative expenses at 17% of net sales. What was the company's net profit on the order?

5. Adrian Fitzgerald, a manufacturer of men's jackets, incurred the following costs in completing an order for 300 jackets at $6.00 each: materials, $499.20; labor, $612.80; overhead, 20% of the combined cost of materials and labor. He estimates his selling and administrative expenses at 16% of net sales. What was his net profit on the order?

REVIEW ASSIGNMENT **69** a

1. a Multiply 82 by $21\frac{1}{2}$.   **c** Divide $\frac{5}{8}$ by 4.
   b Multiply $81\frac{1}{4}$ by $20\frac{1}{2}$.   **d** Divide $2\frac{3}{4}$ by $3\frac{1}{7}$.
   e Change 40% to a common fraction in lowest terms.
   f Change $\frac{9}{20}$ to a percent.
   g Find the due date of an 80-day note dated July 3.

2. In producing an order for 200 women's suits, the manufacturer's costs were as follows: material, $2,656.80; labor, $2,851.35; factory expense, $971.85. The suits were sold at $60 less 25% and 10%. Selling and general expense is figured at 13% of net sales. What percent of the sales price is the net profit?

3. The annual heating expense of a factory is $3,900. This expense is charged to the four departments in proportion to the floor space occupied, which is as follows:

Department A, 5,200 sq. ft.   Department C, 2,600 sq. ft.
Department B, 6,500 sq. ft.   Department D, 1,300 sq. ft.

Find the amount of expense to charge to each department.

4. Simpson, a bankrupt, owed the following creditors:

J. E. Cahill $1,332.11   R. C. Owen $2,140.25
L. P. Ives   1,052.74   E. A. Tripp   1,589.90

The cash distributed to these creditors was $2,323.70. What amount was paid to L. P. Ives?

PART 69b   Problems in Pricing

▶ **To find the manufacturer's selling price of an article.** The manufacturer's calculations in pricing a manufactured article are similar to those of the retailer in pricing merchandise purchased for resale.

Example

In the Ferris and Maitland factory, the manufacturing cost of a line of bowling shoes is $5.25 per pair. Selling and general administrative expenses average 20% of the firm's net sales. At what price should they sell the shoes to realize a net profit of 10% on the selling price?

Solution

The gross profit is 20% + 10%, or 30% of the selling price.

$$100\% \text{ of selling price } = \text{ Selling price}$$
$$\underline{- \ \ 30\% \text{ of selling price } = \text{ Gross profit}}$$
$$70\% \text{ of selling price } = \text{ Factory cost } = \$5.25$$
$$\text{Selling price } = \$5.25 \div 70\%$$
$$= \$5.25 \div .7 = \$7.50. \quad \textbf{Ans.}$$

Check: Selling Price − Gross Profit = Cost
$7.50 − 30% of $7.50 = $7.50 − $2.25 = $5.25

▶ **Exercise 2   Written**

1. The factory cost of a kitchen stove is $79.30. The manufacturer's selling and general administrative expense averages 21% of the selling price. At what price should the manufacturer sell the stove in order to make a net profit of 14% on the selling price? $122

2. The manufacturing cost of an electric appliance is as follows: material, $5.85; labor, $7.80; factory expense, $1.95. Selling and general management expense averages 25% of sales. The manufacturer wants to make a net profit of $8\frac{1}{3}$% on his sales. At what price should he sell each appliance?

3. In figuring the selling price of lamps, the Vanguard Company uses the following manufacturing costs per lamp: material, $1.79; labor, $2.47; factory overhead, $1.02. The company estimates the selling and management expenses at 22% of sales. At what price per dozen should the company sell the lamps to dealers in order to make a net profit of 14% on the selling price?

4. The factory cost of a certain exhaust fan is $34.84. The selling and general administrative expense per fan amounts to $15.10. The manufacturer sells each fan so as to make a net profit of 12% on the selling price.

    a The total of the factory cost and the selling and general administrative expense is what percent of the selling price?

    b What is the manufacturer's selling price of the fan?

5. The cost of manufacturing and selling a 45-piece set of dinnerware is as follows: material, $3.53; labor, $7.88; factory expense, $2.74; selling and general administrative expense, $5.20. If the manufacturer desires to realize 10% net profit on sales, at what price must he sell each set?

6. The combined cost of manufacturing and selling a golf bag is $7.14. At what price must the manufacturer sell each bag in order to make a net profit of 16% on the selling price?

◉   **To find the manufacturer's list price of an article, given the selling price and rate of trade discount.** The price quoted by a manufacturer is often a list price less a trade discount or discount series.

    In setting the list price, the manufacturer first finds his selling price or invoice price in the manner explained on page 464.

    He then finds the list price which will give that invoice price after subtracting the trade discounts.

    Example

    A manufacturer of table and chair sets wants to receive $25.80 for each set after allowing trade discounts of 25% and 20% from the list price. At what price should the manufacturer list the sets in his catalog?

Solution

$$100\% \text{ of list price} = List\ price$$
$$\underline{\ 25\% \text{ of list price} = 1st\ discount\ (25\%\ of\ 100\%)}$$
$$\ 75\% \text{ of list price} = 1st\ remainder$$
$$\underline{\ 15\% \text{ of list price} = 2d\ discount\ (20\%\ of\ 75\%)}$$
$$\ 60\% \text{ of list price} = Invoice\ price = \$25.80$$
$$List\ price = \$25.80 \div 60\%$$
$$= \$25.80 \div .6 = \$43. \quad \textbf{Ans.}$$

Check: $43 − 25%$ of $43 = $43 − $10.75 = $32.25, 1st remainder

    $32.25 − 20%$ of $32.25 = $32.25 − $6.45 = $25.80, invoice price

> **Exercise 3**   Written

   1. Find the price at which each of the following should be listed in the catalog of the Elektro Products Corporation.

	Article	Invoice Price	Trade Discount	List Price
a	Broiler	$25.35	35%	$39.00
b	Can opener	10.50	30%	
c	Power shop	98.10	40%	
d	Table saw	75.00	25% and 20%	$125.00
e	Waffle iron	23.40	20% and 10%	
f	Hand mixer	11.90	20% and 15%	

   2. A manufacturer wishes to receive $3.45 for a certain style of gloves after allowing the wholesaler a trade discount of 40%. What should be the manufacturer's catalog price of these gloves?

   3. A manufacturer wishes to list an article so that the invoice price will be $4.75 after allowing discounts of 20% and 5%. What should the list price be?

> REVIEW ASSIGNMENT **69 b**

   1. a What number multiplied by $\frac{2}{3}$ gives 330?
   b $24.42 is 165% of what amount?
   c What amount decreased by 15% of itself gives $21.25?

   2. A manufacturer desires a gross profit of 18% on the selling price. What should be his selling price of an article that costs $26.65 to manufacture?

   3. A manufacturer wishes to receive $22.75 for an article after allowing the wholesaler a trade discount of 35%. What should be the manufacturer's list price of this article?

   4. The factory cost of a certain article is $11.25. What should be the manufacturer's list price of this article in order that he may allow a trade discount of 25% and realize a gross profit of 20% on the factory cost?

   5. A bankrupt firm paid its creditors 31% of the amount of their claims. Rockwell, one of the creditors, received $292.64. What was the amount of Rockwell's original claim?

PART 69c Additional Trade Discount

▷   **To find the additional trade discount necessary to reduce the invoice price of an article to a lower price level.** The manufacturer sometimes finds it necessary to lower his selling price because of competition, lower production costs, or other reasons. This is done by allowing another discount in addition to the present discounts. The additional discount is based on the present invoice price.

Example

The Comako Company produces coffee percolators and sells them to dealers at $15, less 20% and 20%. To meet the prices of competitors, the company must reduce the invoice price to $8.40.

a What additional trade discount, expressed as a percent, must the company allow?

b What will be the new discount series?

Solution

(a)

$15.00 list price	*$9.60 present selling price*
3.00 1st disc. (20% of $15)	*8.40 new selling price*
$12.00 1st remainder	*$1.20 additional discount*
2.40 2d disc. (20% of $12)	$\frac{\$1.20}{\$9.60} = \frac{1}{8} = 12\frac{1}{2}\%.$ **Ans.**
$ 9.60 invoice price	

(b) *20%, 20%, and $12\frac{1}{2}$%.* **Ans.**

▷   **Exercise 4** Written

1. In each of the following, find the present selling price, the amount of the additional discount that must be offered, the rate of the additional discount, and the new discount series.

	List Price	Present Discounts	Present Selling Price	New Selling Price	Additional Discount Amount	Additional Discount Rate	New Discount Series
a	$30	40%	$18	$15.00	$3	$16\frac{2}{3}\%$	40%, $16\frac{2}{3}\%$
b	45	$33\frac{1}{3}\%$		24.00			
c	60	30%		31.50			
d	50	25, 20%		27.00			
e	90	20, $12\frac{1}{2}\%$		59.85			

2. The Faraday Manufacturing Company has been selling "Colorbrite" televisions at $540, less $33\frac{1}{3}\%$. To meet competition, the company decides to allow an additional discount so that the invoice price to the dealer may be $306. What additional discount, expressed as a percent, must the company offer?   15%

3. A faucet is listed in a manufacturer's catalog at $8.96, less 25%. Because of lower production costs, the manufacturer decides to reduce the invoice price to $5.88. What additional trade discount, expressed as a percent, should be allowed?

4. Golf clubs are listed at $125, less 20% and $12\frac{1}{2}\%$. The market price of the clubs drops to $70. What additional discount, expressed as a percent, must be offered to meet this price?

◉ REVIEW ASSIGNMENT **69** c

1. a $29.25 is 130% of what amount?
b $55\frac{5}{6}$ is what part greater than $33\frac{1}{2}$?
c What amount increased by $\frac{3}{8}$ of itself equals $5.28?
d $7.56 is 5% more than what amount?

2. The Roberts Furniture Company has been selling desks at $110 less 35%. To meet competition the company decides to allow a second discount so that the selling price will be $64.35. What additional rate of discount must the company offer?

3. The manufacturing cost of a tote bag is as follows: materials, $1.07; labor, $1.69; factory expense, $.32. Selling and administrative expenses are 20% of the selling price. At what price must the manufacturer sell the tote bag in order to make a net profit of 10% on the selling price?

4. A manufacturer wishes to receive $21.25 for an article after allowing a trade discount of $37\frac{1}{2}\%$. What should be his list price for this article?

5. What must be the catalog price of a rug that costs $38.25 to manufacture, so that the manufacturer may make a profit of 25% on the selling price after allowing a discount of 40%?

6. A profit of 60% on the cost is equivalent to what rate of profit on the selling price?

7. A dealer bought a filing cabinet for $68, less 15% and 10% and paid a freight charge of $2.38. At what price must he sell the filing cabinet in order to make a gross profit of 36% on the selling price?

GENERAL REVIEW

1. a Add: $5\frac{1}{4}$, $3\frac{1}{3}$, $18\frac{1}{2}$, $9\frac{5}{6}$.   **d** Divide $3\frac{2}{3}$ by $3\frac{1}{7}$.

b Subtract $1\frac{5}{8}$ from $3\frac{1}{4}$.   **e** Multiply 116.83 by 4.9.

c Multiply 56 by $41\frac{1}{2}$.   **f** Divide 1,760.64 by 8.4.

g Express .375 as a common fraction in lowest terms.

h Change $2\frac{1}{2}\%$ to a decimal.

2. Two business partners, Emmons and Finch, share profits in the ratio of 3 to 2, respectively. What percent of the profits does Finch receive?

3. For the first five months of the year, a salesman's monthly sales were $6,980, $7,540, $8,160, $7,800, and $7,145, respectively. What must be the amount of his sales for the sixth month in order that his monthly average for the six months may be $7,500?

4. Waterman, a factory worker, is paid $2.88 an hour for an 8-hour day with time and a half for overtime. During one week he worked the number of hours shown below. Find his gross earnings for that week.

Mon., 6; Tues., 8; Wed., 9; Thurs., $10\frac{1}{2}$; Fri., 8

5. Using the tables on pages 106 and 108, find the income tax and social security tax that should be deducted from the gross earnings of each of the two employees listed below.

	Gross Earnings	Exemptions
Robert Hoag	$129.32	4
Elmer Stewart	118.97	3

6. Markson, a salesman, is paid a salary of $90 a week and a commission of 2% of his net sales. Last week his gross sales were $1,883, and customer returns amounted to $58. His employer deducted $13.50 for withholding taxes, 4.8% for social security, and $2.35 for insurance. What amount of money did Markson receive as take-home pay last week?

7. Karpel receives a monthly salary of $550 and 5% commission on all sales. In addition, he receives a commission of $1\frac{1}{2}\%$ on all sales in excess of $7,000 in any single month. His sales in March amounted to $9,452. What were Karpel's total earnings for March?

8. Ruth Liston borrowed $250 from a consumer finance company and repaid it in 12 monthly payments of $23.35 each. What was the amount of the finance charge on this loan?

9. A washer can be purchased for $175 cash or on the install-ment plan by paying $19 down and $17 a month for 10 months. By what percent is the installment price greater than the cash price?

10. Bliss can purchase a record player for $150 cash or on the installment plan by paying 10% more. He chooses the installment plan and makes a down payment of $30. The balance will be paid in equal monthly payments of $6.75 each. How many months will it take him to pay for the record player?

11. Mitchell is offered a set of furniture on the installment plan for a total cost of $450 by paying 10% of this cost as a down payment and the balance in 15 equal monthly payments. What will be the amount of each monthly payment?

12. Doane can purchase an electric refrigerator for $450 cash, or for a down payment of $100 and $31.50 a month for 12 months. He has enough cash for the down payment and can borrow the balance at a bank for one year at a total interest cost of $21. How much will he save by borrowing and paying cash for the refriger-ator?

13. An investor pays $900 for a $1,000 bond bearing $4\frac{1}{2}\%$ in-terest. What is his rate of income on his investment?

14. Peters bought 80 shares of Inland Metals stock at $32\frac{1}{8}$. Brokerage on the transaction amounted to $30. The stock pays regular quarterly dividends of $32\frac{1}{2}$¢ per share. What annual rate of income does Peters receive on his investment?

▶ **15.** Hatt's checkbook balance on July 1 was $418.35. The bank statement he received on that date showed a balance of $552.41. A service charge of $1.80 and a deposit of $32.66 had not been recorded in the checkbook. Checks were outstanding for $72.17, $8.64, and $22.39. Prepare a reconciliation statement.

▶ **16.** A salesgirl is paid a salary of $75 per week and a commis-sion of 5% on all sales in excess of $800 in any single week. What must be the amount of her sales for one week in order that her total earnings for the week may be $90?

▶ **17.** Balian insured his house, valued at $12,000, for $8,000 under a policy which contained an 80% coinsurance clause. A fire loss of $2,100 occurred. What amount of money did Balian collect from the insurance company?

▶ **18.** A merchant saved $20.25 by taking a cash discount of 3%. What was the invoice price of the merchandise he purchased?

▶ **19.** A bicycle sold for $67.95 after a 10% discount had been deducted from its original price. What was its original price?

UNIT Sixteen

Business Ownership and Farm Problems

SECTION 70

Distributing Partnership Income

A business owned by one person is known as a *sole proprietorship*. A business owned by two or more persons is known as a *partnership*.

A sole proprietorship and partnership

When a partnership is formed, the partners usually sign a *partnership agreement* which states, among other things, the way in which the partners are to share the net income (net profit) or net loss.

PART 70a   Distributing Income in Proportion to Investments

Methods of distributing partnership net income (net profit). The common methods of distributing or sharing the income or loss are:

1. In proportion to investments.
2. In a fixed ratio.
3. By allowing interest to the partners on their investments.
4. By allowing salaries to the partners.
5. By combinations of two or more of these methods.

Net income distributed in proportion to investments. To find the amount a partner should receive when net income, or net profit, is shared in proportion to investments:

1. Express his investment, or capital, as a fractional part of the total capital of the partnership.
2. Multiply that fraction by the total partnership net income.

Example

Atwood and Wall entered into a partnership with investments of $35,000 and $25,000, respectively. They agree to share net income in proportion to their investments. At the end of the first year, the partnership books show a net income of $24,000.

Find each partner's share of the net income.

Solution : *Atwood's investment* $35,000
            Wall's investment   25,000
            Total investment $60,000

Atwood's share $= \dfrac{\$35,000}{\$60,000} \times \$24,000 = \frac{7}{12} \times \$24,000 = \$14,000$

Wall's share $\quad= \dfrac{\$25,000}{\$60,000} \times \$24,000 = \frac{5}{12} \times \$24,000 = \$10,000$

Check: $14,000 + $10,000 = $24,000, total net income

Exercise 1   Written

In each of the following problems, the net income is to be divided in proportion to the partners' investments.

1. Find how much of the net income each partner will receive.

	Investments			Net Income
	Partner A	Partner B	Partner C	
a	$ 5,500	$16,500		$ 9,600
	2,400	7,200		
b	16,000	24,000		8,000
c	52,000	28,000		12,400
d	13,500	24,000		10,750
e	9,000	27,000	$36,000	32,400
	4,050	12,150	16,200	
f	24,000	18,000	12,000	24,372
g	18,000	12,000	16,000	14,260

2. Kenny and Miner, partners, invested $12,000 and $20,000, respectively. The net profit for one year was $12,560. Find each partner's share of the net profit. $4,710; $7,850

3. In the partnership of McHugh & Shade, McHugh's investment is $27,500 and Shade's, $22,000. Their net income for the first year is $12,240. What is each partner's share?

4. The investments of three partners are: Lacey, $16,000; Roland, $20,000; Kaye, $24,000. For the year ended June 30 the firm's net sales were $160,400. The cost of goods sold was $98,700, and the operating expenses amounted to $40,340. How much of the net profit should each partner receive?

REVIEW ASSIGNMENT **70** a

1. a Express 1.375 as a percent.

b Express 16% as a common fraction.

c What percent is equal to 5/200?

d What is the due date of a 70-day note dated December 9?

e Find the number of days from May 7 to August 28.

2. Abel, Byers, and Cain invested $18,000, $24,000, and $30,000, respectively, in a retail business. Their gross profit for a year was $62,400, and their expenses were $39,600. They share net profits and losses in proportion to their investments. How much of the net profit should each partner receive?

3. A watch that formerly cost $37.50 sold for $60. Today the same watch costs $45. For how much must it now be sold to make the same rate of profit on the cost?

4. Benson went into bankruptcy owing a total of $12,310. The cash distributed to his creditors was $3,446.80. How many cents on the dollar did the creditors receive on their claims?

5. Colson shipped 500 boxes of apples to a commission merchant. The merchant sold 100 boxes at $3.80, 100 boxes at $3.50, and the remainder at $3.25. He charged Colson 35 cents per box commission. Freight, storage, and other charges amounted to $112.30. What average price per box, to the nearest cent, did Colson receive as net proceeds?

▶ **6.** It costs a manufacturer $31.50 to make a chair. At what price must he list the chair in his catalog to make a profit of 25% on the selling price after allowing a trade discount of 40%?

PART | 70b | Distributing Income by Other Methods

Net income distributed equally after allowing interest on investments. When the partners' investments are different, it is often the practice to allow each partner interest on his investment and then to divide the remainder of the net income equally.

Example

Ross Lowe and C. B. Ruff form a partnership, investing $24,000 and $16,000, respectively. They agree to allow each partner 6% interest on his investment and to divide the remainder of the net income equally. The net income for the first year is $12,400. Find each partner's share of the net income.

Solution

(1) *Lowe's interest (6% of $24,000)*   *$1,440*
    Ruff's interest (6% of $16,000)   *960*
    Total interest   *$2,400*

(2) *Net Income*   *$12,400*
    Interest   *2,400*
    Remainder   *$10,000*

(3) *$10,000 ÷ 2 = $5,000, each partner's share of remainder*

(4) *Lowe's interest*   *$1,440*   *Ruff's interest*   *$ 960*
    Share of remainder   *5,000*   *Share of remainder*   *5,000*
    Lowe's total share   *$6,440*   *Ruff's total share*   *$5,960*

Check: $6,440 + $5,960 = $12,400, total net income

Exercise 2   Written

1. Find each partner's share of the net income in each of the following. Interest at the given rate is allowed on the investments, and the remainder of the net income is divided equally.

	Investments			Inter-est	Net Income for the Year
	Partner A	Partner B	Partner C		
a	$15,000	$ 8,000		7%	$ 8,850
	4,670	4,180			
b	20,000	30,000	$25,000	6%	16,950
c	37,500	32,000	26,500	5%	23,775

2. Jonas and Heath formed a partnership with investments of $35,000 and $25,000, respectively. In the division of the net profit, each partner receives $7\frac{1}{2}\%$ annually on his investment. The remaining profit is divided equally. The net profit the first year was $15,700. What amount did each partner receive as his total share of the net profit? $8,225; $7,475.

3. Lloyd and Roth are partners with investments of $28,000 and $42,000, respectively. Each partner receives 8% annually on his investment and the remainder of the net income is divided equally between them. Last year the firm made a net income of $17,548. What is each partner's total share of this net income?

4. Kean, Mund, and Poal formed a partnership to conduct a retail business. They invested $8,500, $12,000, and $25,000, respectively. For the first year, their gross profit was $76,530, and their expenses were $50,550. Each partner received 6% on his investment, and the remaining net profit was shared equally. What was each partner's total share of the net profit?

Using other methods of distributing income. In some partnerships, profits are shared in a fixed ratio, such as 3 to 2. In others, each partner's share may be stated as a certain percent of the profits, such as 60% to one partner and 40% to the other. In still others, the partners may be granted salaries, with the remainder of the profit divided equally or on some other equitable basis.

Exercise 3   Written

1. Two business partners, Ahern and Baron, divide their profits in a ratio of 5 to 3 in favor of Ahern. Find the amount of each partner's share of a profit of $27,672.

The profit is divided into eight equal parts, with five of the parts going to Ahern and three to Baron.

2. During the last year, the partnership of Dennis and Farley had total sales of $274,690. Cost of goods sold was $221,760. The operating expenses were $36,280. Dennis received 45% of the net profit as his share for the year. What amount of money did he receive?

3. Hicks and O'Neil are partners with investments of $24,000 and $36,000, respectively. The partnership agreement provides that each partner is to receive a salary of $900 per month plus a share in the remainder of the profit that is in proportion to his investment. The profit for last year was $28,750. How much did each partner receive as his total share of the profit?

4. Nagel and Sabin formed a partnership, Nagel investing $18,000 and Sabin $26,000. It was agreed that each should receive 6% interest on his investment, Nagel a salary of $8,400 a year, Sabin a salary of $7,200 a year, and the remainder of the net income should be divided equally. The net income for the first year was $21,680. Find each partner's total share of the net income.

5. In the Knott-Young Company, Knott invested $20,000 and Young, $35,000. Out of the last year's profit of $23,520, Knott received a salary of $600 a month, and Young received a salary of $750 a month. The remainder of the profit was divided equally. What was each partner's total income from the business for the year?

REVIEW ASSIGNMENT **70 b**

1. a Multiply $80\frac{1}{4}$ by $21\frac{1}{2}$.   **b** Divide $8\frac{1}{3}$ by $12\frac{1}{2}$.

c What percent is equal to 2.5?

d Express 1.6% as a common fraction.

e What percent is equal to $3/400$?

2. Gleason and Dole invested $25,000 and $35,000, respectively, in a partnership. Out of the last year's profit of $16,490, each partner received 6% interest on his investment. The remainder of the profit was divided equally. Find each partner's total share of the profit.

3. Snyder, a bankrupt, owes a total of $7,120. The cash to be distributed to the creditors is $3,702.40. How many cents on the dollar will the creditors receive on their claims?

4. A commission merchant sold merchandise for Prescott for $3,468.50. The agent charged 8% for his commission and $189.68 for freight, storage, and other expenses. What amount did Prescott receive as net proceeds from the sale?

5. A commission merchant purchased merchandise for Brayton for $2,745 and charged 6% commission. Freight, storage, and other expenses amounted to $98.46. What was the total cost of this merchandise to Brayton?

6. Find the proceeds of a 90-day, non-interest-bearing note for $980, dated March 25, and discounted on April 8 at 5%.

● **7.** For how much must goods that cost $180 be sold to gain $16\frac{2}{3}\%$ of the selling price?

● **8.** A chair that had been selling for $80 less 30% was marked down to $49. What additional percent of discount was given?

SECTION 71

Distributing Corporation Income

Corporation charter. Many businesses operate as corporations. Authority to form a corporation is granted by the state in a charter or certificate of incorporation which is issued to the parties who wish to incorporate. The charter states the nature of the corporation's business and the par value and number of shares that may be issued.

Formation of a corporation. In the picture on page 472, you saw Weber's fruit store, a proprietorship, next to the Martin and Bard meat and grocery business, a partnership. Let's assume that these three men now decide to join together in a bigger enterprise.

Realizing that more capital will be required, Martin, Bard, and Weber make application to the secretary of state for a charter to incorporate for $100,000 under the name of Webmar Supermarket, Inc.

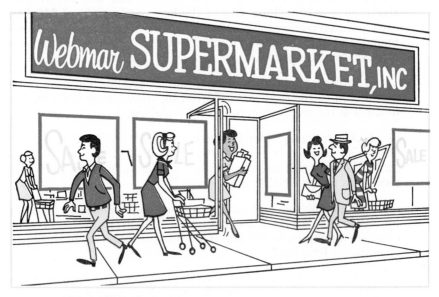

A corporation is formed

The capital stock of $100,000 is to be divided into 1,000 shares, each with a par value of $100. The three incorporators are to receive shares in exchange for the value of their present businesses as follows:

Martin, 250 shares; Bard, 200 shares; Weber, 150 shares. The 400 shares remaining are to be sold as additional cash is needed.

As soon as the corporation charter is received, the building is altered to include the space recently occupied by Mr. Weber.

At the end of the first year the corporation has sold all of its 1,000 shares. The financial condition of the company is shown by the following balance sheet.

WEBMAR SUPERMARKET, INC.
BALANCE SHEET, DECEMBER 31, 19—

Assets			Liabilities	
Cash	3,200		Accounts Payable	9,200
Accounts Receivable	2,900			
Merchandise Inventory	30,400		*Proprietorship*	
Supplies	600		Capital Stock	100,000
Office Equipment	2,400		Retained Earnings	12,500
Store Equipment	19,300			
Delivery Equipment	5,500			
Land and Buildings	57,400			
Total Assets	121,700		Total Liab. and Prop.	121,700

Retained earnings and dividends. At regular intervals, at least as often as once a year, the net income is calculated and recorded in an account called *retained earnings*.

In the foregoing balance sheet, the item "Retained Earnings" is shown in the proprietorship section and is seen to be $12,500.

The directors of the corporation then decide how much of the net income is to be distributed to the shareholders and how much is to be retained by the corporation for expansion and improvements or for future emergencies.

The net income distributed to the shareholders is called a *dividend*. The *rate of dividend* may be expressed as a percent of the par value of the shares or in terms of dollars and cents per share.

To find the rate of dividend. To find the rate of dividend, expressed in percent, divide the total dividend by the par value of the capital stock. To find the rate in dollars and cents per share, divide the dividend by the number of shares.

In the following examples and problems it is assumed that the corporation has sold all the shares of authorized stock.

Example

The Webmar Supermarket, Inc., with capital stock of $100,000 (1,000 shares at $100 par value per share) has a net income of $12,500 for the first year's operations. What rate of dividend may be declared if the entire net income is to be paid to the shareholders?

Solution

$12,500 ÷ $100,000 = .125 = 12.5%, rate expressed in percent

or

$12,500 ÷ 1,000 = $12.50, rate in dollars and cents per share

Exercise 1   Written

1. The Slater Corporation, whose capital stock amounts to $400,000, has a net income of $64,000 for one year. What rate of dividend, expressed in percent, may be declared if the entire net income is to be distributed to the shareholders? 16%

2. The capital stock of the Oakley Corporation amounts to $165,000. Last year the corporation paid a total dividend of $8,250 to the shareholders. What rate of dividend, expressed as a percent, was paid?

3. A corporation capitalized at $600,000 paid a total dividend of $39,000 for the year. What was the rate of dividend?

4. The capital of the Weaver Corporation consists of 4,500 shares of stock. The directors voted a dividend of $2,475. What was the rate of dividend in cents per share? 55¢

5. A bank, whose capital stock consists of 32,000 shares, paid a dividend of $43,200. What was the rate per share?

▶ **6.** The capital stock of the Vu-Easy Gage Company consists of $50,000 of preferred stock and $200,000 of common. The dividend rate on the preferred stock is fixed at 6%. If the company's net income for one year is $20,165, what is the largest even percent of dividend that can be paid on the common stock?

To find the total dividend and the amount retained in the retained earnings account. As a rule only a part of the net income is distributed to the shareholders. The remainder is retained by the corporation.

Example

The Webmar Supermarket, Inc., with capital stock of $100,000, has a net income of $12,500 for the first year's operations. The directors vote to pay a 5% dividend and to keep the remainder of the net income in the retained earnings account. Find (a) the total dividend and (b) the amount kept in the retained earnings account.

Solution

(a) *5% of $100,000 =*
    $5,000, total dividend

(b) *$12,500, net income*
    5,000, total dividend
    $ 7,500, kept in retained earnings

Exercise 2 Written

1. Find the missing amounts in each of the following:

	Capital Stock		Total Par Value	Net Income	Dividend		Kept in Retained Earnings Account
	Shares	Par Value			Rate	Total Paid	
a	3,000	$100	$300,000	$26,435	7%	$21,000	$5,435
b	1,700	100		14,784	5%		
c	1,350	100		12,623	6%		
d	2,225	100		23,509	8%		
e	5,250	50		22,425	6%		
f	3,450	25		7,234	4%		

2. The capital of the Bitner Corporation consists of 3,500 shares of stock, each with a par value of $100. Last year the corporation had a net income of $20,132.38. The directors voted to pay a dividend of $12,250 to the shareholders and to keep the remainder of the net income in the retained earnings account. What amount was kept in the retained earnings account? $7,882.38

3. Last year the Kolbey Corporation, which is capitalized at $650,000, earned a net income of $52,981.96. The directors declared a 7% dividend and voted to keep the remainder of the net income in the retained earnings account. What amount was kept in the retained earnings account?

4. A corporation, whose capital consists of 145,000 shares of stock, shows a net income of $35,052.35 for a certain period. The directors decide to declare a dividend of 18 cents a share and to keep the remainder of the net income in the retained earnings account. Find the amount to be kept in the retained earnings account. $8,952.35

5. The capital stock of a corporation consists of 3,000 shares of 5% preferred stock (par value $100 per share) and 60,000 shares of common stock ($10 par value per share). The corporation's net income for last year was $67,916.47. The directors declared the regular 5% dividend on the preferred stock and a dividend of 45¢ per share on the common. The remaining net income was kept in the retained earnings account. How much was kept in the retained earnings account?

Cooperatives. A cooperative is usually organized as a corporation with the shareholders as the patrons of the business. The net income is distributed among the shareholders in two parts:

(1) A dividend on the capital stock, which is distributed to each shareholder in proportion to the number of shares he owns.

(2) A patronage or participation dividend, which is distributed to each shareholder in proportion to the amount of business he has done with the cooperative.

Exercise **3**   Written

1. Alvin Hahn, a farmer, is a member of the Midland Farmers Cooperative Store. At the end of one year's operations, the directors of the cooperative declared a 6% dividend on the capital stock and a 5% patronage dividend on the sales to the store's customers.

Hahn owns five shares of the stock, each with a par value of $25; and he purchased $635.95 worth of goods from the cooperative during the year. What is the total dividend he should receive from the cooperative? $39.30

2. At the end of last year's operations, the Gainway Retail Cooperative declared a 5% dividend on the capital stock and a 3% participation dividend. Nora Beck owns fifteen shares of the capital stock, par value of each share $20; and she purchased $983.64 worth of merchandise from the cooperative last year. What total dividend should she receive?

3. K. C. Garma owns thirty-five shares of the local cooperative stock, par value of each share $5. He buys most of his groceries, gasoline, and oil from the cooperative. On December 31 the cooperative declared a 4% dividend on the capital stock and a 3% patronage dividend. What is the total dividend Garma should receive if his purchases from the cooperative totaled $1,624.33?

4. A cooperative retail store declared a $5\frac{1}{2}\%$ dividend on the capital stock and a 4% participation dividend on the net sales. How much dividend did Noah Dodd receive if he owned 25 shares of the cooperative stock (par value of each share $10) and if his purchases from the cooperative during the year amounted to $485?

REVIEW ASSIGNMENT 71

1. a Multiply $81\frac{1}{2}$ by $20\frac{1}{4}$. **b.** Divide $18\frac{3}{4}$ by $22\frac{1}{2}$.

c Express 1.4 as a percent.

d Express .16 as a common fraction in lowest terms.

e What percent is equal to $\frac{100}{125}$?

f What percent is equal to 4?

g Find the interest at 5% on $225 for 91 days.

2. The Keller Corporation, whose capital consists of 6,500 shares at $100 each, earned a net income of $62,328 last year. A dividend of 5% was paid to the shareholders and the remaining net income was kept in retained earnings. How much was kept in retained earnings?

3. Casey, Doyle, and Ford, with partnership investments of $14,000, $16,000, and $20,000, respectively, share profits and losses in proportion to their investments. How much of the net profit of $17,600 should each partner receive?

4. D. E. Corning borrowed $1,900 on his 7% note dated September 10. He paid the note and the interest on the following December 1. What total amount did he pay?

5. The assessed valuation of property in Pineville is $11,201,000. $807,710 is to be raised by taxation. What tax rate per $100 is required, to the nearest tenth of a cent?

6. On May 1, Hoy discounted at 6% at the bank his 90-day, non-interest-bearing note for $985. Find the proceeds of the note.

7. Graham gave you a 90-day, 5% note for $1,300, dated April 26. You discounted the note on May 4 at the bank at 6%. How much did you receive as net proceeds from the note?

8. At what price should a retailer mark an article in order that he may receive $42 for it after allowing an advertised discount of 20%?

9. The manufacturing cost of a cosmetic case is $10.44. Selling and administrative expenses are estimated at 18% of the selling price. What price should the manufacturer quote for the article in order to make a net income of 10% on the selling price?

Problems of the Farmer

Income statement of a farmer. The farmer is in the business of raising and selling farm products at a profit. He should keep a record of his sales and expenses and, at regular intervals, prepare an income statement to show the amount of his net income or net loss for the period.

An income statement of a farmer is shown below.

ANDREW JACOBSON

INCOME STATEMENT

FOR THE YEAR ENDED DECEMBER 31, 19 - -

Farm Income:

Livestock Sales	$12,139	
Produce Sales	4,895	
Merchandise Received for Produce	161	
Miscellaneous Income	329	
Total Farm Income		$17,524

Farm Expenses:

Labor Hired	$3,046	
Feed Purchased	2,149	
Seed	494	
Fertilizer	986	
Fuel and Oil (Farm Machinery)	520	
Repairs and Maintenance	255	
Taxes and Insurance	570	
Interest Expense	385	
Depreciation of Buildings	250	
Depreciation of Livestock	558	
Depreciation of Machinery and Equipment	736	
Miscellaneous Expense	347	
Total Farm Expenses		10,296
Net Farm Income		$ 7,228

Income statement of a farmer

Cost of production. When more than one product is raised, separate income and expense records are kept for each product.

Expenses for taxes, insurance, depreciation, and farm supplies used apply to the farm as a whole. They are in the nature of overhead expenses and must be distributed among the costs of the various products. The table below shows the percents used on one farm for distributing these expenses.

Production Expense	Poultry	Live-stock	Grain	Dairy Products
Taxes	5%	40%	40%	15%
Insurance	10%	50%	30%	10%
Depr. of Farm Equip.	5%	10%	60%	25%
Depr. of Farm Bldgs.	12%	60%	12%	16%
Farm Supplies Used	15%	50%	10%	25%

Exercise 1   Written

1. Kurt Ewing, a farmer, incurs the following costs in producing a crop of 280 bushels of potatoes: seed, $36.96; fertilizer, $49.42; man labor, $77.84; tractor labor, $14.79; spraying and dusting, $14.10; land use, $6.24; equipment, $25.29; other expenses, $4.96. What was Ewing's production cost per bushel?

2. Taxes on Angus Everett's farm are $480. His expense is distributed according to the percents in the table shown above. Find the amount that is charged to the cost of producing poultry, livestock, grain, and dairy products.

3. The depreciation of the buildings on Conrad Seward's farm amounts to $930. Using the percents in the table shown above, find the amount charged to the cost of producing poultry, livestock, grain, and dairy products.

4. In producing 1,560 bushels of corn on a 20-acre field, a farmer incurred the following expenses: seed, $55.74; fertilizer, $475.20; man labor, $342.10; tractor labor, $184.20; other equipment, $166.20; hired harvesting, $45.36; land use, $198.10; storing and selling, $74.70; interest, $8.60; other expenses, $33.20. He sold the entire crop at $1.16 a bushel.

   a What was his average net income per bushel?
   b What was his average net income per acre?

Farm management problems. Problems in farm management involve many applications of mathematics. They concern the profitable use of the land and equipment, costs and returns from the different farm enterprises, and the marketing of the products.

Exercise 2   Written

1. Seth Hunt was offered $2,500 in cash as rent of his farm. He decided, however, to rent the farm on a profit-sharing basis. During the season, his share of the expense was: seed, $335; fertilizer and lime, $715; repairs and replacements of tools and machinery, $255; miscellaneous expenses, $165. His share of the crop was sold for $4,910. How much did he gain or lose through renting his farm on a profit-sharing basis?

2. A farmer purchased 60 steers for fattening purposes, total purchase weight 40,230 lb., at $27.50 per cwt. At the end of 260 days he sold them at $33 per cwt., total sales weight 64,370 lb. Expenses were: feed, $5,820; labor, $678; interest, $620; buying and marketing expenses, $270; use of buildings and equipment, $630; general farm expenses, $372; miscellaneous expense, $75. What was his net income on the venture?

3. In June, the dairy herd of Harold Gustafson produced 25,000 pounds of milk. The average milkfat content of this milk was 4.8%, and the price of milkfat was 67 cents a pound. What was the value of the milkfat produced by the herd?

4. When milkfat is churned, there is an overrun of about 21%; that is, the weight of the butter produced is about 21% greater than the weight of the milkfat churned. How many pounds of butter can be produced from 7,500 pounds of milkfat?

5. If butter is worth 72¢ a pound, find the value of the butter produced from a mixture of 2,000 pounds of milk containing 4.6% milkfat, 1,500 pounds of milk containing 4.4% milkfat, and 800 pounds of cream containing 24% milkfat. The overrun is the same as in Problem 4.

6. On a 12-acre piece of land, Ole Johnson harvested 2,100 crates of cauliflower which he sold at an average price of $4.75 a crate. The growing costs totaled $4,964, and the harvesting and selling costs totaled $2,617. Find the average net income per acre.

Marketing farm products. A farmer may sell his products through a local cooperative marketing association, through a wholesaler or commission merchant, or directly to the processor or the consumer.

Exercise 3   Written

1. Jacob Flansberg harvested 930 boxes of pears from a 6-acre orchard. His costs were: growing, $1,682.34; harvesting, $1,568.20;

packing and hauling, $942.26. He sold the entire crop through a commission merchant for net proceeds of $5,375.40.

a What average price did he receive per box?

b What was his average net income per acre?

2. A grower shipped 1,500 crates of lettuce to a commission merchant. The agent sold the lettuce for $6,880. After deducting 8% commission and $479.60 for freight and other charges, the agent remitted the proceeds to the grower. What average price per crate did the grower receive for the lettuce?

3. During May, Roy Kem sent to the Co-op Association 8,950 pounds of milk testing 4.2% milkfat. The association paid $6.47 a hundred pounds for milk testing 4% milkfat or better, less 85¢ a hundred pounds for expenses. How much did Kem receive?

4. During one season a cooperative grain elevator handled 235,600 bushels of wheat. At the end of the season there was a profit of $12,805.80 to be distributed as a patronage dividend.

a Find the dividend in cents per bushel. (Carry the result correct to five decimal places.)

b Find the dividend paid to Gerald Alpert, who had delivered 3,265 bushels to the cooperative.

REVIEW ASSIGNMENT **72**

1. Lind, a farmer, incurs the following costs in producing a crop of 250 bushels of tomatoes: plants, $77.15; fertilizer, $81.60; labor, $60.70; spraying, $40.35; equipment, $65.80; other expenses, $14.40. What was the production cost per bushel?

2. Last year, Bradley's weekly earnings averaged $120. The year before, they averaged $108. By what percent, to the nearest whole percent, did his earnings increase or decrease?

3. Total sales of the Williams Company increased to $150,000 from $125,000 the year before. With the same percent of growth, what total sales can the company expect for next year?

4. Dealer A offers a rug for $450, less $33\frac{1}{3}\%$ and 20%. Dealer B offers a rug of equal value for $500, less 30%, 20%, and 10%. Which is the better offer and how much better?

5. Gilbert had a bank balance of $1,341.16 on May 17. On the next transaction, the bank paid his 50-day, 7% note for $635 and charged the payment to his account. What was the new balance of Gilbert's bank account?

GENERAL REVIEW

1. a Add $9\frac{2}{3}$, $12\frac{5}{6}$, $5\frac{4}{9}$, $11\frac{1}{2}$.

    d Divide $12\frac{1}{4}$ by $5\frac{3}{5}$.

  b Subtract $1\frac{9}{16}$ from $3\frac{1}{4}$.

    e Multiply 265.1 by 10.4.

  c Multiply $76\frac{1}{3}$ by $6\frac{1}{4}$.

    f Divide 30.732 by 118.2.

g Express $\frac{3}{20}$ as a percent.

h Change .625 to a common fraction in lowest terms.

i Express .029 as a percent.

j Change $4\frac{1}{2}\%$ to a decimal.

2. The balance on Tyler's bank statement was $481.63. His checkbook balance was $361.16. The bank had deducted a service charge of $1.72. Checks for $41.82, $72.15, and $8.22 were outstanding. Prepare a reconciliation statement.

3. For the first 10 weeks of the year, a salesman's average sales were $1,231 a week. For the next 3 weeks, his sales were $991, $1,047, and $1,278, respectively. What were his average weekly sales for these 13 weeks?

4. Lurie paid a total of $1,702 for 40 shares of stock. He kept the stock three years during which time he received regular quarterly dividends of $.45 per share. He then sold the stock and received $1,621 after all expenses had been deducted. What was Lurie's net gain from owning and selling this stock?

5. Deyo started on an automobile trip at 9:15 a.m. He drove 187 miles and arrived at his destination at 2:45 p.m. On the way he spent a total of one hour and fifteen minutes for lunch and buying gasoline. Find the average speed that he traveled in miles per hour, for the actual driving time.

6. On March 1, Mr. Aiken's gas meter read 89,900 cubic feet. On April 1 it read 101,200 cubic feet. At the rate of 17¢ per 100 cubic feet, what is the amount of Mr. Aiken's gas bill for the month of March, including a sales tax of 5%?

7. Earl Mossman purchased for $18,000 the home he had been renting at $180 a month. He withdrew $6,000 from a savings account that was paying interest at 5% per year. With this amount as a down payment, he gave a 7% mortgage for the balance of the purchase price. In addition to the interest on the mortgage and the loss of interest on the cash investment, annual expenses for taxes, insurance, repairs, depreciation, and miscellaneous items are estimated at $1,180. How much does Mr. Mossman save or lose annually by buying the home instead of renting it?

8. The total assessed valuation of taxable property in a certain town is $11,340,000. The tax to be raised for the town budget is $829,180.80. What tax rate per $1,000 will need to be levied to raise this tax?

9. Parr can buy some equipment for his store from Wolfe Bros. for $1,100, less 10% and 10%. The Dell Company offers the same type of equipment for $1,200, less 25%; terms 2/10, n/60. Parr is prepared to pay cash for this equipment. How much will he save by accepting the better of the two offers?

10. On an invoice amounting to $1,240, Hopkins is offered a choice of 90 days credit or a 5% discount for cash. How much would he save by borrowing the needed amount for 90 days at 6% and paying the invoice in cash?

11. Emerson, Farley, and Murray invested $32,000, $28,000, and $20,000, respectively, in a partnership. Profits are divided in proportion to the partners' investments. What percent of the profits does Farley receive?

12. Gayton purchased a shipment of goods amounting to $2,142 and sold it for $2,437. Operating expenses connected with this shipment amounted to $413. What was the amount of Gayton's net loss on the transaction?

13. What is the highest price a store can pay for ladies' handbags that retail for $8.75 each, if the store must have a markup of 44% of the selling price?

14. A commission merchant sold some produce for Morrison for $1,761.20. The agent's commission was 8%. Other expenses connected with the sale were: freight, $92.48; storage, $67.25; miscellaneous expenses, $8.66. What amount did Morrison receive as net proceeds from this sale?

15. A fruit dealer buys 20 crates of strawberries (24 baskets to the crate) at $13.50 a crate. Spoilage is estimated at 5%. At what price per basket, to the nearest cent, must he sell the remainder to gain $33\frac{1}{3}$% of the cost of the 20 crates?

16. A dealer bought 15 crates of lettuce, 2 dozen heads to the crate, at $2.45 per crate. Twenty heads spoiled and had to be thrown away. The dealer sold the remaining heads at 2 for 29 cents. What rate of gross profit, based on the selling price, did he make on the entire transaction, to the nearest tenth of a percent?

17. Cyr, a retailer, bought 40 blankets at $15 each, less 30%. He sold 20 at $18.50, 15 at $16, and the remainder at $14. Operating expenses are estimated at 33% of the selling price. What average net profit per blanket did Cyr make on the entire transaction?

18. In the Peerless Products Company, Bell invested $35,000, Clark $30,000, and Grant $25,000. The net income last year was $43,620. Out of this net income each partner was allowed 5% interest on his original investment, plus a salary of $850 a month. The remainder of the net income was divided equally among the partners. How much was Bell's total share of the net income?

19. The monthly rent of a department store is $3,600. This expense is distributed over four departments on the basis of the floor space each department occupies, which is as follows:

Department A, 3,000 sq. ft.　　　　Department C, 2,400 sq. ft.

Department B, 1,000 sq. ft.　　　　Department D, 1,600 sq. ft.

What amount should be charged to each department?

❯ **20.** On April 30, Eric Mull's checkbook balance was $914.02· On the same date the bank statement showed a balance of $809.30. The following checks were outstanding: No. 52, $21.48; No. 58, $17.55. The statement showed that $18.75 had been deducted for a U.S. Savings Bond purchased for him by the bank. A deposit of $125 had been mailed to the bank too late to be recorded on the bank statement. Prepare a reconciliation statement.

❯ **21.** Elting deposited $850 in the Federal Savings Bank on January 2 and $475 on the following July 1. The bank pays 4% interest per year, compounded quarterly. Interest was added to Elting's account on April 1, July 1, and October 1. What total amount did Elting have on deposit on October 1?

❯ **22.** A dealer bought a door chime for $28 less 25% and 10%. The express charge amounted to $.60. At what price must he sell the chime to make a gross profit of 35% of the selling price?

❯ **23.** Boyer, a hardware dealer, bought a weather vane for $32, less 25%. In addition he paid a transportation charge of $1.16. His operating expenses average 24% of sales. At what price should he sell the weather vane in order to make a net profit of 8% on the selling price?

❯ **24.** An aquarium outfit sold for $43.75 after a markup of 40% of the original cost had been added. What was the original cost of this aquarium outfit?

❯ **25.** A department store purchased 50 beach umbrellas at $4.35 each. After the umbrellas had been marked up 60% on the cost, 40 were sold. To the nearest cent, what should be the selling price of each of the remaining umbrellas in order that the store's net profit will be 50% of the cost of the entire lot?

❯ **26.** An article is listed at $50 less 20%. What additional percent of discount must be given to reduce its price to $34?

UNIT Seventeen

Everyday Measurements

SECTION 73

Denominate Numbers

Tables of denominate numbers. Some of the most commonly used tables of measurement are given below.

Linear Measure

12 inches (in.) = 1 foot (ft.)	$16\frac{1}{2}$ feet = 1 rod
3 feet = 1 yard (yd.)	320 rods = 1 mile (mi.)
$5\frac{1}{2}$ yards = 1 rod (rd.)	5,280 feet = 1 mile

Square Measure

144 sq. in. = 1 sq. ft.	160 sq. rd. = 1 acre (A)
9 sq. ft. = 1 sq. yd.	640 acres = 1 sq. mi. or section
$30\frac{1}{4}$ sq. yd. = 1 sq. rd.	36 sq. mi. = 1 township

Cubic Measure

1,728 cubic inches (cu. in.) = 1 cubic foot (cu. ft.)
27 cubic feet = 1 cubic yard (cu. yd.)
128 cubic feet = 1 cord of wood
1 cubic foot = $7\frac{1}{2}$ gallons

Dry Measure

2 pints = 1 quart
8 quarts = 1 peck (pk.)
4 pecks = 1 bushel (bu.)

Liquid Measure

4 gills (gi.) = 1 pint (pt.)
2 pints = 1 quart (qt.)
4 quarts = 1 gallon (gal.)

Avoirdupois Weight

16 ounces = 1 pound (lb.)
100 pounds = 1 hundred-
weight (cwt.)
2,000 pounds = 1 ton (T)

Time Measure

60 seconds (sec.) = 1 minute (min.)
60 minutes = 1 hour (hr.)
24 hours = 1 day

To change a denominate number to units of lower or higher denomination. A denominate number is changed to units of lower denomination by multiplication. Thus, 3 ft. = 3 × 12 in. = 36 in.

A denominate number is changed to units of higher denomination by division. Thus, 36 in. = 36 ÷ 12 = 3 ft.

Examples

1. Change 5 yd. 2 ft. 4 in. to inches.	2. Change 208 inches to yards, feet, and inches.

<table>
<tr><th>Solution</th><th>Solution</th></tr>
<tr><td>

5×3 ft. $= 15$ ft.
15 ft. $+ 2$ ft. $= 17$ ft.
17×12 in. $= 204$ in.
204 in. $+ 4$ in. $= 208$ in.

Ans. *208 inches*

</td><td>

12) 208
3) 17 $- 4$ *in.*
5 $- 2$ *ft.*

Ans. *5 yd. 2 ft. 4 in.*

</td></tr>
</table>

Exercise 1   Written

Change each of the following as indicated.

1. 3 ft. 7 in. to inches
2. 3 yd. 1 ft. 7 in. to inches
3. 59 in. to feet and inches
4. $15\frac{1}{4}$ sq. ft. to square inches
5. 350 sq. in. to square feet and square inches
6. $181\frac{1}{2}$ sq. yd. to square feet
7. 176 sq. ft. to square yards and square feet
8. 320 cu. ft. to cubic yards and cubic feet
9. 8 bu. 5 qt. to quarts

10. 7 bu. 13 qt. to pints
11. 22 pk. 4 qt. to quarts
12. 4 bu. 3 pk. 5 qt. to quarts
13. 8 gal. 3 qt. to quarts
14. 4 gal. 2 qt. 1 pt. to pints
15. 47 pt. to quarts and pints
16. 77 qt. to gallons and quarts
17. 3 lb. 7 oz. to ounces
18. 100 oz. to pounds and ounces
19. 3 hr. 27 min. to minutes
20. 204 min. to hours and minutes

Adding and subtracting denominate numbers. The addition and subtraction of denominate numbers are shown below.

Examples

1. Add:	2. Subtract:
3 ft. 8 in. *2 ft. 10 in.* *5 ft. 9 in.* *10 ft. 27 in.,* or *12 ft. 3 in.* **Ans.** *12 ft. 3 in.*	*8 hr. 10 min.* $=$ *7 hr. 70 min.* *3 hr. 45 min.* $=$ *3 hr. 45 min.* *4 hr. 25 min.* **Ans.** *4 hr. 25 min.*

Exercise 2   Written

1. Add the following:

a 7 ft. 5 in.; 4 ft. 10 in.; and 8 ft. 5 in.
b 9 lb. 10 oz.; 7 lb. 13 oz.; and 4 lb. 14 oz.
c 4 hr. 55 min.; 2 hr. 37 min.; and 3 hr. 52 min.
d 8 bu. 3 pk.; 3 bu. 2 pk.; and 7 bu. 1 pk.
e 4 yd. 2 ft. 11 in.; 8 yd. 1 ft. 7 in.; and 6 yd. 10 in.
f 8 gal. 1 qt. 1 pt.; 9 gal. 3 qt. 1 pt.; and 7 gal. 2 qt. 1 pt.

2. Subtract the following:

a 8 ft. 5 in.	**c** 7 hr. 15 min.	**e** 12 lb.
3 ft. 9 in.	2 hr. 55 min.	3 lb. 7 oz.
b 11 ft. 3 in.	**d** 9 lb. 7 oz.	**f** 8 yd.
4 ft. 10 in.	5 lb. 12 oz.	3 yd. 1 ft. 7 in.

Multiplying and dividing denominate numbers. The multiplication and division of denominate numbers are shown below.

Examples

1. Multiply 3 ft. 7 in. by 4.	2. Divide 14 ft. 5 in. by 4.
Solution	**Solution**
3 ft. 7 in.	*3 ft. 7¼ in.*
4	*4)14 ft. 5 in.*
12 ft. 28 in., or 14 ft. 4 in.	*12 ft.*
	2 ft. = 24 in.
Ans. *14 ft. 4 in.*	*29 in.*
	28 in.
	1 in. 1 ÷ 4 = ¼
	Ans. *3 ft. 7¼ in.*

Exercise 3   Written

1. Multiply

a 7 ft. 8 in. by 9
b 5 gal. 3 qt. by 5
c 3 lb. 13 oz. by 12
d 3 hr. 20 min. by 8
e 3 yd. 2 ft. 1 in. by 5

2. Divide:

a 28 ft. 10 in. by 2
b 15 hr. 40 min. by 5
c 12 ft. 7 in. by 4
d 26 lb. 4 oz. by 6
e 7 yd. 2 ft. 4 in. by 2

SECTION 74

Rectangles and Rectangular Solids

To find the perimeter of a rectangle. The perimeter (P) of a rectangle, which is the distance around it, equals 2 times the length $(2l)$ plus 2 times the width $(2w)$.

$$P = 2l + 2w$$

Thus, if a room is 15 ft. long and 12 ft. wide, the perimeter of the floor or ceiling is 54 ft.

$$P = 2l + 2w = (2 \times 15) + (2 \times 12) = 30 + 24 = 54 \text{ ft.}$$

To find the area of a rectangle. The area (A) of a rectangle equals the product of the length times the width $(l \times w)$.

$$A = l \times w, \text{ or } A = lw$$

For example, the area of the floor or ceiling of a room 15 ft. long and 12 ft. wide is 180 sq. ft.

$$A = l \times w = 15 \times 12 = 180 \text{ sq. ft.}$$

To find the volume of a rectangular solid. The volume (V) of a rectangular solid equals the length times the width times the height. $(l \times w \times h)$.

$$V = l \times w \times h, \text{ or } V = lwh$$

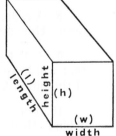

Thus, the volume of a rectangular solid 8 ft. long, 6 ft. wide, and 2 ft. high is 96 cu. ft.

$$V = l \times w \times h = 8 \times 6 \times 2 = 96 \text{ cu. ft.}$$

The length times the width represents the area of the base. The formula for the volume may therefore be expressed in the form,

$$V = B \times h, \text{ or } V = Bh$$

In this new form of the formula, B stands for the area of the base, $l \times w$.

Exercise 1 Written

1. A living room is 23' 10" long and 15' 8" wide. How many feet of molding are needed to go around the room just below the ceiling?

2. At $5.50 a square yard, what will be the cost of installing a concrete floor 45 ft. long and 18 ft. wide?

3. The living room of a home is 18 ft. long and 12 ft. wide.

a What is the square foot area of the floor of the room?

b If a rug 9 ft. wide by 12 ft. long is placed on the floor, how many square feet of the floor will remain uncovered?

4. At 80¢ a square foot, what will be the cost of a stone walk 5 ft. wide around the outside of a rectangular flower plot that is 35 feet long and 20 ft. wide?

5. At $5.40 a gallon, what will be the cost of paint for the four outside walls of a building 60 ft. long, 30 ft. wide, and 18 ft. high if the first coat is estimated to require one gallon to 48 sq. yd. and the second coat one gallon to 72 sq. yd.?

6. A room is 18 ft. long, 12 ft. wide, and 8 ft. high. At $1.25 a square yard, what will be the cost of painting the four walls and ceiling, deducting 80 sq. ft. for door and window openings? (Count a fraction of a square yard as one square yard.)

7. A driveway 60 feet long and 9 feet wide is to be surfaced with a 3-inch layer of topping. How many cubic yards of topping will be needed?

8. A cellar 42 ft. long and 24 ft. wide is to be excavated 6 ft. deep. How many cubic yards of earth must be removed?

9. S. T. Carson wishes to build a bin 12 ft. long and 5 ft. wide that will have a capacity of 400 cu. ft. What must be the height of the bin in feet and inches?

10. For a building development, a builder purchased $87\frac{1}{2}$ acres of land. He divided the area into plots of $2\frac{1}{2}$ acres each. How many of these plots did he have?

11. A swimming pool is 32 feet long by 16 feet wide. The depth of the water averages 6 feet. At 45¢ per hundred cubic feet, what will be the cost of the water that is needed to fill the pool to this level?

Triangles

To find the area of a triangle. The area of a triangle equals $\frac{1}{2}$ times the base (*b*) times the altitude (*h*).

$$A = \tfrac{1}{2} \times b \times h, \text{ or } A = \tfrac{1}{2}bh$$

Exercise 1 Written

1. The base of a triangle is 30 feet and the altitude is 15 feet. What is the area of the triangle?

2. A city lot in the shape of a triangle has a base of 150 feet and an altitude of 110 feet. At $2.10 a square foot, what is the value of the lot?

3. A triangular plot has a base of 70 feet and an altitude of 40 feet. At $1.95 a pound, what will be the cost of grass seed for the plot if 1 lb. is used for each 200 square feet?

4. A triangular sail on a boat has a height of $14\frac{1}{2}$ ft. and a base of $9\frac{1}{2}$ ft. What is the area of the sail to the nearest square foot?

5. The sketch at the left shows the gable of a barn. A gable is the vertical triangular portion of the end of a building, from the eaves to the ridge of the roof.

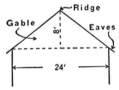

Using the dimensions shown in the sketch, find the area of the gable.

6. Find the total number of square feet in the gables at both ends of a house that is 28 ft. wide, with the ridge 10 ft. above the eaves.

7. Find the cost, at $1.20 a square yard, of painting the two gables of a house 36 ft. wide. The height of the ridge above the eaves is 12 ft.

8. At 75¢ per sq. yd., find the cost of painting the two sides and two ends of a barn 30 ft. wide, 50 ft. long, and 18 ft. high to the eaves. The height of the ridge above the eaves is 15 ft.

9. It has been decided to paint the two sides and two ends of a barn 26 ft. wide, 36 ft. long, and 20 ft. high to the eaves. The height of the ridge above the eaves is 13 ft. It is estimated that for the first coat one gallon of paint will cover 300 square feet of surface and that for the second coat one gallon will cover 450 square feet. Deducting 118 square feet for openings, find how much the paint for two coats will cost at $5.25 a gallon.

Scale Drawing

Drawing to scale. Shown at the right is a scale drawing of the floor plan of John Appelton's garage. It is drawn to the scale of $\frac{1}{16}$ in. = 1 ft. This means that each $\frac{1}{16}$ in. on the drawing represents an actual length of 1 foot.

Scale: $\frac{1}{16}$ in. = 1 ft.

Exercise 1   Written

1. Using a ruler divided into sixteenths of an inch, find the length and width (outside dimensions) of the garage shown above.

2. A set of house plans is drawn to the scale of $\frac{1}{4}$ in. = 1 ft. What actual length is represented by a line $2\frac{1}{4}$ inches long on the plans?

3. When the scale of a scale drawing is $\frac{1}{8}$ in. = 1 ft., what actual lengths are represented by the following lengths on the drawing?

a 3 in.   **b** $1\frac{3}{4}$ in.   **c** $2\frac{5}{8}$ in.   **d** $4\frac{1}{2}$ in.

4. A room is 18 ft. by 13 ft. Make a scale drawing of the room, using the scale of $\frac{1}{4}$ in. = 1 ft.

5. The sketch at the right shows the floor plan of a house. Make a scale drawing of the floor plan, using the scale $\frac{1}{16}$ in. = 1 ft.

6. At a scale of $\frac{1}{4}$ in. = 1 ft., how long a line should you draw to represent a wall 27 ft. long?

7. If the scale is $\frac{1}{8}$ in. = 1 ft., how long a line should you draw to represent a distance of 33 ft.?

8. A garage is 22′ × 19′. Give the dimensions of a scale drawing of the garage if a scale of $\frac{1}{4}$ in. = 1 ft. is used.

UNIT Eighteen

Computer Mathematics and Probability

.333

.52

$1.64

.7

Mortality Table

Age	Number Living
0	100,000
10	98,000
18	97,000
30	95,000
40	92,000
50	88,000
60	77,000
70	56,000
80	26,000

Decimal System of Numeration

Numerals and numbers. You have seen on page 7 that the marks we make to represent numbers are called numerals. Thus, 3, 8, 35, X, and XV are numerals. Numerals are symbols or names for numbers.

Decimal system of numeration. Numerals like 3, 8, and 25 are Hindu-Arabic numerals. The Hindu-Arabic system of numerals consists of the ten basic symbols 0, 1, 2, 3, 4, 5, 6, 7, 8, and 9.

These symbols are called *digits*. Because there are ten digits, this system is called a *decimal* system of numeration. The word "decimal" comes from a Latin word meaning ten. By *decimal system of numeration* we mean a method that uses ten digits for writing numerals.

Place value in the decimal system. With the ten digits of the decimal system we can write the numeral for a number of any size. This is possible because the value of a digit depends upon its position in the numeral. We call this the *place value* of the digit.

The chart at the right shows the place value of each digit in the numeral 3,333.

The 3 at the extreme right has a value of 3 *ones*, or 3.

The next 3 to the left has a value of 3 *tens*, or 30, which is ten times 3.

The next 3 has a value of 3 *hundreds*, or 300, which is ten times 30.

The next 3 has a value of 3 *thousands*, or 3,000, which is ten times 300.

Notice that moving a digit one place to the left multiplies its value by ten.

Exercise 1 Written

1. a In 7,584, what digit is in the thousands place?
b What digit is in the hundreds place?
c What digit is in the tens place?
d What digit is in the ones place?

2. The chart at the right shows the place value of each digit in the numeral 42,683.

The chart shows that there are 4 ten-thousands.

a How many thousands are there?

b How many hundreds?

c How many tens?

d How many ones?

3. In the numeral 4,823, the 4 has a value of 4,000
the 8 has a value of   800
the 2 has a value of   20
the 3 has a value of   3

In 3,629, what is the value of —

a the 3?   **b** the 6?   **c** the 2?   **d** the 9?

4. The numerals 243, 324, 432, 234, 423, and 342 are all made up of the same digits.

a Which numeral represents the largest number?

b Which numeral represents the smallest number?

5. a What is the largest number you can write with the digits 5, 3, and 7, using each digit only once?

b What is the smallest number?

6. The value of any numeral is equal to the sum of the values of the digits in the numeral.

For example, the table at the right shows that 3,627 is equal to 3,000 + 600 + 20 + 7.

Prepare similar tables to show the value of each digit and the sum of the digits in each of these numerals.

3,000
600
20
7
3,627

a 456   **c** 4,307   **e** 8,002   **g** 12,000

b 9,475   **d** 7,540   **f** 12,823   **h** 234,451

7. To find the numeral consisting of 8 *thousands*, 0 *hundreds*, 6 *tens*, and 4 *ones*, find the sum of the values of the digits, as shown at the right.

In like manner find the numeral consisting of:

a 9 thousands, 5 hundreds, 0 tens, 7 ones.

b 6 thousands, 4 hundreds, 3 tens, 0 ones.

c 4 ten-thousands, 0 thousands, 2 hundreds, 9 tens, 8 ones.

d 5 thousands, 7 hundreds, 9 tens, 2 ones.

e 4 ten-thousands, 8 thousands, 2 hundreds, 3 tens, 6 ones.

f 13 thousands, 0 hundreds, 3 tens, 8 ones.

g 3 hundred-thousands, 7 ten-thousands, 4 thousands, 6 hundreds, 9 tens, 8 ones.

SECTION

Binary System of Numeration

We use the decimal system of numeration in our everyday calculations in the home, store, factory, and office. Present-day electronic computers, however, make extensive use of what is called the binary system of numeration.

PART 78a   Interpreting Binary Numerals

Principal facts about the decimal system. In the decimal system we use *ten* symbols: 0, 1, 2, 3, 4, 5, 6, 7, 8, 9. Also, the value of each place in a numeral is *ten* times the value of the place to the right of it. Because of these two features, the decimal system is said to be a *base-ten system* or a system with the *base ten*.

The binary system. As noted above, many electronic computing machines make use of a *base-two system* of numeration called the *binary system*.

In the binary system only *two* digits are used. They are 0 and 1, and each digit in a binary numeral is either a 0 or a 1. Also, the value of each place in a binary numeral is *two* times the value of the place to the right of it.

Binary numerals represented in a panel of lights. Since there are only two different digits, a binary numeral can be indicated in a panel of electric lights. A light that is *on* represents a *1*. A light that is *off* represents a *0*. Because *on* and *off* can be represented by 1 and 0, many electronic computers use the binary system.

In the panel of lights at the right, the first and third lights from the right are *on*. The rest of the lights are off. In their present state of illumination, the lights represent the binary numeral 101, which is equal to 5 in base 10.

Binary place-value chart. Shown below is a place-value chart for base 2 through five places. The place values in the column headings (16, 8, 4, 2, 1) are expressed in terms of base-10 numerals.

		Place-Value Chart — Base 2				
Sixteens	Eights	Fours	Twos	Ones		Equivalent
(2x8)	(2x4)	(2x2)	(2x1)			in
16	8	4	2	1		Base 10
				1 = 1	=	1
			1	0 = 2 + 0	=	2
			1	1 = 2 + 1	=	3
		1	0	0 = 4 + 0 + 0 =		4
		1	0	1 = 4 + 0 + 1 =		5

Meaning of the binary numerals in the place-value chart. The first three numerals in the chart shown above are 1, 10, and 11. They are read "one," "one, zero," and "one, one."

The first numeral in the chart is 1, and is in the "1" column. This means that it is equal to 1 in base 10.

The second numeral is 10. The 1 is in the "2" column, and the 0 is in the "1" column. It means *one 2 + no 1's*. It is therefore equal to 2 + 0, or 2, in base 10. Notice that, as the symbol 1 shifts one place to the left, its value is multiplied by 2.

The third numeral, 11, has 1 in the "2" column and 1 in the "1" column. It is therefore equal to 2 + 1, or 3, in base 10.

The fourth numeral is 100 and is read "one, zero, zero." It has 1 in the "4" column, 0 in the "2" column, and 0 in the "1" column. It is therefore equal to 4 + 0 + 0, or 4, in base 10.

The fifth numeral is 101 and is read "one, zero, one." It has 1 in the "4" column, 0 in the "2" column, and 1 in the "1" column. It is therefore equal to 4 + 0 + 1, or 5, in base 10.

Exercise 1 Written

Shown below are the column headings of a binary place-value chart through nine places.

256   128   64   32   16   8   4   2   1

Practice writing the headings from right to left until you can write them without looking at the sample. Proceed this way:

First, write the numeral 1   1
Next, multiply 1 by 2 and write 2 to the left of the 1 . .   2   1
Next, multiply 2 by 2 and write 4 to the left of the 2 .   4   2   1
Continue in this manner through nine places.

PART 78b Changing the Base of a Numeral

Changing a base-2 numeral to a base-10 numeral. Persons working with computers sometimes need to change a base-2 numeral to a base-10 numeral, and a base-10 numeral to a base-2 numeral.

To change a base-2 numeral to a base-10 numeral, write the base-2 numeral in a place-value chart, and then add the values of the base-2 digits.

Example

Change 110101, base 2, to a base-10 numeral.

Solution

Step 1. Write a base-2 place-value chart through six places, which is the number of digits in 110101.

32 16 8 4 2 1

Step 2. Write 110101 in the chart.

32 16 8 4 2 1
1 1 0 1 0 1

Step 3. Add the decimal values of the digits in the base-2 numeral as indicated by the column headings, omitting the zeros. From left to right: 32 + 16 + 4 + 1 = 53.

Hence, 110101, base 2, equals 53, base 10. **Ans.**

Exercise 2 Written

Change each of the following base-2 numerals to a base-10 numeral. You may use the same place-value chart, through seven places, for all the problems in the exercise, using one line for each problem.

1. 1 1 1 1   5. 1 1 1 0 1   9.   1 0 0 1 1 1
2. 1 0 1 1   6. 1 1 0 1 1   10. 1 1 0 1 1 0 1
3. 1 0 0 0 0   7. 1 0 1 1 1   11. 1 0 0 1 0 1 1
4. 1 0 1 1 0   8. 1 0 0 0 0 0   12. 1 0 1 1 0 1 0

Changing a base-10 numeral to a base-2 numeral. Shown at the top of page 505 are the steps and procedures in changing the base-10 numeral, 25, to a base-2 numeral.

Step 1. In 25 there is 1 sixteen and 9 left over. Write   16 8 4 2 1
1 in the "16" column of a place-value chart.   *1*

Step 2. In 9 there is 1 eight and 1 left over. Write 1 in   16 8 4 2 1
the "8" column.   *1 1*

Step 3. In 1 there are 0 fours, 0 twos, and 1 one. Write   16 8 4 2 1
0 in the "4" column, 0 in the "2" column, and   *1 1 0 0 1*
1 in the "1" column.

Hence the base-2 numeral equal to 25, base 10, is 11001.

Check: 16 + 8 + 1 = 25

Exercise **3**   Written

Change each of the following base-10 numerals to a base-2 numeral. You may use the same place-value chart, through seven places, for all the problems, using one line for each problem.

1. 31	**5.** 27	**9.** 25	**13.** 14	**17.** 12	**21.** 64
2. 15	**6.** 47	**10.** 19	**14.** 62	**18.** 21	**22.** 87
3. 63	**7.** 29	**11.** 51	**15.** 28	**19.** 43	**23.** 110
4. 13	**8.** 39	**12.** 30	**16.** 60	**20.** 32	**24.** 117

Binary-coded decimals. In some computers, each digit in a base-10 numeral, rather than the numeral as a whole, is changed to a binary numeral. For example, 98 is expressed as 1001-1000. The latter is called a *binary-coded decimal*. The 1001 represents the base-10 digit 9; the 1000 represents 8. 1001 and 1000 are called *binary-coded decimal digits*. Each coded digit contains four places. Zeros are prefixed to fill out four spaces if needed. Thus, for the base-10 digit 0, the coded digit is 0000; for 1, it is 0001; for 2, 0010; and so on.

Exercise **4**   Written

1. Write the base-10 numeral expressed by the binary-coded decimal in each of the following:

a 0001-0010-0000   **d** 0010-0100-0111-0101   **g** 0010-1000-1000

b 0011-0100-0101   **e** 1000-0110-1001-0000   **h** 0100-0101-0011

c 0110-1000-0111   **f** 0011-0001-0010-0110   **i** 1000-0111-0001

2. Change each of the following base-10 numerals to a binary-coded decimal.

a 24	**c** 142	**e** 954	**g** 6740
b 36	**d** 306	**f** 587	**h** 3081

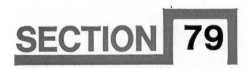

Binary Arithmetic

Addition with base-2 numerals. There are four basic addition facts that we need to know for performing addition with base-2 numerals. They are:

$$0 + 0 = 0 \qquad 0 + 1 = 1 \qquad 1 + 0 = 1 \qquad 1 + 1 = 10$$

Notice in the place-value chart on page 503 that the base-2 numeral 100 represents a number that is 1 more than the base-2 numeral 11. This means that $11 + 1 = 100$. We use this addition fact occasionally in column addition.

We perform column addition with base-2 numerals in the same manner as with base-10 numerals. First, we add the ones column. Then we add successively the columns at the left.

Example

Find the sum of the numbers represented by the base-2 numerals in the column below at the left.

Solution	Explanation	Check
1 1 1 1 1 1 1 1 ———— $1\ 0\ \overset{10}{0}\ \overset{1}{0}\ 1$ 10001 **Ans.**	Begin with the ones column and add from the bottom up. 1. In the ones column: $1 + 1 = 10; 10 + 1 = 11$. Write 1; carry (1). 2. In the twos column: $(1) + 1 = 10; 10 + 1 = 11$; $11 + 1 = 100$. Write 0; carry (10). 3. In the fours column: $(10) + 1 = 11; 11 + 1 =$ 100. Write 100.	Base 2 Base 10 $\ 111 = 7$ $\ 111 = 7$ $\ \ 11 = 3$ ———————— $10001 = 17$ $16 + 1 = 17$

Exercise **1**   Written

1. Find the sums with the base-2 numerals given below.

a 1000	**b** 1010	**c** 1	**d** 10	**e** 100	**f** 101
101	101	1	10	100	1

2. Find the sums with the base-2 numerals given below.

a 11	**d** 11	**g** 11011	**j** 1	**k** 10	**l** 101
1	11	10111	1	11	111
			1	10	110

b 101	**e** 111	**h** 10101
11	111	11011

m 1	**n** 101	**o** 1011
1	111	1101

c 111	**f** 1110	**i** 11101
1	1111	10111

m 1	**n** 101	**o** 1011
1	111	1101
1	10	1011
1	100	1001

Multiplication with base-2 numerals. There are four multiplication facts that we need for performing multiplication with base-2 numerals. They are:

$$0 \times 0 = 0 \quad 0 \times 1 = 0 \quad 1 \times 0 = 0 \quad 1 \times 1 = 1$$

We perform multiplication with base-2 numerals in the same manner as with base-10 numerals. We first obtain partial products by multiplying the multiplicand by each digit in the multiplier, starting with the digit in the ones position. We then find the sum of the partial products.

Example

Multiply 1011 by 101, base 2.

Solution	Explanation	Check
1011	$1 \times 1011 = 1011$, the first partial product.	Base 2 Base 10
101		1011 = 11
1011		101 = 5
10110	$0 \times 1011 = 0$. Write 0 in the twos column of the second partial product.	110111 = 55
110111		
	$1 \times 1011 = 1011$. Write 1011 to the left of the 0 in the second partial product.	$32 + 16 +$ $4 + 2 + 1 = 55$
110111 **Ans.**		
	Add the partial products.	

Exercise 2 Written

1. Find the products with the base-2 numerals given below.

a 111	**b** 101	**c** 101	**d** 11	**e** 111	**f** 1101
10	100	11	11	101	11

2. Find the products with the base-2 numerals given below.

a 111	**c** 1101	**e** 1101	**g** 111	**i** 1011
11	101	110	111	1101

b 1111	**d** 1111	**f** 1011	**h** 1011	**j** 1111
11	101	1100	111	111

Subtraction with base-2 numerals. In subtraction with base-2 numerals we use the following facts:

$$0 - 0 = 0 \quad 1 - 0 = 1 \quad 1 - 1 = 0 \quad 10 - 1 = 1$$

Frequently, a 1 in the subtrahend has to be subtracted from a 0 in the minuend. There are several methods of procedure when this is the case. One method is shown in the example given below.

Example

Subtract 10101 from 1001000, base 2.

Solution	Explanation
1 0 0 1 0 0 0 1 0 1 0 1	The 1 in the ones column cannot be subtracted from 0.

0 1 1 10
1 0 0 1̸ 0̸ 0̸ 0̸
    1 0 1 0 1
      0 0 1 1
	Step 1. Move to the left in the minuend until a 1 is reached. Change this 1 to 0. Change each intervening 0 to 1. Change the 0 at the point of subtraction to 10. Then subtract until a point is reached where a 1 must again be subtracted from 0. This point is in the sixteens column.

0 1 10 0 1 1 10 1̸ 0̸ 0̸ 1̸ 0̸ 0̸ 0̸ 1 0 1 0 1 1 1 0 0 1 1 **Ans.**	*Step 2.* Move to the left in the minuend until the next 1 is reached. Then proceed again in the manner described above.
Check:	Base 2 Base 10 1001000 = 72 10101 = 21 110011 = 51 32 + 16 + 2 + 1 = 51

Exercise 3   Written

1. Find the differences with the base-2 numerals given below.

a 10	**b** 11	**c** 110	**d** 101	**e** 111	**f** 1111
10	10	10	1	101	11

2. Find the differences with the base-2 numerals given below.

a 10	d 101	g 100	j 1000	m 1101
1	10	1	101	1011

b 110	e 101	h 1000	k 100	n 10000
1	11	1	11	11

c 100	f 1010	i 100001	l 110	o 11101
10	100	10	11	1011

Division with base-2 numerals. We perform division with base-2 numerals in the same manner as with base-10 numerals. Observe the examples given below.

Example 1	Example 2
In base 2, 1111 ÷ 101 = ?.	In base 2, 10010 ÷ 11 = ?.

Example 1:
```
        11   Ans.
101 )1111
     101
     ‾‾‾‾
     101
     101
     ‾‾‾‾
```

Example 2:
```
       110   Ans.
11 )10010
    11
    ‾‾
    11
    11
    ‾‾
    00
```

Check (Example 1):
```
            Base 2    Base 10
            1111  =  15
             101  =   5
1111 ÷ 101 = 11    15 ÷ 5 = 3
            11 = 2 + 1 = 3
```

Check (Example 2):
```
              Base 2    Base 10
              10010  =  18
                 11  =   3
10010 ÷ 11 = 110    18 ÷ 3 = 6
             110 = 4 + 2 = 6
```

Notice in Example 2 that the divisor is 11, whereas the first two digits in the dividend are 10. Since 11 cannot be subtracted from 10, the 11 is placed under and subtracted from the 100 in the dividend.

Exercise 4 Written

Find the quotients with the base-2 numerals given below.

1. 10)1110   4. 11)11011   7. 11)100001   10. 110)110110

2. 100)11000   5. 11)10101   8. 111)110001   11. 110)110000

3. 101)1111   6. 111)100011   9. 1011)110111   12. 1110)101010

SECTION 80

Probability

Meaning and uses of probability. *Probability* is a branch of mathematics concerned with predicting the likelihood of events whose occurrence is uncertain. It has many uses in business, industry, and science. Although the mathematics of most of the applications are too advanced for us to consider here, in this section you will become acquainted with the basic ideas of probability and how they may be used in some of their simpler applications.

Chance events. Suppose a bag contains two colored marbles of the same size, one red and one white. Without looking, you are to draw one of the marbles from the bag. You have no way of knowing which one is red and which one is white, and you have no way of drawing one in preference to the other. Under these conditions, we say that your selection is a *random choice* and that the outcome is a *chance event.*

Measure of probability of a chance event. In the situation just described, what are the chances that you will draw the red marble? Two outcomes of the draw are possible: (1) you draw the red marble; or (2) you draw the white marble.

Since your selection is a random choice, one outcome is just as likely to occur as the other. The chance that you will draw the red marble is therefore 1 out of 2, which we may express as a fraction, $\frac{1}{2}$. We say that the probability of the event, "draw the red marble," is $\frac{1}{2}$. If we prefer, we may say that the probability is .5 or 50%.

Suppose a bag contains 6 red marbles, 3 white marbles, and 1 blue marble, making a total of 10. The marbles are identical except for color. What are the chances of your drawing a red marble? Since there are 6 red marbles, there are 6 ways, out of 10, in which you can succeed in drawing a red one. The probability of the event, "you draw a red marble," is therefore 6/10, or 3/5.

Since 4 of the marbles are *not* red, there are 4 ways, out of 10, in which you can fail to draw a red marble. The probability of your *not* drawing a red marble is therefore 4/10, or 2/5. Stated formally, we may say that the probability of the event, "you do not draw a red marble," is 4/10, or 2/5.

Events that are certain or impossible. If a bag contains nothing but 5 green marbles, the chances of drawing a green marble are 5 out of 5, which is 5/5, or 1. The event, "draw a green marble," is certain to occur, because no other outcome is possible. Any event that is certain therefore has a probability of 1.

From a bag containing nothing but green marbles, the event, "draw a white marble," is an impossible outcome. The chances of drawing a white marble are 0 out of 5, which is 0/5, or 0. Any event that is impossible therefore has a probability of 0.

Conclusions regarding the measure of probability. From the preceding examples we see that probability is a fraction which measures the likelihood that a particular event will occur. The numerator is the number of ways the event can occur or succeed. The denominator is the total number of possible outcomes.

The probability of an event can be 0, 1, or any fraction between 0 and 1. It can never be less than 0 or greater than 1.

Probability may be expressed as a fraction, a decimal, or a percent, whichever is more convenient or desirable.

Exercise 1   Oral

1. If a coin that is perfectly balanced is given a toss and allowed to fall freely, it is as likely to turn up heads as tails. What is the probability of its turning up heads?

2. A bag contains 1 red marble, 1 white marble, and 1 blue marble. If one marble is drawn at random,

a What is the probability that it will be white?

b What is the probability that it will not be white?

3. A box contains 5 black checkers and 4 red checkers. If one checker is drawn at random,

a What is the probability that it will be red?

b What is the probability that it will not be red?

c What is the probability that the checker will be yellow?

4. For a raffle, 20 tickets have been sold. What is the probability of your winning if you have

a 1 ticket?   **b** 2 tickets?   **c** 3 tickets?

5. A bag contains 4 peppermint wafers, 6 orange wafers, and 7 lemon wafers, all the same size. One wafer is drawn at random. What is the probability that it will be

a Peppermint?   **b** Orange?   **c** Lemon?   **d** Lime?

e What is the probability that the wafer will not be lemon?

Probability and the principle of large numbers. The probability of an event tells us approximately how many times we can expect the event to occur out of a large number of trials.

For example, if a coin that is perfectly balanced is to be given a toss, we can assume that it is just as likely to come up heads as tails. We can therefore say that the probability of its coming up heads is $\frac{1}{2}$.

This does not mean that out of say 20 tosses we are sure to get 10 heads. We may get several more or several less than 10. What it does mean is that, if we toss the coin many times, say 1,000 times, the number of heads will not be far from $\frac{1}{2}$ of 1,000. The longer we keep tossing, the nearer the number of heads will come to equaling $\frac{1}{2}$ of the number of tosses. This is the *principle* or *law of large numbers*, and it is one of the central ideas of probability. For a large number of trials of the same kind, we can predict the outcome with a relatively small amount of error.

Exercise 2   Written

1. The probability of a certain event is $\frac{1}{4}$. Approximately how many times would you expect the event to occur in 3,600 trials?

2. Three cards, marked 1, 2, and 3, respectively, are placed in a hat.

   a If one card is drawn at random, what is the probability that the card drawn will be the one marked 2?

   b Assume that a card is drawn and placed back in the hat, and that this operation is repeated 3,450 times. Approximately how many times would we expect the card drawn to be the one marked 2?

3. A small cube has its six faces marked 1, 2, 3, 4, 5, and 6, respectively. The cube is perfect in every respect so that, if you give it a toss, it will fall with each of the six numerals equally likely to show on top.

In one toss of the cube, how many possible outcomes are there in terms of the number of different ways the cube can fall?

4. In one toss of the cube described in Problem 3, what is the probability of throwing

a a 7?   **d** a number greater than a 4?

b a number less than 7?   **e** a number less than a 4?

c a 4?   **f** a number that is not a 3?

5. Assume that the cube in Problem 4 is tossed 4,500 times. Exactly how many times would we expect the events listed in **a** and **b** to occur? Approximately how many times would we expect the events listed in **c**, **d**, **e**, and **f** to occur?

Probability determined by experiment. In all the preceding examples, the conditions in each situation were such that we could determine in advance the probability of the event from the description of the conditions. In most applications of probability, however, such information is not available; and the probability measure has to be found by experiment or from experience.

For example, if a coin is unevenly worn and not perfectly balanced, heads and tails are not equally likely to come up if the coin is tossed. The probabilities for this coin must be determined by experiment; that is, by actually tossing the coin and recording the results.

Let us suppose that we get 821 heads and 179 tails in 1,000 tosses. From this data, we can estimate the probability of tossing a head as $821/1,000$, or .821; and the probability of tossing a tail as $179/1,000$, or .179. For a series of future tosses of this coin, we can predict that approximately 82.1% of the tosses will show heads and approximately 17.9% will show tails.

Factories often make tests on random samples of each particular product to see what percent is up to standard or what percent is not. In a test of 100 random samples of a particular article, suppose 2 are found defective. This is 2% of the 100 samples. On the basis of the test, it may be assumed that approximately 2% of the entire batch from which the samples were selected will turn out to be defective. In a lot of 500 of these articles, it can be expected that the number defective will be approximately 2% of 500, or 10.

Probability determined from experience. From their records of deaths among their policyholders, insurance companies compile mortality tables which show, among other things, the number still living in each age group. A portion of a mortality table is shown on page 514.

The table shows how many persons in a sample group of 100,000 live births reached certain ages. The numbers for each age except the first have been rounded to the nearest thousand for convenience in making calculations.

Mortality Table	
Age	Number Living
0	100,000
10	98,000
18	97,000
30	95,000
40	92,000
50	88,000
60	77,000
70	56,000
80	26,000

From the table we can determine the probability that a person will reach a given age. For example, the table shows that 95,000 of the original 100,000 reached the age of 30. We may say, then, that at birth the probability of living to be 30 is 95,000 ÷ 100,000, or .95.

Of the 95,000 who were living at age 30, the table shows that 56,000 were still living at age 70. The probability that a person now 30 will live to be 70 is therefore 56,000 ÷ 95,000, or .59, to the nearest hundredth.

Exercise 3   Written

1. On a factory test of 200 random samples of a particular electric switch, 3 of the samples were found defective. In a lot of 450 of these switches, how many might be expected to be defective? (Express the answer to the nearest whole number.)

2. **a** What is the probability that a person born today will live to be 60?

   b What is the probability that he will not live to be 60?

3. What is the probability that a 40-year old man will live to be 50? 60? 70? 80? (Give your answer to the nearest hundredth.)

4. In a high school graduating class, 400 of the graduates are 18 years old.

   a What is the probability that a member of this group will live to be 70? (Give the answer to the nearest hundredth.)

   b Approximately how many of the group can be expected to reach age 70?

5. During the last 360 days, a weather forecaster's predictions have been correct on 288 days.

   a What is the probability that his forecast of tomorrow's weather will be correct?

   b Over the next 30 days, approximately how many times would you expect him to forecast correctly?

Drills for Accuracy and Speed

The following drills are of two kinds — written and mental.

A written drill is one in which the student writes all the calculations and the answers on his answer paper.

A mental drill is one in which he performs all the calculations mentally and writes only the answers on his answer paper.

Drills 1 and 2 are mental drills.

Drills 3 to 13 are written drills.

Drills 14 to 37 are mental drills.

Drill 1   Addition   Mental

Place a sheet of paper across the page so that the upper edge of the paper is under the sixth item of each column. Then add each column of exposed numbers from the bottom up, using combinations wherever possible, and write the sum on the sheet of paper. Repeat the drill, adding the columns from the top down.

Proceed in a similar manner with the edge of a piece of paper placed under the seventh row of addends, then under the eighth row, and so on, as directed by your teacher.

	a	b	c	d	e	f
1.	76	89	86	456	$ .86	$129.35
2.	94	76	679	5,794	.29	87.29
3.	81	21	48	76,532	.31	3.50
4.	27	48	63	967	.42	16.48
5.	43	37	99	87,658	12.95	194.76
6.	59	52	75	4,369	.87	8.95
7.	84	19	32	2,123	.64	69.83
8.	26	87	21	35,254	.72	100.00
9.	29	31	198	4,683	.27	7.26
10.	74	55	54	28,765	1.46	35.42
11.	83	83	37	5,124	.35	472.19
12.	19	49	89	71,676	.92	107.24
13.	79	23	75	3,782	.88	86.28
14.	85	53	42	52,497	.83	55.24
15.	92	18	783	870	5.47	423.42

Drill 2   Subtraction   Mental

Place a sheet of paper across the page so that the upper edge of the paper is under the subtrahends of the first horizontal row of problems given below. Then subtract and write the differences on the sheet of paper. Prove the result in each case by adding the difference to the subtrahend.

Do the same with Problems 2 to 4.

	a	b	c	d
1.	8,965,395	$57,630.00	12,806,638	$877,151.58
	7,360,273	40,534.75	9,707,553	480,561.92
2.	9,789,489	$76,700.00	91,313,904	$120,121.17
	5,608,029	39,410.12	35,296,808	20,250.89
3.	8,437,482	$374,422.08	82,104,006	$105,074.27
	1,105,381	268,370.09	64,008,009	99,257.35
4.	9,491,459	$200,907.00	95,016,102	$121,025.19
	2,441,251	107,358.81	89,067,304	96,865.37

Drill 3   Multiplication of whole numbers   Written

Perform the indicated multiplication in each of the following problems and prove the result.

1. 268×341
2. 722×307
3. 623×504
4. 431×208
5. 822×702

6. $3,206 \times 2,105$
7. $4,013 \times 3,402$
8. $5,204 \times 4,021$
9. $6,051 \times 5,014$
10. $7,003 \times 1,008$

11. $5,009 \times 3,007$
12. $6,008 \times 4,002$
13. $7,102 \times 6,004$
14. $6,203 \times 5,006$
15. $4,022 \times 2,009$

Drill 4   Multiplication involving decimals   Written

Perform the indicated multiplication in each of the following problems and prove the result.

1. 74.1×82
2. 6.32×44
3. 4.08×67
4. 6.42×25.4
5. 8.07×4.23

6. 3.61×5.04
7. 71.1×30.8
8. $.406 \times .205$
9. $72.9 \times .0301$
10. $81.5 \times .0142$

11. $4.63 \times .107$
12. $.347 \times .026$
13. $1.202 \times .208$
14. $.4127 \times 1.001$
15. $.3413 \times 3.008$

Drill 5   Multiplication involving end zeros   Written

Perform the indicated multiplication in each of the following problems and prove the result.

1. 264 × 3,800
2. 314 × 1,300
3. 232 × 4,100
4. 422 × 2,300
5. 280 × 76

6.   510 × 3,300
7.   420 × 5,300
8. 94,000 × 570
9. 24,000 × 360
10. 52,000 × 180

11.   930 × 3.75
12. 1,700 × 4.06
13.   6.50 × 1,700
14.   8.20 × 1,400
15. 12.10 × 1,600

Drill 6   Multiplication involving dollars and cents   Written

Perform the indicated multiplication in each of the following and prove the result.

1. $8.50 × 45
2. $9.40 × 350
3. $6.50 × 1,300
4. $1.90 × 1,450
5. $ .70 × 1,750

6. $ .45 × 180
7. $ .52 × 2,100
8. $ .34 × 14,000
9. $ 1.02 × 10,500
10. $10.50 × 3,040

11. $ 8,500 × .02542
12. $12,400 × .10205
13. $16,700 × .035
14. $34,000 × .01912
15. $65,000 × .00915

Drill 7   Division with whole numbers   Written

Perform the indicated division in each of the following and prove the quotient.

1. 1,134 ÷ 27
2. 1,504 ÷ 32
3. 2,294 ÷ 37
4. 1,739 ÷ 37
5. 7,392 ÷ 84

6.   6,322 ÷ 58
7.   9,729 ÷ 47
8. 11,778 ÷ 39
9. 25,920 ÷ 64
10. 46,816 ÷ 77

11. 94,094 ÷ 143
12. 10,032 ÷ 114
13. 10,912 ÷ 176
14. 22,016 ÷ 128
15. 48,222 ÷ 171

Drill 8   Division involving decimals   Written

In each of the following problems, divide correct to the number of decimal places indicated and prove the quotient.

To 1 decimal place	To 2 decimal places	To 3 decimal places
1. 500 ÷ 2.2	6. 70 ÷ 13.2	11. 7.66 ÷ 2.6
2. 15 ÷ 6.3	7. 1.02 ÷ 5.4	12. .892 ÷ 3.9
3. 84.8 ÷ 1.15	8. 13.3 ÷ 8.4	13. 2 ÷ 5.7
4. 57.1 ÷ .09	9. 6.6 ÷ .37	14. 1.52 ÷ .54
5. 70.7 ÷ .87	10. 2.19 ÷ .079	15. .776 ÷ .69

Drill 9   Division involving end zeros in the divisor   Written

In each of the following problems, divide correct to the number of decimal places indicated and prove the quotient.

To 1 decimal place	To 2 decimal places	To 3 decimal places
1. $3,815 \div 180$	5. $2,000 \div 4,700$	9. $330 \quad \div 7,900$
2. $2,855 \div 490$	6. $824.5 \div 3,500$	10. $21.85 \quad \div 1,500$
3. $8,325 \div 2,600$	7. $460 \quad \div 280$	11. $17,150 \div 17,000$
4. $4,800 \div 4,400$	8. $25.9 \quad \div 730$	12. $200 \quad \div 6,700$

Drill 10   Addition of fractions and mixed numbers   Written

Find the sum of each of the following.

1. $\frac{1}{2}$ $\frac{2}{3}$ $\frac{3}{4}$

2. $8\frac{1}{4}$ $12\frac{1}{2}$ $9\frac{1}{3}$

3. $5\frac{1}{3}$ $16\frac{1}{2}$ $6\frac{1}{4}$

4. $12\frac{1}{5}$ $7\frac{1}{2}$ $9\frac{1}{4}$

5. $4\frac{1}{4}$ $7\frac{2}{5}$ $8\frac{1}{8}$

6. $6\frac{1}{4}$ $4\frac{1}{3}$ $5\frac{1}{5}$

7. $12\frac{1}{2}$ $5\frac{5}{6}$ $12\frac{1}{3}$ $20\frac{3}{4}$

8. $4\frac{1}{4}$ $4\frac{1}{3}$ $19\frac{1}{2}$ $18\frac{5}{6}$

9. $3\frac{5}{16}$ $6\frac{1}{8}$ $13\frac{3}{4}$ $6\frac{1}{2}$

10. $10\frac{1}{3}$ $15\frac{5}{9}$ $2\frac{1}{6}$ $7\frac{1}{2}$

11. $10\frac{2}{3}$ $11\frac{5}{6}$ $4\frac{4}{9}$ $12\frac{1}{2}$

12. $24\frac{5}{8}$ $5\frac{2}{3}$ $11\frac{1}{4}$ $18\frac{1}{6}$

13. $6\frac{7}{12}$ $7\frac{3}{4}$ $2\frac{1}{8}$ $11\frac{5}{6}$

14. $4\frac{2}{3}$ $10\frac{5}{12}$ $11\frac{1}{9}$ $6\frac{1}{4}$

15. $7\frac{5}{6}$ $12\frac{1}{3}$ $5\frac{4}{9}$ $15\frac{1}{2}$

16. $8\frac{2}{7}$ $6\frac{3}{4}$ $15\frac{1}{2}$ $3\frac{1}{14}$

17. $15\frac{3}{4}$ $10\frac{1}{5}$ $22\frac{1}{2}$ $3\frac{7}{10}$

18. $4\frac{1}{2}$ $16\frac{1}{4}$ $8\frac{1}{8}$ $9\frac{5}{16}$

Drill 11   Subtraction of fractions and mixed numbers   Written

Perform the subtraction in each of the following.

1. $18\frac{7}{12}$ $7\frac{1}{2}$

2. $16\frac{9}{10}$ $\frac{3}{5}$

3. $27\frac{7}{15}$ $9\frac{1}{3}$

4. $16\frac{1}{2}$ $\frac{1}{3}$

5. $21\frac{3}{4}$ $6\frac{2}{3}$

6. $19\frac{5}{6}$ $8\frac{3}{4}$

7. $24\frac{11}{12}$ $\frac{5}{8}$

8. $10\frac{7}{15}$ $2\frac{3}{10}$

9. $21\frac{3}{4}$ $\frac{4}{5}$

10. $10\frac{3}{8}$ $2\frac{2}{3}$

11. $12\frac{3}{4}$ $\frac{7}{8}$

12. $18\frac{1}{3}$ $4\frac{1}{2}$

13. $12\frac{1}{2}$ $8\frac{7}{8}$

14. $13\frac{1}{4}$ $\frac{7}{8}$

15. $10\frac{2}{3}$ $3\frac{3}{5}$

16. $14\frac{1}{2}$ $5\frac{5}{8}$

17. $15\frac{1}{2}$ $9\frac{4}{5}$

18. $28\frac{2}{3}$ $5\frac{3}{8}$

Drill **12** Multiplication of fractions and mixed numbers Written

Find the product in each of the following.

1. $12\frac{1}{2}$	2. $14\frac{1}{3}$	3. $12\frac{2}{3}$	4. $16\frac{1}{2}$	5. $12\frac{1}{3}$	6. $15\frac{1}{4}$
$16\frac{1}{4}$	$15\frac{1}{2}$	$9\frac{1}{4}$	$5\frac{1}{4}$	$8\frac{1}{2}$	$9\frac{2}{3}$

7. $27\frac{1}{2}$	8. $21\frac{2}{3}$	9. $32\frac{1}{4}$	10. $27\frac{1}{2}$	11. $21\frac{2}{3}$	12. $32\frac{1}{4}$
$22\frac{2}{3}$	$12\frac{1}{3}$	$8\frac{3}{4}$	$15\frac{2}{3}$	$10\frac{1}{3}$	$7\frac{3}{4}$

13. $20\frac{3}{4}$	14. $15\frac{3}{4}$	15. $18\frac{1}{4}$	16. $12\frac{1}{4}$	17. $16\frac{3}{4}$	18. $21\frac{3}{4}$
$9\frac{1}{2}$	$20\frac{2}{3}$	$16\frac{2}{3}$	$13\frac{2}{3}$	$7\frac{1}{2}$	$9\frac{2}{3}$

19. $36\frac{3}{8}$	20. $32\frac{2}{3}$	21. $27\frac{3}{4}$	22. $25\frac{3}{8}$	23. $18\frac{2}{3}$	24. $17\frac{3}{4}$
$24\frac{1}{3}$	$15\frac{1}{8}$	$20\frac{1}{3}$	$16\frac{1}{3}$	$12\frac{1}{8}$	$24\frac{1}{3}$

Drill **13** Division of fractions and mixed numbers Written

Perform the indicated division in each of the following.

1. $47 \div \frac{2}{3}$	**13.** $270 \div 9\frac{3}{8}$	**25.** $58\frac{11}{12} \div 25\frac{1}{4}$
2. $28 \div \frac{3}{4}$	**14.** $140 \div 11\frac{1}{4}$	**26.** $70\frac{5}{16} \div 18\frac{3}{4}$
3. $42 \div \frac{4}{5}$	**15.** $126 \div 13\frac{1}{2}$	**27.** $35\frac{8}{15} \div 16\frac{2}{5}$
4. $92 \div \frac{8}{9}$	**16.** $153 \div 15\frac{3}{4}$	**28.** $40\frac{5}{8} \div 12\frac{3}{16}$
5. $39 \div \frac{5}{6}$	**17.** $29\frac{3}{8} \div 3\frac{1}{8}$	**29.** $48\frac{3}{4} \div 7\frac{7}{8}$
6. $31\frac{1}{3} \div 4$	**18.** $126\frac{2}{3} \div 13\frac{1}{3}$	**30.** $37\frac{1}{8} \div 16\frac{1}{2}$
7. $52\frac{1}{2} \div 6$	**19.** $86\frac{1}{4} \div 18\frac{3}{4}$	**31.** $154\frac{1}{6} \div 24\frac{2}{3}$
8. $45\frac{1}{3} \div 8$	**20.** $204\frac{1}{6} \div 29\frac{1}{6}$	**32.** $58\frac{1}{3} \div 12\frac{1}{2}$
9. $69\frac{3}{4} \div 9$	**21.** $81\frac{1}{4} \div 43\frac{3}{4}$	**33.** $46\frac{2}{3} \div 17\frac{1}{2}$
10. $124\frac{1}{2} \div 12$	**22.** $56\frac{7}{8} \div 16\frac{1}{4}$	**34.** $151\frac{2}{3} \div 16\frac{1}{4}$
11. $35 \div 4\frac{2}{3}$	**23.** $45\frac{5}{6} \div 18\frac{1}{3}$	**35.** $95\frac{1}{4} \div 21\frac{1}{6}$
12. $117 \div 6\frac{3}{4}$	**24.** $44\frac{1}{4} \div 29\frac{1}{2}$	**36.** $43\frac{1}{8} \div 19\frac{1}{6}$

Drill **14** Multiplication by 10, 100, and 1,000 Mental

Perform the indicated multiplication in each of the following.

1. 7.38×10	7. 9.85×100	13. $.085 \times 100$
2. 9.21×100	8. 5.345×10	14. $.071 \times 10$
3. $4.72 \times 1,000$	9. 5.63×10	15. $4.98 \times 1,000$
4. 6.3×100	10. 4.2×100	16. 5.08×100
5. 3.27×10	11. $3.4 \times 1,000$	17. 9.76×10
6. $.596 \times 1,000$	12. 42.7×10	18. $.021 \times 1,000$

Drill **15**   Multiplication by multiples of 10 and 10¢   Mental

Find the cost of each of the following:

1. 20 @ 65¢	7. 20 @ $.70	13. 80 @ $.45
2. 60 @ 45¢	8. 40 @ $.35	14. 60 @ 52¢
3. 23 @ $.30	9. 65 @ 60¢	15. 22 @ 70¢
4. 30 @ $.15	10. 40 @ $.32	16. 20 @ $.17
5. 80 @ $.35	11. 70 @ 15¢	17. 30 @ 55¢
6. 35 @ 40¢	12. 31 @ 80¢	18. 115 @ $.20

Drill **16**   Division by 10, 100, and 1,000   Mental

Perform the indicated division in each of the following.

1. 348 ÷ 10	7. 73.8 ÷ 10	13. 7.3 ÷ 100
2. 1,987 ÷ 1,000	8. 9.2 ÷ 100	14. 9.16 ÷ 10
3. 847 ÷ 100	9. 4.7 ÷ 1,000	15. 5.9 ÷ 1,000
4. 7,240 ÷ 1,000	10. 5.63 ÷ 100	16. 80 ÷ 100
5. 360 ÷ 10	11. 7.2 ÷ 10	17. 7.8 ÷ 10
6. 93.4 ÷ 10	12. 20 ÷ 1,000	18. 30 ÷ 1,000

Drill **17**   Multiplication and division by 10, 100, and 1,000   Mental

Perform the operation indicated in each of the following.

1. 7.38 × 10	7. 198 ÷ 1,000	13. 64.7 ÷ 1,000
2. .042 × 1,000	8. .38 ÷ 10	14. .069 × 100
3. 348 ÷ 10	9. 6.47 × 1,000	15. .38 × 10
4. 420 ÷ 1,000	10. 6.9 ÷ 100	16. .21 ÷ 100
5. 9.20 × 100	11. .74 ÷ 1,000	17. 5.63 ÷ 100
6. .38 × 10	12. 56.3 × 100	18. .0074 × 1,000

Drill **18**   Multiplication by .1, .01, and .001   Mental

Perform the indicated multiplication in each of the following.

1. 73.8 × .1	6. 362 × .001	11. 4.22 × .01
2. 9.2 × .01	7. 83.4 × .1	12. 713 × .001
3. 647 × .001	8. 3.85 × .01	13. 62.4 × .1
4. 34.1 × .01	9. 53.4 × .1	14. 3,420 × .001
5. 5.31 × .1	10. 863 × .1	15. 4.8 × .01

❯ Drill **19** Division by .1, .01, and .001 Mental

Perform the indicated division in each of the following.

1. 73.8 ÷ .1	6. .485 ÷ .001	11. 4.33 ÷ .01
2. 8.2 ÷ .01	7. 72.36 ÷ .1	12. 6.54 ÷ .001
3. 46.7 ÷ .001	8. 2.74 ÷ .01	13. 33.6 ÷ .1
4. 21.4 ÷ .01	9. 6.456 ÷ .1	14. .706 ÷ .001
5. 3.61 ÷ .1	10. 5.74 ÷ .1	15. .263 ÷ .01

❯ Drill **20** Multiplication and division by .1, .01, and .001 Mental

Perform the indicated operation in each of the following.

1. 6.31 ÷ .1	6. .27 ÷ .1	11. .95 × .001
2. .042 ÷ .001	7. 183 × .001	12. 62.5 ÷ .01
3. 348 × .1	8. .52 × .1	13. 8.5 × .001
4. 420 × .001	9. 3.25 ÷ .001	14. .012 ÷ .01
5. 9.20 ÷ .01	10. 7.4 × .01	15. .27 ÷ .1

❯ Drill **21** Multiplication and division by 10, 100, and 1,000; and .1, .01, and .001 Mental

Perform the indicated operation in each of the following.

1. 2.6 ÷ 100	10. 27.8 ÷ 10	19. 4.4 × .1
2. .086 ÷ .01	11. 6.1 ÷ .01	20. 4.32 × 1,000
3. 9.7 × 10	12. .021 × 100	21. 52.4 ÷ 10
4. .325 ÷ .001	13. .275 ÷ .01	22. .084 × .01
5. .55 × 1,000	14. 4.2 × 100	23. 3.6 ÷ 100
6. 7.15 × .01	15. .45 × .001	24. .002 × 10
7. 4.72 ÷ 10	16. .073 × 10	25. .84 ÷ .001
8. 6.5 ÷ .1	17. 2.6 × 100	26. .012 × .1
9. 3.4 ÷ 10	18. .02 ÷ 10	27. .045 × 10

Drill **22** Articles purchased in quantities of 10, 100, or 1,000 Mental

Find the cost of each of the following.

1. 10 @ $.16	8. 100 @ $.01¼	15. 10 @ $.33⅓
2. 100 @ $.18	9. 100 @ $.06¼	16. 10 @ $.83⅓
3. 1,000 @ $.12	10. 1,000 @ $.02½	17. 10 @ $.16⅔
4. 10 @ $.02½	11. 1,000 @ $.01¼	18. 10 @ $.66⅔
5. 10 @ $.07½	12. 1,000 @ $.06¼	19. 10 @ $.06¼
6. 10 @ $.12½	13. 100 @ $.33⅓	20. 10 @ $.03¾
7. 100 @ $.02½	14. 100 @ $.83⅓	21. 10 @ $.08¾

Drill **23**   Articles priced at 10¢, $1, $10, etc.   Mental

Find the cost of each of the following.

1. 65 @ 10¢
2. 32 @ $1
3. 17 @ $10
4. $2\frac{1}{2}$ @ $1
5. $37\frac{1}{2}$ @ $10
6. $7\frac{1}{2}$ @ $100
7. $1\frac{1}{4}$ @ $100

8. $6\frac{1}{4}$ @ $100
9. $3\frac{3}{4}$ @ $100
10. $8\frac{3}{4}$ @ $100
11. $1\frac{1}{4}$ @ $10
12. $6\frac{1}{4}$ @ $10
13. $3\frac{3}{4}$ @ $10
14. $8\frac{3}{4}$ @ $10

15. $33\frac{1}{3}$ @ $1
16. $3\frac{1}{3}$ @ $1
17. $66\frac{2}{3}$ @ $1
18. $1\frac{1}{4}$ @ 10¢
19. $6\frac{1}{4}$ @ 10¢
20. $3\frac{3}{4}$ @ 10¢
21. $8\frac{3}{4}$ @ 10¢

Drill **24**   Articles priced per C, Cwt., M, or T   Mental

Find the cost of each of the following.

1.   300 articles @ $9 per C.
2.   125 cans   @ $6 per C.
3.   750 articles @ $4 per C.
4.   150 articles @ $12 per C.
5. 1,200 pounds @ $3.50 per cwt.
6.   750 pounds @ $4 per cwt.
7.   450 pounds @ $2 per cwt.
8.   250 pounds @ $4 per cwt.
9.   350 pounds @ $6 per cwt.
10. 175 pounds @ $12 per cwt.

11. 1,400 articles @ $15 per M.
12. 1,300 articles @ $9 per M.
13. 2,500 articles @ $12 per M.
14. 9,000 pounds @ $14 per T.
15. 5,000 pounds @ $18 per T.
16. 3,000 pounds @ $26 per T.
17. 6,000 pounds @ $22 per T.
18. 1,800 pounds @ $10 per T.
19. 1,300 pounds @ $14 per T.
20. 800 pounds @ $24 per T.

Drill **25**   Addition and subtraction of fractions   Mental

Perform the operation indicated in each of the following.

1. $\frac{1}{4} + \frac{3}{16}$
2. $\frac{1}{3} + \frac{5}{6}$
3. $\frac{1}{6} + \frac{11}{12}$
4. $\frac{1}{8} + \frac{15}{16}$
5. $\frac{7}{8} + \frac{1}{16}$
6. $\frac{5}{6} + \frac{7}{12}$

7. $\frac{5}{6} + \frac{11}{12}$
8. $\frac{1}{2} + \frac{2}{3}$
9. $\frac{5}{6} + \frac{1}{8}$
10. $\frac{2}{3} + \frac{3}{4}$
11. $\frac{3}{4} + \frac{1}{6}$
12. $\frac{2}{3} + \frac{1}{5}$

13. $\frac{5}{8} - \frac{3}{16}$
14. $\frac{2}{3} - \frac{1}{6}$
15. $\frac{11}{12} - \frac{1}{4}$
16. $\frac{5}{6} - \frac{1}{3}$
17. $\frac{7}{12} - \frac{1}{4}$
18. $\frac{2}{3} - \frac{1}{5}$

19. $\frac{1}{4} + \frac{1}{8} + \frac{1}{2}$
20. $\frac{1}{3} + \frac{1}{6} + \frac{1}{2}$
21. $\frac{1}{4} + \frac{3}{8} + \frac{1}{2}$
22. $\frac{7}{8} + \frac{1}{2} + \frac{3}{4}$
23. $\frac{1}{3} + \frac{1}{2} + \frac{5}{6}$
24. $\frac{1}{2} + \frac{1}{4} + \frac{5}{8}$

Drill **26**   Multiplication and division of fractions   Mental

Perform the operation indicated in each of the following.

1. $\frac{1}{3} \times \frac{2}{3}$
2. $\frac{1}{2} \times \frac{1}{3}$
3. $\frac{1}{4}$ of $\frac{4}{5}$
4. $\frac{1}{3} \times \frac{3}{8}$
5. $\frac{1}{2}$ of $\frac{4}{5}$
6. $\frac{1}{3}$ of $\frac{15}{16}$

7. $\frac{2}{3}$ of $\frac{9}{25}$
8. $\frac{2}{3} \times \frac{3}{8}$
9. $\frac{2}{5}$ of $\frac{15}{16}$
10. $\frac{3}{4} \times \frac{8}{15}$
11. $\frac{3}{8}$ of $\frac{15}{16}$
12. $\frac{5}{6}$ of $\frac{12}{25}$

13. $\frac{1}{3} \div \frac{1}{2}$
14. $\frac{3}{8} \div \frac{2}{3}$
15. $\frac{1}{6} \div \frac{1}{4}$
16. $\frac{3}{8} \div \frac{5}{8}$
17. $\frac{2}{5} \div \frac{4}{5}$
18. $\frac{1}{9} \div \frac{2}{3}$

19. $\frac{3}{8} \div \frac{1}{2}$
20. $\frac{4}{15} \div \frac{2}{3}$
21. $\frac{3}{5} \div \frac{9}{10}$
22. $\frac{2}{3} \div \frac{8}{9}$
23. $\frac{1}{2} \div \frac{1}{4}$
24. $\frac{1}{3} \div \frac{1}{4}$

25. $\frac{3}{4} \div \frac{3}{10}$
26. $\frac{2}{3} \div \frac{1}{3}$
27. $\frac{9}{10} \div \frac{3}{10}$
28. $\frac{5}{8} \div \frac{3}{8}$
29. $\frac{2}{3} \div \frac{2}{9}$
30. $\frac{3}{4} \div \frac{5}{8}$

Drill **27** Review of fractions   Mental

Perform the operation indicated in each of the following.

1. $\frac{7}{8} - \frac{1}{4}$ 11. $\frac{3}{4} \times \frac{16}{25}$ 21. $\frac{3}{4} - \frac{5}{12}$ 31. $\frac{3}{4} + \frac{1}{8} + \frac{1}{2}$

2. $\frac{1}{4} \div \frac{1}{3}$ 12. $\frac{5}{6} - \frac{1}{12}$ 22. $\frac{4}{5} \div \frac{3}{5}$ 32. $\frac{1}{4} + \frac{7}{8} + \frac{1}{2}$

3. $\frac{1}{2} \times \frac{6}{7}$ 13. $\frac{2}{5} + \frac{5}{6}$ 23. $\frac{3}{4} + \frac{1}{6}$ 33. $\frac{5}{6} + \frac{1}{2} + \frac{2}{3}$

4. $\frac{4}{5} + \frac{7}{10}$ 14. $\frac{5}{9} \div \frac{7}{9}$ 24. $\frac{3}{15} \div \frac{2}{5}$ 34. $\frac{3}{4} + \frac{1}{2} + \frac{3}{8}$

5. $\frac{3}{5} \div \frac{3}{4}$ 15. $\frac{1}{2} - \frac{3}{16}$ 25. $\frac{5}{6} \times \frac{4}{7}$ 35. $\frac{1}{2} + \frac{1}{6} + \frac{2}{3}$

6. $\frac{5}{12} - \frac{1}{3}$ 16. $\frac{2}{3}$ of $\frac{9}{16}$ 26. $\frac{2}{3} - \frac{1}{4}$ 36. $\frac{1}{3} \times \frac{3}{4} \times \frac{4}{5}$

7. $\frac{2}{3} + \frac{1}{4}$ 17. $\frac{3}{10} \div \frac{9}{10}$ 27. $\frac{7}{9} \div \frac{2}{3}$ 37. $\frac{2}{3} \times \frac{3}{8} \times \frac{1}{2}$

8. $\frac{3}{5}$ of $\frac{15}{32}$ 18. $\frac{5}{12} - \frac{1}{6}$ 28. $\frac{3}{5} - \frac{1}{4}$ 38. $\frac{5}{6} \times \frac{2}{3} \times \frac{2}{5}$

9. $\frac{3}{4} \div \frac{5}{6}$ 19. $\frac{2}{5}$ of $\frac{15}{32}$ 29. $\frac{2}{3} \div \frac{8}{9}$ 39. $\frac{3}{4} \times \frac{2}{3} \times \frac{6}{7}$

10. $\frac{2}{5} + \frac{3}{4}$ 20. $\frac{2}{9} \div \frac{2}{3}$ 30. $\frac{1}{8} + \frac{5}{12}$ 40. $\frac{2}{3} \times \frac{7}{8} \times \frac{4}{5}$

Drill **28**   Changing decimals to percents   Mental

Express each of the following as a percent.

1. .25   5. .004   9. 3   13. $1\frac{1}{2}$ 17. $1\frac{3}{4}$

2. .37   6. .0035   10. 2   14. $1\frac{1}{3}$ 18. $1\frac{2}{3}$

3. .123   7. 1.25   11. .425   15. .20   19. .001

4. .03   8. 2.45   12. .0075   16. .0625   20. 1.5

Drill **29**   Changing percents to decimals   Mental

Express each of the following as a decimal or a whole number, as the case may be.

1. 75%   5. 175%   9. 1%   13. 200%   17. $\frac{2}{5}$%

2. 46%   6. 225%   10. $\frac{1}{2}$%   14. $\frac{3}{4}$%   18. $\frac{1}{8}$%

3. 3.5%   7. 300%   11. $\frac{1}{4}$%   15. 100%   19. .125%

4. .2%   8. 4%   12. $\frac{2}{3}$%   16. .15%   20. $\frac{1}{3}$%

Drill **30**   Changing percents to fractions   Mental

Express each of the following as a fraction in lowest terms.

1. 17%   5. 6%   9. 1.3%   13. 1.5%   17. 24%

2. 3%   6. 14%   10. 1.4%   14. 5%   18. 2.8%

3. 2.3%   7. 8%   11. .8%   15. 4%   19. 1.2%

4. 1.9%   8. 12%   12. .5%   16. 35%   20. 34%

Drill **31**   Multiplication by aliquot parts of 100%   Mental

Perform the indicated multiplication in each of the following.

1. $12\frac{1}{2}\%$ of $32	7. $33\frac{1}{3}\%$ of $36	13. 25% of $26
2. 75% of $28	8. $87\frac{1}{2}\%$ of $72	14. $12\frac{1}{2}\%$ of $65
3. $83\frac{1}{3}\%$ of $42	9. $62\frac{1}{2}\%$ of $40	15. 25% of $29
4. $66\frac{2}{3}\%$ of $33	10. $33\frac{1}{3}\%$ of $129	16. 50% of $43
5. $87\frac{1}{2}\%$ of $48	11. $16\frac{2}{3}\%$ of $78	17. $16\frac{2}{3}\%$ of $39
6. $37\frac{1}{2}\%$ of $64	12. $66\frac{2}{3}\%$ of $45	18. $12\frac{1}{2}\%$ of $50

Drill **32**   Multiplication by 1%, 10%, etc.   Mental

Perform the indicated multiplication in each of the following.

1. 1% of $40	7. 1% of $120	13. 1,000% of $.56
2. 10% of $82	8. 10% of $65	14. 1% of $6.95
3. 100% of $39	9. 1% of $125	15. 100% of $35.40
4. 1,000% of $32	10. 1,000% of $2.15	16. 10% of $8.17
5. 10% of $24	11. 100% of $78	17. 1% of $35.40
6. 1% of $76	12. 1% of $150	18. 1,000% of $4.60

Drill **33**   Multiplication of a percent by 1, 10, 100, etc.   Mental

Perform the indicated multiplication in each of the following.

1. 25% of $1	7. 1% of $100	13. $66\frac{2}{3}\%$ of $1
2. $66\frac{2}{3}\%$ of $10	8. $87\frac{1}{2}\%$ of $1	14. 25% of $10
3. $62\frac{1}{2}\%$ of $100	9. 75% of $10	15. 75% of $1,000
4. $83\frac{1}{3}\%$ of $1,000	10. $16\frac{2}{3}\%$ of $100	16. $1\frac{1}{2}\%$ of $100
5. 75% of $100	11. $12\frac{1}{2}\%$ of $10	17. $1\frac{1}{4}\%$ of $1,000
6. $37\frac{1}{2}\%$ of $10	12. $83\frac{1}{3}\%$ of $100	18. $7\frac{1}{2}\%$ of $10

Drill **34**   Multiplication by fractional parts of 1%   Mental

Perform the indicated multiplication in each of the following.

1. 1% of $700	7. 1% of $525	13. $\frac{1}{10}\%$ of $1,828
2. $\frac{1}{2}\%$ of $600	8. $\frac{2}{3}\%$ of $1,500	14. $\frac{1}{2}\%$ of $100
3. $\frac{1}{4}\%$ of $800	9. $\frac{1}{2}\%$ of $1,250	15. $\frac{2}{3}\%$ of $100
4. $\frac{1}{3}\%$ of $1,200	10. $\frac{3}{4}\%$ of $600	16. $\frac{3}{4}\%$ of $520
5. $\frac{1}{5}\%$ of $1,000	11. $\frac{3}{8}\%$ of $1,600	17. $\frac{3}{4}\%$ of $100
6. $\frac{1}{8}\%$ of $2,400	12. $\frac{1}{10}\%$ of $1,575	18. $\frac{3}{8}\%$ of $400

Drill 35 Aliquot parts — $\frac{1}{4}$, $\frac{1}{2}$, and $\frac{3}{4}$ of $1 Mental

Find the cost of each of the following.

1. 36 @ 25¢	6. 210 @ 50¢	11. 24 @ $.75
2. 16 @ 75¢	7. 48 @ $.25	12. 230 @ 50¢
3. 160 @ $.50	8. 32 @ 75¢	13. 16 @ $.25
4. 28 @ $.75	9. 28 @ $.25	14. 290 @ 50¢
5. 120 @ $.25	10. 180 @ $.50	15. 280 @ 75¢

Drill 36 Aliquot parts — $\frac{1}{8}$, $\frac{3}{8}$, $\frac{5}{8}$, and $\frac{7}{8}$ of $1 Mental

Find the cost of each of the following.

1. 72 @ $.12$\frac{1}{2}$	7. 64 @ 12$\frac{1}{2}$¢	13. 40 @ $.62$\frac{1}{2}$
2. 24 @ 62$\frac{1}{2}$¢	8. 32 @ $.87$\frac{1}{2}$	14. 96 @ 12$\frac{1}{2}$¢
3. 32 @ 37$\frac{1}{2}$¢	9. 16 @ 62$\frac{1}{2}$¢	15. 48 @ $.62$\frac{1}{2}$
4. 16 @ $.87$\frac{1}{2}$	10. 24 @ 87$\frac{1}{2}$¢	16. 24 @ 37$\frac{1}{2}$¢
5. 56 @ $.37$\frac{1}{2}$	11. 48 @ $.37$\frac{1}{2}$	17. 56 @ $.12$\frac{1}{2}$
6. 72 @ $.62$\frac{1}{2}$	12. 32 @ $.12$\frac{1}{2}$	18. 80 @ 87$\frac{1}{2}$¢

Drill 37 Aliquot parts — review Mental

Find the cost of each of the following.

1. 36 @ 75¢	8. 56 @ $.87$\frac{1}{2}$	15. 350 @ $.50
2. 64 @ $.62$\frac{1}{2}$	9. 84 @ 25¢	16. 48 @ 87$\frac{1}{2}$¢
3. 250 @ 50¢	10. 160 @ 75¢	17. 364 @ $.25
4. 72 @ $.37$\frac{1}{2}$	11. 88 @ $.37$\frac{1}{2}$	18. 64 @ $.37$\frac{1}{2}$
5. 120 @ $.25	12. 32 @ 62$\frac{1}{2}$¢	19. 88 @ 75¢
6. 48 @ 12$\frac{1}{2}$¢	13. 240 @ $.12$\frac{1}{2}$	20. 320 @ 12$\frac{1}{2}$¢
7. 80 @ 62$\frac{1}{2}$¢	14. 40 @ $.87$\frac{1}{2}$	21. 218 @ 50¢

Drill 38 Aliquot parts — $\frac{1}{3}$, $\frac{2}{3}$, $\frac{1}{6}$, and $\frac{5}{6}$ of $1 Mental

Find the cost of each of the following.

1. 27 @ 33$\frac{1}{3}$¢	7. 36 @ $.83$\frac{1}{3}$	13. 45 @ $.33$\frac{1}{3}$
2. 18 @ 66$\frac{2}{3}$¢	8. 24 @ 66$\frac{2}{3}$¢	14. 126 @ $.16$\frac{2}{3}$
3. 72 @ $.16$\frac{2}{3}$	9. 42 @ $.33$\frac{1}{3}$	15. 36 @ 66$\frac{2}{3}$¢
4. 24 @ $.83$\frac{1}{3}$	10. 120 @ 16$\frac{2}{3}$¢	16. 120 @ $.33$\frac{1}{3}$
5. 21 @ 66$\frac{2}{3}$¢	11. 48 @ 83$\frac{1}{3}$¢	17. 240 @ 16$\frac{2}{3}$¢
6. 39 @ $.33$\frac{1}{3}$	12. 540 @ $.16$\frac{2}{3}$	18. 600 @ $.66$\frac{2}{3}$

Drill **39**   Aliquot parts — review   Mental

Find the cost of each of the following.

1. 32 @ $.12½
2. 54 @ 83⅓¢
3. 64 @ $.87½
4. 80 @ 75¢
5. 48 @ 16⅔¢
6. 56 @ $.62½
7. 84 @ $.50

8. 27 @ 66⅔¢
9. 40 @ $.37½
10. 88 @ 25¢
11. 24 @ $.33⅓
12. 72 @ $.62½
13. 92 @ 50¢
14. 60 @ 66⅔¢

15. 96 @ $.37½
16. 124 @ 25¢
17. 150 @ $.33⅓
18. 88 @ $.12½
19. 72 @ 87½¢
20. 84 @ 75¢
21. 96 @ $.16⅔

Drill **40**   Aliquot parts — $\frac{1}{12}$, $\frac{1}{15}$, and $\frac{1}{16}$ of $1   Mental

Find the cost of each of the following.

1. 72 @ 8⅓¢
2. 30 @ 6⅔¢
3. 48 @ 6¼¢
4. 60 @ $.06⅔

5. 32 @ $.06¼
6. 96 @ $.08⅓
7. 75 @ 6⅔¢
8. 84 @ 8⅓¢

9. 45 @ $.06⅔
10. 64 @ $.06¼
11. 240 @ 8⅓¢
12. 96 @ $.06¼

Drill **41**   Aliquot parts — review   Mental

Find the cost of each of the following.

1. 180 @ 33⅓¢
2. 48 @ 75¢
3. 120 @ $.08⅓
4. 160 @ 87½¢
5. 140 @ 50¢
6. 120 @ $.83⅓
7. 32 @ $.62½
8. 128 @ 25¢
9. 360 @ 16⅔¢
10. 480 @ 37½¢

11. 48 @ $.06¼
12. 180 @ $.66⅔
13. 64 @ $.12½
14. 45 @ 6⅔¢
15. 480 @ $.16⅔
16. 56 @ 37½¢
17. 80 @ 6¼¢
18. 600 @ 66⅔¢
19. 120 @ $.12½
20. 150 @ 6⅔¢

21. 450 @ $.33⅓
22. 240 @ $.75
23. 360 @ 8⅓¢
24. 240 @ $.87½
25. 180 @ 50¢
26. 36 @ $.83⅓
27. 160 @ 62½¢
28. 240 @ 25¢
29. 540 @ $.16⅔
30. 32 @ $.12½

Drill **42**   Combinations of aliquot parts of $1   Mental

Find the cost of each of the following.

1. 24 @ $1.12½
2. 14 @ $2.50
3. 48 @ $1.25
4. 15 @ $1.10
5. 80 @ $1.50
6. 60 @ $1.25
7. 72 @ $1.12½

8. 25 @ $1.10
9. 90 @ $1.50
10. 16 @ $2.50
11. 160 @ $1.50
12. 120 @ $1.25
13. 140 @ $2.50
14. 35 @ $1.10

15. 96 @ $1.12½
16. 320 @ $2.50
17. 250 @ $1.50
18. 120 @ $1.10
19. 240 @ $1.25
20. 104 @ $1.12½
21. 420 @ $1.50

Drill **43** Aliquot parts of 100 Mental

Find the cost of each of the following.

1. $33\frac{1}{3}$ @ 15¢
2. 75 @ 28¢
3. $87\frac{1}{2}$ @ $.48
4. 50 @ $.38
5. $83\frac{1}{3}$ @ 24¢
6. $62\frac{1}{2}$ @ $.32
7. 25 @ 48¢
8. $16\frac{2}{3}$ @ $.18

9. $37\frac{1}{2}$ @ $.32
10. $66\frac{2}{3}$ @ 24¢
11. $12\frac{1}{2}$ @ $.48
12. $16\frac{2}{3}$ @ $.42
13. $37\frac{1}{2}$ @ 64¢
14. $66\frac{2}{3}$ @ 36¢
15. $12\frac{1}{2}$ @ 64¢
16. $33\frac{1}{3}$ @ $.45

17. 75 @ $.88
18. $87\frac{1}{2}$ @ $2.40
19. 50 @ $.84
20. $83\frac{1}{3}$ @ 36¢
21. $62\frac{1}{2}$ @ 56¢
22. 25 @ $1.60
23. $16\frac{2}{3}$ @ $.48
24. $12\frac{1}{2}$ @ 72¢

Drill **44** Combinations of aliquot parts of 100 Mental

Find the cost of each of the following.

1. 125 @ 16¢
2. 250 @ 12¢
3. 150 @ 22¢
4. 175 @ $.12
5. 250 @ $.14
6. 150 @ 18¢
7. 125 @ 12¢
8. 150 @ $.24

9. 175 @ $.16
10. 125 @ $.28
11. 250 @ 16¢
12. 150 @ 14¢
13. 125 @ $.24
14. 250 @ 18¢
15. 150 @ $1.40
16. 125 @ $1.20

17. 150 @ $1.80
18. 175 @ $1.20
19. 250 @ $1.40
20. 125 @ $1.60
21. 150 @ $4.40
22. 125 @ $2.40
23. 175 @ $1.60
24. 250 @ $1.20

Drill **45** Aliquot parts — general review Mental

Find the cost of each of the following.

1. 150 articles @ $33\frac{1}{3}$¢
2. 25 bushels @ $2.16
3. 87 bushels @ $33\frac{1}{3}$¢
4. 56 crates @ $37\frac{1}{2}$¢
5. $16\frac{2}{3}$ yards @ 72¢
6. 84 bushels @ 75¢
7. 104 yards @ 25¢
8. 75 dozen @ 60¢
9. 64 bushels @ $87\frac{1}{2}$¢
10. 315 feet @ $33\frac{1}{3}$¢
11. 125 bushels @ 60¢
12. 125 articles @ 40¢
13. 48 bushels @ $16\frac{2}{3}$¢
14. 120 yards @ $1.25
15. 330 bushels @ $33\frac{1}{3}$¢
16. 320 dozen @ $87\frac{1}{2}$¢
17. 120 gallons @ 50¢

18. 75 yards @ 56¢
19. 125 bushels @ 80¢
20. 56 dozen @ $1.25
21. 120 articles @ 75¢
22. 660 yards @ $.66$\frac{2}{3}$
23. 240 yards @ $.87$\frac{1}{2}$
24. 96 yards @ 25¢
25. 72 dozen @ $1.25
26. 48 bushels @ $.66$\frac{2}{3}$
27. 175 articles @ 32¢
28. 640 dozen @ $1.25
29. 360 articles @ 75¢
30. 48 articles @ $2.50
31. 125 articles @ $.16
32. 72 articles @ $.37$\frac{1}{2}$
33. 630 articles @ $.66$\frac{2}{3}$
34. 1,240 dozen @ $1.50

Drill **46**   Making extensions — general review   Mental

Find the cost of each of the following.

1. 360 bushels @ $16\frac{2}{3}$¢
2. 32 quarts @ $62\frac{1}{2}$¢
3. 240 bushels @ $1.25
4. 25 pounds @ 96¢
5. 20 yards @ $.65
6. 120 articles @ $.12$\frac{1}{2}$
7. 180 bushels @ 50¢
8. 72 yards @ 1.12\frac{1}{2}$
9. $16\frac{2}{3}$ feet @ 42¢
10. 56 quarts @ $37\frac{1}{2}$¢
11. 360 bushels @ $.08$\frac{1}{3}$
12. 75 pounds @ 88¢
13. 160 pounds @ $.87$\frac{1}{2}$
14. $12\frac{1}{2}$ bushels @ $.72
15. $62\frac{1}{2}$ pounds @ $.64
16. 80 feet @ 35¢
17. 120 gallons @ $33\frac{1}{3}$¢

18. 280 bushels @ 75¢
19. 140 bushels @ $2.50
20. 50 gallons @ 36¢
21. 60 quarts @ $.45
22. 160 bushels @ 25¢
23. 600 gallons @ $.66$\frac{2}{3}$
24. 250 yards @ $1.50
25. $37\frac{1}{2}$ pounds @ 64¢
26. 40 pounds @ $.65
27. 450 pounds @ $10 per cwt.
28. 1,500 cards @ $6 per M.
29. 4,500 pounds @ $10 per ton
30. 650 pounds @ $4 per cwt.
31. 3,500 feet @ $12 per M.
32. 3,000 pounds @ $18 per ton
33. 250 pounds @ $2 per cwt.
34. 1,200 pounds @ $15 per ton

Drill **47**   Making extensions — general review   Mental

Find the cost of each of the following.

1. 370 bushels @ 50¢
2. 120 bushels @ $1.25
3. $37\frac{1}{2}$ pounds @ 72¢
4. 60 gallons @ 35¢
5. 450 feet @ $33\frac{1}{3}$¢
6. 96 bushels @ 1.12\frac{1}{2}$
7. 25 bushels @ $.88
8. 40 pounds @ 62¢
9. 720 bushels @ $.25
10. 360 articles @ 75¢
11. $12\frac{1}{2}$ pounds @ $.48
12. 75 quarts @ $.64
13. 30 yards @ $12\frac{1}{2}$¢
14. 160 bushels @ $62\frac{1}{2}$¢
15. 420 yards @ $1.50
16. 50 gallons @ $.86
17. 80 quarts @ 45¢

18. 480 gallons @ $37\frac{1}{2}$¢
19. 325 pounds @ $8 per cwt.
20. 1,500 feet @ $40 per M.
21. 320 bushels @ $2.50
22. 1,600 pounds @ $20 per ton
23. $62\frac{1}{2}$ bushels @ $1.60
24. 650 pounds @ $3 per cwt.
25. 1,200 pads @ $30 per M.
26. 240 pounds @ $16\frac{2}{3}$¢
27. 1,200 lbs. @ $3.50 per cwt.
28. 180 bushels @ $66\frac{2}{3}$¢
29. 800 pounds @ $35 per ton
30. $16\frac{2}{3}$ yards @ $.48
31. 20 quarts @ 85¢
32. 1,600 pounds @ $25 per ton
33. 240 bushels @ $.87$\frac{1}{2}$
34. 120 yards @ $8\frac{1}{3}$¢

Drill **48**   Interest for multiples of 6, 60, and 600 days   Mental

Find the interest at 6% on:

1. $350 for 6 da.
2. $1,300 for 18 da.
3. $200 for 48 da.
4. $220 for 12 da.
5. $500 for 42 da.
6. $800 for 24 da.
7. $300 for 54 da.
8. $400 for 18 da.
9. $400 for 36 da.
10. $310 for 120 da.
11. $200 for 180 da.
12. $80 for 420 da.
13. $150 for 240 da.
14. $210 for 360 da.
15. $105 for 540 da.
16. $100 for 120 da.
17. $41 for 1,200 da.
18. $37 for 1,800 da.
19. $17 for 4,800 da.
20. $25 for 3,600 da.
21. $29 for 2,400 da.
22. $21 for 4,200 da.
23. $13 for 5,400 da.
24. $16 for 1,800 da.

Drill **49**   Interest for aliquot parts of 6, 60, and 600 days   Mental

Find the interest at 6% on:

1. $1,500 for 2 da.
2. $1,800 for 1 da.
3. $3,600 for 2 da.
4. $2,400 for 1 da.
5. $2,800 for 3 da.
6. $390 for 20 da.
7. $420 for 30 da.
8. $720 for 10 da.
9. $840 for 15 da.
10. $525 for 12 da.
11. $240 for 45 da.
12. $270 for 40 da.
13. $620 for 300 da.
14. $390 for 200 da.
15. $210 for 400 da.
16. $320 for 150 da.
17. $440 for 450 da.
18. $480 for 100 da.
19. $180 for 500 da.
20. $1,220 for 30 da.
21. $2,760 for 2 da.
22. $160 for 150 da.
23. $120 for 15 da.
24. $180 for 10 da.
25. $3,400 for 3 da.
26. $150 for 200 da.
27. $6,900 for 2 da.
28. $6,600 for 1 da.
29. $340 for 30 da.
30. $350 for 12 da.
31. $540 for 20 da.
32. $80 for 450 da.
33. $280 for 300 da.

▶ Drill **50**   Interest for combinations of 6 and 60 days with parts of 6 and 60 days   Mental

Find the interest at 6% on:

1. $160 for 9 da.
2. $210 for 8 da.
3. $720 for 7 da.
4. $1,400 for 9 da.
5. $660 for 7 da.
6. $2,700 for 8 da.
7. $400 for 90 da.
8. $1,500 for 9 da.
9. $160 for 75 da.
10. $360 for 80 da.
11. $180 for 70 da.
12. $250 for 72 da.
13. $500 for 66 da.
14. $270 for 80 da.
15. $360 for 66 da.
16. $800 for 90 da.
17. $360 for 70 da.
18. $250 for 90 da.
19. $240 for 75 da.
20. $1,250 for 90 da.
21. $65 for 72 da.
22. $990 for 80 da.
23. $42 for 70 da.
24. $180 for 90 da.

❯ Drill **51**   Interchange of principal and time   Mental

By the interchange method, see page 199, find the interest at 6% on:

1. $60 for 21 da.	**16.** $360 for 41 da.	**31.** $200 for 21 da.
2. $600 for 19 da.	**17.** $240 for 17 da.	**32.** $800 for 21 da.
3. $6,000 for 13 da.	**18.** $480 for 23 da.	**33.** $600 for 51 da.
4. $600 for 26 da.	**19.** $180 for 34 da.	**34.** $1,200 for 51 da.
5. $6,000 for 37 da.	**20.** $540 for 16 da.	**35.** $3,600 for 14 da.
6. $60 for 46 da.	**21.** $600 for 34 da.	**36.** $2,400 for 43 da.
7. $30 for 46 da.	**22.** $300 for 34 da.	**37.** $1,800 for 35 da.
8. $90 for 46 da.	**23.** $200 for 39 da.	**38.** $3,600 for 25 da.
9. $15 for 160 da.	**24.** $400 for 27 da.	**39.** $1,200 for 83 da.
10. $75 for 160 da.	**25.** $150 for 56 da.	**40.** $6,000 for 69 da.
11. $30 for 108 da.	**26.** $450 for 32 da.	**41.** $2,000 for 69 da.
12. $90 for 62 da.	**27.** $100 for 96 da.	**42.** $1,500 for 64 da.
13. $15 for 128 da.	**28.** $600 for 29 da.	**43.** $2,000 for 126 da.
14. $75 for 124 da.	**29.** $300 for 26 da.	**44.** $1,500 for 108 da.
15. $120 for 65 da.	**30.** $900 for 26 da.	**45.** $3,000 for 19 da.

❯ Drill **52**   Interest review   Mental

Find the interest at 6% on:

1. $600 for 36 da.	**19.** $90 for 320 da.	**37.** $850 for 30 da.
2. $450 for 30 da.	**20.** $150 for 18 da.	**38.** $1,200 for 74 da.
3. $1,850 for 90 da.	**21.** $200 for 9 da.	**39.** $960 for 20 da.
4. $90 for 218 da.	**22.** $200 for 1 mo.	**40.** $400 for 18 da.
5. $60 for 97 da.	**23.** $2,786 for 6 da.	**41.** $800 for 33 da.
6. $1,800 for 30 da.	**24.** $60 for 113 da.	**42.** $50.50 for 60 da.
7. $3,050 for 6 da.	**25.** $720 for 12 da.	**43.** $900 for 22 da.
8. $8,400 for 60 da.	**26.** $900 for 1 mo.	**44.** $150 for 72 da.
9. $15 for 280 da.	**27.** $420 for 9 da.	**45.** $800 for 27 da.
10. $460 for 1 mo.	**28.** $30 for 112 da.	**46.** $250 for 90 da.
11. $350 for 12 da.	**29.** $4,897 for 6 da.	**47.** $100 for 18 da.
12. $500 for 9 da.	**30.** $800 for 4 mo.	**48.** $1,200 for 49 da.
13. $60 for 57 da.	**31.** $2,400 for 11 da.	**49.** $16 for 45 da.
14. $250 for 3 mo.	**32.** $900 for 3 mo.	**50.** $260 for 9 da.
15. $5,429 for 6 da.	**33.** $600 for 46 da.	**51.** $650 for 72 da.
16. $186 for 20 da.	**34.** $300 for 45 da.	**52.** $360 for 26 da.
17. $3,600 for 3 da.	**35.** $100 for 96 da.	**53.** $660 for 40 da.
18. $450 for 2 mo.	**36.** $30 for 73 da.	**54.** $250 for 72 da.

● Drill **53** Interest for fractional parts of 6%   Mental

In solving each of the following problems, first find the interest mentally at 6%, and then multiply that result by the fraction that is equal to the given rate.

1. $800 for 60 days at $1\frac{1}{2}\%$

2. $1,000 for 2 months at $4\frac{1}{2}\%$

3. $180 for 60 days at 5%

4. $240 for 30 days at 4%

5. $3,600 for 30 days at 1%

6. $360 for 60 days at 2%

7. $600 for 30 days at 3%

8. $2,400 for 20 days at $1\frac{1}{2}\%$

9. $560 for 15 days at 3%

10. $2,400 for 30 days at 2%

11. $440 for 60 days at 3%

12. $480 for 20 days at $4\frac{1}{2}\%$

13. $1,200 for 30 days at 7%

14. $480 for 15 days at 5%

15. $1,600 for 30 days at $1\frac{1}{2}\%$

16. $680 for 2 months at 3%

17. $800 for 30 days at $4\frac{1}{2}\%$

18. $750 for 12 days at 2%

19. $240 for 30 days at 7%

20. $8,400 for 6 days at $1\frac{1}{2}\%$

21. $560 for 75 days at 3%

22. $880 for 2 months at $1\frac{1}{2}\%$

● Drill **54** Interest for fractional parts of 6%   Mental

When the interest rate is a fractional part of 6%, some problems are most easily solved by finding the interest at 6% for a fractional part of the days or months given in the time.

By this method, the interest on $840 for 20 days at $4\frac{1}{2}\%$, for example, would be calculated in the following manner:

$4\frac{1}{2}\% = \frac{3}{4}$ of 6%
$\frac{3}{4}$ of 20 da. = 15 da.
Int. at 6% on $840 for 15 da. = $2.10

In each of the problems given below, find the interest mentally by the method shown above.

1. $327 for 80 days at $4\frac{1}{2}\%$

2. $360 for 6 months at 2%

3. $1,000 for 72 days at 5%

4. $437 for 4 months at 3%

5. $240 for 90 days at 4%

6. $900 for 36 days at 5%

7. $420 for 45 days at 4%

8. $480 for 15 days at 4%

9. $840 for 40 days at $1\frac{1}{2}\%$

10. $420 for 3 months at 2%

11. $250 for 6 months at 3%

12. $630 for 8 days at $4\frac{1}{2}\%$

13. $660 for 20 days at 3%

14. $250 for 90 days at 4%

15. $1,800 for 40 days at $1\frac{1}{2}\%$

16. $1,600 for 90 days at 2%

17. $260 for 4 months at $4\frac{1}{2}\%$

18. $5,400 for 30 days at 2%

19. $3,600 for 40 days at $4\frac{1}{2}\%$

20. $720 for 36 days at 5%

21. $450 for 80 days at $1\frac{1}{2}\%$

22. $320 for 3 months at 4%

❯ Drill **55** Interest review   Mental

Find the interest on:

1. $800 for 15 days at 6%
2. $1,500 for 120 days at 6%
3. $500 for 6 days at 6%
4. $840 for 60 days at 2%
5. $800 for 2 months at 3%
6. $480 for 30 days at 6%
7. $400 for 15 days at 6%
8. $578.90 for 6 days at 6%
9. $750 for 60 days at 2%
10. $1,200 for 15 days at 6%
11. $280 for 60 days at 3%
12. $5,000 for 120 days at 6%
13. $600 for 60 days at 2%
14. $300 for 58 days at 6%
15. $1,700 for 1 yr. at 5%
16. $700 for 120 days at 6%
17. $1,400 for 15 days at 6%

18. $1,915 for 6 days at 6%
19. $1,250 for 60 days at 3%
20. $500 for 15 days at 6%
21. $280 for 30 days at 6%
22. $230 for 60 days at 3%
23. $3,000 for 4 months at 6%
24. $600 for 19 days at 6%
25. $5,800 for 30 days at 6%
26. $240 for 18 days at 6%
27. $1,000 for 2 months at 6%
28. $60 for 470 days at 6%
29. $3,600 for 60 days at 7%
30. $80 for 75 days at 3%
31. $240 for 3 months at 6%
32. $750 for 1 year at 2%
33. $2,400 for 30 days at 5%
34. $3,488 for 6 days at 6%

❯ Drill **56** Interest review   Mental

Find the interest on:

1. $1,450 for 60 days at 3%
2. $5,900 for 6 days at 6%
3. $5,600 for 30 days at 6%
4. $600 for 126 days at 6%
5. $1,200 for 90 days at 2%
6. $500 for 4 months at 6%
7. $950 for 12 days at 6%
8. $150 for 30 days at 6%
9. $950 for 60 days at 3%
10. $1,600 for 15 days at $4\frac{1}{2}$%
11. $1,000 for 120 days at 6%
12. $60 for 113 days at 6%
13. $600 for 178 days at 6%
14. $7,858 for 6 days at 6%
15. $1,500 for 60 days at 2%
16. $320 for 60 days at 3%
17. $1,800 for 90 days at 6%

18. $900 for 1 year at 3%
19. $1,000 for 60 days at $4\frac{1}{2}$%
20. $600 for 26 days at 6%
21. $750 for 30 days at 2%
22. $920 for 15 days at 6%
23. $800 for 4 months at 3%
24. $6,000 for 15 days at 6%
25. $400 for 90 days at 3%
26. $450 for 3 months at 6%
27. $810 for 60 days at 2%
28. $600 for 47 days at 6%
29. $60 for 129 days at 6%
30. $1,000 for 1 year at 3%
31. $486 for 30 days at 6%
32. $600 for 137 days at 6%
33. $1,500 for 1 year at 4%
34. $800 for 90 days at $4\frac{1}{2}$%

Supplementary Problems

The following problems have been adapted from problems given on various final examinations in business mathematics. They are classified by sections and units to correlate with the text.

Sections **1–3**   Unit One

1. On July 2, Hubert's checkbook balance was $814.83. The statement he received from his bank on that date showed a balance of $928.54. Checks outstanding were: No. 35 for $75.21; No. 38 for $16.50; No. 39 for $25. Further comparison of the checkbook with the statement showed that a service charge of $3 had been deducted by the bank. Prepare a reconciliation statement.

2. On April 30, Edwin Slate had a checkbook balance of $345.65 and a bank statement balance of $504.25. There was a service charge of $1.95 reported on the bank statement. The outstanding checks amounted to: $24.15; $38.90; $46.50; $51. Prepare a reconciliation statement.

3. Mr. Henderson's bank statement as of January 31 showed a bank balance of $1,165.75. His checkbook balance was $1,319.05. Checks were outstanding for $16.60; $23.10; $34.60. A deposit of $170.50, mailed on January 31, was not recorded on the bank statement. Among the canceled checks was one for $57.10 that Mr. Henderson had failed to record in his checkbook. Prepare a reconciliation statement.

4. On May 31, Mr. Albert Cook's checkbook balance was $336. On the same date his bank statement showed a balance of $568. The following checks were outstanding: $100; $23.50; and $19.50. It was also discovered that a deposit for $91.50 had not been entered in the checkbook. The bank had deducted a service charge of $2.50 for which a voucher was enclosed with the canceled checks. Prepare a reconciliation statement.

5. Frazier's checkbook had a balance of $151.37 at the end of last month. His bank statement balance on the same date was $307.98. A service charge of $1.32 had been made. A comparison of canceled checks with check stubs showed that the following checks were outstanding: $28.54; $19.29; and $101.10. One of the canceled checks written for $45 had been mistakenly entered on the checkbook stub as $54. Prepare a reconciliation statement.

❯ **6.** On March 31, Mr. Wooden's bank statement showed a balance of $327.97. His checkbook balance for that date was $345.97. A deposit for $56.20 on March 31 had not been recorded yet by the bank, and the following checks were outstanding: $17.50; $6.80; $14.25. In addition, a service charge of $.35 had been made during the month by the bank. Prepare a reconciliation statement.

❯ **7.** On June 1, Dawson's checkbook balance was $575. His bank statement on that date showed a balance of $620.30. Checks for $63.80 and $49 were outstanding. The statement showed that the bank had deducted a service charge of $3 for the month. Dawson discovered that a deposit of $64.50 had been recorded twice in his checkbook by mistake. Prepare a reconciliation statement.

❯ **8.** On December 1, J. C. Allen's checkbook balance was $1,417.50. On the same date the monthly statement from the bank showed a balance of $1,578.40. Checks for the following amounts were outstanding: $74.50; $91.42; $27.48. A comparison of the statement with the checkbook showed that the following items, which were not recorded in the checkbook, had been paid: a canceled check for $20.10 and a charge of $3.40 for banking services. The amount of one of the canceled checks was $421, while the amount on the checkbook stub was $412. Prepare a reconciliation statement.

Sections **4–9** Unit Two

1. The Acme Sales Company conducted a contest for its salesmen. Potter's average sales for the last nine weeks of last year were $379.65. For the first four weeks of this year, his sales amounted to $376.14, $625.32, $429.53, and $374.52, respectively. Find Potter's average weekly sales for the 13 weeks.

2. Mr. Smallman sold merchandise as follows: first week $750; second week $850; third week $600; fourth week $900. How much merchandise must be sold during the fifth week in order that Mr. Smallman will have an average of $800 in sales per week for the five-week period?

3. A salesman earned $82, $96, $78, and $92 each week for four weeks. What amount will he need to earn the fifth week in order to have a final average earnings for five weeks of $85?

4. A ticket seller at a school track meet was given 300 75-cent tickets for adults, 400 50-cent tickets for students, and $15 in cash for change. After the meet, he turned back to the office 28 adult tickets, 22 student tickets, and $409 in cash. By what amount of money was his actual cash short or over?

5. Miss Lee, a cashier at a summer theater, had the following money in the cash box of the ticket-selling window at the start of a particular working day: 2 five-dollar bills, 10 one-dollar bills, 15 half dollars, 42 quarters, 55 dimes, 90 nickels. At the close of the day when she was proving her day's cash receipts, she found that she had sold 179 adults' tickets at 60¢ each and 57 children's tickets at 30¢ each.

How much money should Miss Lee have in the cash box at the conclusion of this day?

Sections **10-12**   Unit Three

1. One side of a room is 145 inches long. Two cabinets already placed along the wall measure $38\frac{1}{8}$ inches and $50\frac{1}{4}$ inches, respectively. How many inches of space are left for a third cabinet to be placed along the wall?

2. In planning the available office space along a wall 27 feet long, the following allowances for machines and work space are needed: $5\frac{1}{4}$ ft.; $3\frac{1}{6}$ ft.; $7\frac{2}{3}$ ft.; $4\frac{1}{2}$ ft. How many feet of space would remain unused?

3. In a furniture factory, it usually takes $58\frac{1}{5}$ hours to build a certain cabinet. Recently, the cabinet was finished in $47\frac{1}{2}$ hours. How much time was saved?

4. A machinist spent $23\frac{1}{2}$ hours working on a part. If he is paid at the rate of $3.90 per hour, what will be the cost of his labor for the part?

5. A customer bought $1\frac{1}{3}$ dozen handkerchiefs at $6.69 a dozen; $\frac{1}{4}$ dozen towels at $13.80 a dozen; $\frac{3}{4}$ dozen washcloths at $5.35 a dozen; and one pair of socks at $1.19. He gave in payment a $20 bill. How much change should he receive?

6. Find the total cost of the following: 375 pineapples @ $39.75 a hundred; 64 bags of sugar, each containing 25 pounds, @ $11\frac{3}{4}$ cents a pound; 3 cases of peas, each containing 2 dozen cans, @ $3.25 a dozen; 74 packages of paper bags, each containing 50 bags, @ $6 per thousand.

7. A builder purchased $32\frac{1}{2}$ acres of land for a building development. He divided the property into plots of $2\frac{1}{2}$ acres each. How many plots did he have?

8. A dress manufacturer requires $3\frac{1}{4}$ yards of cloth to complete one dress. How many dresses can be made from a bolt of cloth containing 65 yards?

Sections **13–17**   Unit Four

1. Mr. Jones, an employee of Robinson & Haitz Co., is employed on a 40-hour-week basis, with time and a half for overtime. The regular rate paid this employee is $3.20 per hour. During the week of January 4 Jones worked 46 hours. The following deductions were made from his gross pay: 4.8% for FICA tax, $16.10 for federal withholding tax, $.30 for disability benefits insurance, $3 for state withholding tax, and $1 for United Appeal contribution. What will be the take-home pay for Mr. Jones?

2. Post is employed on the basis of 8 hours a day with time and one-half for all overtime hours worked beyond 8 hours. His regular hourly pay rate is $2.30. Last week he worked the following hours:

Mon. 8 hr.; Tues., 9 hr.; Wed., 8 hr.; Thurs., 6 hr.; Fri., 10 hr.

From Post's total earnings, 4.8% was deducted for FICA taxes. In addition, $7.70 was deducted for federal withholding tax, $1.30 for state withholding tax, and $.30 for disability benefits. What net amount of money did Post receive as take-home pay?

3. Lamb is paid $.16⅔ for each acceptable part he makes at work. On Monday he completed 131 pieces; on Tuesday, 136; on Wednesday, 137; on Thursday, 139; and on Friday, 113. Fourteen parts were rejected for defects. What were Lamb's total earnings for that week?

4. Doris Zimmer is employed by the Eagle Mills and is paid $.07½ for each article completed and accepted. During the last week in April she completed the following:

Mon., 210; Tues., 220; Wed., 228; Thurs., 234; Fri., 222

A total of 18 articles were not accepted. What were her gross earnings for that week?

5. Mr. Jacobs is employed in a shoe factory where employees are paid on a piece work basis. The rate of pay for the type of work performed by Mr. Jacobs is 9½ cents per pair of shoes processed. During one week Mr. Jacobs processed the following: Monday 260 pairs; Tuesday 225 pairs; Wednesday 204 pairs; Thursday 224 pairs; Friday 267 pairs. His payroll deductions were: withholding taxes $12.20; FICA tax $5.33, and state disability tax $.30. What was Mr. Jacobs' take-home pay?

6. Deere, Fisher, and Griffin earned $124.37, $125.25, and $124.19, respectively, during the week ending February 14. By using the Social Security Employee Tax Table on page 108, determine the total amount of FICA tax withheld from the gross wages of each of the three employees.

Sections **18–21** Unit Five

1. During the first week in September, Ralph sold 72 aluminum storm windows at $17.25 each. How much did he earn if his rate of commission was 20% of sales?

2. Hogan, a salesman, sold 5 boats in July when the selling price was $429.50 each. In August, when the price was reduced to $399.50, he sold 7 boats. Hogan's commission is 6% of his sales. What was the amount of the difference between the commissions he received in July and those he received in August?

3. Alpert's sales for the Acme Supply Company for the months of April, May, and June were $3,750, $2,840, and $3,225. He is paid a salary of $300 per month and a commission of 4% on that part of his sales in excess of $3,000 for any one month. What was the amount of Alpert's total earnings for the three months?

4. A salesman is paid $4\frac{1}{2}$% commission on all sales up to and including $5,500, and $6\frac{1}{2}$% on that portion of his sales in excess of $5,500 in any one month. Last month his sales were $8,000.

   a What amount of commission did he earn at the $4\frac{1}{2}$% rate?

   b What amount of commission did he earn at the $6\frac{1}{2}$% rate?

5. Edwards, a salesman, is paid a salary of $300 per month and commission as follows:

10% on all sales in excess of $2,000 per month
An additional commission of 2% on all sales in excess of $3,500 per month

Last month Edwards' sales amounted to $5,850. What were Edwards' total earnings for that month?

6. Avery, a book salesman, is paid a salary of $85 per week. He is also paid a commission of 25¢ per book on all sales and an additional commission of $12\frac{1}{2}$¢ per book on all sales in excess of 80 books per week. During a recent week, he sold 124 books. What were Avery's total earnings for that week?

7. Albright, a salesman, receives a monthly salary of $300 and is also paid commissions of varying rates on different sales. His total earnings, including both salary and commissions, were $7,870 during 1970. If Albright's sales for the year were $61,000, what average percent of commission did he earn?

◗ **8.** A salesman was paid a commission of $480 for his services in selling a plot of ground. What was the selling price of the plot if the commission was figured at the rate of 5%?

9. A real estate agency engaged R. Lewis as a salesman. **Mr.** Lewis sold a house for $21,500. The agency's commission was 6% of the selling price of the house. Mr. Lewis is paid 40% of the agency's commission. How much did Mr. Lewis receive?

10. The Apex Collection Agency collected 70% of an outstanding bill of $935 owed to the Leone Printing Company. If the collection agency charged 12% commission, what was the amount of the check remitted to the Leone Printing Company?

11. The student population of a school district was 2,400 in 1969. The student population increased to 3,000 in 1970. With the same percent of growth over 1970, what will be the anticipated school population in 1971?

◖ **12.** The September 1970 registration in typing in a school was 184 pupils. This represents a decrease of 8% from the September 1969 registration in typing in the same school. What was the September 1969 registration in typing?

Sections **22–28** Unit Six

1. The cash price of an electric heater is $40. The heater can be purchased on the installment plan by paying $17 down with monthly payments of $3.10 each for ten months. By what percent is the installment price greater than the cash price?

2. Smith can buy a television set on the installment plan for a total cost of $337.50, including finance charges. If he pays 20% of the total cost as a down payment and the balance in equal monthly payments of $15 each, how many months will it take to pay for the television set?

3. Mrs. Julian purchased a living room suite on the installment plan for a total cost of $480. She paid 15% of the total cost as a down payment and promised to pay the unpaid balance in 15 equal monthly installments. What will be the amount of each monthly payment?

4. Mr. Green purchased a car on the installment plan. The cash price of the car was $3,100. His old car was taken in trade for $1,600 as the down payment, the balance to be paid in 24 monthly installments. The finance charges were $120. What was the amount of each payment due monthly for this purchase?

5. Mr. Evans has arranged to purchase a new refrigerator listed at $390. An allowance of $40 is being given Mr. Evans for his old refrigerator as a down payment. The installment sales contract provides for 6% interest on the original unpaid balance and a service charge of $5.80. How much will the monthly payment be on a 12-month contract?

6. Atkins, a furniture dealer, offers for sale a living room suite on the deferred-payment plan for $169.20 down and the balance in 12 monthly installments of $18.80 each. Landers, another furniture dealer, offers a suite of the same quality for $151 down and the balance in 52 weekly payments of $4.50 each. How much money would be saved by taking advantage of the better of the two offers?

7. A photographic shop offers a camera for $99.50 cash or on the installment plan for a total cost of $106.52 by paying $8.52 down and the balance in 8 equal monthly payments.

a If Kane buys the camera on the installment plan, what will be the amount of each monthly payment?

b In order to pay cash for the camera, Kane borrows the money from the bank at a cost of $4.79. How much money will this enable Kane to save?

8. Deere can buy an air conditioner for $269 cash, or on the installment plan by paying $55 down and making 12 equal monthly payments of $19.50 each. Deere has $55 in cash. He borrows the balance of the cash price from the bank for one year at 6% interest. What amount of money does Deere save by borrowing from the bank and paying cash instead of paying on the installment plan?

Sections **29–35**   Unit Seven

1. For a 6-month period a student received $6 as interest on his savings account of $300. What annual percent of interest did this savings bank pay him?

2. On January 2, Barnes deposited $1,500 in a bank that pays 4% interest per year, compounded quarterly. Interest was added to the account on April 1 and July 1. What amount did he have on deposit on July 1?

3. The Thruway Authority sold $8,000,000 worth of bonds to raise funds for road construction. The bonds paid interest at the rate of $3\frac{3}{4}\%$ per year. What is the total cost of interest per year on these bonds?

4. Johnson invested $600 in North Pacific stock, which sold at $39 a share. If the total cost of the brokerage was $15, how many shares did Johnson buy?

5. Stevens owns 65 shares of preferred stock which pays a quarterly dividend of $.45 per share. What amount of money should he receive as dividends during a one-year period?

6. Gordon bought stock in a corporation at a total cost, including brokerage and other expenses, of $76 per share. This stock paid him an annual dividend of 5% on a par value of $50 per share. What actual percent of return did Gordon receive on his investment, to the nearest tenth of a percent?

7. Peterson had an investment in several different stocks that had a total cost of $6,650. The dividends received from his stocks last year amounted to: $42.40, $78, $22, $150.20. The total dividends received last year were what percent of the total cost of Peterson's stocks?

8. Mr. George Clancy purchased 20 shares of common stock at a total cost of $1,722.50, including brokerage charges. He kept the stock 3 years and received regular quarterly dividends of $2 per share. He then sold this stock and received $1,912 as net proceeds from the sale. What was the amount of Clancy's total gain from owning and selling this stock?

9. Mr. Jones purchased 50 shares of New Era Plastics stock at $11\frac{1}{4}$ per share on January 18. The brokerage charges were $10.63. On July 28, Mr. Jones sold the 50 shares of New Era Plastics stock at $8\frac{1}{8}$ per share, and $10.22 was deducted for brokerage charges and taxes. Including the expense of buying and selling the stock, what was the amount of the net loss in this transaction?

❿ **10.** A certain stock quoted at 88 pays a dividend of 6% annually. This stock has a par value of $100 per share. How much money should be invested in this stock in order to obtain a yearly income of $2,100? (Disregard brokerage and transfer taxes.)

11. Hallenbeck purchased a two-family house for $24,000, paying $10,000 in cash and giving a mortgage for the balance. He rented each apartment for $120 a month. His expenses during the year were as follows: insurance, $90; taxes, $635; depreciation and repairs, $615; interest on the mortgage, $840. What was Hallenbeck's annual rate of return that year based on his original cash investment?

12. Mr. Stone purchased a two-family house with the intention of renting it as an investment. The total cost was $20,000 (land $5,000 and building $15,000). The taxes and insurance are estimated at $550 per year, repairs $200, and depreciation 3% of the cost of the building. Mr. Stone paid cash for the property. For how much must he rent each apartment per month in order to receive a net return of 6% on the investment?

Sections **36–42**   Unit Eight

1. Instead of buying a completed house for $16,500, Johnson had a similar house built by paying a contractor for all expenses incurred in building the house. The expenses were as follows: lot, $1,100; excavating and landscaping, $500; masonry, $1,060; lumber and carpentry, $6,655; painting, $630; plumbing, $950; heating, $1,300; electrical work, $730; other expenses, $475.

The contractor added 15% to the total expenses for his services. How much did Johnson save by having the house built?

2. Mr. Adams obtained a $5,000 mortgage loan on his new home and agreed to repay the principal and interest in payments of $40 per month over a period of 15 years. What amount of money will he have paid in interest during the life of this mortgage?

3. Mr. Ross owns a house and lot valued at $22,000 in a community where property is assessed at 45% of its true value. The rate of taxation in the current year is $3.527 per $100 of assessed value. How much will Mr. Ross have to pay as his tax on this property, to the nearest cent?

4. When purchasing a fire insurance policy, the rate in a certain community is $.42 per $100 of coverage. The rate for a 3-year policy is 2.7 times the annual rate. What amount of money is saved by purchasing a single 3-year policy for $8,500 rather than three 1-year policies for the same coverage?

5. A building was insured with the Auburn Insurance Company for $32,000, with the Elmira Insurance Company for $24,000, and with the Norwood Insurance Company for $14,000. A fire loss of $21,000 occurred. What amount of money should the owner of the building collect from the Auburn Insurance Company?

6. The owner of a ski shop insured his store with three companies: Atlas Insurance Co., $10,000; Beacon Insurance Co., $20,000; Congress Insurance Co., $30,000. If a fire occurs, for what percent of the total loss will the Atlas Insurance Co. be liable?

7. A house valued at $30,000 was insured for $16,000 under a policy containing an 80% coinsurance clause. A fire loss of $12,000 occurred. What amount of money should the insurance company be expected to pay?

8. Last month Mr. Watson's water bill was $5.40. The water company charges $3 for the first 6,000 gallons of water and $.40 for each additional thousand gallons thereafter. How many gallons of water did Mr. Watson use last month?

Sections **43–46**   Unit Nine

1. An automobile dealer offers to accept Green's old car and $1,800 in cash in exchange for a new car worth $2,850. Green purchased his old car 4 years ago for $1,850. What was the amount of average annual depreciation on Green's old car?

2. Seven years ago, New Forest High School purchased 12 calculators for $178 each. This year, the school purchased 12 new calculators priced at $235 each and received a trade-in allowance of $45 on each of the older machines.

   a What was the amount of average annual depreciation on each of the old calculators?

   b What net amount of money did the school have to pay for the new calculators?

3. A car costing $2,850 was estimated to depreciate in value at the annual rate of 18% of the original cost. What was the amount of the average monthly depreciation on this car?

4. Mr. Dugan estimated the average annual depreciation on his automobile to be 20% of the cost. If he paid $3,850 for the car when it was new, what was its estimated value after 3 years of use?

5. An automobile costing $2,600 when new has an estimated trade-in value of $1,400 after three years of use. What was the estimated value of this car after two years' depreciation had been deducted?

6. The average annual depreciation on an adding machine is $37.92. If the machine cost $252.80 when new, what is the value of the adding machine after four years of use?

7. Before buying an automobile costing $1,825, a man estimates his first year's expenditures as follows: license plates, $18.50; insurance, $130; gasoline and oil, $125; interest at 6% on the cost of the car; repairs, $65; depreciation, 35% of the cost of the car. Find the total estimated cost of operating the car the first year.

8. A salesman drove his automobile 9,840 miles in one year. If he averaged 16 miles to the gallon and paid $.30 per gallon (tax included) for gasoline, how much did he spend for gasoline, including tax, that year?

9. On five successive days a deliveryman listed his mileage as follows: 64, 138, 92, 28, 56. If his truck averaged 14 miles per gallon of gasoline, how many gallons should he have used during these five days?

Sections **47–50**   Unit Ten

1. In the village of Whitesburg the amount of money needed for the total estimated expenses for the year was $286,875. Of this amount, $3,150 was expected to be received from licenses and other income. If the total assessed valuation of all taxable property in the village was $9,750,000, what tax rate per $100 would need to be levied in order to raise the necessary funds?

2. The total assessed value of real property in a community is $32,000,000. The school budget shows anticipated expenses for the coming year of $1,579,040. State aid and other revenue to the school system is expected to amount to $540,000. In this community Mr. Burke owns real estate valued at $10,000. The property is assessed at 60% of valuation.

   a Determine the tax rate. (Express your answer as the rate per $1,000.)

   b Determine the amount of school tax to be paid by Mr. Burke.

3. Graves paid a real estate tax of $202.98 on his house, which had an assessed valuation of $6,800. What was the tax rate per $1,000 which Graves paid on his house?

◗ 4. Eton paid $28.56 for a new automobile tire. This price included a 2% retail sales tax based on the original marked price. What was the original marked price of this tire?

◗ 5. Mrs. Jones purchased a refrigerator in a county having a 3% sales tax. The total cost of the purchase, including the sales tax, amounted to $412. What was the amount of the sales tax on Mrs. Jones' purchase?

◗ 6. In a county having a 3% sales tax, a wearing apparel store had cash register readings totaling $18,540, which included the sales tax for the first quarter of 1970. What was the amount of the sales tax for this store for the period indicated?

7. Mr. Stanton's state income tax return for last year showed a total income for the year of $5,286. He was entitled to deduct the following items before determining his tax liability:

Family allowance — self, wife and one child at $600 each, totaling	$1,800
Real estate taxes	384
Interest on debts	68
Contributions to charity	165

His taxable income was subject to a tax of 2% on the first $1,000 and 3% on the next $2,000 or any fraction thereof. What was the total of Mr. Stanton's state income tax?

Sections **51–54**   Unit Eleven

1. Jane Boel, treasurer of the student council, reported a balance of $867.65 in the student council account before the annual awards dinner. Expenses in connection with this dinner were as follows:

235 dinners served at $1.75 each
Decorations, $305.73
3 corsages at $2.50 each
Programs, $80
Invitations, $16

After all expenses in connection with this dinner had been paid, what balance remained in the student council account?

2. The following information is selected from the weekly payroll of the Whitson Company. Their employees work on a 40-hour-per-week basis with time and a half for overtime.

Employee	Total Hours	Hourly Rate	FICA Tax	Federal With-holding Tax	State With-holding Tax
Brett, C.	43	$1.80	$3.86	$11.40	$1.40
Doyle, R.	40	$2.10	$4.03	$12.00	$1.60

a What is the amount of Brett's gross earnings?

b What is the amount of Doyle's net pay?

3. The chart below shows the departmental sales of The Skyway Supermarket for the week ending September 29.

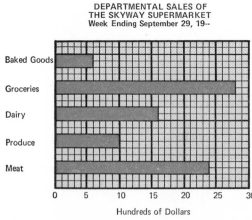

DEPARTMENTAL SALES OF
THE SKYWAY SUPERMARKET
Week Ending September 29, 19--

Hundreds of Dollars

a What was the amount of sales of the department that had the largest sales for the week?

b What was the amount of sales of the department that had the least sales for the week?

c If this store is in operation six days each week, what is the amount of the average sales of the Meat Department?

d If the Dairy Department is planning a sales promotion next week to increase their sales by 5%, what will be the Dairy Department's expected sales next week?

e This week's Produce Department sales represent a 25% gain based on last week's Produce Department sales. What was the amount of last week's sales for that department?

f What were the total sales for all departments for the week?

4. The production record of the Delta Shirt Manufacturing Company for the years 1960 through 1970 is shown in the chart below.

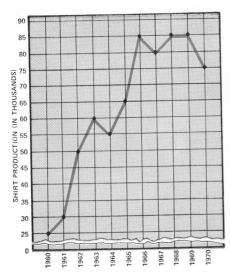

Delta Shirt Manufacturing Company
Production Record
1960-1970

a What was the number of shirts manufactured in 1960?

b What was the decrease in number of shirts manufactured between the years 1963 and 1964?

c If, in 1966, the cost of manufacturing a shirt was $3, what was the total production cost of the shirts manufactured during that year?

d The company plans to increase its production in 1971 $33\frac{1}{3}\%$ over that of 1970. How many shirts will therefore be manufactured in 1971?

5. Robert Clark, treasurer, in submitting information on the proceeds of a movie show for the benefit of his high school athletic association, reported that 197 adult tickets at $.45 each and 344 children's tickets at $.25 each were sold. The expenses for the performance were as follows: $15 for rental of a 90-minute movie; $2.50 each for two cartoon reels; $14 for the services of the projectionist. What net profit did the athletic association receive from this benefit performance?

6. The payroll record of Jackson's service station showed the information given below for the week ending March 30. By using the income tax withholding table on page 106, determine the total amount of federal income tax withheld by the owner of the service station from the earnings of all the employees.

Employee	Earnings	No. of Exemptions
T. Lyons	$107.50	3
J. Rietz	$125.00	2
M. Watson	$115.90	2

7. The chart below shows the annual sales of the Permaset Plastics Company for the years 1966 through 1970.

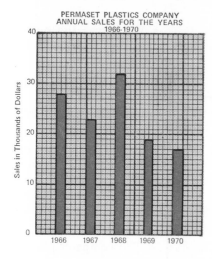

PERMASET PLASTICS COMPANY
ANNUAL SALES FOR THE YEARS
1966-1970

a What was the amount of the sales during the year with the lowest annual sales?

b If the company's salesmen are to increase sales in 1971 by 20% over the 1970 sales, what will be the amount of expected sales in 1971?

c What was the amount of the total sales for 1966 through 1970?

d What was the amount of the average yearly sales for the period shown?

8. The annual sales of the Good Manufacturing Company amounted to $240,000 in 1970. The chart below shows how each sales dollar is used.

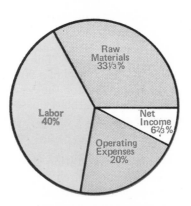

DISTRIBUTION OF SALES
1970

a What amount of money was spent for labor?

b What amount of money was earned as net income?

c If the gross profit may be found by subtracting raw materials and labor from sales, what is the amount of the gross profit?

d Next year sales are expected to increase by 8%. What should the expected sales amount to next year?

9. The treasurer of a club reports a cash balance on hand of $87 and debts of $17. If the club wishes to end the year with a cash balance of $200 and no debts, what additional sum of money should each of the 52 members pay?

10. Mr. Harvey operates a retail store. His sales for the year were $65,750. The cost of the goods which he sold was $47,225. His operating expenses amounted to $10,635. His net income was what percent of the sales for the year?

Jackson & Sons

Analysis of Total Sales Income in 1967, 1968, 1969, 1970

11. From the information shown on the above chart, determine the following:

a In what year was the greatest net profit earned?

b In what year was the least net profit earned?

c In what year was the amount of the expenses largest?

d In what year did the firm have the largest sales income?

e What was the percent of net profit in 1970 based on sales income?

12. On a bar chart, a one-inch line represents $50. How long a line must be drawn to represent $325?

13. On a bar chart, a line one inch long represents $500. What amount of money would be represented on this chart by a line $6\frac{1}{2}$ inches long?

14. Using the title and tabulated information, prepare a bar chart to show the facts in each of the following.

<table>
<tr><td colspan="2">a Beach Manufacturing Co.</td><td colspan="2">b Ann's Dress Shop</td></tr>
<tr><td colspan="2">Sales Contest Results</td><td colspan="2">Dresses Sold</td></tr>
<tr><td colspan="2">Week of May 7, 19—</td><td colspan="2">During the Week</td></tr>
<tr><td></td><td>Total</td><td colspan="2">Ending March 22, 19—</td></tr>
<tr><td>Salesman</td><td>Sales</td><td></td><td></td></tr>
<tr><td>Abbott</td><td>$560</td><td>Monday</td><td>27</td></tr>
<tr><td>Clark</td><td>890</td><td>Tuesday</td><td>39</td></tr>
<tr><td>Decker</td><td>700</td><td>Wednesday</td><td>32</td></tr>
<tr><td>Merton</td><td>480</td><td>Thursday</td><td>25</td></tr>
<tr><td>Stevens</td><td>550</td><td>Friday</td><td>42</td></tr>
<tr><td>Vincent</td><td>940</td><td>Saturday</td><td>56</td></tr>
<tr><td>Young</td><td>820</td><td></td><td></td></tr>
</table>

15. Using the title and information, prepare a curve or broken-line chart to show the facts in each of the following.

a Average Daily Temperatures — April 9–April 15, 19—

Sunday	41 degrees	Thursday	44 degrees
Monday	36 degrees	Friday	50 degrees
Tuesday	27 degrees	Saturday	46 degrees
Wednesday	47 degrees		

b Daily Lunch Counter Sales — June 20–June 26, 19—

Sunday	$370	Thursday	$330
Monday	280	Friday	350
Tuesday	260	Saturday	410
Wednesday	290		

16. The payroll record of the Brite Laundry showed the information given below for the week ending January 24. By using the Social Security Employee Tax Table on page 108, determine the total FICA tax withheld for this payroll period.

Employee	Gross Earnings	Employee	Gross Earnings
R. Hutton	$119.00	J. Moore	$128.65
M. Lyons	129.75	C. Peterson	124.90

Sections 55–58   Unit Twelve

1. The Johnson Appliance Company is able to buy refrigerators from the Mount Distributing Company for $420 each, less a trade discount of 35%. They are also able to buy identical refrigerators from the Westover Distributing Company for $380 each, less trade discounts of 20% and 15%; but freight charges of $11 for each refrigerator must be paid to the Westover Distributing Company. How much will be saved on each refrigerator by taking advantage of the better offer?

2. A dealer advertised house paint at $4.90 per gallon. If he allows a discount of 10% for quantity buying, what will be the cost of a 4-gallon case of paint?

3. In order to encourage retailers to purchase in larger quantities, the Syracuse Manufacturing Company grants a quantity discount of 15% if 150 units are purchased. If the units cost $22.60 each, how much will Raymond save if he takes advantage of the quantity discount by buying 150 units?

4. Mr. Forster can purchase an air conditioner for his store from an out-of-town firm for $1,700 less 10% and 10%, plus freight and installation charges totaling $75. A local firm offers similar equipment completely installed for $1,800 less 15% and 10%, terms 1/10, n/30. If Mr. Forster is prepared to pay cash, how much will be saved by taking advantage of the better offer?

5. In order to raise money, the junior class of a certain school decided to sell basketball booster buttons. On November 15, the class purchased 3,000 buttons at a cost of $7.50 per 100, terms 2/10, n/30. On November 22 the treasurer of the class reported that all buttons had been sold at $.10 each and that a check had been sent to the manufacturer in payment for the buttons. What net profit did the junior class realize in selling these buttons?

6. Johnson is billed $375 for a purchase. If he pays within 10 days, he needs to pay only $363.75. What percent of cash discount does he earn?

7. The Tri-City Supply Company purchased fixtures amounting to $2,100, terms 2/10, n/30. In order to take advantage of the cash discount, the firm borrowed the amount of money needed to pay the invoice, less the cash discount, from the bank for 20 days at 6%. How much did the firm save by borrowing the money from the bank with interest, rather than paying the full amount of the invoice?

8. Mr. James can obtain $21 cash discount by borrowing $679 at 6% for 60 days. How much will he actually save by borrowing?

9. By borrowing $768 for 30 days at 5% interest, Mr. Fellows obtained a $32 cash discount on an invoice. What net amount did he save by borrowing the money and taking the cash discount?

10. If a merchant saved $19.50 by taking a cash discount of 2%, what was the invoice price of the merchandise he purchased?

Sections **59–63**   Unit Thirteen

1. A merchant bought a shipment of goods for $3,865 and sold it for $4,392. His operating expenses in connection with this shipment amounted to $712. What was the amount of this merchant's net loss on the transaction?

2. The Foster Department Store bought chairs for $18 each and placed a retail price tag of $31.50 on each chair. The salesmen in the furniture department receive a commission of 10% of the selling price of each item sold. What amount of profit is made by the store on the sale of one chair after the commission is paid to the salesman?

3. The Good Friends Store bought ladies' blouses for $4 each and marked them to sell at $7 each. At that price, the store sold 8 blouses a day. In order to increase daily sales, the selling price was reduced to $6 and sales increased to 15 blouses per day.

   a What was the amount of the total daily gross profit when the blouses were sold at $7 each?

   b What was the percent of markup, based on the selling price, when the blouses were sold at $6 each?

4. A store uses the code phrase BEAUTY SHOP with an X for repeating numbers in pricing its merchandise.

   a Write the code marking for a shirt that costs $3.35.

   b What is the price of an article which bears the code ESOH?

5. A store selling bicycles places code letters under the selling price to mark the cost of its merchandise. The code words MELODY HITS are used as the key for numbers 1 through 0. What is the amount of the gross profit on a bicycle marked $42.95?

$$\overline{\text{LEDS}}$$

▶ **6.** For how much should an article that cost $21 be sold in order for the merchant to make a profit of 30% based on the selling price?

▶ **7.** A storekeeper buys television sets for $225 less 20% and 10%. The freight charges on each set average $2. At what price must the dealer sell each set in order to make a gross profit of 20% of the selling price?

▶ **8.** An electric stove is billed to a retailer at $150 less 25% and 10%, plus a delivery charge of $3.75. From experience the retailer knows that overhead expenses amount to 30% of the selling price.

At what price should the retailer mark this stove in order to make a net profit of 10% on the selling price?

9. Johnston, a clothing dealer, bought a shipment of 700 women's coats at $16.50 per coat. He sold 325 of them at $29.50 each, 200 at $24.50 each, and the remainder at $19.50 each. What percent of the cost of these coats did Johnston make as gross profit on the entire transaction to the nearest whole percent?

10. Randolph purchases bowling balls for $10.26 each. He sells each bowling ball for $15.39.

    a What is Randolph's percent of gross profit on each bowling ball if he bases the markup on the cost?

    b What is Randolph's percent of gross profit on each bowling ball if he bases the markup on the selling price?

11. The Lewin Appliance Company purchased a washing machine for $236, less 25%. Freight and trucking charges amounted to $23. At what price should the washing machine be sold in order to make a gross profit of 38% of the total cost price?

12. An article costing $121.50 had to be sold for $97.20. What was the percent of loss, based on the cost?

13. A grocer buys 5 crates of fresh eggs (30 dozen to the crate) at $15 per crate. Express charges are $2.90. The grocer estimates that 5 dozen will be broken and have to be thrown away. At what price per dozen, to the nearest whole cent, must he sell the remainder in order to gain a net income of 30% on the total cost of the eggs?

14. Hulbert has been buying lamps at a cost of $16, and selling them for $20. The price which Hulbert pays for these lamps was recently increased to $18. At what price per lamp must he sell them in the future in order to continue makng the same percent of gain on their cost?

⬤ **15.** Freeman, the proprietor of a clothing store, bought 600 dresses at $12.50. He sold 300 of these dresses at $21.95 each, and the remainder at $13.95 each. Operating expenses connected with this transaction amounted to $2,557.50. What percent of net profit, based on the original cost of these dresses, did Freeman gain?

⬤ **16.** Lewis bought 550 dresses for $10.80 each, less 10%. He sold 475 of these dresses for a total price of $6,750. At what price, to the nearest cent, must he sell each of the remaining dresses in order to make a markup of 40% on the cost of the entire 550 dresses?

Sections **64–67**   Unit Fourteen

1. On July 21, Elwell discounted at his bank a customer's two-month promissory note dated June 10. The face of this note was $360, and it bore interest at the rate of 5% per year. The bank charged Elwell 6% discount. What amount of money did Elwell receive as net proceeds from discounting this note?

2.

```
┌────────────────────────────────────────────────────────────┐
│ $1,500                        Albany, New York, March 15, 19-- │
│                                                              │
│ Ninety days after date I promise to pay to the order of      │
│ Joseph Mackin ---------------------------------------------- │
│ One thousand five hundred and 00/100---------DOLLARS         │
│ Value received with interest at the rate of 5% per annum.    │
│                        (Signed)    Thomas Atwood             │
└────────────────────────────────────────────────────────────┘
```

On April 20, 19--, Mr. Mackin discounted the above note at the First National Bank. The rate of discount was 6%. What amount did Mr. Mackin receive as net proceeds from discounting this note?

3. Mr. Goade discounted his customer's 90-day noninterest-bearing note for $690 at the bank. The note was dated April 6 and discounted on May 26 at 6%. Find the net proceeds of the note.

4. What is the bank discount on a $720, non-interest-bearing promissory note that is discounted at 4% 30 days before it is due?

5. A merchant discounted at his bank, at 6%, his own 90-day promissory note for $800. What sum of money did he receive as net proceeds from discounting this note?

6. Jones, a bankrupt, has assets of $12,500 and liabilities of $50,000. How much can Jones pay on each dollar owed?

7. Under a bankruptcy agreement, the firm of Nelson and Pickard is ordered to pay its creditors $.58 on each dollar that is due them. How much would a creditor receive as his settlement for a claim of $2,700?

8. Mr. Manter has filed a petition in bankruptcy. His liabilities amount to $5,000. His assets consist only of cash amounting to $1,500. How much money can a creditor with a claim of $500 expect to receive?

9. Hudson went into bankruptcy, owing a total of $92,800. The net cash distributed to his creditors was $21,344. What amount of money was paid to a creditor with a claim of $11,600?

10. Kearney, a bankrupt, owed the following creditors:

Foster Corporation.... $2,595   Fiske and Son........ $6,530
Morton Brothers...... 2,887   R. J. Jackson......... 1,638

The net cash distributed to these creditors amounted to $5,050.50. What amount of money was paid to R. J. Jackson?

❯ **11.** An insolvent debtor, after liquidating his assets, was able to pay $128 to one of his creditors. This amount represented 32% of the original account. How much was the original account?

12. A farmer sent a commission merchant 900 bushels of potatoes to be sold. The commission merchant sold the potatoes at $.90 a bushel. He deducted 6% commission on sales, $15.50 for trucking, and $.02$\frac{1}{2}$ per bushel for storage. What amount did this farmer receive as the net proceeds from this sale?

13. Mr. Bourne sent a consignment of 200 bushels of apples to a commission merchant to sell. The commission merchant sold 68 bushels at $2.25 per bushel; 42 bushels at $2.05 per bushel; and the remainder at $1.90 per bushel. The expenses of selling were: trucking $8.75; cost of containers $21.50; commission 10% for selling. What were the net proceeds of the transaction to Mr. Bourne?

14. The Davison Corporation asked a commission merchant to purchase 1,500 bushels of potatoes for the corporation. The potatoes were purchased at $1.75 a bushel. Expenses involved in this purchase were: commission 4%, freight and trucking $225. Find the total cost of the potatoes to the Davison Corporation.

15. Thompson employed a commission merchant to buy 650 crates of oranges for him. The merchant purchased 400 crates at $5.25 per crate, 150 crates at $5.80 per crate, and the remainder at $6.10 per crate. The agent charged Thompson 45¢ per crate commission. Express and other charges amounted to $34.50. What average total cost per crate, to the nearest whole cent, did Thompson pay for the oranges?

❯ **16.** A commission broker was paid $46.26 commission. The commission was 3% of the money he received from selling eggs at 60¢ per dozen for his employer. How many dozens did he sell?

Sections **68-69** Unit Fifteen

1. A merchant owns a building that cost $45,000 and depreciates at the rate of 2% annually. In addition, he has delivery equipment costing $4,000 with an estimated life of 5 years and an estimated scrap value of $400. What is the total depreciation expense for one year on both the building and the delivery equipment?

2. The Arnold Company bought a machine for $7,600. After using it for four years, the company bought a new machine for $12,000 by trading in the old machine and paying $7,200 in cash. What was the amount of the average annual depreciation of the old machine?

3. A machine costing $1,800 was estimated to depreciate in value at the annual rate of 7% of the original cost. What was the amount of the average monthly depreciation on this machine?

4. A printing press costing $5,860 was estimated to depreciate 9% of its original cost each year. What would be the estimated value of the machine after 5 years of use?

5. A building has a total usable floor space of 51,000 square feet. The space used for various purposes is as follows:

Offices	17,000 square feet
Salesrooms	6,375 square feet
Retail stores	12,750 square feet
Storage	remainder of the space

Expenses amounting to $6,000 are to be divided in proportion to the amount of floor space used for each purpose. How much should be charged to each?

6. The cost of manufacturing a certain household item was as follows: labor $3.40, materials $3, overhead $2.80. The manufacturer desired to make a profit of 30% on his cost. An excise tax of 5% was added to the manufacturer's selling price. How much would a retailer have to pay for this item, including tax?

❯ **7.** A machine depreciates at the rate of $280 a year, which is equal to 8% of the cost of the machine. What was the original cost of the machine?

❯ **8.** Merchandise listed at $60 had a trade discount of 20%. What additional rate of discount would be necessary to sell the merchandise at $40?

❯ **9.** In figuring the retail price for shoes, The Smith Shoe Company used the following manufacturing costs per pair: labor, $1.90;

leather and trimmings, $2.30; factory overhead, $.60. They estimate the selling and management expenses at 15% of sales. What price per pair should the company quote for the shoes in order to make a net profit of 10% of the selling price?

❿ **10.** An article listed at $50 is now being sold with a 20% discount. What additional rate of discount must be offered in order to reduce the selling price to $36?

❿ **11.** The manufacturing cost of a certain article is as follows: factory expense, $6.25; materials, $28.50; labor, $16.50. A net profit of 20% on the cost is desired. The selling expense amounts to 15% of the selling price. What must be the selling price?

❿ **12.** It costs a manufacturer $17 to make a rug. At what price should he list the rug in his catalog to make a profit of 15% of the selling price after allowing a trade discount of $33\frac{1}{3}\%$?

Sections **70-72** Unit Sixteen

1. Howarth and Smythe are partners in a supermarket, with investments of $14,000 and $8,000, respectively. Profits and losses are shared in proportion to each partner's investment. In a recent year, the firm had sales of $87,460 and costs and expenses of doing business of $66,340. What amount of money did Smythe receive as his share of the net profit?

2. Blair, Thomas, and Cone are members of a partnership with investments of $12,000, $18,000, and $30,000, respectively. The partners have agreed that profits are to be shared in proportion to the investments. In 1970 the firm had net sales of $102,000. The cost of goods sold was $62,300. The operating expenses were $18,000. What was the net profit for the year? How much did each partner receive as his share of the net profit?

3. Watson and Blume formed a partnership with investments of $9,000 and $6,000, respectively. The partnership agreement provided that the net income would be divided as follows: each partner was to receive 6% interest annually on his investment with the remaining net income to be shared equally. Last year the firm's net income was $11,500. What amount did Watson receive as his total share of this net income?

4. Arthur, Perry, and Forbes invested $6,000, $10,000, and $20,000, respectively, in a partnership business. They agreed that each partner was to receive 6% interest on his investment and that the remaining net income was to be divided equally. The net income for the year was $10,260. How much money did each partner receive as his total share of the net income?

5. Edwards and Bryan are partners in a retail shoe business, with investments of $8,500 and $12,500 respectively. The net profit for a recent year amounted to $5,700. The partners have agreed that Edwards is to receive 40% of the net profit and Bryan is to receive 60%. What amount of money would Edwards receive as his share of the net profit for that year?

6. Bassit and Spencer were partners in a wholesale business. During last year the total sales amounted to $285,640. The cost of goods sold was $247,847. Operating expenses were $20,450. Bassit received 60% of the net profit as his share for the year. How much money did he receive?

7. Sparr invested $15,000 and Chase invested $25,000 in a retail paint business. In May, the partnership made a net profit of $6,488. If Sparr receives a monthly salary of $750 and Chase a monthly salary of $1,250, with any remaining profit to be divided equally, what is the total amount of money that Sparr would receive?

8. Last year, Holmes, Blake, and Iverson were partners in a retail furniture business with investments of $16,000, $12,000, and $8,000, respectively. The partnership agreement provides that, from the net profit, Holmes is to receive a salary of $620 per month, Blake is to receive a salary of $440 per month, and Iverson is to receive a salary of $360 per month. The remainder of the net profit is to be shared equally. Last year the firm made a net profit of $29,400. What amount did Holmes receive as his total share of the net profit for last year?

9. Mr. Ames, Mr. Morton, and Mr. Earle, partners in a wholesale business, invested $30,000, $15,000, and $5,000, respectively. The partnership agreement provides that each partner is to receive a salary of $500 per month plus a share in the remainder of the net income in proportion to the investment of each partner. The net income for last year was $28,600. How much did each partner receive for the year as his total share of the net income?

10. A partner who had invested $20,000 in a business was to receive 5% on his original investment, plus a salary of $100 per week, and was to share equally in any remaining net income. His share of the remaining net income last year was $3,300. What were his total earnings for the year?

❯ 11. The Peerless Corporation had capital stock consisting of 500 shares of preferred stock paying 6% dividends, and 500 shares of common stock. The par value of each type of stock is $100 per share. A dividend of $7,000 is to be paid the shareholders. After the dividends have been paid to the preferred shareholders, how much will be paid as the dividend on each share of common stock?

Civil Service Problems

The following problems have been adapted from various civil service examinations.

For each problem, perform the necessary calculations on your answer paper. Then select the one best answer and write the letter of that answer in the answer column on your paper.

1. The number of decimal places in the product of .4266 and .3333 is

(A) 8 (B) 6 (C) 4 (D) 2 (E) None of these

2. Of the following, the correct solution of 3.48 × .009 is

(A) 3.132 (B) .3132 (C) .03132 (D) .003132 (E) None of these

3. 72 divided by .009 is

(A) .125 (B) 800 (C) 8,000 (D) 80 (E) None of these

4. Of the following, the correct solution of $\frac{.52}{.0004}$ is

(A) 1.300 (B) 13.00 (C) 130.0 (D) 1,300 (E) None of these

5. The sum of $87\frac{1}{2}$, $33\frac{1}{3}$, $12\frac{1}{2}$, $88\frac{1}{3}$, $66\frac{2}{3}$, $37\frac{1}{2}$, and $62\frac{1}{2}$ is

(A) 398 (B) $388\frac{1}{3}$ (C) $380\frac{8}{17}$ (D) 390 (E) None of these

6. The product of 23 and $9\frac{3}{4}$ is

(A) $191\frac{2}{3}$ (B) $224\frac{1}{4}$ (C) $213\frac{3}{4}$ (D) $32\frac{3}{4}$ (E) None of these

7. $\frac{7}{8}$ divided by $\frac{2}{7}$ is

(A) $\frac{1}{4}$ (B) $3\frac{1}{16}$ (C) $\frac{9}{15}$ (D) $4\frac{1}{16}$ (E) None of these

8. When a number larger than 1 is divided by a fraction having a value less than 1, the result will

(A) always be a smaller number (B) usually be a smaller number

(C) usually be a larger number (D) always be a larger number

9. The number which when increased by $\frac{1}{3}$ of itself equals 212 is

(A) 128 (B) 71 (C) 159 (D) 106 (E) None of these

10. The number .03125 reduced to a common fraction is

(A) $\frac{3}{64}$ (B) $\frac{1}{16}$ (C) $\frac{1}{32}$ (D) $\frac{1}{13}$ (E) None of these

11. What is the common fraction equivalent (in its lowest terms) of .58⅓?

(A) $\frac{5}{12}$ (B) $\frac{174}{300}$ (C) $\frac{175}{100}$ (D) $\frac{7}{12}$ (E) None of these

12. $\frac{27}{64}$ expressed as a percent is

(A) 40.6250% (B) 43.7500% (C) 42.1875% (D) 54.3133%
(E) None of these

13. What is .127 expressed as a percent?

(A) 12.7% (B) 1.27% (C) $12\frac{7}{100}$% (D) $12\frac{1}{2}$% (E) None of these

14. What percent of 4 is 5?

(A) 80% (B) 120% (C) 125% (D) 25% (E) None of these

15. What percent of $26\frac{2}{3}$ is $6\frac{2}{3}$?

(A) $66\frac{2}{3}$% (B) 25% (C) 48% (D) $33\frac{1}{3}$% (E) None of these

16. 200% of 800 equals

(A) 2,500 (B) 71 (C) 1,600 (D) 4 (E) None of these

17. The percentage of increase from 2 to 3 is

(A) 50% (B) $66\frac{2}{3}$% (C) $133\frac{1}{3}$% (D) $33\frac{1}{3}$% (E) None of these

18. Men's white linen handkerchiefs cost $1.29 for 3. The cost per dozen handkerchiefs is

(A) $7.74 (B) $3.87 (C) $14.48 (D) $5.16 (E) None of these

19. Pencils used in an office may be bought at the price of two for five cents or, when bought in large quantities, at the price of $1.38 for six dozen. What is the saving per dozen when pencils are bought at the lower rate?

(A) $.07 (B) $.10 (C) $.37 (D) $.78 (E) None of these

20. If 10 protractors are purchased at $1.20 a dozen and 15 protractors are purchased at $.84 a dozen, the average price paid for each protractor is

(A) $.06 (B) $.07½ (C) $.08⅕ (D) $.08 (E) None of these

21. If the average of a series of forty-five items is 225, what is the sum of the items?

(A) 270 (B) 10,125 (C) 180 (D) 11,125 (E) None of these

22. During one week a personnel agency receives 192 applications on Monday, 213 on Tuesday, 218 on Wednesday, 215 on

Thursday, 102 on Friday, and 194 on Saturday. If the agency has seven branch offices, what is the daily average of applications received in each office for the entire week?

(A) 29   (B) 27   (C) 149   (D) 47   (E) None of these

23. Folders, each containing the same number of sheets, are filed alphabetically in a 4-drawer cabinet. The inside length of each drawer is 35 inches and all 4 drawers are packed full. Filed under A are 43 folders occupying 7 inches. How many folders are there in the whole cabinet?

(A) 20   (B) 215   (C) 860   (D) 645   (E) None of these

24. If a card file of 1,000 cards contains 72 cards to the inch and $3\frac{5}{8}$ inches of cards are removed, how many cards are left in the file?

(A) 739   (B) 836   (C) 780   (D) 690   (E) None of these

25. A machine operator is paid at the rate of $2.96 per hour if his hourly average of production is 350 written bills. For any day in which his hourly average is below 350 his hourly rate of pay is reduced by one-eighth. What would be his pay for a seven-hour day in which he produced 2,415 written bills?

(A) $20.72   (B) $18.03   (C) $18.13   (D) $17.85   (E) None of these

26. A clerk divided his 35 hour week as follows: $\frac{1}{5}$ of his time in sorting mail; $\frac{1}{2}$ of his time in filing letters; and $\frac{1}{7}$ of his time in reception work. The rest of his time was devoted to messenger work. The percentage of time spent on messenger work by the clerk during the week was most nearly

(A) 6%   (B) 10%   (C) 14%   (D) 16%   (E) None of these

27. If a supply of typewriting paper is being reduced each week by $12\frac{1}{2}\%$ of the original number of sheets, in how many weeks will the supply be used up?

(A) 2   (B) $4\frac{1}{2}$ (C) 6   (D) 8   (E) None of these

28. During a three-day sleet storm in January, $\frac{2}{5}\%$ of the operators of motor cars in a metropolitan area met with accidents. What fraction of the operators met with accidents?

(A) $\frac{2}{5}$ (B) $\frac{1}{40}$ (C) $\frac{2}{500}$ (D) $\frac{5}{200}$ (E) None of these

29. John Doe borrowed $225,000 for 5 years at $3\frac{1}{2}\%$. The annual interest charge was

(A) $1,575   (B) $1,555   (C) $7,875   (D) $39,375   (E) None of these

30. A salesman gets a commission of 6% on sales. If he wants his commission to amount to $72 he will have to sell merchandise totaling

(A) $142   (B) $1,200   (C) $120   (D) $12   (E) None of these

31. Property worth $8,400 is assessed for 75% of its actual value. If the city tax is $2.48 per $100 assessed valuation, the county tax 64 cents per $100 assessed valuation, and the state tax 45 cents per $100 assessed valuation, find the total tax paid by the property owner who also pays a $12 improvement tax.

(A) $246.62   (B) $236.91   (C) $163.68   (D) $311.88   (E) None of these

32. Assume that you are a mail clerk in a state office. A shipment of letter paper is to be made by railway express between two points. The express rate book shows a rate of $.80 for this class of shipment. The gross weight of the shipment is 145 pounds. The charges for prepaying this shipment will be

(A) $1.18   (B) $1.16   (C) $116.00   (D) $1.60   (E) None of these

33. If $3\frac{1}{2}$% of a clerk's annual salary of $4,680 is deducted for retirement and if his salary is paid in equal monthly amounts, how much does he contribute toward retirement each month?

(A) $6.60   (B) $10.80   (C) $13.65   (D) $163.80   (E) None of these

34. If retirement deductions from salaries are increased from $3\frac{1}{2}$% to 6%, what is the monthly amount of the increase in the deduction from a $4,800 salary?

(A) $3.06   (B) $10.00   (C) $12.00   (D) $4.50   (E) None of these

35. An invoice dated January 15 for merchandise you bought added up to $876. The terms were 3/10, n/60, *f.o.b. destination.* When the goods arrived, you paid freight amounting to $8.50. On January 20 you returned goods billed at $26, and received credit therefor. You paid the bill on January 24. The amount of your check was

(A) $815.22   (B) $816   (C) $829.50   (D) $850   (E) None of these

36. A clerk saved $8\frac{1}{3}$% of his salary. If his salary was $480 a month, how many years and months did he work to save $1,800?

(A) 3 yr. 9 mo.   (B) 3 yr. 6 mo.   (C) 4 yr.   (D) 3 yr. 3 mo.   (E) None of these

37. Add 5 hr. 13 min.; 3 hr. 49 min.; and 14 min. The sum is

(A) 8 hr. 16 min.   (B) 9 hr. 16 min.   (C) 9 hr. 76 min.

(D) 8 hr. 6 min.   (E) None of these

38. In September, 1,235 gallons of milk for school lunches cost $1,659.84. The average cost per half pint is

(A) $.086   (B) $.085   (C) $.087   (D) $.084   (E) None of these

39. A floor is 25 ft. wide by 36 ft. long. To cover this floor with carpet will require

(A) 100 sq. yd. (B) 300 sq. yd. (C) 900 sq. yd. (D) 25 sq. yd.

(E) None of these

40. In taking dictation a stenographer averages eight words per line in her notebook, each page of which contains 20 lines. In transcribing the notes she averages ten words of typing per line. How many lines of typing will she require to transcribe 16 pages of notes?

(A) 257   (B) 246   (C) 256   (D) 255   (E) None of these

41. A clerk sorted 900 file cards at the rate of 150 per hour and later sorted 720 file cards at the rate of 80 per hour. His average rate of sorting the 1,620 file cards was

(A) 115 per hour   (B) 230 per hour   (C) 180 per hour

(D) 108 per hour   (E) None of these

42. A stenographer transcribes her notes at the rate of one line typed in ten seconds. At this rate, how long (in minutes and seconds) will it take her to transcribe notes which will require seven pages of typing, 25 lines to the page?

(A) 29 min. 10 sec.   (B) 17 min. 50 sec.   (C) 40 min. 10 sec.

(D) 20 min. 30 sec.   (E) None of these

43. An office has been using ordinary lead pencils that cost 35 cents a dozen. In an average month, 444 pencils are used up. If mechanical pencils costing 10 cents apiece were used, it would be necessary to purchase 90 of them without leads each year. Leads for these mechanical pencils cost one cent apiece. Three hundred leads would be needed by the office each month if only mechanical pencils were used. By buying and using the mechanical pencils rather than the ordinary lead pencils, in a year's time the office would save

(A)$210.40 (B) $11.30 (C) $90.50 (D) $110.40 (E) None of these

44. In the series 22, 19, 16, 13, 10, ___, 4, 1, the number which should appear in the blank space is

(A) 5   (B) 7   (C) 6   (D) 8   (E) None of these

45. A man invested $150,000 in a new business enterprise. The first year he lost $33\frac{1}{3}\%$ of his original investment. The next year he made a profit of $\frac{1}{4}$ of his net worth at the beginning of that year. His net worth at the end of the second year was what part of his original investment?

(A) $8\frac{1}{3}\%$ (B) 75%   (C) $16\frac{2}{3}\%$ (D) $83\frac{1}{3}\%$ (E) None of these

46. A city department has set up a computing unit and has rented 5 computing machines at a yearly rental of $640 per machine. In addition, the cost to the department for the maintenance and repair of each of these machines is $60 per year. Five computing machine operators, each receiving an annual salary of $9,000, and a supervisor, who receives $11,000 a year, have been assigned to this unit. This unit will perform the work previously performed by 10 employees whose combined salary was $92,800 a year. On the basis of these facts, the savings that will result from the operation of this computing unit for 5 years will be most nearly

(A) $120,000   (B) $166,000   (C) $170,000   (D) $196,000
(E) None of these

47. A staff member working on applications can handle an average of 168 a day working $5\frac{1}{2}$ days per week. If the rate of work remains the same and 83,160 applications must be processed in 5 weeks, how many staff members must be assigned to the handling of applications for this period?

(A) 90   (B) 99   (C) 12   (D) 18   (E) None of these

48. In a box $3' \times 2'$ by $2\frac{1}{4}'$ are to be placed smaller boxes $3'' \times 5'' \times 6''$. The maximum number of the smaller boxes which may be placed in the larger box is

(A) 224   (B) 240   (C) 252   (D) 259   (E) None of these

49. Twelve clerks are assigned to enter certain data on index cards. This number of clerks could perform the task in 18 days. After these clerks have worked on this assignment for 6 days, 4 more clerks are added to the staff to do this work. Assuming that all the clerks work at the same rate of speed, the entire task, instead of taking 18 days, will be performed in

(A) 9 days (B) 12 days (C) 15 days (D) 16 days (E) None of these

Interest Tables

SIMPLE INTEREST TABLE

($100 on a 360-Day Year Basis)

Time	4%	4½%	5%	6%	Time	4%	4½%	5%	6%
1 da.	.0111	.0125	.0139	.0167	21 da.	.2333	.2625	.2917	.3500
2 da.	.0222	.0250	.0278	.0333	22 da.	.2444	.2750	.3056	.3667
3 da.	.0333	.0375	.0417	.0500	23 da.	.2556	.2875	.3194	.3833
4 da.	.0444	.0500	.0556	.0667	24 da.	.2667	.3000	.3333	.4000
5 da.	.0556	.0625	.0694	.0833	25 da.	.2778	.3125	.3472	.4167
6 da.	.0667	.0750	.0833	.1000	26 da.	.2889	.3250	.3611	.4333
7 da.	.0778	.0875	.0972	.1167	27 da.	.3000	.3375	.3750	.4500
8 da.	.0889	.1000	.1111	.1333	28 da.	.3111	.3500	.3889	.4667
9 da.	.1000	.1125	.1250	.1500	29 da.	.3222	.3625	.4028	.4833
10 da.	.1111	.1250	.1389	.1667	1 mo.	.3333	.3750	.4167	.5000
11 da.	.1222	.1375	.1528	.1833	2 mo.	.6667	.7500	.8333	1.0000
12 da.	.1333	.1500	.1667	.2000	3 mo.	1.0000	1.1250	1.2500	1.5000
13 da.	.1444	.1625	.1806	.2167	4 mo.	1.3333	1.5000	1.6667	2.0000
14 da.	.1556	.1750	.1944	.2333	5 mo.	1.6667	1.8750	2.0833	2.5000
15 da.	.1667	.1875	.2083	.2500	6 mo.	2.0000	2.2500	2.5000	3.0000
16 da.	.1778	.2000	.2222	.2667					
17 da.	.1889	.2125	.2361	.2833					
18 da.	.2000	.2250	.2500	.3000					
19 da.	.2111	.2375	.2639	.3167					
20 da.	.2222	.2500	.2778	.3333					

TABLE SHOWING NUMBER OF DAYS BETWEEN DATES

From Any Day of	To the Same Day of the Next											
	Jan.	Feb.	Mar.	Apr.	May	June	July	Aug.	Sept.	Oct.	Nov.	Dec.
January.......	365	31	59	90	120	151	181	212	243	273	304	334
February......	334	365	28	59	89	120	150	181	212	242	273	303
March........	306	337	365	31	61	92	122	153	184	214	245	275
April.........	275	306	334	365	30	61	91	122	153	183	214	244
May..........	245	276	304	335	365	31	61	92	123	153	184	214
June.........	214	245	273	304	334	365	30	61	92	122	153	183
July..........	184	215	243	274	304	335	365	31	62	92	123	153
August........	153	184	212	243	273	304	334	365	31	61	92	122
September....	122	153	181	212	242	273	303	334	365	30	61	91
October.......	92	123	151	182	212	243	273	304	335	365	31	61
November.....	61	92	120	151	181	212	242	273	304	334	365	30
December.....	31	62	90	121	151	182	212	243	274	304	335	365

When February contains 29 days, add one day to the figure obtained from the table.

Glossary

Account. A record of receipts and payments, or debits and credits.

Account purchase. A report of costs and expenses sent by an agent to a principal for whom he has made a purchase.

Account sales. A report of receipts and expenses by an agent to a principal for whom he has made a sale.

Accrued interest. Interest earned but not due for payment.

Accurate interest. Simple interest based on exact time and 365 days to the year.

Addend. A number to be added to another.

Agent. A person authorized to act for another.

Amortization. The gradual, systematic reduction of a debt by periodic payments so that the entire debt is paid off in a certain length of time.

Amount financed. The amount of credit extended on an installment loan or purchase.

Annual percentage rate. The true interest rate represented by the finance charge on an installment loan or purchase.

Arrears. Amounts remaining unpaid after the date due for payment.

Assessed value. The value placed upon property for tax purposes.

Assessor. One appointed to place a value on property for tax purposes.

Asset. Anything of value owned by a person or a business.

Balance. The difference between the two sides of an account.

Bank discount. Interest deducted in advance by a bank when it makes a loan.

Bankrupt. Unable to pay one's debts; insolvent.

Bank statement. A copy of the bank's record of a depositor's account which is given to the depositor at regular intervals.

Base. The number which may be multiplied by a fraction or a percent; of a numeration system, the number by which the place value of a digit in a numeral is multiplied when the digit is shifted one place to the left.

Bonus. A payment over and above what is due.

Broker. An agent who executes orders for the purchase or sale of property or goods for others usually for a commission.

Brokerage. The commission charged by a broker.

Budget. An estimate of income and expenditures for a future period of time.

Canceled check. A check that has been marked paid by the bank.

Capital. The net worth of a business; the amount of money or property owned by an individual or a business.

Cashbook. A book for recording cash receipts and payments.

Cash discount. A deduction given for prompt payment of a bill.

Cash surrender value. The amount that may be received if a life insurance policy is canceled.

Change sheet. A form showing the number of each denomination of money for a payroll.

Charge sale. A sale made with an agreement that payment is to be made at a later date.

Check. A written order directing a bank to pay out money for a depositor.

Clearinghouse. An association of local banks for exchanging checks and settling accounts.

Coinsurance. A type of fire insurance under which, if property is not insured up to a certain percent of its value, the insured cannot collect the full amount of the loss.

Collateral. Stocks, bonds, or other personal property given as security for the repayment of a loan or other debt.

Commission. A payment to an agent or salesman, based on the value or quantity of goods purchased or sold.

Commission merchant. A middleman who buys or sells on a commission basis.

Common stock. Stock that has no preferences over other shares.

Compound amount. The value of a sum of money at the end of a period of time when earned interest has been added to the principal at regular intervals.

Compound interest. Interest calculated on interest after it has been added to the principal.

Consignment. Any shipment of goods; also, a shipment of goods by a principal to his agent.

Cooperative. A business organized as a corporation whose shareholders are its patrons.

Corporation. A type of business organization in which ownership is represented by shares of stock.

Cost-plus. A plan under which a contractor does a piece of work at actual cost, plus a certain percent of the cost for his services or profit.

Credit memorandum. A form showing the amount allowed a customer for returned or unsatisfactory goods, overcharges, and similar items.

Creditor. One to whom a debt is owed.

Date of maturity. The date on which an obligation falls due.

Decimal (or decimal fraction). Any numeral containing a decimal point, as .52 or 7.52.

Decimal numeral. Same as decimal or decimal fraction; also, a numeral written under the decimal system of numeration.

Deficit. A shortage in money, income, or resources.

Demand note. A note that is payable at whatever time payment is requested.

Deposit slip. A form on which to list the currency and checks that are deposited.

Depreciation. Decrease in value through use and passage of time.

Difference. The number obtained by subtracting one number from another.

Digit. Any one of the symbols 0, 1, 2, 3, 4, 5, 6, 7, 8, 9.

Discount. A reduction in price or in the amount of a bill; interest deducted in advance.

Dividend. The number that is to be divided by another; earnings distributed to shareholders of a corporation or to holders of participating insurance policies; interest on a bank account.

Divisible. Capable of being divided.

Divisor. The number by which another number is to be divided.

Drawee. The party who is directed to pay a check.

Drawer. The party who orders the payment of a check.

Endorse. To write one's signature on the back of a check or note.

Exact interest. Same as accurate interest.

Exact time. The number of calendar days between two dates.

Exchange. A charge for collecting a check or note; a place where stocks, bonds, or commodities are traded.

Expense. An amount of money paid out; the cost of goods or services used up or consumed; a decrease in proprietorship resulting from the operation of a business.

Extension. On a bill or invoice, an amount obtained by multiplying the quantity sold by the unit price; additional time allowed by a creditor to a debtor for the payment of a debt.

Face value. The amount stated on a business paper, as a note, bond, or insurance policy.

Finance charge. The total amount charged by a creditor for extending credit on an installment loan or purchase.

Fiscal period. A period of time for which the net income or net loss of a business is figured.

Fiscal year. A fiscal period of twelve months beginning on any date.

Fraction. A symbol or numeral, such as $\frac{2}{3}$, $\frac{5}{4}$, or $\frac{6}{2}$, representing the quotient of two numbers, or indicating the division of the numerator (upper number) by the denominator (lower number); symbol or name for a fractional number.

Fractional number. The quotient of two whole numbers when the quotient is not a whole number.

Gross. The total without any deduction; as, gross profit, gross income, gross sales, etc.; twelve dozen.

Gross profit. The amount by which the selling price of an article exceeds the cost; the net sales less the cost of goods sold.

Income. The return, measured in terms of money, from labor, business, property, or capital.

Installment buying. Paying for a purchase by a series of partial payments at stated intervals over a period of time.

Inventory. A list of things on hand.

Investment. Property purchased or acquired for long-term use or as a source of income or profit; the amount of money invested.

Invoice. An itemized statement of goods shipped or sold, including quantity, prices, and charges.

Liability. A debt that is owed.

List price. A quoted price or a price given in a catalog or price list before any trade discounts have been deducted.

Maker. One who signs a promissory note and thus promises to make payment.

Margin. Gross profit.

Market value. The value or price of an article in the open market.

Markup. The amount by which the selling price of an article exceeds the cost; gross profit.

Maturity. See date of maturity.

Merchandise inventory. An itemized list showing the cost or market value of the merchandise on hand at a particular time.

Middleman. One who performs a marketing service between the producer and the consumer, as a wholesaler, commission merchant, or retailer.

Minuend. The number from which another is to be subtracted.

Mixed number. A number represented by a numeral consisting of the numerals for a whole number and a fractional number, as $3\frac{1}{2}$.

Mortgage. A paper signed by the borrower that gives the lender the right to ownership of certain property of the borrower if the principal or interest, or both, are not paid.

Multiplicand. The number that is to be multiplied by another.

Multiplier. The number by which another number is multiplied.

Net. The amount remaining after all deductions have been subtracted; a fixed price, not subject to discount or deduction, at which a firm will sell an article.

Net income (net profit). The amount remaining after deducting the operating expenses from the gross profit.

Note. A written promise to pay a specified sum of money at a definite time.

Numeral. A symbol or name for a number.

On account. A term used to indicate that a purchase or a sale is to be paid for at a later date, or to describe a payment that is made in partial settlement of the amount owed.

Outstanding check. A check that has been issued but not presented to a bank for payment.

Overdue. Unpaid at the time when payment is due.

Partner. A member of a partnership.

Partnership. An association of two or more persons who combine their property or their skill, or both, in one business and agree to share in the profits or losses.

Par value. Face value.

Payee. The one to whom a check or note is made payable.

Percent. By the hundred.

Piecework. Work paid for on the basis of the quantity produced.

Policy. A contract of insurance.

Preferred stock. Stock that has the first claim on the dividends or assets of a corporation.

Price list. A sheet or booklet which lists the name and price of each article that a company offers for sale.

Prime cost. The cost of goods before any buying expenses or other charges are added.

Prime number. A number that cannot be divided without a remainder by any whole number other than itself and 1.

Principal. The amount on which interest is paid; the one for whom an agent acts.

Probability. A branch of mathematics concerned with predicting the likelihood of events whose occurrence is uncertain.

Proceeds. The amount received from a business transaction; as, the proceeds of a note; the proceeds of a sale.

Product. The result obtained by multiplication.

Promissory note. See **Note.**

Pro rata. In proportion; proportionately.

Proving cash. Counting the cash on hand and checking its accuracy with the record of cash received and paid out.

Quarterly. Once every three months or quarter of a year.

Quota. A specified amount, number, or share, often set as a standard of accomplishment.

Quotation. The price and terms on which a supplier offers to furnish an article; the published or stated market price of a stock, bond, or commodity.

Quotient. The number resulting from the division of one number by another.

Real estate. Land and everything attached to it, such as buildings, trees, etc.

Reciprocal. The reciprocal of a given number is a number whose product with the given number is 1. For example, the reciprocal of 5 is $\frac{1}{5}$; of $\frac{1}{5}$, it is 5; of $\frac{2}{3}$, it is $\frac{3}{2}$.

Reconciliation statement. A statement whereby the bank statement balance and the checkbook balance are brought into agreement.

Refund. Money paid back.

Remainder. That part of the dividend which is left over when the divisor is not contained a whole number of times in the dividend.

Remittance. Money sent from one person to another in part or full payment of an amount due.

Retail discount. The discount a retailer allows from the marked price of an article.

Retailer. One who sells in small quantities direct to the consumer.

Sales slip. A form used by a retailer that shows all the details about a sale to a particular customer.

Security. Something given to guarantee the payment of a debt or the fulfillment of a promise or contract.

Semiannually. Once every six months or half year.

Shareholder (or stockholder). One who owns shares of the capital stock of a corporation.

Stock. A quantity of goods or supplies on hand; shares of ownership in a corporation.

Stockbroker. One who buys and sells stocks for others.

Subtrahend. The number to be subtracted from another.

Sum. The number obtained by adding two or more numbers; a total; an amount of money.

Terms. The conditions or arrangements regarding the payment for goods agreed to by the buyer and seller; the numerator and denominator of a fraction.

Trade in. To give or turn in a used article in part payment of the purchase price of a new one.

Trade-in value. The amount allowed toward the purchase price of a new article for a used one traded in.

Unit. A single thing.

Unit price. The price of one unit.

Upkeep. The act or cost of keeping property in good repair.

Whole number. Any one of the numbers zero, one, two, three, four, five, and so on.

Wholesaler. One who buys goods in large quantities for resale to retailers or other middlemen.

Withdrawal. Money taken out of a bank account by the depositor.

Withholding tax. The income tax that the employer deducts from an employee's earnings.

Yield. The percent that the annual income is of the amount invested; the quantity produced, as of farm crops.

Business Abbreviations and Symbols

acct.............account
a.m.............before noon
amt.............amount
art.............article
bal.............balance
bbl.............barrel
bdl.............bundle
bu.............bushel
bx.............box
chg.............charge
c.i.f.......cost, insurance, freight
ck.............check
c.l.............carload
Co.............company
C.O.D.........cash on delivery;
                  collect on delivery
coll.............collection
com.............commission
coml.............commercial
corp.............corporation
cr.............credit; creditor
crt.............crate
cs.............case
csk.............cask
ctf.............certificate
ctn.............carton
cts.............cents
cu.............cubic
cwt.............hundredweight
da.............day
deg.............degree
dept.............department
dft.............draft
dis., disc., disct...discount
div.............dividend
do.............ditto; the same
doz.............dozen
dr.............debit; debtor
ea.............each

e.g.............for example
e.o.e.............errors and
                  omissions excepted
e.o.m.............end of month
etc.............and so forth
exch.............exchange
ex. div.........without
                  dividend
exp.............expense;
                  express
f.o.b.............free on board
frt.............freight
ft.............foot; feet
fwd.............forward
gal.............gallon
g. gr.............great gross
gi.............gill
gr.............grain; gross
gro.............gross
gr. wt.............gross weight
guar.............guarantee
hf.............half
h.p.............horsepower
hr.............hour
hund.............hundred
in.............inch
inc.............incorporated
ins.............insurance
int.............interest
inv.............invoice
invt.............inventory
kw.............kilowatt
K.W.H., kw-hr...kilowatt hour
lb.............pound
l.c.l.............less than car-
                  load lots
l.p.............list price
max.............maximum
mdse.............merchandise

mem., memo.	memorandum
mfg.	manufacturing
mfr.	manufacturer
mi.	mile
min.	minute
misc.	miscellaneous
mo.	month
m.p.h.	miles per hour
mtg.	mortgage
n.g.	no good
no.	number
N.S.F.	not sufficient funds
O.K.	all correct
on a/c.	on account
oz.	ounce
payt.	payment
pc.	piece
pd.	paid
pfd.	preferred
pk.	peck
pkg.	package
p.m.	after noon

p.p.	parcel post
pr.	pair
prem.	premium
pt.	pint
qr.	quarter; quire
qt.	quart; quantity
quot.	quotation
rd.	rod
rec.	receipt
recd.	received
reg.	registered
retd.	returned
rm.	ream; room
ship.	shipped
shipt.	shipment
shtg.	shortage
sig.	signature
T.	ton
tb.	tub
wk.	week
wt.	weight
yd.	yard
yr.	year

---

a/c	account
( )	aggregation
&	and
@	at
B/D	bank draft
B/L	bill of lading
c/o	care of
¢	cents
√	check mark; correct
°	degree
$	dollar; dollars
'	foot; feet; minutes
>	greater than
C	hundred
"	inch; inches; seconds

<	less than
#	number, if written before a numeral; pounds, if written after a numeral
o/c	overcharge
o/d	on demand
o/s	out of stock
%	percent
p/c	petty cash
:	ratio
S/D	sight draft
S/D-B/L	sight draft, bill of lading attached
√	square root
M	thousand

Index